D1104946

Recent Borzoi Fiction

The Sea of Grass
BY CONRAD RICHTER

The Invaders
BY STUART DAVID ENGSTRAND

August Folly
BY ANGELA THIRKELL

Alli's Son
BY MAGNHILD HAALKE

Published by Alfred A. Knopf

THE BROTHERS ASHKENAZI

THE BROTHERS

Ashkenazi

BY I. J. SINGER

*Translated from the Yiddish
by Maurice Samuel*

NEW YORK · ALFRED · A · KNOPF

1937

PUBLISHED SEPTEMBER 12, 1936
FIRST AND SECOND PRINTINGS BEFORE PUBLICATION
THIRD PRINTING, OCTOBER 1936
FOURTH PRINTING, NOVEMBER 1936
FIFTH PRINTING, DECEMBER 1936
SIXTH PRINTING, JANUARY 1937
SEVENTH PRINTING, FEBRUARY 1937
EIGHTH PRINTING, JUNE 1937
NINTH PRINTING, OCTOBER 1937

MANUFACTURED IN THE UNITED STATES OF AMERICA

DEDICATED TO THE MEMORY OF MY SON

YASHA

Book One

Book One

Along the sandy roads which lead from Silesia and Saxony into Poland, through townlets and villages laid waste by the Napoleonic wars, passed a long procession of wagons and carriages bearing men, women, children, and household goods.

The Polish peasants in the fields, the serfs of the local nobility, stood motionless behind their ploughshares, shielding their eyes from the sun and the dust, to stare at the strange vehicles and their strange burdens. The peasant women leaned on their pointed spades and pushed the coloured kerchiefs back on their foreheads to see better. Flaxen-haired children, dressed in nothing more than coarse linen shirts, crawled out from the earthen huts and through the wattled fences, and together with the village dogs improvised a noisy reception for the travellers. In front of the Jewish village inns groups of little Jewish boys, with curled black ear-locks hanging down their faces and ritual fringes hanging over their tattered trousers, gathered with wide-open dark eyes to observe the interminable line of carriages moving ceaselessly forward.

Queer vehicles they were, such as the roads of Poland had seldom seen before. They were not like the glittering carriages of the Polish nobility, nor like the long, narrow carts of the villagers, with latticed sides, nor yet like the wagons of the Jewish draymen, patched up with planks and surrounded by dangling buckets. They did not resemble, either, the massive mail-phaetons of the Government, drawn by four horses and accompanied by trumpeters. Equally queer was the har-

[3]

ness, with a multitude of reins, bridles, and leather straps unknown to Polish usage. But strangest of all to the watchers in the fields were the travellers themselves.

The carriages were by no means all alike. Some were broad and heavy, with high, massive wheels, and drawn by two powerful horses; some were flimsy, rickety affairs, drawn by a single horse; some had high walls and a roof, like the caravans of circuses and travelling comedians; some were covered with canvas stretched over iron arches, like the wagons of the gypsies. Here and there were little go-carts drawn by dogs, while some were pulled along by the family of travellers, the father and mother harnessed in front, the children pushing from behind.

On the large, solid carriages sprawled big-bellied Germans, their blond beards protruding from under their chins; curved pipes hung down from their mouths, and watch-chains glittered on their chests. Near them, always busy with some household task, sat their wives, strapping women with wimples drawn over their heads and wooden clogs on the well-filled red woollen stockings. These carriages were piled high with bedding, clothes, tapestries, utensils, pictures of German kings, Bibles and prayer-books, cages of geese and ducks which kept up a perpetual quacking, and rabbits and guinea-pigs in hay-filled baskets. Following on a long line hitched to the back of the carriage were usually several well-fed big-uddered cows.

In the small carts the men and women were as lean and weary as the single beast which dragged them along, its muzzle bowed to the heavy sand. Wherever a cow followed, it was meagre and empty-uddered. The father and mother and the older children were as often on foot as in the cart. Yet these were in better case than the poorest, who either used dogs or were their own beasts of burden. On these carts the bundles were few and small, and the live-stock consisted at most of a few hens and rabbits. Very rarely was there seen a half-starved goat hitched to the go-carts of the poorest.

But rich or poor, well fed or hungry, there was one article which was to be found with all of them, and that was the

[4]

wooden loom made of smooth boards and held together with rope.

"Praised be the name of our Lord Jesus!" was the greeting of Polish wayfarers to the travellers. "Where do you come from, strangers, and where are you going?" The only answer they received from the strangers was in German. *"Grüss Gott, guten Tag!"* The Poles, understanding no German, spat out, crossed themselves, and said: "Pagans! Not a Christian word among them!"

The Jewish innkeepers scattered along the roads did manage to strike up a conversation with the wanderers. They invited them into the inns, to take a rest and a bite of food. But the travellers did not get down from their vehicles, not for so much as a noggin of whisky. They had brought along with them whatever they needed. At night they slept in their carts. Not a groschen did they spend.

These were weavers, part from Germany, part from Moravia, coming to settle in Poland.

For in the German countries there were many mouths and little bread, while in Poland there was plenty of bread but almost no merchandise. The unskilled Polish peasants wove their coarse linen from the native flax, but the city-dwellers, who wanted good cotton, woollen, and silk stuffs, had to import them from abroad. Whatever the country needed in the way of bed and table linens, clothes, army uniforms, was imported by the Jews, who brought the shipments mostly down the Vistula, from the port of Danzig. Vast sums flowed out of the country for these commodities. The Government therefore sent agents into Germany to persuade weavers to come into Poland, where they would be given free land and special conditions and where they would be able to sell easily whatever their looms could produce.

The weavers, who were half-peasants, brought everything with them into the new country, from chickens to cats, from ploughshares to concertinas. Among the richer carriages were those of the pastors in their long black coats, who came with wives and children to sustain the Protestantism of their flocks in a Catholic land and to keep green and fresh the memory

[5]

of the German kings to whom the wanderers owed allegiance.

The road of the immigrants lay across the flatlands, in the direction of the city of Warsaw and of the townlets of Zhyrardov, Kalisz, Pabianits, Zgresh, and Piotrkov. Some of the newcomers settled in the village of Lodz, which took its name from the near-by lake called Lodka. At one end of the village, close to the fir woods, they put up houses, laid out gardens, planted potatoes and cabbages, sowed wheat, and erected their wooden looms. Their privileges were many. The Polish Government, under the direction of the Tsar of Russia, who was also King of Poland, freed them for a number of years from all taxes, exempted them from military service, secured them in their freedom of religious customs and the use of their mother tongue, and—not least—excluded the Jews from this new townlet of Vilki, as it was named from the Polish word for wolves, which were frequently seen hereabouts on the cold winter days.

The Jews of Lodz, two or three dozen in number, lived in a little street of their own among the "burghers." They were without exception tailors, and they had only been allowed to settle in Lodz because there was no one else to make clothes for the Poles. Other Jews were not admitted to Lodz.

The Jews of Lodz had a guild of their own, and a guildhouse—a hut, actually—where they gathered to take counsel, chiefly against the hostile measures of the gentile guilds. In this guildhouse, on a wooden table, stood a simple box containing a scroll of the law, for the place was also used as a synagogue. They had neither a rabbi, nor a ritual bath, nor a cemetery. Questions of ritual and ceremonial were settled by the village teacher, who taught the Jewish children the rudiments of Hebrew. When one of the Jewish wives had to take a ritual bath, her husband accompanied her to the lake outside the village and stood on guard while she made the prescribed immersions. In the winter-time they took axes along to break through the ice, and the women dipped themselves in the freezing water. When someone died the body had to be carted to the near-by Jewish community of Lentchitz, to which the Jews of Lodz were supposed to belong.

But there was bad blood between the community of Lentchitz and the tailors of Lodz. The Jews of Lentchitz were poor, and there were too many tailors among them. Between the Feast of Passover in the spring, and the Feast of Tabernacles in the late autumn, when Jews usually ordered new coats, the tailors of Lentchitz had little to do except try to sleep away their hunger. Things were better in Lodz, and so, from time to time, tailors would steal out of Lentchitz into Lodz and work there at impossibly low prices. The tailors of Lodz protested in vain that the bread was being taken out of their mouths, and finally the struggle came into the open. The tailors of Lodz complained to the sub-prefect of the village and begged that exalted official, for whose welfare they would ever pray, to expel the newcomers, who, apart from the fact that they were utterly without skill, did not belong to the authorized guild, paid no taxes, and had no right to settle in Lodz. The petition was accompanied by a gift of tallow candles for the church and a present for the noble sub-prefect. The latter at once sent round a posse of police who hunted up the intruding tailors and took away their scissors and press-irons. If any of them were found a second time in Lodz they were put in chains, flogged, and thrown out of the village.

The community of Lentchitz retaliated by refusing to bury the dead of Lodz unless payment were made at the rate of a rouble a head, whereupon the tailors of Lodz stopped paying community taxes to Lentchitz. The heads of Lentchitz, in turn, complained to the authorities, and soldiers were sent into the homes of the tailors of Lodz.

The soldiers were a dreadful scourge. They brought forbidden food into the houses, they snatched up kosher knives and used them to cut pig's meat, they used foul language, they forced themselves on the women, and they mocked the Jews as they stood at prayer. Worst of all, the Passover week was approaching, during which it is dangerous to have a gentile in the house lest he bring in the forbidden leaven. Busy as they were, for the Passover coincides with Easter, when the gentiles also ordered new clothes, the tailors of Lodz had to go in a body to the community of Lentchitz to beg the Rabbi to call off the soldiers.

The heads of the community of Lentchitz would do noth-

[7]

ing until the tailors of Lodz had taken off their shoes and begged forgiveness in their stocking-feet. There was no way out of it: the tailors pulled off their boots, stood in their tattered stockings, and begged forgiveness. They also paid up the arrears of taxes and took a solemn oath never again to lodge complaint with the sub-prefect. Then they went home.

The soldiers were called off, and from that time on, Jewish tailors of Lentchitz began to settle in numbers in the village of Lodz.

But in Vilki, where the Germans lived, the Jews did not dare to settle. If a Jew ventured into that section, blond-haired boys would set the dogs on him and chase him out with stones raising the immemorial cry of *"Hep! Hep! Jude!"*

ℛℯ𝓫 Abraham Hirsh Ashkenazi, merchant of Lodz and head of the Jewish community of that city, sat, distressed and ill-tempered, over a volume of the Talmud, and plucked at the hair of his thick, black beard.

It was not the state of his business that was responsible for his distress and ill temper. No, business was good, both for him and for the other Jews of Lodz. In the several decades which had passed since the Germans had settled in Vilki, a flourishing community had grown up in Lodz. True, the Vilki district was still forbidden to the Jews, but Lodz itself had expanded, and the Jews were now numerous enough to support a Rabbi, an assistant Rabbi, several synagogues and ritual slaughterers, a ritual bath, and a cemetery. The German weavers who had settled in Poland still did not produce the finer type of goods demanded by the nobility, high dignitaries, army officers, and the richer classes. These were still imported from abroad, and rich Jews travelled by post, as of old, or on the new trains, to make purchases in Danzig and Leipzig. The poorer Jews, in partnership with the frontier guards, smuggled in heavy quantities of foreign goods and sold them at high prices. Still others, pedlars and general dealers, went barefoot from village to village and bought wool from the peasants; this they resold to the merchants of Lodz, who sent it abroad to be spun into thread. The Polish peasants, who used to neglect their sheep, letting the fleeces become dirty and tangled, and shearing them irregularly, were learning

[9]

to produce a higher grade of fleece. Jewish innkeepers and lessees turned to the woollen business and bought up in advance the produce of entire flocks belonging to the nobility.

The German master weavers blamed the Jews for the demand for foreign goods. They liked even less the widespread practices of Jewish cotton-dealers, who let out work to the poorest German workers and forced down the prices of merchandise. These Jewish dealers, to whom the state bank extended no credits, were usually short of cash, and when the week-end came they could not pay their workers. They therefore issued credit slips, written in bad Hebrew and stamped with a home-made seal which consisted of a scratched stone. The credit slips were readily accepted by Jewish tailors, shoemakers, grocers, and innkeepers, and so every Saturday night the Jewish stores were filled with German workers exchanging the Hebrew credit slips against supplies of food, drink and clothing. The German master weavers denounced the Jews to the authorities for making their own Jewish money. The authorities forbade the Jews to issue any more credit slips. At the same time an official was sent to England to bring back a large supply of cotton, so that the Jews would be forced out of the trade, but before it reached Lodz the English cotton was stolen by the officials. Local officials also accepted bribes from the Jews, and before long, poor German weavers were again working for Jewish cotton-dealers and taking the Hebrew credit slips into Jewish stores. The very officials who denounced the importation of foreign goods would wear only the foreign goods which the Jews brought into the country—and they were the same ones who took bribes from smugglers who did not even pay duty on the foreign goods.

Reb Abraham Hirsh Ashkenazi, who was likewise known by the name of Danzig, because of his frequent business visits to that city, was one of the most distinguished Jews in the community. He had just returned, shortly after the Festival of Purim, from an unusually successful trip, bringing with him an excellent assortment of fine silks and woollens to be distributed among the shopkeepers of Lodz and the pedlars who went out to the villages. He had also brought back handsome presents for his wife and his little daughters. Best of all, he had bought a huge silver goblet as a present for the Rabbi of Vorka, of whom he was an ardent follower. There was much that Reb Abraham Hirsh Ashkenazi had to be thankful for, and the distress of his soul had to do more with community affairs than with his own. Young as he was, his reputation for wealth, learning, and piety had given him the place of leadership in the Jewish community of Lodz, and during the time of his absence in Danzig public troubles and problems without number had accumulated.

First, the Passover was approaching, and the special charities connected with that festival were heavier than usual. There were not only the professional beggars to be looked after. Decent workers, who as a rule managed to make ends meet, found themselves after a year of labour unable to induct the Passover festival into their homes. Someone would have to supply them with the matzos, wine, eggs, meat, and chicken fat. And almost on the day of his return from Danzig Reb Abraham Hirsh had co-opted a committee of respected householders, and with his big red kerchief in his hand he had gone from one door to another among the well-to-do and gathered contributions. But the more he gathered, the more he needed. The poor beleaguered the community house, wept on the doorsteps, and complained bitterly that the community overseers were heartless and incompetent.

And then money was needed to ransom Jews from prison. On the roads and lanes of Poland the Cossacks were at war with the Polish nobility, who had risen in revolt against the Russian overlordship and dreamed of an independent Poland and a Polish king. Bands of rebels frequented the dense forests, and such as the Cossacks captured they hanged out of hand. But there were also Jews, stewards and lessees of the Polish nobility, who supplied their employers with ammunition, and those who fell into the hands of the Cossacks suffered the same fate as the rebels. Shortly before this Passover a number of Jews—survivors of such a raid—had been brought in chains to Lodz and flung into the prison. They had been travelling along the road with barrels of apples at the bottom of which was packed loose gunpowder. Cossacks had stopped

[11]

them, searched the wagons, thrust their bayonets through the barrels, and found nothing. Dissatisfied, they were about to free the Jews when it occurred to them that it would be a pity to let such a good supply of apples pass through their fingers. But when they had lifted out a few layers of the fruit, they discovered the gunpowder. Some of the Jews were hanged on the nearest trees; the remainder were brought to Lodz. Now widows, orphans, and relatives stood weeping before the community house of Lodz; they implored the officials to provide decent Jewish burial for the dead and to rescue the living from a like fate.

Large sums were needed for this purpose. But before anything could be done to ransom the captives, a supply of matzos would have to be bought for them lest, God forbid, they be compelled to eat bread on the Passover.

Third, dreadful sins had been committed in the community. A group of so-called enlightened, modernizing Jews, belonging to the well-to-do class, had turned their backs on the traditional Jewishness of their fathers and petitioned the Government to open godless, secular schools for their children, where the latter would sit with uncovered heads, learn the heathenish lore of the gentiles, and forsake the way and the life. The Government did not take kindly to the idea, but these modernizing Jews were obstinate and had money, whence it was clear that they would probably get what they wanted. It was reported further that these same Jews were planning to build a so-called synagogue of their own after the fashion of the German Jews, a synagogue with an organ —just like the abomination of the churches—where a modernized pastor would bleat sermons just like a priest. To Reb Abraham Hirsh such a synagogue was worse than a church; the latter was used only by gentiles or by the few wretched Jews who had apostatized; the former might be frequented by plain, ignorant Jews who would not understand that they were being tempted into the path which ultimately led to apostasy.

This did not finish the count of evil. Jewish pedlars and general dealers who tramped through the villages to sell their goods and to buy in wool, pelts, and bristles had learned that the Jewish boy Naphthali, called "the apostate" because he was hardly better than one, had hired himself out to a German weaver and was learning the trade. More than once Naphthali had been pitched out of the synagogue for his shameless transgressions of the Jewish Law, but this was beyond anything he had ever done before, for if he had become the apprentice of a German weaver he undoubtedly worked on the Sabbath and ate food that was not kosher—perhaps even pork.

Long before this journey of his, Reb Abraham Hirsh had sent messengers to Naphthali and had had him brought to the community house, where, with much banging of the table, he had threatened the lad that if he did not mend his ways, he, Reb Abraham Hirsh Ashkenazi, head of the community, would turn him over to the military and make a soldier of him. But Naphthali had answered impudently that he was going to be a weaver whatever anyone thought or said. So Reb Abraham Hirsh had actually tried to get the military to take the lad, but the military had turned him down. The result had been that quite a number of Jews whose attachment to the true tradition was not of the strongest had apprenticed themselves to Germans or had begun to consort with them in dangerous intimacy. Thus, for instance, young Mendel Flederbaum, who as a small entrepreneur had employed several weavers, had learned the trade from his own workers and had applied for membership in the German guild of master weavers. The authorities supported him because he had shorn his beard close—one might almost say that he had shaved—and changed the long, pious caftan of the Jew for the short, heathen coat of the gentile. Likewise he had learned to read and write the gentile language with a perfection wholly unbecoming to a pious Jew. Seeing his example, plain, ordinary Jewish workers had felt their appetites awaken for the pleasures, privileges, and customs of the non-Jewish world. All this had been accentuated during the brief absence of Reb Abraham Hirsh; and to cap it all an epidemic of scarlet fever had broken out in the Jewish quarter and many children had been carried off; it was clear to anyone who had eyes to see that this was God's

[13]

punishment and His warning to the sinful community.

These were the worries that tormented the head of the community as he sat plucking the hairs of his thick black beard over a huge folio of the Talmud—these and one more, a purely personal one. It was his wife. She was carrying on dreadfully because her husband was going away to Vorka to spend the Passover in the company of his beloved Rabbi. Not that this was anything new. Pious even among the pietists, or Chasidim, Reb Abraham Hirsh went to this Rabbi for the festivals of the New Year, the Day of Atonement, Tabernacles, Pentecost, and even Passover. Every Passover his wife wept and complained; she was compelled to go for the week to her father, the Rabbi of Ozerkov, as if she were a widow without a man to conduct the Passover ceremonies for her. As a rule Reb Abraham Hirsh paid little attention to his wife's tears. Was she not a woman? Were a woman's tears anything out of the ordinary? But this time it was something special; she was big with child and expecting to be brought to bed almost any day. Moreover, it was going to be a boy, her first boy, for she had felt the child stirring on her right side. She did not want to be left alone now; she did not want her husband to be away during the circumcision ceremony.

"I'll do something to myself," she sobbed. "So help me God, I'll do something to myself."

She wept so long that she became feverish, and Reb Abraham Hirsh did not know where to hide from her importunities. Every now and again he would pull out the lovely silver goblet which he had bought for his Rabbi. It was a special Passover goblet, to be placed on the table during the ceremonies and filled with wine for the prophet Elijah. As often as he saw it he thought of it standing, lustrous and prominent, on the long table at which the Rabbi and his followers were seated: *his* goblet, Reb Abraham Hirsh's goblet, *his* gift to the Rabbi. And thinking thus, he would bite his beard in irritation.

Others, too, were trying to dissuade him from the journey to the Rabbi. The country was restless, the roads were infested with rebels and Cossacks, innocent wayfarers had been set upon and maltreated, even hanged. But Reb Abraham

[14]

Hirsh refused to listen. Last time he had visited his Rabbi, on the festival of Tabernacles, he had made mention of his wife's pregnancy, and the Rabbi had said:

"Abraham Hirsh, your generations will be rich men."

"Rabbi," he had answered, terrified, "I want them to be God-fearing Jews."

But the Rabbi had added nothing more, and Reb Abraham Hirsh had not dared to question him. It was a bad sign, a very bad sign. And now, when the son was about to be born, he felt that he had to go to his Rabbi and repeat his petition for God-fearing, pious children. The dangers of the journey did not worry him; Reb Abraham Hirsh was no coward, and in many years of travel he had passed through all sorts of perils. Only one thing gave him pause—the child that was coming into the world. And, yes, he thought of his wife too: it would be hard on her, for she would not even be able to go to her father for the Passover ceremonies. Besides, the latter would never forgive his son-in-law for such behaviour.

Then the Rabbi came into his mind again, and Reb Abraham Hirsh could not sit still. There were several poor pietists in Lodz, Chasidim, followers of the Rabbi of Vorka, who wanted to go along and who could not do it at their own expense. They were waiting for Reb Abraham Hirsh to take them, as he always did. What would they say? They would laugh at him for letting a woman interfere with his duties and wishes. Their pious holiday would be spoiled. And what sense would there be in waiting for the next festival, Pentecost, to bring the Rabbi a Passover goblet? But the chief thing was the question of the children that were to come. While they were still unborn, perhaps something could be done for their future through the Rabbi. Reb Abraham Hirsh did not want sons who would be rich but not God-fearing. He would rather have them poor, teachers or what not, but pious. If his wife had any sense, she would herself urge him to go on this journey. But she was only a foolish woman, with tears instead of counsel.

And so Reb Abraham Hirsh rose from his Talmud and began to pack again the big leather valises with which he had returned only a few days before from his journey to Danzig. He put in prayer-shawl and phylacteries, his silk caftan, the silver goblet, some clothes, and several volumes of the Talmud to study on the way. Like a true Chasid, he remembered also to include a few bottles of fiery whisky. Then he sent Leah Sarah, the servant, for the drayman.

His wife, standing by, burst loudly into tears. "Abraham Hirsh," she sobbed, "I won't survive the shame of it."

Reb Abraham Hirsh did not look at her. He went to the door and kissed the mezuzah on the door-post. Then he turned back and wished her an easy delivery. "And don't forget," he added, "if it's a boy he's to be named Simcha Bunim, after the Rabbi of Pshiska, blessed be his memory. Simcha Bunim. Those are my orders."

ii

$\mathcal{R}eb$ Abraham Hirsh's wife had made no mistake; the stirring on her right side during the last months of her pregnancy had foretold, according to the tradition, a male child. But instead of one son she brought forth two.

Her pains began on the first evening of Passover and lasted through the night. With the dawn a child came. The women of the courtyard, who attended her, caught up the tiny bundle, slapped it to make it cry louder, carried it to the lamp, and called out joyfully to the suffering mother:

"Good luck! It's a boy!"

But the mother's screams continued as loud as before, and the women tried in vain to pacify her. Only Leah Sarah, the servant, an experienced midwife, perceived that another child was coming, and she called out: "Hold on to the head of the bed, mistress darling. That'll make it easier." And in a few minutes she was delivered of a second child, a big, heavy boy. There was no need to slap this one, for it filled the house with its crying. Leah Sarah caught it up, carried it to the lamp, and exclaimed ecstatically: "Good luck, mistress, another boy, a great big one, like a bear."

The women rummaged around for two threads, a red and a blue, and tied the first to the older, the second to the younger child. But no such precautions were necessary, for it would have been impossible to confuse the two. The older one was small, lean, with light, scanty hair on his pointed head and with grey eyes, like the mother's. The younger was

[17]

plump and solid, with a round, thickly covered head and merry black eyes. Their voices were different, too. The older one wailed in a high, thin treble which died away into a choking despair; the younger one bellowed like a steer.

"One the dead spit of his mother, and the other the dead spit of his father," crowed Leah Sarah, as she brought the washed babies to the mother. The latter looked at them closely and anxiously and gave her breast first to the older and weaker one. "Quiet, you little rascal," she whispered to the younger one, who had set up a tremendous howl, as though he were already jealous of his brother. One after the other she besprinkled their mouths with milk, to teach them to take the breast. The younger one set to at once and drew lustily, pressing his mouth hard against the breast; the older one could not take hold of the nipple, and when he did he squeezed it between his tiny gums, but did not suck. Then, after a minute, he would let go and wail chokingly in his thin, weak treble. "Hush, hush, you poor little darling," his mother whispered.

During the eight days which preceded the ceremony of the circumcision the mother lay restless and worried on the high pile of cushions. She was worried about the names to give her new-born sons. Once or twice during her pregnancy she had dared to suggest to her husband that if she gave birth to a boy she would like to call him Jacob Meyer, in memory of her sainted grandfather, the Rabbi of Voidislav. But her husband had cut her short. If it was a boy he was to be called Simcha Bunim, after the great Chasidic Rabbi of Pshiska. "If it's a girl," he said, "you can do whatever you like. Girls belong to you. But boys belong to me." Now that her husband was away, there was no one to contradict her. Still, she did not know what to do. For she had given birth to two sons and therefore had four names to dispose of, two for each. She was certain that whatever she did, she would fail to please her husband, and the surest way to make him angry would be to choose one name from her side of the family. Her neighbours advised her to dispatch a courier to her husband during the week-days of the Passover holiday, asking him to come home in time for the circumcision ceremony. But she would not do it. Her heart was sore. She had never had much joy of her husband. When he wasn't away on business, he was visiting his Rabbi. When he wasn't visiting his Rabbi, he either shut himself in his own room, to study the Talmud, or was to be found in the little club-house of the particular group of Chasidim or pietists to which he belonged. There they would eat improvised meals, take a few drinks, talk of the wonders of their Chasidic rabbis, exchange stories from the Talmud, and carry on late into the night. She did not expect much from a husband, for she was herself a daughter of a Chasidic house, and she knew that among the pietists a wife counted for little. So it had been in her childhood home; her father had never had time for her mother, except in the nights. They never went out visiting together, never spent time in each other's company. What was there for a man, a scholar, skilled in the Talmud and the wisdom of the sages, to say to a silly woman, and what could she reply in return? And if she had nothing to say to her husband, she had even less to say to other men.

All this she knew and was more or less resigned to, like all Chasidic wives. Like all wives she would include in her morning prayers the grateful acknowledgment to the Almighty that He had made her according to His will: to wit, a female. Yet there were times when she suffered, too. True, she was a rich man's wife, a highly respected matron; she was envied; she was fruitful, bringing forth a child almost every year, and the children, though females until the birth of the twins, were excellent specimens. Her husband would never fail to bring her a present from the road; sometimes a Turkish shawl, sometimes a piece of jewellery. But he had no time for her. On the Sabbath there would always be a guest at table, either a passing traveller or one of the poor pietists belonging to Reb Abraham Hirsh's clique. It would have been improper to ask the guest to sit at table with a woman; so the wife would come in at the beginning of the meal to listen to the Sabbath benediction and be given a sip of wine from the beaker which her husband half emptied before, according to the custom. After that she and the servant, Leah Sarah, would each receive a slice of the benediction bread, and they would retire

[19]

to the kitchen to eat by themselves.

They hardly ever went out together. He could not have conversed with her women friends; she would not have dared to speak with his men friends. And if it so happened that they had to visit some relative or put in an appearance at a wedding or circumcision ceremony, they would walk apart, she a few paces behind him. As soon as they entered the house they would separate, he going at once to the men, she to the women. On Sabbath mornings he would stay long in the synagogue, and she would wait for the noonday meal till she was faint with hunger. What hurt her most, however, was his haughtiness toward her, for Reb Abraham Hirsh's piety and pride went beyond the practice even of the world she had been born into. After all, there were godly Chasidim who, if they could not talk Talmud with their wives, did occasionally ask their advice on business matters, tell them of a piece of good fortune, or come for consolation when things went badly. No, this was not Reb Abraham Hirsh's custom. Only once a week he would pull out his big purse, and hand her a few banknotes for the household. He did not even address her by her name. It was always "you," or "wife," after the fashion of the very fanatical pietists. Even when he returned from a long journey he had nothing to say. He would kiss the mezuzah on the door-post and say: "Good morning. Anything new in the house?" Then he would hold out to her the present which he invariably brought her. If she took it from his hand it was a sign that she could be a wife to him after his long absence; if not, he would turn away darkly and hurry out of the house to the club-house of his Chasidic group, to hear about the latest sayings and doings of his beloved Rabbi.

She was afraid of him; she feared his silence, she feared the sound of his voice when he sat alone in his room chanting over the Talmud, she feared his very bearing, masculine and haughty. She did not want much from her husband; an occasional friendly word, an occasional smile; it would have been enough to repay her for her empty woman's life in the perpetual company of the servant. But these were things which Reb Abraham Hirsh could not spare for a woman. Yes, he was her husband, and she had brought him many children;

he even loved her in his way, but that was only in the nights, in accordance with the Law. For the rest she, being a woman, had to be content with conducting household affairs, and with maintaining the rigid standards of Jewishness expected of her. He treated her as if she were a servant. It might happen that, late in the night, his pietist clique would suddenly take a notion to pay him a visit and improvise a little celebration. Reb Abraham would then call into the kitchen: "Wife, make us a good beet soup with garlic and potatoes!" and she would sit up with the servant, cooking for the group.

On the high holidays Reb Abraham Hirsh was not at home. At the seasons when most Jewish houses were filled with festivity and the family was united round the table, Reb Abraham Hirsh was on a visit to his Rabbi. Alone, like a widow, God help her, she said the woman's benediction, and ate with her children in the kitchen. Yes, she was more or less resigned to this grey life of hers, and she knew only too well that there would have been no point in pleading with her husband, or remonstrating with him. But this that had happened now was out of the ordinary. She had been pregnant; she had been close to delivery; she had expected a son. So she had wept and pleaded, and it had done her no good. Her husband had gone off as usual to his Rabbi in Vorka. And now that she had brought two men-children into the world, a feeling of pride awoke in her, and all the bitterness of all the years came to a head, and her heart was hot within her. She would not send a courier to her husband, asking his advice about the names or begging him to return for the circumcision ceremony. Besides, she was not even sure that he would leave his Rabbi before the end of the Passover!

She lay there in the childbirth bed, piled high with cushions and behung with white sheets, protected by psalms from the evil spirit which haunt new mothers and new-born babies. In the room stood perpetually a number of young boys from the schoolroom, saying prayers loudly, and to these she answered with a loud, firm amen, feeling, hour after hour, her dignity and worth and importance increasing. She made the first preparations in her life for the circumcision of a son—of two sons at once—and she made them alone. She issued com-

[21]

mands, just like a man; and as the days went by, her determination, weak and terrified at first, to push in at least one name from her side of the family became clear and unfaltering. She would defy her husband. She would be independent. She was a mother with rights.

The rebellion did not go too far. She had not the courage to appropriate an entire name. She contented herself with slipping in a part of the name for each boy. She divided the older boy's name: Simcha, as her husband had ordered, and then Meyer, after her sainted grandfather, the Rabbi of Voidislav. To the younger boy she gave the second half of the names—Jacob Bunim.

The first thing Reb Abraham Hirsh asked for when he came into the house after the Passover was to be shown the children.

"Which is the older one?" he asked his wife, staring in astonishment at his two sons, who lay there wrapped tight in swaddling-clothes.

"The littler one," said the midwife, timidly, and lifted up the child.

"And what's his name?" asked the father.

"Simcha," replied the mother, all her courage deserting her.

"What? One name?" asked Reb Abraham Hirsh, incredulously.

"No. Simcha Meyer. The Meyer is for my sainted grandfather, the Rabbi of Voidislav," said the mother.

"Here, take it away," said Reb Abraham Hirsh, angrily.

Leah Sarah picked up the second child and lifted it to its father. "Jacob Bunim," she said, "go to your father."

Reb Abraham Hirsh looked on the younger son, and his looks became softer. Well, the Pshiska Rabbi's second name was here, after all. It was ridiculous, of course, to have taken a holy man's name and divided it up like that, between two children, bolstering it with the names of another man, so that it was neither here nor there. But there was nothing to be done now.

"The dead spit of his master," said Leah Sarah, wheedlingly. "A beautiful child, God bless it."

[22]

"Put it down, put it down," said Reb Abraham Hirsh, and left the room irritated and confused.

The mother burst into tears and pressed the babies to her, one at each breast. "Bless you, bless you, my little Meyer," she wept, calling the older one by the name of her dead grandfather. "Suck, my little darling." She did not have to coax the younger one, but the older one merely hung on, closing his tiny gums on the tender nipple, so that the mother cried out with the pain of it. Leah Sarah picked up the child and wagged an admonitory finger under its wrinkled nose. "You bad little boy!" she exclaimed. "Why don't you behave like your brother?" She looked at her mistress's inflamed breast and shook her head. "I've never seen the like of it," she said, shocked. "Such a baby should bite so hard! All he does is bite and cry, the little ruffian." And the baby set up a thin, wild wail which was heard all over the house. Reb Abraham Hirsh could not bear it. "Leah Sarah!" he shouted angrily from his room. "Close the door! I can't study with that noise going on."

All the joy of his double gain had been spoiled for him by his wife and her ridiculous division of names. He was already thinking of the time when the two boys would be grown up and he would introduce them into the club-house of his pietist sect and would have to announce their absurd names right in front of the Rabbi, Simcha Meyer and Jacob Bunim, names that were neither here nor there. He repeated the names several times, and they even had a queer taste in his mouth. He could not forgive his wife. And though she still lay in her childbirth bed, weak from her ordeal, he would not go in to her.

From that day on, Reb Abraham Hirsh flung himself with renewed energy into his double activities, business and study. He made up his mind that henceforth he would travel no more to Danzig, but concentrate wholly on his home town. Business was good in Lodz. The town was growing from day to day. When a few Jewish pioneers had, through their non-Jewish ways and associations, broken a path into the weaving trade, not simply as employers, but as workers and masters, others followed in larger and larger numbers, and Jewish looms became a common thing in Lodz. The legal difficulties in the way of this expansion were easily overcome. With the suppression of the Polish rebellion by hordes of Cossacks, the Russian Government sent into Poland a swarm of officials, typical Russians whose first thought was of bribes. The German weavers objected; their guilds remained hostile to the Jews; they complained to the authorities; but Jewish looms hummed louder and louder in the old sections of the city.

The Jewish quarter became fearfully congested. Overnight new attics, balconies, and storeys were added to the crazy houses, to accommodate looms and workers. There was a constant stream of Jews who were deserting the countryside for the wages to be earned in Lodz. Without permits, without plans, day and night, the building went on; houses were pulled down, others put up, rooms were divided, walls were erected; a crooked jumble of patchwork, jerrybuilt structures covered the old city. Finally nothing more could be added, and the Jews began to edge over into the German section itself, Vilki, where they were specifically forbidden to settle. First the rich stepped over the boundary, wheedling and bribing their way in; then, when a number of precedents had been established, the poorer and less courageous followed.

Like a river in thaw, bursting its banks and carrying before it the dams and barriers which had long held it in, the Jewish population of Lodz and the surrounding country swarmed to the weaving trade, overthrowing in the rush of their hunger all the barriers, the special laws, ukases, prohibitions which a hostile Government had erected against them. Thousands of country innkeepers, pedlars, and village merchants had been ruined with the ruin of the nobility. In the general movement which ensued—the search for bread—it was Lodz that sucked in the largest part of the unsettled population. In the little towns the Jewish dry-goods stores either were closed or stood empty from morning to night; young sixteen-year-old wives, the supports of scholarly husbands who gave all their time to study of the Talmud, sat there waiting for customers who came no more. For the nobility was either impoverished or exiled, and the liberated serfs were as poor as ever. Steadily the weaving business spread out of Lodz, and looms were set up in the townlets and villages; but Lodz remained the metropolis and chief centre of attraction. The Jews of the villages, long accustomed to the meannesses and brutalities of the nobility and their servants, made light of the obstacles which the Germans and the officials placed in their way in the city; they came pouring in, setting up their looms everywhere.

At first they had to employ many Germans, the poorer kind of workers, and these were glad to work for the Jews— much more so than for their own kind. The Jewish boss did not make them kiss his hand every morning when they came to work and every evening when they left. If a Jewish boss caught a German worker stealing a spool or a piece of woven cloth, he did not thrash the thief, as a German boss would have done. He merely took the stolen article and threw it back into the heap. On Saturday nights the German weavers would sit in the kitchens of their Jewish employers, smoking their big, hooked pipes while they waited for their pay, spitting on the floor, carrying on a Yiddish conversation with the wife of the house and the servants.

"Hey, Reb employer," they said in excellent Yiddish, "get through with your Sabbath and give us our few groschen. They'll be closing the inns soon."

Steadily the number of Jews who could work a loom increased. Fathers brought their sons in from the villages to learn the trade. Barefoot they came on all the roads leading into Lodz. They came with sticks in their hands to beat off the village dogs, and on the outskirts of the town they put on their boots, which they had been carrying all the way. It was the custom to apprentice the boys for three years. A sum of money, the savings and scrapings of God knew how many seasons, was paid into the hand of the master weaver. The boys would receive no pay during the apprenticeship. They would get their meals and a place to sleep in, and from morning to night they would learn.

They stood in the hundreds at their looms, their skull-caps on their heads, the ritual fringes hanging over their cheap canvas trousers, pieces of coloured thread clinging to their

[25]

curly hair and sprouting beards, while their hands flew swiftly over the looms, weaving from before sunrise till long after sunset the piece goods which were to be made into dresses and women's kerchiefs. As they worked they sang snatches from the synagogue services, trilling the bravura passages like real cantors, pausing with special joy on the sacred words of the high festivals. The master weavers paraded up and down the aisles, keeping an eye on the heaps of merchandise, urging the workers on, infuriated if one of them stopped to wipe the perspiration from his forehead or to roll himself a cigarette.

In the kitchens of these home factories sat the wives and daughters of the employers, peeling potatoes, frying onions, preparing the food for the workers and apprentices. Here and there sat an apprentice rocking a cradle with his foot while his hands were busy wrapping the woollen thread on spools.

In the market-places Jews were busy selling piece goods, remnants, wool and cotton. The groceries were crowded with the wives of the workers. Rag-merchants made the rounds of the workshops in town and village, gathering the waste to be made into wadding. Women and girls sat wrapping thread on coloured spools, seamstresses treadled their sewing-machines, stocking-weavers turned out by the tens of thousands the heavy, bright-coloured stockings which women wore in those days. The synagogue melodies of the men mingled with the sentimental love-songs of the women.

When the city of Lodz became too small for all this activity, the Jews began to build a new suburb.

To one side of Lodz there stretched big, sandy fields on which the grain grew very sparsely. Even the grass was meagre and sandy, and the animals which pastured there were lean and small-uddered, yielding little milk. The peasants who worked this soil were mostly the former serfs of the two Canarski brothers, of the Polish nobility. After their liberation they had not the means with which to buy the land, nor were they able to scrape a livelihood out of their allotments. They remained with their former owners, living in dreadful poverty, going around half-naked and hungry, glad if they could fill their stomachs with potatoes between harvest times.

Reb Solomon David Preiss, the rich and pious Chasid of Kotzk, who had made his money selling Polish grain to Prussia, lay awake one night and, thinking of a thousand and one things, he also thought that it would be an excellent idea to buy up the fields of the brothers Canarski and to build there a suburb for the poorer class of workers who were living on top of one another in Lodz. The next morning, right after prayers, he told his servant to harness the gig and to drive him over to the Canarski estate.

Clever business-man that he was, Reb Solomon David Preiss did not go straight to the two noblemen. He stopped at the steward's lodge to have a friendly talk on the subject of the grain he was buying from him, and, chewing a sample of the purchase, he asked as it were abstractedly how things were going with the Canarski brothers. The steward tugged at his long, blond moustaches, sighed heavily, and asked in return how anyone could expect things to go well when his employers neglected the estate, threw out money right and left, gambled, ran off every now and then to Paris for a wild time, and left everything to him, the steward. Reb Solomon listened quietly, commiserating with him.

When he approached the brothers themselves he had nothing to say about a suburb to be built on their lands. Oh, no. All he had in mind, he said, was to put up a glass-factory; he was looking for a suitable location, one with plenty of sand. And if he could get such a location, at the right price, he might consider it. The faces of the two noblemen suddenly became radiant.

"Pan Solomon!" they exclaimed, forgetting in their enthusiasm that it was unbecoming for a Polish nobleman to call a Jew Pan, or Mister, "our estate Balut has sand enough for fifty glass-factories."

Reb Solomon David did not show himself too eager. He let himself be persuaded with difficulty. In the end he bought up the tremendous stretch of fields for the sum of twenty thousand roubles, cash. The brothers could hardly wait to collect the money; and the moment they had it they set out for Paris, where it could be spent easiest. While they were in Paris they heard from their steward that Reb Solomon David was building, not a glass-factory, but a suburb, and they came running back to Lodz to cancel the sale for breach of contract. The judge and assessors before whom the case was laid were friends of the Canarskis, and they began to look for precedents which would permit them to push out the Jew. Reb Solomon David Preiss had no palace where he could entertain judges and assessors and their wives and daughters, nor could he converse with them on their favourite subjects of hares and hunting dogs. But Reb Solomon had money, golden imperials, which appealed to judges and assessors even more than dances and hunting dogs. So that very soon the judges and assessors were looking for precedents which would not permit them to push out the Jew. The brothers Canarski, finding themselves in a tight place, denounced Reb Solomon to the high authorities for putting up buildings in a place where Jews were, according to the law, not permitted to live: to wit, in a village. Officials from the capital came down in carriages and visited the Canarskis. They drank wine at their table, danced with their daughters, went hunting, and promised everything. But the golden imperials of Reb Solomon were irresistible, and the high officials went back and forth between Lodz and Warsaw, consulted authorities, filled out reports, prepared learned commentaries, and made such a marvellous tangle of the business that even they forgot what it was all about.

And meanwhile, on the sand fields of Balut, the suburb grew, house by house, hut by hut, street by street. The building went on ceaselessly, day and night, swiftly, formlessly. Every man who bought himself a lot built according to his own taste, and the chief consideration was to crowd as many houses and rooms as possible into each lot. Houses and walls ran crookedly into narrow lanes and blind alleys. Before the rooms had been whitewashed they were already filled. Peasants brought sand in carts, pulled out the roots of trees, slaked lime, sawed logs, planed planks, cut tiles. Jewish carpenters, plasterers, tinsmiths, locksmiths, glaziers, were busy night and day. The dossiers of the case *Canarski Brothers* vs. *Solo-*

[28]

mon David Preiss went from office to office in the Senate, and meanwhile there arose a city, with streets, houses, squares, market-places, which no law would ever be able to destroy.

The streets in this new Jewish city usually went under two names: those given officially, by the municipality, and those given in advance by the plain folk who anticipated or ignored the authorities—homely names which subsisted side by side with the dignified titles used by the post office; the earliest settler in a street, or the richest man, or the little synagogue, was usually the namesake. There was the Street of Reb Mordecai the Beadle, the Synagogue Street, Jonah Piltzer's Square, Grossman's Lane, Pepper Alley, and so forth. On some of the corners still lingered the straw-covered huts of the peasants, and for a while there wandered through the noisy streets a few lean cows, an occasional pig, a scraggy chicken, a half-starved dog. But very rapidly these last rural vestiges were wiped out, the peasants themselves being pulled into the city life. They did unskilled work, digging lime, carrying bricks and mortar, digging out roots of trees. And gradually they lost their peasant character, too, discarding their peasant clothes and buying the ready-made city suits. They made money for the first time in their lives and learned how to spend it. Their children mingled with the children of the Jews and learned to speak Yiddish; they also earned a little small change, or a piece of white bread, for doing certain Sabbath services forbidden to the Jews, such as removing the candlesticks, lighting an oven in the winter-time, putting out lamps, and other odd jobs connected with the touching of fire. The poorest class of German weavers came into the Jewish city and lived in the houses of the former peasants. Soon after, the agents of the German master weavers began to comb the villages and townlets round Lodz for peasants to work in the steam factories which had begun to spring up.

On the Vilki side of the city, hard by the fields, the German master Heinz Huntze, who had become rich in the days of the hand-looms, built the first steam factory, a huge red-brick building with many windows and a tremendous chimney. His was the first siren to scream into the quiet morning air of Lodz, waking the city to its work. Before this factory was quite completed Reb Solomon David Preiss, who had made an immense fortune in the building of Balut, made himself a rich broadcloth coat, ordered himself a new and imposing silk hat and a silk umbrella, sewed a fistful of banknotes into his vest—which he never took off, not even in his sleep—and set out for England. With no knowledge of foreign languages, speaking only a Polish Yiddish which he distorted into what he thought was German, he hired himself an engineer and a chemist, purchased great machines, and brought them all back with him to Lodz. He built the second steam factory in Lodz, and his chimney, towering above that of Heinz Huntze's, added a richer quota of smoke to the clear morning air.

Reb Solomon David Preiss did not employ Jews in his factory, for the Englishmen refused to work on Sunday, and Reb Solomon David would not have Jews working for him on the Sabbath. In fact, it is even forbidden to a Jew to make gentile employees work for him on the Sabbath, for it is written: "The seventh day is the Sabbath of the Lord thy God; in it thou shalt not do any work, thou, nor thy son, nor thy daughter, thy manservant nor thy maidservant, nor thy cattle nor thy stranger that is within thy gates." Therefore Reb Solomon David, who was a scholar as well as a businessman, went to his Rabbi and had the latter make out a deed of sale in a mixture of Hebrew and Aramaic. The document stated that Reb Solomon David Preiss, of the holy community of Lodz, by Lake Lodka, sold his factory to his gentile servant Voitchech Smoluch. Reb Solomon David called in the servant, who stood terrified before the Rabbi while his employer proposed the "sale."

"Panie," he stammered, when his employer had translated the document to him, "how can I buy the factory? I'm a poor man."

"Idiot," answered his employer, "do as I tell you. You'll pay me a rouble for the factory."

"I haven't got a rouble," pleaded the servant.

Reb Solomon David took a silver rouble out of his big purse and handed it to his servant. "Here, I'll lend you a rouble and you'll pay me for the factory. You'll give me back the rouble when you can."

The Pole did not understand. He was afraid of a trick; maybe these Jews were practising some sort of sorcery on him. But he yielded to the anger of his employer and touched gingerly the tip of the red kerchief which the Rabbi held out to him, according to custom, in sign of the completion of the deal. Then the Rabbi told him to sign the document, which the Pole did not know how to do, so he merely put down three little crosses. Both the Rabbi and Reb Solomon David were annoyed by the timidity of the gentile and by the sacrilegious crosses which appeared at the bottom of the Hebrew document, but the sale was legal. Reb Solomon David gave the Pole a ten-groschen tip—a whole tenth of a rouble—and the deed of sale, and the servant shoved the document into his hat and hurried off to the nearest saloon. To the Rabbi Reb Solomon David gave, for his services, three roubles. And now that the factory belonged not to him, to Reb Solomon David the Jew, but to Voitchech Smoluch the gentile, it could be kept going on the Sabbath—and, for that matter, on every other holy day—and no sin would be committed.

The factory which no longer belonged to Reb Solomon David Preiss thundered and trembled with activity on Sabbath and week-day. The smoke belched into the sky, the sirens screamed across the city. The German hand-loom workers, who had begun to feel the competition of the steam factories, concentrated their resentment on the Jew. Machines were inventions of the Devil, with whom the Jews were in league. The German masters, for their own good reasons, encouraged the workers in their hatred of the Jewish manufacturer. And so one Saturday night a horde of infuriated workers, with torches, axes, and knives in their hands, poured out of the saloons and made for the Jewish factory. At the head of the procession went the masters, carrying the flags of the guilds; behind them followed the drunken workers. They poured barrels of kerosene on the doors and walls of the factory and set fire to it; then they turned to the Jewish quarter and rioted through the narrow streets, attacking workers and shopkeepers, smashing windows, and setting fire to houses. The cry of their mediæval ancestors was on their lips:

"Hep! Hep! Jude!"

A regiment of Cossacks appeared, cleared the streets, and with naked swords and gigantic whips drove the rabble out of town, toward the banks of Lake Lodka.

Reb Solomon David Preiss's factory was not seriously damaged. Before long the smoke belched from it thicker than ever, the sirens screamed more loudly. German master weavers, seeing they could not get rid of their Jewish competitor, decided to follow his example. They borrowed money from the state bank and built factories. Jews who had made money importing foreign goods also entered the home industry and added new factories. The chimneys of Lodz clustered like the trees of a forest, but they blossomed in smoke and poisoned the air. Cesspools formed near every factory, and sent up their poison from the ground. A second wave of immigration set in from the countryside, and thousands of peasants became city workers. The textiles of Lodz flowed out over Russia and into the Far East. And still there was work enough both for the steam factories and for the hand-looms, and they subsisted side by side.

Lodz went on growing, and with it grew the house of Reb Abraham Hirsh Ashkenazi, also known as Reb Abraham Hirsh Danzig.

From childhood, almost from babyhood, on, little Simcha Meyer led a lonely and sundered life, estranged from his twin brother and little sisters and even from his father and mother. He went his own way. In the sandy courtyard behind his father's brick house in the old town the children of the families played together, but Simcha Meyer stood off and watched them from a distance. The yard was a huge one, cobbled only in part. On three sides it was closed in by houses, and on the fourth by a wall. It was not rectangular in shape, but irregular, for houses and walls had never been built according to any plan. The rich house was the one in front, the house of Reb Abraham Hirsh Ashkenazi; the houses at the sides were those of workmen, and all the day long the hum and rattle of looms issued from the windows and open doors. A thick dust floated into the air, particularly from the houses of the dealers who bought rags to pluck into wadding. Across the entire length of the yard a rope-maker drew and twisted the long strands of hemp. He worked with three sons, and all day long their voices would be heard: "Draw! Hold fast! Draw! Hold fast!"

All the children, rich and poor, loved the yard; but most of all it was loved by Simcha Meyer's twin brother, Jacob Bunim.

"Simcha Meyer," he would cry out joyfully, "let's play tag!"

"I don't want," Simcha Meyer would answer, curtly.

There is no friendship between the two. Jacob Bunim would like to be friends. He is a big, sturdy youngster, always full of laughter.

"Jacob Bunim," the older people ask him, "what makes you laugh like that?"

"I don't know," the youngster answers. "I like it." And he laughs again, so that others must laugh with him. He plays with heart and soul. No one runs faster than he, and no one is as skilful in finding hiding-places under the wooden foundations of the house. He is the strongest boy in the yard; he pulls out the cobbles and holds them above his head, to the terror and admiration of all. He stands side by side with the rope-maker's boys and pulls as hard as any of them. He does not like to play alone or laugh alone; he must have others to laugh and play with him. He wants even his brother Simcha Meyer to join; but Simcha Meyer turns away from him.

The soul of little Simcha Meyer is filled with pride and ambition. He won't play in the yard where his brother is king. He can't run as fast as his brother, he can't stand on his head like him, and he can't turn cartwheels. On rare occasions when, despite himself, he is drawn into a game of tag, he is the first to be caught, and when he runs fast he's almost sure to trip up on one of the cobble-stones and fall full-length, hitting his nose on the ground, so that the blood streams from it.

The sight of blood terrifies him. He begins to scream: "Blood! Blood!" and run around with his eyes shut. Only Jacob Bunim doesn't lose his head. He takes his brother by the arm and leads him to the pump. He fills his two hands with water, holds it up to Simcha Meyer's nose and says: "Draw in!" Jacob Bunim is still laughing, though he is really sorry for his brother. "You mustn't be afraid of blood," he says. "I'm not afraid of it. Look!" And picking up a piece of glass, he scratches his hand so that the blood comes out, and he laughs more loudly than ever.

The children standing around are filled with admiration, especially the little girls. "He's so strong!" they gasp.

And Simcha Meyer, hearing them, is filled with bitterness and anger.

[34]

Only in the house, and when there are no other children around, does he let Jacob Bunim play with him, and then only at games in which Jacob Bunim must carry him around. He sits astride his brother then, and digs in with his heels, uses a straw from the broom as a whip, and shouts ecstatically: "Giddy up!" Leah Sarah, the servant, can't bear to see this. "You big fool!" she shouts at Jacob Bunim, who is her favourite. "Do you want to tear your guts out?"

"I can carry two like him," brags Jacob Bunim, and laughs.

In these games Simcha Meyer is happy, but when he goes out in the yard where the other children are, his face becomes sullen. He would play with them if they would let him be leader, if they would gather round him admiringly, as they do round Jacob Bunim. But there's only one Jacob Bunim, and all the boys follow him around, and the little girls, too, just like a lot of chickens following a big red rooster. First and most adoring among them is little Dinah, the daughter of Reb Chaim Alter, whose wooden house stands next to Reb Abraham Hirsh's yard. She is plump and pretty, with hair of chestnut brown, done into a hundred rings and curls and tied up with a bright blue ribbon. She loves play, and she loves Jacob Bunim. And he—he carries her around pick-a-back or trundles her up and down the yard in the wheelbarrow which the janitor uses for garbage.

Whenever Leah Sarah looks at the two of them, a wide happy grin spreads over her face, and she sighs to the other women: "What a sweet bride and bridegroom they'd make!"

"Dinah, who's going to be your bridegroom?" the women ask the little girl.

"My daddy," she answers, shaking her ringlets.

"And who else?"

"Him!" And she points with her plump little hand at Jacob Bunim.

Leah Sarah is filled with such joy that she must blow her nose into her apron to hide her emotions.

And Simcha Meyer stands on one side and sees how the whole world turns round Jacob Bunim. The yard is full of happy noises. From the open windows of the houses which make up two sides of it float the synagogue melodies

[35]

which the workers sing at the looms. From other windows, those of the wadding-makers, float out softer, sweeter voices, those of the girls whose heads, bent over their work and covered with dust and fluff, are full of dreams about the princes and queens' daughters whose marvellous adventures are contained in the little paper-covered Yiddish books which they read of evenings. They sing sad songs about Jewish girls, loved and shot dead by high army officers, or about other girls who fell in love with gentiles and turned Christian for them, only to be cast off later, so that they had to wander from house to house and do washing and other menial work. It is all very sweet and sad, and the children love to listen.

But the greatest source of joy in the yard is the rope-maker. He is an immense Jew, covered with a wild growth of light hair, which looks like the hemp he twists. It grows all over his face and neck, it stands out in wads from his ears and nostrils, it lies along his bare legs. Side by side with the ritual fringes which hang over his trousers dangle bundles of rope. The rope-maker and his sons are giants, and they are as good and jolly as they are huge. They never chase away the children who gather to watch them with eyes and mouths wide open, and if one of the boys wants to catch the rope and twist and pull, or turn the wheel, the old man lets him. He laughs, in a big thunderous voice: "Hold on tight, there. Don't be scared, I won't pull your whiskers off!"

There are other pleasures which keep the children in the yard, so that their mothers can hardly get them into the house to eat. Only part of the yard is cobbled; more than half of it is sand, in which you can dig down deep, till the sand gets all yellow, and even water oozes out. The boys build castles of the sand; the girls make loaves and cakes. On the low roof of the janitor's hut there is a dovecote, and all day long the bright-coloured doves circle above the yard or come down into the sand to look for crumbs and worms. The cats suddenly wake up from their dozing in the sun and begin to crawl stealthily toward the pigeons, and the pigeons don't seem to know or care, and the cats come nearer and nearer and nearer—and then they leap. But always too late. The pigeons are gone.

[36]

Jacob Bunim's heart brims with joy. "Simcha Meyer, Simcha Meyer," he shouts, "I'll get you some crumbs and you can feed the pigeons. They'll come right up to your hand."

"I don't want," mutters Simcha Meyer.

The children see him standing alone, and they begin to mock him. "Simcha Meyer, very big liar, buys for lower and sells for higher!" He walks away from them.

Small-built, lean, his face lightly freckled, with thin lips and grey eyes which change into a queer green when he grows angry, Simcha Meyer stands to one side, pretending not to watch. His hands are thrust into the pockets of his well-made alpaca coat. His silk cap is pushed back on his head, leaving clear the high forehead, which is fringed with close-cut light hair falling into two flaxen ear-locks at either side. His big ears stand out from his head like those of a rabbit; they seem to be listening to everything. In the same way his eyes, too, seem to be everywhere. If you look at them carelessly they seem to be gentle enough; but suddenly the green light comes into them, and you see all the distrust and obstinacy and dislike in them. They are restless eyes, darting always from side to side; there is something fantastic in them, they are even slightly mad.

He longs with all his heart to join in the games with the other children, to run and shout with them, dig in the sand, dance in a ring; but something hard and obstinate, something which isn't himself, won't let him budge. His mother calls to him from the window: "Meyer, darling, play with the children!" He throws back a curt "I don't want!" But he does want; only just because mother asks him he won't do it.

If he plays at all, he plays alone. He gathers and sorts labels out of his father's store. He collects bobbins and threads them on a cord. In the house he has a china rooster, a savings-bank; he takes the coins out and sits counting them intently. Then he puts them back and takes them out again. From the merchants who come to visit his father he gets little gifts, three-kopeck pieces, ten-kopeck pieces, and sometimes even a whole silver rouble. He does not spend. He saves and counts. He takes the china rooster with him into

[37]

the yard and shakes it, so that all the children may hear, though he seems to pay no attention to them.

For though he will not play with the children, he cannot avoid them wholly. He needs them sometimes because he needs someone he can make angry. It's not safe to interfere with the boys, but the girls can't do anything to him. So when he feels like it he walks deliberately into their sand-cakes or sneaks up on them, snatches playthings from their hands, and runs away. He does this to all the girls, his own sisters included; but most of all to Dinah, who loves his brother Jacob Bunim so.

He can't do these things to Jacob Bunim or the other boys, but he has other ways of teasing them. He comes out into the yard with a big piece of sugar candy and stations himself near Jacob Bunim and sucks it loudly. "It's good," he says, "it's good."

Jacob Bunim has already had his piece of candy, but he wants more. And he never wants anything except passionately.

"Simcha Meyer," he says, "give me a lick."

"No." And Simcha Meyer sucks more loudly.

"Didn't I let you lick mine?" shouts Jacob Bunim, his heart swelling with anger.

"I can lick your candy, you can't lick mine," says Simcha Meyer, and sticks out his tongue.

This is more than Jacob Bunim can stand. He throws himself on Simcha Meyer and tears the piece of candy from him, leaving the marks of his finger-nails on Simcha Meyer's cheek. Jacob Bunim is good-hearted, and he wants others to be good-hearted, and if they refuse to be good-hearted he hits them. His anger doesn't last long. It dies with the first blow, and he is ready to make friends again. He hates not being friends with someone; it makes him feel like not himself. No sooner has he knocked Simcha Meyer down than he is sorry for it, and says so, and asks to be friends again. He holds out his little finger, as a sign that he is offering his friendship. Simcha Meyer pays no attention. He picks himself up, his eyes green with fury, and he runs to tell his father.

[38]

Reb Abraham Hirsh has one simple rule: children are always in the wrong and parents are always in the right. So when Simcha Meyer comes to complain about Jacob Bunim, he decides that both ought to get a taste of the strap, which he slowly takes from round his trousers. But Simcha Meyer knows a trick worth two of that. When Jacob Bunim has been punished and his own turn comes, he falls suddenly on the floor and goes into convulsions. His mother comes running in, picks him up, and holds him close.

"Meyer, my little darling, my treasure!" She begins to weep.

Reb Abraham Hirsh is baffled. "How is it he gets those convulsions only when he's going to be punished?" he shouts.

The mother does not hear him. She carries off her elder son and puts him to bed. She gives him her gold watch and chain to play with. She bends over him tenderly, and tears fill her eyes.

"Murderer!" she mutters. "Brute!" And to Simcha Meyer she whispers: "Mother won't let anything happen to her darling."

The walls of the private office of Heinz Huntze are covered with portraits, pictures, medals, and diplomas. Right above the massive oak desk hang the pictures of two monarchs: on the right, Alexander II, Autocrat of the Russias, King of Poland, Grand Duke of Finland, etc., etc.; on the left, William I, Emperor of Germany. And in the middle, right under the two rulers, hangs the portrait of the great industrialist Heinz Huntze.

The portrait of Heinz Huntze is not quite as imposing as those of the two kings. His bosom does not glitter, like theirs, with orders and crosses; his face, too, lacks the high repose and dignity which stamps the faces of kings. His bullet-head, close cropped, with the short hair standing up stiffly in front, like bristles, is somewhat too reminiscent of the poor weaver Heinz Huntze who came out of Saxony so many years ago with two poor hand-looms on his cart. Likewise the lines on his face, which the artist could not wholly suppress, bespeak a life of worry and labour not at all suggestive of royalty. His stiff black coat, his starched shirt, and, more than anything else, his high collar, which almost touches his ears, are, in fact, typical of the German master workman dressed up for a golden wedding or some other solemn celebration. No, it is impossible to say that this full-length portrait of Heinz Huntze is imposing; it is all the less so by contrast with the two magnificent personages above him; but it is certainly not without character.

[40]

There is only a single ribbon on his vest, that of the Order of St. Anna. The Governor of Piotrkov got that for him from St. Petersburg, in recognition of his high services to the industrial development of Poland. It cost him a good round sum of money—presents from Heinz Huntze's daughters to the Governor, his wife and daughters. Not that Heinz Huntze himself would have spent a cracked groschen on such rubbish; still, he must admit that it looks good on his snow-white vest, that ribbon of the Order of St. Anna. Far more important, however, are the great gold, silver, and bronze medals which cover the walls, testifying to the quality of the work turned out by the factory of Heinz Huntze. As far as appearance goes, Heinz Huntze is even overshadowed by his man Melchior, who, with his lofty form, his vast red moustaches and sideburns, his green huntsman's uniform with gilt buttons, his dazzling high boots with silver tassels, stands at attention near the door of the office, ready to carry out his master's orders.

But if Heinz Huntze lacks majesty of face and bearing, he does not lack the substance of royalty, which is power. He is not a king in title; he is a king in reality, and though his rule covers less than a thousandth part of the territory of the Emperors, his decisions cut closer and more deeply into the lives of his subjects. The thousands of workers, together with their wives and children, are in his hands. It depends on him whether they work late into the night or can spend the evening in a tavern. If he is exceptionally gracious, he lets them have their holidays, when they can lie around in the grass near the factory or gather in the *Gesangverein* to sing the hymns, ballads, and homeland songs of their beloved Germany. It depends on him entirely whether a worker who has seduced a factory girl shall marry her to cover up her shame or whether the girl shall trail a bastard after her to the derision of her fellow-workers. He alone decides whether the workers shall put in double shifts, so that they crawl home almost too exhausted to swallow the soup, made with real lard instead of cheap oil, which their wives prepare with the extra earnings; or whether they shall not work at all, and so have plenty of time to eat in, but nothing to eat.

[41]

To him, to Heinz Huntze, come expectant mothers, asking him to be godfather to the unborn child; his employees likewise come to him for permission to marry, and when they expect a new mouth to feed they come again, hat in hand, to beg for a little increase in pay.

To him belong the huge factory, the rows of red-brick dwellings which house his workers, the surrounding fields in which the women plant potatoes and cabbages, the woods where the children go for bark and branches and firewood in winter, the church where all assemble on Sundays, the hospital to which a man is rushed when he has been caught in a machine, the cemetery in which he is buried, and even the *Gesangverein* where the workers sing the ballads of their homeland. Here he is king, old Heinz Huntze, with a kingship unknown to the rulers of the land. Of him, much more than of those abstract figures—and with greater awe, too—speak the old, toothless workers, recalling the far-off days when he was one of them, standing with them at a loom, talking with them like an equal, and even sitting down with them to a glass of beer. The young men speak of him, and the young women, and even the babies in the cradles. Every word he utters is caught up, repeated, carried from street to street, interpreted and reinterpreted.

Like every ruler Heinz Huntze cannot tolerate competition from those who were his former subjects. He has never been able to forgive Fritz Goetzke, his one-time employee, for working himself up and erecting a steam factory just like his own. As often as he thinks of this piece of impudence his face goes red and his voice rises. Besides, this unspeakable Goetzke has the habit of stealing every one of old Huntze's innovations, whether it be a type of fabric, a design, or a model. And he turns them out cheaper, the devil knows how. The struggle has been going on for a long time, and it is beginning to tell on Heinz Huntze. He has met every attack with a counter-attack; he has sworn a dozen times to undersell Fritz Goetzke if it cost him his last penny. But Fritz Goetzke refuses to be undersold, and if Heinz goes down a groschen on the dozen, Goetzke goes down another groschen.

[42]

It was in one of his bitterest moods that Reb Abraham Hirsh Ashkenazi found him one day. The latter sat opposite him in the office, his hat off, his head covered only with a little skull-cap.

"I'll shoot the dog," screamed old Huntze, lapsing, in spite of all the efforts spent on him by his daughters, into the heavy dialect of Saxony. "I'll shoot the *Schweinehund,* I'll put an end to it!"

"Herr Huntze," said Reb Abraham Hirsh, softly, "don't you think it's gone far enough? Don't you think you ought to make peace with him?" Reb Abraham Hirsh spoke a Yiddish German, and for "peace" said *"sholom,"* in good Hebrew, and not *"Frieden."* He went on: "You know, Herr Huntze, it is written in our sacred books that the world is founded on *sholom.*" He remembered suddenly that *sholom* was not a German word, and Heinz Huntze would not understand it. But he could not think of the German equivalent.

Heinz Huntze almost leapt out of his seat. "What?" he howled. "*Sholom?* You want me to make *sholom* with that *Scheisskerl?* Not I, Reb Abraham Hirsh. I'll die first."

Reb Abraham Hirsh was deeply touched to hear the old German use a Hebrew word, likewise to hear the full title with which the other addressed him. But he could not agree that Fritz Goetzke ought to be shot. He stroked his thick, black beard and tried to pacify old Huntze. He understood Huntze's rage. It was, if you like, indecent and ungrateful of Fritz Goetzke to compete so bitterly with his former employer. But one mustn't expect decency and gratitude in business. Only money counted. And if money ceased to count, it was only to give way to something worse. For there was something more than rapacity in Fritz Goetzke's bitter competition and in old Heinz Huntze's counter-attacks: there was ambition and personal rivalry. The fact he had once been old Huntze's employee made Fritz Goetzke the more relentless. But what was the sense of it all, Reb Abraham Hirsh asked himself. The only gainers were the shopkeepers. They got merchandise for next to nothing—or, in the case of those who got easy credit, for nothing at all. If it went on like this the two factories would face ruin. Better make peace, he thought. And he daringly suggested a combination: one firm—Heinz Huntze and Fritz Goetzke.

Heinz Huntze leaned over his desk and bellowed: "I won't listen to that *Quatsch,* that rubbish!" And he went round the table and almost put his hand on Reb Abraham Hirsh's mouth. "I'd rather die than go into business with that louse."

Reb Abraham Hirsh got up, with a sigh, and went to the door. He paused and turned back. He would have liked, before he left, to quote the old German something from the wisdom of the Jewish sages, a parable, a proverb, a deep saying, to show how evil was anger, and how, because of it, cities and countries and nations had been destroyed. But he could not think of the German words. In particular he would have liked to tell Huntze the story of Kamtza and Bar-Kamtza, the two Jewish enemies in Jerusalem at the time of the Roman siege, for the sake of whose obstinate hatred for each other the city and the homeland were destroyed. But he doubted whether the old German would understand these pieces from the Talmud, especially in Yiddish. He gave it up and made a helpless gesture with his hand. He said, simply: "Herr Huntze, I hope to persuade you yet, with God's help. Think it over. It's the only way out."

But Heinz Huntze was so enraged that he could not fill his pipe. "Hey, you," he shouted to the servant in the green hunting costume, "don't stand there like an idiot. Fill it for me!" And the angrier he grew, the more thickly did the old peasant dialect sound in Heinz Huntze's voice.

ℛℯ𝒷 Abraham Hirsh Ashkenazi's sons do not attend the same Hebrew school or study under the same teacher.

Although in the matter of age they are separated by only a few minutes, in the matter of study they are separated by an unbridgeable gulf. Jacob Bunim is a normal boy, and like all boys of his age he is already learning the Talmud, but it is quite clear that nothing is going to come of it. He gets it laboriously, page by page, without quite understanding it. He isn't expected to do more than repeat his weekly lesson when Saturday afternoon comes and his father examines him, after his Sabbath nap.

"All right, all right, it'll have to do," says Reb Abraham Hirsh, shrugging his shoulders. "Now go to Mamma and tell her to give you your Sabbath fruit. And try to be a better student."

Jacob Bunim knows only too well that he is a disappointment to his father, and for a few moments after his Sabbath examination his face is overshadowed. But not more than for a few moments. He sits down in front of the cookies and cake which the children get every Sabbath afternoon, and he forgets. He smacks his lips. He loves food as he loves play and as he loves everything else physical. Before long he is laughing again at the top of his voice, his father's discontent forgotten.

Very different is it with Simcha Meyer.

Already the word *ilui*, the word precious and beloved

among Jewish parents, meaning *young genius, young scholar, young master of learning, prodigy,* is being applied to Simcha Meyer. At the age of ten he had exhausted the scholarship of the ordinary children's *melamed,* or teacher, and Reb Abraham Hirsh separated him from his brother, took him out of the elementary *cheder,* or schoolroom, and placed him under the care of Reb Boruch Wolf Lentchitzer, who taught older children, such as were preparing for their confirmation, and sometimes youths who were already engaged to be married. Every Saturday afternoon Reb Boruch Wolf comes to Reb Abraham Hirsh's house to examine his pupil in the presence of the father. Reb Boruch Wolf drinks countless cups of the Sabbath tea, which has been prepared the day before, of course, and is kept hot in a huge stone jug wrapped in rags. He enjoys the tea, and he enjoys displaying the ingenuity of his remarkable pupil. This isn't a straightforward examination, such as suffices for other pupils. It is an examination *de luxe,* with pitfalls, misleading questions, hairsplitting distinctions—in fact, it is almost a disputation between two scholars of equal age and erudition. The boy catches up the questions, caps the quotations, challenges the precedents, gives parable for parable, meets casuistry with casuistry. Reb Boruch Wolf perspires with tea and happiness.

"Reb Abraham Hirsh," he murmurs in an aside, "the boy's an *ilui,* a head of gold."

Happiness fills the heart of Reb Abraham Hirsh, too, but he gives no outward sign.

"See to it, Reb Boruch Wolf," he pleads, "that he grows up a good Jew, too, with the fear of God in him."

He has not forgotten what the Rabbi of Vorka told him, that his generations would be rich men—and no mention of piety and the fear of God. He is troubled in his happiness, and he worries more about Simcha Meyer than about Jacob Bunim, just because the boy has a "golden" head, is considered a prodigy, and is held in respect. He has noticed that the boy has his own ways, that he pokes his nose everywhere, picks up everything, understands things far beyond his years, and is restless, acquisitive, eager. He knows, too,

[46]

that all *iluis,* all prodigies, are like that, but that does not reassure him. He knows that piety is above learning, and better a starving school-teacher who fears God than a mighty scholar who has departed from the path of Jewishness. He sends Simcha Meyer away to the kitchen to get his Sabbath fruit, and he turns to the teacher with a deep sigh.

"Reb Boruch Wolf," he says, "the boy needs a firm hand. Don't spare the rod."

He has chosen Reb Boruch Wolf among all the teachers in Lodz for his boy Simcha Meyer. The mother, timid in all things except where her oldest boy was concerned, objected, for Reb Boruch Wolf is famous for his cruelty not less than for his piety and learning. Besides, he overworks the boys. He holds them in the schoolroom from early morning till late at night. On Thursday, which is repetition day, he works with them beyond midnight and sometimes until the morning hours. He crams into the children not only the Talmud with its accepted commentaries, but all kinds of super-commentaries on the commentaries themselves. He gets them out of obscure books, or invents them himself. As usual, Reb Abraham Hirsh pays no attention to his wife's objections. He wants the boy to learn early how to carry the heavy burden of *Torah* and Jewishness, and no one could teach that better than Reb Boruch Wolf Lentchitzer.

He is no youngster, no beginner, this Reb Boruch Wolf. He is in the late sixties, but still strong, with a lean, bony body and fingers like pincers. His face is slightly twisted as the result of a stroke of paralysis. He got that from a cold which he caught one bitter winter when he went on foot to his Rabbi all the way from Lentchitz to Kotzk. The right side of his face is higher than the left side; one pointed eyebrow goes up, the other down. Slightly twisted, too, is Reb Boruch Wolf's brain. He never teaches the boys the interesting parts of the Talmud, the legends and stories and adventures of the great teachers in Israel. These he considers fit only for women, or for anti-Chasidic Jews, or for others with weak heads. He doesn't like to teach the Bible in class, either, not even the most sacred part of it, the Pentateuch. The boys can study that for themselves, at home, on the Sabbaths, when they have no *cheder*. He goes further, Reb Boruch Wolf; he avoids those tractates of the Talmud which deal with bright and cheerful things, like holy days, festivals, and jolly customs. He concentrates on the purely legalistic and formalistic tractates, which have to do with business, bills, notes of exchange, and damages. He likes, best of all, the tractates which deal with the complicated ceremonial laws of purity and impurity, sacred and profane, in the Holy Land and in the lands of exile; with the ritual of sacrifice and slaughter, and the duties of the priests and Levites. He sits in front of his pupils, for ever puffing at his tremendous pipe with its three-foot stem, and the thick smoke creeps into the eyes and throats of the boys, making them think of the smoke of sacrifice.

His learning is as dry and bony and harsh as his own old body. He hates the simple and the straightforward, the obvious meaning of a text or interpretation. If it isn't complicated, it isn't learning to him. And he never finishes his sentences. It's the business of a good pupil, he says, to finish the teacher's sentences, to catch the lead and go on by himself. Even the few words which he does throw them, by way of hint, are half-swallowed by his thick whiskers or get lost in the stem of his pipe. He is full of casuistries, contradictions, paradoxes, questions, quotations, precedents. He twists the texts until he can't untwist them, and then he bangs the table with the stem of his pipe or brings it down on the shoulders of his pupils.

"Faster, you yokels, you blockheads!" he cries, and grinds his few remaining yellow teeth. "Heathens! Donkeys! You should be washing horses, not learning Talmud!"

He swipes with the hard, heavy pipe-stem right and left, and, unlike other teachers, he does not care whom he hits; the children of the rich are not more important to him than the children of the poor. He cares nothing for the age of his pupils; he is as liable to slap a young bridegroom as a beginner. The boys sway backward and forward in the traditional Talmud chant, they rub their eyes, they drag onward from line to line like weary horses which hear the whip whistling over them.

[48]

"*Eretz de-chutz le-aretz metame,* the lands outside the Holy Land bring uncleanliness," they mumble. "Wherefore the teachers ask this question . . ."

But they don't know the question, and they don't know the answer. In vain does Reb Boruch Wolf ply the pipe-stem right and left. The yokels, the heathens, the blockheads don't budge. Then Reb Boruch Wolf turns in despair to his favourite pupil, his prodigy, Simcha Meyer, with the cry: "You tell them, Simcha Meyer, tell the idiots!"

Simcha Meyer is by far the youngest in the schoolroom. After him are the thirteen-year-olds who are preparing for confirmation. But Simcha Meyer is the one bright spot in the life of Reb Boruch Wolf. Not that he follows the text and the teaching with any closeness. Far from it. While the Rabbi is explaining, or half-explaining, what happens to the purity of a Jew when he sets foot outside of the Holy Land, Simcha Meyer is busy in the back row playing at cards under the desk. Not real cards, that is, but pieces of paper marked with the names of the cards. He sways back and forth above the tattered pages of the Talmud, but under the desk his quick fingers are sorting the pieces of paper, collecting winnings, paying out losses. It's very seldom he does the last. He has an uncanny knack—if it's only that—of winning. The other boys know that something is wrong somewhere; there's something suspicious about those streaks of luck. But they never catch him. For that matter, neither does his Rebbi, Boruch Wolf. For no sooner does he cry: "You tell them, Simcha Meyer," than the boy's eyes fly back to the folio of the Talmud and he's off on a brilliant exposition of the question which the sages ask concerning the impurity of the lands outside Palestine.

Reb Boruch Wolf derives special joy from throwing his pupils into confusion. He'll get them to fix their eyes and ears on him, while he's explaining or half-explaining a difficult text; and while they're most absorbed in his words he'll suddenly exclaim: "Where's the sentence we're talking about?" for he, like all the other Talmud-teachers of his school, demands that the boys learn not only the text, but the place of each sentence and each word on the page of

[49]

the Talmud—all Talmuds being printed alike. But the boys, all confused, haven't the slightest idea where the text is, on the first line or on the tenth. And then a wild, hilarious joy comes into the soul of Boruch Wolf. He points the pipe-stem at one of the boys and howls: "Find it! Find it!" and when the boy's hand crawls helplessly over the page, brings the pipe-stem down on the fingers with a vicious crack.

Reb Boruch Wolf's dearest ambition is 'to catch Simcha Meyer in that way. But he never does. The boy manages, in some miraculous way, to keep his eyes both on his games and on the page of the Talmud. Nor does Reb Boruch Wolf ever succeed in giving him a false lead. That's another favourite trick of his. He puts a question concerning a legal dispute between Reuben and Simon, the traditional John Doe figures of all Talmudic cases, and, winding up his explanation, he chants: "Now it is obvious that Simon is—" and from the lilt in his voice it would appear that the next word is "guilty"—and all the boys follow with "guilty!" Thereupon, with a howl of mingled rage and glee, he gives the right answer: "No, you yokels, it's Reuben who is guilty." The trick succeeds with everyone but Simcha Meyer. It's hard to tell whether Simcha Meyer gives the right answer because he knows it or because, with a diabolic intuition, amazing in one of his years, he always reads his Rebbi's intention behind the misleading intonation.

This warfare between the Rebbi and his brilliant pupil rises to astonishing climaxes. Sometimes old Boruch Wolf takes up a complicated case, which he has thought out well in advance, and tries to confuse the youngster. But Simcha Meyer gives better than he gets. He remembers texts and precedents which have slipped from his Rebbi's mind; he quotes a host of authorities, twists the decision from all semblance of its original meaning, begins to shout enthusiastically, so that Reb Boruch Wolf becomes utterly confused and yields ground, losing the offensive to his pupil. His right eyebrow goes up higher and higher, till it threatens to disappear into his skull-cap, and the hair on the right side of his face bristles up like a cat's whiskers when a mouse has slipped away from between its claws. He is ashamed to give way in the presence of his pupils, he is in a daze, he would like to retreat with honour, but Simcha Meyer presses the advantage till the old man begins to stammer and contradict himself. Reb Boruch Wolf is lost between rage, shame, and admiration.

After one of these disastrous skirmishes he leaves Simcha Meyer alone for a few days. Then Simcha Meyer becomes shameless. He chants with the other boys, but mingles the words of the Talmud with the words of his game, hardly bothering to lower his voice.

"*Chelev u-shlemim,* a fat offering and a whole offering shall ye bring, *yaktir,* I've got thirty-one, pay me!"

The boys dislike him. They are older than he. Some of them are already engaged to be married, and one of them sports a gold watch and chain, even on week-days. But they are all in his hands. At home their fathers reproach them, saying: "Look at little Simcha Meyer; why can't you be like him?" But it is to Simcha Meyer they must come on Thursdays, when they are reviewing the week's studies, for explanation of the texts. Simcha Meyer does not give them his help for nothing. One boy must buy him a glass of ice-cream, another must let him play with his watch and take it to pieces. If Simcha Meyer dislikes one of the boys, he'll refuse to help, or else he'll give him a false translation of the text, and giggle when the boy repeats it to the Rebbi. But what can they do? And what can the Rebbi himself, Reb Boruch Wolf, do to him? At heart he is as afraid as the rest, and in spite of Reb Abraham Hirsh's injunction, he never lays a finger on Simcha Meyer, not even when the latter plays tricks which no other boy in the *cheder* would dream of trying.

Reb Boruch Wolf is married to a second wife, much younger than himself, a miserable creature, and barren at that, which is why her first husband divorced her. She is short-sighted, hard of hearing, absent-minded, and dreadfully clumsy. She keeps her husband in a perpetual rage. She doesn't understand his way of talking, his ironies and half-sentences.

"Boruch Wolf," she asks him in a drawn-out, whining

voice, "will you come in to eat?"

"Donkey!" he replies, "did you expect the food to come in to me?"

"Boruch Wolf, what would you like to eat?"

"Soup with noodles."

"I haven't got any, Boruch Wolf, it's the middle of the week."

"Idiot! Then why do you ask me?"

She never answers back, she is too frightened. And if her husband continues yelling at her she bursts into tears and wipes her eyes with a corner of her apron. Her tears drive Reb Boruch Wolf into a frenzy of rage. He can't bear tears, either his wife's or his pupils'. He becomes frantic. He gives a mighty blow with his pipe-stem on the table, and yells:

"Go home, everybody, go home! I'm not a Rebbi any more, I don't want to teach! I can't teach with a wife who's always wailing and snivelling. Get out, all of you!"

The boys don't wait until he has finished. They're outside before he has time to change his mind.

Reb Boruch Wolf's wife does her poor best not to irritate her husband, and she tries hard to swallow her tears. But if she isn't there to drive her husband into a frenzy, Simcha Meyer will sometimes take her place, with tricks of his own. He is quite skilful at bringing on a fight between the two. He steals into the kitchen and puts dishes in unexpected places, on the edge of the table or in a dark corner, so that she, absent-minded and short-sighted as she is, is bound to knock them over. And when the crash is heard in the *cheder,* Reb Boruch Wolf leaps as if he has been shot, and screams: "Another dish! You squinting fool, you'll ruin me, I'll have to go begging from door to door!"

He runs into the kitchen and of course finds his wife in tears. This is the last straw. And Reb Boruch Wolf comes back into the *cheder,* his face distorted with fury. He bangs the pipe-stem on the table, and gasps rather than howls: "Get out, everybody! I've had enough. I don't want to be a Rebbi any more!"

The boys scuttle out, slide down the banisters, and run

[52]

into the street, happy in their unexpected freedom. They go to the market-place, which is full of life; peasants are there, with horses and wagons, cattle, pigs, chickens, bags of grain; housewives wearing night-caps on their close-cropped heads —for every orthodox Jewish wife must cut off her hair when she marries—cluster round the carts; they pick up the hens and examine them, blowing into their behinds or even sticking in a finger to find out if there's an egg there. Jews shake hands with peasants, argue, bargain, and try the grains of wheat between their teeth. From the market-place the boys go off into some side street where building is going on. They watch the bricklayers and plasterers at work. Lodz is still growing, house by house, alley by alley, street by street. Then the boys make for Balut, where the alleys are narrowest and most crowded, and where day and night are heard the hum and rattle of the looms, the buzz and treadle of sewing-machines, the synagogue melodies of the weavers, the heart-breaking love-songs of the seamstresses. The boys with pocket-money buy little bags of almonds or of sugar candy, in tiny shops thick with flies. Simcha Meyer makes every boy give him a kopeck, and he marches into the shop of the Turk who wears a red skull-cap, and buys there a whole loaf of sweet raisin cake. The boys hesitate to touch it; it probably isn't kosher. Simcha Meyer has no scruples; he breaks off chunks and stuffs them into his mouth. Then from Balut the boys make in a crowd for the open fields, where the goats are at pasture, and they sit down in the grass and play cards.

When they've had enough of this, they run off to the sandy square near the barracks, to see the soldiers drilling and the officers cracking them over the head with the scabbards of their swords. Or they go back to the market-place, where the town crier gathers the crowd around him, beats his drum loudly, and announces the news of the day: a theft has been committed in so-and-so's house, so-and-so has lost a pig, so-and-so has been sent to prison, so-and-so has been distrained upon for taxes, and his candlesticks or bed-clothes are for sale.

And finally, toward evening, they go in a body to the whore-house district, narrow dirty little streets which did not

[53]

exist a few years before. The houses are small and flimsy, huts rather than houses, with low windows and uneven roofs. Once upon a time the place where these houses now stand was used by the good people of Lodz as an open-air comfort station. Some still retain the habit, but when they come round they are chased away by the owners of the whore-houses. The girls are for the use of soldiers and of the poorest peasants who come to town to work there, leaving their wives in the villages; Jewish apprentices are also among the clients.

The boys know that they're not supposed to go through these streets, which is of course why they are attracted to them. But they run quickly through the narrow alleys, casting hasty glances at the unkempt girls sitting on the doorsteps cracking sunflower seeds. They don't stop to speak to the girls. God forbid! They run past, with burning cheeks and beating hearts, ashamed to stop. But they like to hear the girls calling them: "Come here, little boys, you'll like it!"

And at last they go home, just in time for the late afternoon prayer, when twilight is falling on the crowded ill-paved streets, and the lamplighters walk about with their long poles lighting the lamps which are scattered sparsely through the city. And they, too, are a sight, these lamplighters. It's wonderful to see them hook their poles into the ropes by which the lamp is pulled down, wonderful to see them wipe the glass chimneys and pour the kerosene into the lamp and then light it with a flourish of the torch and finally pull it up again to its place by the rope.

Every time a lamp is lit the boys chant, in Yiddish: "A happy week!" just as they do at home when the lamps are lit at the end of the Sabbath and a new week begins. The lamplighter, who doesn't understand Yiddish, thinks they are making fun of him, and he puts down pole and torch to chase them away. The boys run, and the lamplighter catches the slowest of them, grabs the hat off his head, and pitches it neatly on top of one of the lamps. The others turn and set up a new chorus. "Bat in the belfry, bat in the belfry!" they sing at the lamplighter, "Angel of Death!" Among them, smallest and quickest and loudest, runs Simcha Meyer.

When he gets home at last, he finds his brother, Jacob

Bunim, crawling around on all fours, giving his sisters a ride. And if it isn't one of his sisters, it's Dinah, who, though she no longer lives in the same street, comes round every day to visit the Ashkenazi girls; at least, so she says, but everyone knows she really comes for Jacob Bunim's sake. Jacob Bunim, though he is ten years old, and looks bigger than his years, still plays with the girls. He has no idea of dignity. He doesn't want to grow up; he wants to go on playing for the rest of his life.

Simcha Meyer, coming into the house and finding his brother playing with the girls, begins to mock him: "Donkey! I'll tell Father you do nothing but play with the girls. Thick-head! You never learn your lessons, you'll never know anything!"

Jacob Bunim gets red in the face. He doesn't mind his sisters, but he squirms to have Dinah hear his brother's words. Most of all he hates to be called thick-head and donkey, because he knows it's true.

"Go on, tell Father," he retorts. "When you die God'll hang you from a tree by your tongue, for being a sneak." But at heart he's afraid, and before long he begins to bribe Simcha Meyer not to tell his father. He brings out his toys and offers them to his brother. The little girls stand around, their hearts bursting with rage. And they sing at Simcha Meyer: "Simcha Meyer is a big liar, he buys for less and sells for higher."

$\mathcal{R}$eb Abraham Hirsh Ashkenazi had his way.

Heinz Huntze yelled with rage, banged the table, stamped with his feet, and swore that he would rather go begging from house to house than come to terms with the *Schweinehund* Fritz Goetzke; but Reb Abraham Hirsh carried on calmly, going from Huntze to Goetzke and from Goetzke to Huntze. He talked quietly, cited the wise words of the sages and the parables of the Talmud; anger, he said, was an evil thing, more sinful than the worship of idols, and peace was the foundation of the world. Finally he wore the contestants out, and a new firm appeared in Lodz, the great combine of Heinz Huntze and Fritz Goetzke.

At the last moment the negotiations were almost broken off because neither of the partners would have his name second. It took all of Reb Abraham Hirsh's diplomacy, scholarship, and ingenuity, and several dozen sayings from the sacred books, to persuade Fritz Goetzke to give way; and when the name had been settled, the documents were signed.

Reb Abraham Hirsh's reward was the general agency of the new firm. Right in the midst of Vilki, where, not many years before, a Jew had not dared to show his face, Heinz Huntze built, on Piotrkov Street, a superb office building and warehouse for his general agent. The doors were as massive as the doors of a palace, the walls as thick as those of a fortress, the windows were barred. There were deep cellars, high lofts, and strong-rooms, packed to bursting with the merchandise turned out on the looms of Heinz Huntze and Fritz Goetzke. On the big sign which hung outside figured the names of the two great industrialists and, in letters almost as large, the name of Abraham Hirsh Ashkenazi. This was not the sign which had originally been planned. The first one had borne the emblem and trade mark of the firm, two naked and bearded Teutons wearing fig-leaves and holding spears in their hands. Reb Abraham Hirsh insisted that they be deleted from the sign. A Jew cannot be associated with images—and such images!

Huntze's daughters, who tried so hard to make their father drop his peasant dialect and speak like a Prussian aristocrat, were disgusted to see the office and warehouse practically turned over to Jews. They are everywhere, those Jews, queer little fellows in long coats, with funny little canes, with unkempt beards and ear-locks, shouting, bargaining, gesticulating. They speak their singsong Yiddish to the old man himself, they grab his lapels, they almost embrace him. And it so happens that the palace of the Huntzes is built close to the factory, and there, too, the little Jews are in swarms, a revolting sight. How often have they not pleaded with their father to have nothing to do with the tribes of Moses? If they had to be his customers, why couldn't he make his contacts only through the agent, who certainly didn't have to be a Jew? But there's a streak in old Huntze which draws him to this outlandish people. He likes to jabber, to bargain, to outwit and outmanœuvre. He has no taste for the solemnities which his daughters want to force on him. He likes his glass of beer, his pipe, and a good argument with a Jewish merchant who thinks he can put something over on the old German. He doesn't want to get rid of the Jews; he doesn't want to get rid of Abraham Hirsh Ashkenazi, who so cleverly brought about the flourishing partnership.

Reb Abraham Hirsh Ashkenazi sits in his own brown little office, his skull-cap on his head, the account-books, big and black and heavy, like his volumes of the Talmud, ranged before him. He is a hard man to see. The door of the office is besieged by hosts of Jewish merchants. When the door opens to let someone out and someone else in, they cry in a chorus:

"Reb Abraham Hirsh! I've got to see you! I can't wait any longer. Every minute costs money."

The assistants run fluttering among the merchants, trying to serve them. No, they've got to see Reb Abraham Hirsh himself. No one else will do.

It happens sometimes that one of the merchants remembers suddenly that he has forgotten to say his memorial prayer that day—it is the anniversary of his father's death. And he cannot say the prayer without the religious quorum of ten. He passes the word round: "I've got to say my memorial prayers! I need nine Jews." Right there, in the noisy stockrooms, with excited buyers rushing in and out, ten Jews stand apart and intone the afternoon prayer, with the addition of the Sanctification which is the memorial to a dead parent. Sometimes Reb Abraham Hirsh happens to be rushing by. His piety will not let him miss the opportunity; he stops and joins the group of impromptu worshippers. But he's in a hurry, just the same. He wants to be in on both worlds simultaneously, so he gabbles his amens at top speed and runs back to his office. His assistants watch him respectfully, whispering to each other. Only one of the employees, Goldlust, the head book-keeper, is derisive. He wears a short coat, and his beard is cut close, like the beard of a gentile. He has no patience with these outlandish practices. When he sees a Jew running around trying to get together his prayer-crowd, he objects furiously. "Listen, Mister," he cries, "this isn't one of your back-street synagogues. If you haven't said your prayers, this isn't the time to say them, you—you—village loon!"

Reb Abraham Hirsh makes little distinction between his home and his place of business. The customers who fail to see him during the day besiege him as obstinately in his home at night. Lodz swarms with merchants from every part of the Empire, and among these buyers of textiles Jews predominate. But they are not all of the pious, old-fashioned type. Among them are such as have cut their beards close and others who have even shaved them off—sign of the last break with orthodoxy, next door to eating ham. Missing a prayer is nothing new to them, nor taking a ride on the Sabbath.

[58]

They are not overfond, these Jews from other parts, of the Polish Jews, with their long gaberdines, their drawling Yiddish, their fanatical piety; and the Polish Jews return the dislike with interest, calling their visitors heathens, unbelievers, blasphemers, and pigs. But that doesn't prevent them from doing business with each other. And since there is only the most primitive hotel accommodation in Lodz, the impious out-of-towners must be accommodated in the homes of the local merchants. So Reb Abraham Hirsh's table is always crowded, noon and evening, with strangers, mostly Litvacks, or Lithuanian Jews, who eat with immense and noisy relish the fat roast goose and the sweet stuffed fish of Poland, hearty dishes which their lean home country hardly knows. Out of respect for Reb Abraham Hirsh they go through the traditional washing of hands before the meals, mumble the prayers and benedictions after the meals; they also do their best to make at least a polite display of Jewish scholarship. But these Lithuanian merchant Jews quote the Bible rather than the Talmud, and for a scholar like Reb Abraham Hirsh this is a puerile exhibition. When they have thus paid tribute to their host, they revert to more natural conversation. They tell stories of business adventures in remote parts of Russia, they describe the customs and manners of the peoples of the Empire on the far-off borders of Persia and China. At night they sit around until late and finally go to sleep on sofas in Reb Abraham Hirsh's house.

Travelling merchants of this kind are not the best influence in a pious Jewish home, and Reb Abraham Hirsh tried hard to keep his boys away from his visitors, with their worldly conversation, their irreligious habits, and even their —God save the mark—Biblical verses. As soon as the meal was over, he would send the youngsters from the table. Jacob Bunim went readily enough to his toys, his pocket-knives, his little girl friends; Simcha Meyer lingered or, if driven away, stole in again, to listen. Sometimes, without his father's knowledge, he would ask one of the merchants to take him along on his various errands. He went ostensibly to show the stranger the location of the various streets and firms, in reality to listen to his talk. Invariably the merchant would

[59]

give him a handsome tip and advise him to drop his ridiculous outmoded Talmudic studies and to turn to modern education.

"It's the only thing in the world," they said, impressively. "Real education!"

Often Simcha Meyer sneaked into his father's office and warehouse, though he was forbidden to set foot there. The salesmen, office workers, and shipping clerks did not betray him. It amused them to watch this odd, restless, sharp-faced youngster studying the business in his own precocious way, fingering the fabrics and learning their names from the attached labels, listening with cocked ears to sales conversations, picking up the jargon of the trade. When his father was out of the building Simcha Meyer stole into the office and peeped into the account-books. Goldlust, the accountant, was irritated and astonished. But, like the others, he helped Simcha Meyer along.

"That kid's got the goods," they murmured. "You just watch him."

Simcha Meyer was indifferent to their opinion of him. He wanted to know everything. He had definitely made up his mind that when he was a grown man he would sit in an office just like his father's. But he would sit there bareheaded and not wearing that silly skull-cap which his father, the pious Jew, always had on his head. And he wouldn't admit the riff-raff, the noisy little merchants that his father dealt with. He would see only the big important people. And even they would have to take off their hats when they came into his office. He wouldn't let them speak Yiddish, either. They would have to speak to him in German.

$\mathfrak{I}t$ is Saturday night in the big, cheerful dining-room of the manufacturer Reb Chaim Alter. Half an hour or more has passed since three stars became visible in the sky outside, indicating that the Sabbath is at an end, but Reb Chaim is only now performing the ceremony of the ushering out of the holy day. He is late as usual because he has been sitting with his Chasidic cronies in their little synagogue and club-house. He loves the atmosphere and the company of the place. He loves to linger there over the Saturday evening feast. He has a good voice and he leads in the singing of the Chasidic hymns and traditional melodies. When the privilege of leading the prayers is being auctioned off, Reb Chaim is usually the buyer.

He comes into the warm, bright dining-room, his face glowing with affection, and chants rather than says: "A happy, happy week to all of us." His smiling eyes rest in turn on his wife, his sons, his daughter, his relatives, all assembled in the massively furnished room. A dozen candlesticks are ranged on the sideboards, and a great copper lamp hangs by three chains above the huge oak dining-table.

Slowly, enjoying every gesture, he pours the wine into the goblet of embossed silver, letting a little run over on to the tray, so that the week which is now opening may likewise run over with happiness and prosperity. Humming a melody, he takes out from the sideboard the heavy silver spice-box, with its green turret and its little silver flags and bells. He

[61]

folds back the sleeves of his rich gaberdine, baring his big, fleshy arms, and he instructs Dinah, his only daughter, to hold the ceremonial candle.

"Hold it higher, little one," he says to the thirteen-year-old girl with the chestnut plaits, "higher still. It means you'll have a tall bridegroom."

A tide of colour washes over the smooth cheeks of the child. She pulls a face—but she holds the spice-box higher. Reb Chaim raises the silver goblet and casts a glance round the room to see if all are present, including Hadassah, the maid. Yes, they are all here. Reb Chaim is content. He begins to intone the prayer of the ushering out of the Sabbath and the welcoming in of the new week. He praises God, who created fire, he shakes the spice-box, he sings at great length, enjoying every word, and he sniffs in the delicious odours which float over the room. Then he passes the spice-box to his wife and his children and lets them smell, and they all say the prayer which praises the Almighty for having created sweet-smelling spices.

Hadassah, the maid, gets the spice-box, too. Invariably she is so confused by the honour that she forgets to stick her nose into the little silver door of the spice-box, and everybody laughs. Even Reb Chaim cannot suppress a smile. He finishes the ceremony. He folds over the end of the table-cloth, pours wine on to the table, extinguishes the flickering candle, dips his fingers into the wine, and puts his wet hands into his pockets—into all of them in turn. Thereby he ensures that the ensuing week will be a happy and a prosperous one and that wealth will flow into his pockets. He also wipes his eyes with the wine of the ceremony, and then he chants, over and over again: "May this be a happy week, a prosperous week, a lucky, joyous, merry week!"

Then he takes off his silk gaberdine and calls to his man: "Samuel Leibish, bring me my dressing-gown."

Samuel Leibish, the servant, a young man with a little blond beard and a paper collar, runs up hastily with the silk dressing-gown and the cigars which Reb Chaim, good Jew that he is, has been deprived of during the twenty-four hours of the Sabbath. It is a great privation for Reb Chaim, and

Samuel Leibish keeps the box of cigars handy, so that his employer may light one as soon as the closing ceremony of the Sabbath is over. Reb Chaim beams with contentment at the good service and the prospect of a smoke. He bites off the tip of the cigar and draws hungrily at the flame which his man brings him. He murmurs the last words of the prayer while he puffs luxuriously at the cigar, and his nostrils, expanding, breathe in the sweet smell of the dews of heaven and of the fatness of the earth, its grain and grapes and fruits and oil, which God will give His people if only it will walk in His ways. And still murmuring the prayer, he opens the telegrams and letters which have arrived during the Sabbath, and which he could not open on the day of rest. The last words of the prayer go at a gallop: he is famished for a cup of good, fresh, strong tea.

"Priveh, my love," he says to his wife, "the tea with the lemon, please. Tell Hadassah."

Priveh, a handsome, clear-skinned buxom matron, dressed in a silk dress with a long trail, her plump neck adorned with strings of pearls, with diamonds on her smooth, soft fingers, and with a light-coloured, curled wig on her head, which makes her look like the pictures of opera stars, walks over to her husband with mincing steps and coquettishly holds out her hand for her week-end money.

"Money, money," grumbles Reb Chaim good-naturedly. "What do you need so much money for?"

An affected, flirtatious smile lingers on Priveh's lips. "For the household, my husband," she answers in Yiddish which she tries to make sound like German, and the smile becomes a trifle contemptuous. She turns and walks out of the room with the expression of an offended queen.

Reb Chaim is terrified. He didn't mean to offend her. He leaps up from his comfortable chair and runs after her. "Priveh! Privishe, darling! I was just joking." But Priveh won't let him get away with that kind of joke. She knows just two things about her Reb Chaim: first, that he's still distractedly in love with her; second, that he can't bear to quarrel. He can't bear any kind of strain or worry. He wants things to go smoothly and pleasantly. Priveh, on the other

[63]

hand, has a weakness for scenes and quarrels. She'll seize on any pretext for one, and though she knows that her husband meant no harm with that remark, she's ready to tell Hadassah, the maid, to fix Reb Chaim's bed on the couch in the dining-room for that night. Reb Chaim can't bear the thought of it. He wants to be near her warm, plump body; and he wants her to speak gently to him. In the end, having felt that his wife does, after all, spend too much on the household, he has to throw good money after bad, because without a present —a new dress, or perhaps even a piece of jewellery—Priveh won't make friends again.

"All right, Priveh, darling," he pleads, "take as much as you like. All the money in the world isn't worth five minutes of worry where you're concerned."

Priveh unbends and takes the wad of banknotes which he offers her. "Is it all right now, darling?" he asks.

"You've forgotten your tea, Chaim, dear," she says, smiling coquettishly. "Let's go back to the dining-room."

Reb Chaim swallows his tea in big gulps, happy that peace has been restored in the house. He asks Samuel Leibish to bring him the accounts, and he begins to review the week's business. The two of them sit side by side, fingering bills, invoices, receipts. They sit there for hours without being able to get the accounts straight. Reb Chaim is his own book-keeper, and the system he uses is the invention of the more old-fashioned of the Jewish merchants of Lodz. The language is a mixture of faulty German and faultier Hebrew. One page of the ledger is marked "Taken," the other "Given." The language would not matter if the accountant had a head for figures, but that is just what Reb Chaim hasn't. Neither has his man, Samuel Leibish. Constitutionally lazy, an epicure, fond of a good time, absent-minded, unsystematic, Reb Chaim keeps books not so much because he thinks it necessary as because he knows it has to be done. His pockets are usually stuffed with bills, receipts, and memoranda which were supposed to be entered in the books the day they were made out or received, but they stay in his pocket—if they don't fall out and get lost—and become more and more illegible, so that by the end of the week he can't read them.

[64]

The pages in the ledger are a remarkable sight. Since the figures don't balance, there have to be special additions and subtractions, insertions on the margins, explanatory remarks which run over on to the next page, and yet never seem long enough. After a couple of hours of painful effort Reb Chaim pushes the books away with a growl of irritation and asks Samuel Leibish to get him the lantern and accompany him to the factory, which lies on the other side of the courtyard.

"The less you bother with figures, the better off you are," he says to his servant. "Isn't that true, Samuel Leibish?"

"Why, certainly, Reb Chaim," answers Samuel Leibish. "It's a well-known fact."

As he steps out into the courtyard he hears from afar the clatter of the looms, going at full speed after the Sabbath pause. There's plenty of work, and the weavers are busy till late in the night. Reb Chaim loves his factory, because it's such a simple thing. The more work, the more money! You don't have to be an accountant to understand that.

Saturday night the weavers stay longer than any other night, to make up for the Sabbath pause. They sit, fifty weavers, at tallow candles, making the women's kerchiefs which are Reb Chaim Alter's specialty. Every weaver must buy his own candles. This is a rule which was introduced long ago by the little employers who had two or three looms, and the rule still holds good. If anyone is going to change that rule, it certainly won't be Reb Chaim. He's not the kind of man to go in for innovations. What was good enough for his father is good enough for him, and that applies not only to the factory, but to all the rules of his life, and especially to his religious outlook. Reb Chaim is not impressed by the steam factories of the Huntzes and Reb Solomon David Preiss and the others. His friends have often tried to persuade him to install a steam factory. He could manage it if he wanted to; but he doesn't feel like it. His hand-looms are still making money; the steam mills hadn't driven the hand-looms from the field. There are other employers who, like Reb Chaim, stick to the old ways.

Reb Chaim's factory is Jewish throughout. On every door there is a mezuzah, the little wooden or metal container

[65]

with the passage from the Pentateuch which the Jews were bidden of old to fasten on the door-posts of their houses. In one of the stockrooms there is a lectern and a small candelabrum, so that Reb Chaim's workers can say their afternoon and evening prayers with some degree of formality. This has two advantages, the one spiritual, the other material. The workers can indulge in group prayer, which is so much more acceptable to the Almighty; also they don't have to go out of the factory to a synagogue. In the winter, when day dawns late and morning prayers must therefore be deferred—since it is forbidden to say the morning prayers until you can distinguish a blue thread from a green thread—the workers must interrupt their work for the services; then the improvised synagogue in the stockroom is especially handy.

Reb Chaim also keeps watch over the individual piety of his employees. No worker may sit at the loom without a hat or skull-cap on his head, not even on the hottest days. Nor must anyone be without the ritual fringes which are part of the dress of every observant Jew. He sees to it, does Reb Chaim, that none of the men shall cut their beards too close or even wear the heathenishly short coats of the modernists. Reb Chaim, though only an indifferent scholar, knows that, as the sages tell, for three pious observances were the Jews delivered from the Egyptian bondage: to wit, their traditional language, their traditional customs, and their traditional clothes. He knows further that sinfulness is contagious, like disease. One sick sheep can infect the whole flock. Therefore Reb Chaim will not let a single one of his workers fall into the ways of the modernist sinners.

"If I should want gentiles in this factory," he tells his workers, "I could have real ones, and not apostate Jews."

"God bless you, Reb Chaim," answer the older weavers, thin, half-starved Jews, whose faces are pale and tired and whose eyes are swollen and red from their long night hours.

Reb Chaim also contributes to the weavers' synagogue in Balut, a dilapidated hut jammed in between factories and coal-yards. He also maintains a Hebrew teacher, who gives lessons every Saturday afternoon to his employees. In the summer he teaches them *Pirke Aboth,* The Ethics of the

[66]

Fathers, and in the winter special prayers from the Psalms. The teacher is a man of great learning, well-informed on the subject of the world beyond the grave. He sits in the little synagogue, which is crowded with tired, sleepy weavers, and tells them all about the insignificance of man and the ugliness of the things of the flesh.

"Know whence thou comest," he quotes from The Ethics of the Fathers, "from a stinking drop. Know whither thou goest, to a place of worms."

On the other side of Balut stretch fresh, open fields, and on them graze the horses of the Jewish draymen. The draymen lie in the grass, dozing, breathing in the scented air. Beyond the meadows lie the fir woods, shadowed and sweet-smelling. But the employees of Reb Chaim Alter don't frequent those places. For on Saturday night Reb Chaim asks the teacher which of the weavers was missing from the Saturday afternoon lesson, and the worker who absents himself a few times is fired. On the holy Sabbath day, says Reb Alter, a Jew is forbidden to waste his time in field and forest, among heathens and factory girls. The Sabbath must be given over to contemplation and the study of sacred things. That is Reb Chaim's own invariable practice. On the Sabbath afternoons of the summer he sits comfortably on the porch of his summer home in the country, reading one of the sacred books or talking of holy things with one of the Chasidim of his clique. For it is written, again, in The Ethics of the Fathers, that if a man walks in the road, his mind fixed on sacred matters, and he pauses to exclaim: "How lovely is that tree!" or "How sweet is that field!" he has forfeited his life. No, no. These are foolish things, which distract the mind and lead to sinfulness. A worker must meditate on the sanctities during the Sabbath, and on the night of the Sabbath he must go back to his loom and work at least until midnight, to make up for the work that wasn't done in the last twenty-four hours.

He is like a father to his workers, Reb Chaim Alter. When a son is born to one of them, he never refuses to attend the circumcision ceremony. He will stand godfather, too. He is a rich man, but he knows that all Jews are brothers, and far be it from him to show himself haughty. He eats the piece

[67]

of cake at the ceremony, though he doesn't like the taste of it, and doesn't show his disgust. When a worker marries off a son, Reb Chaim is there, and he always has a present for the bridegroom. When Passover comes round, he presents every worker with a bottle of raisin wine which he gets cheap from one of his Chasidim. On the Feast of Tabernacles he buys a palm-branch for the weavers' synagogue. True, it isn't one of those handsome, thick-leaved palm-branches such as he uses in his own synagogue; but he will not have it said that in the synagogue of his workers there was no palm-branch for the Feast of Tabernacles. When one of his workers dies, Reb Chaim walks in the funeral procession as far as the very cemetery. He also contributes to the grave-clothes for the dead man, and he sends something to the bereaved family.

He does everything that a man can do for his workers, and in his little synagogue he is praised loudly by his Chasidic clique. Therefore Reb Chaim loves his factory, for it is at once the source of his livelihood, the outlet for the goodness of his heart, and the foundation of his honourable reputation among his fellow-Jews.

In dressing-gown and skull-cap Reb Chaim walks across the courtyard to the factory, Samuel Leibish walking in front with the lantern.

"Is everything in order, Samuel Leibish?" asks Reb Chaim.

"Everything is in order, master," the other answers. "Two looms were out of commission, but they've been fixed."

"Who fixed them?" asks Reb Chaim.

"Tevyeh the-world-isn't-coming-to-an-end-yet," answers Samuel Leibish. "He worked on them till they're as good as new."

"A clever lad," murmurs Reb Chaim. "If it weren't for that tongue of his."

"Reb Chaim," says Samuel Leibish with cringing reproachfulness, "what can you expect if you pay him five whole roubles a week. It's unheard of."

"A happy week to all of you," says Reb Chaim as he steps into the factory. "A happy week to all of you and to all Jews."

Sudden activity breaks out in the long, dim-lit room. The elderly Jews, who have been talking casually about one thing

[68]

or another, but chiefly about their daughters, whom it is so difficult to marry off these days, turn hastily to the looms. They push down from their foreheads the spectacles which most of them wear, they stretch their lean, thick-veined hands to the looms, they work the treadles with their tired feet, they rock right and left on their seats. "A happy week to you, Reb Chaim," they answer in chorus.

The young men, who have been singing a synagogue melody, break off the chorus, throw themselves into the work, and make the thread fly across the loom. Reb Chaim walks from loom to loom, watching closely, testing the cloth, correcting, reproving. Sometimes a weaver lets fall a drop of perspiration on the kerchief he is weaving; sometimes the weave is uneven.

"Let's have no botching, boys," he cries. "And no eating at the looms. Get that, Samuel Leibish."

"Certainly, Reb Chaim," answers Samuel Leibish loudly, looking round angrily at the weavers. "That's what I'm always telling them. Everything has to be absolutely clean."

Reb Chaim listens contentedly to the clatter of the looms. It sounds to him like the clinking of coins. He walks past the looms and looks into the stockrooms, filled with wool and with finished merchandise, thousands and thousands of kerchiefs ready for shipment. His heart is filled with pride. Let them say what they like, let them repeat a hundred times that there's no future in hand-looms, and steam's the thing. Hand-looms are good enough for him. They bring him a handsome income. Of course, he could make more money—there's no limit to that—but if they go on producing the same income for him, not less, why, he has enough to be thankful for to God. These women's kerchiefs of his are selling throughout the length and breadth of Russia. The orders grow from week to week; he'll have to increase the hours, there's no help for it. What of that? These workers are better than machines. Let Germans and apostate Jews have their steam and their engines and their factory whistles and all the noise and excitement—Reb Chaim sticks to his good old hand-looms and his Jewish workers and his Jewish ways.

And Reb Chaim walks back along the length of his factory, his man Samuel Leibish following him like a sinister shadow. And finally he reaches the loom of young Tevyeh, whom everybody calls "Tevyeh the-world-isn't-coming-to-an-end-yet." This Tevyeh, with his little new-sprouting beard, his white paper collar on his scraggy neck, his thin, wiry body, his shaggy eyebrows, this Tevyeh is the only one who doesn't pay any attention to the boss. He goes on throwing red threads into the border of a black kerchief which he is weaving, and he sings, not a synagogue melody, such as the others always sing, but something in Yiddish, with rhymes. The only sign he gives of being aware of the boss's presence is to lower his voice, so that the song is only half-audible.

A very odd song it is, such as weavers have never sung before. It isn't taken from one of the traditional Queen Esther plays; it isn't something heard at the services; it isn't even a German love-song, such as the seamstresses have made popular. It's quite a strange song, and yet it has something intimate and familiar about it. Nobody knows where it comes from or who composed it. Tevyeh brought it into the factory a few weeks ago, and he has been singing it ever since, so that everyone knows it by heart now. It's a song about a rich factory-owner who sits drinking beer and smoking cigars, and when his workers weep at their looms he warns them:

"God damn you, don't weep while you're working,
    The tears leave a stain on the thread.
    I'll fire every worker who snivels,
    And get me another instead."

Reb Chaim knows about that song. Samuel Leibish told him that his workers were being corrupted by an indecent and subversive composition which had recently become popular in Lodz. Reb Chaim can't make out the words which Tevyeh is humming to himself, but the melody is familiar, and he suspects that this is the famous song with the disrespectful allusion to a cigar-smoking boss, who can't be anyone but Reb Chaim himself.

[70]

"What's that you're singing, Tevyeh?" he asks.

"A song," answers Tevyeh, without turning his head.

"Is it a new synagogue melody?" asks Reb Chaim, playing the simpleton. "Sing it louder. I'd like to learn it, too."

Tevyeh does not answer. He stops singing. Reb Chaim looks at him closely, observes how thin, neglected, and flimsy are the ritual fringes which the young man wears. His face darkens. He mutters, just loud enough to be heard: "Tevyeh, Tevyeh, you'll—" but he does not finish. He walks out of the factory without another word. The incident of the song, and the sight of that contemptuously maltreated set of fringes, have introduced a jarring note into his cheerful Sabbath-night mood. But Reb Chaim isn't the kind of man to remain ill-humoured long. By the time he has crossed the yard, he has recovered his gaiety. Besides, on entering the house, he perceives a visitor he is always glad to see, young Simcha Meyer, the son of Reb Abraham Hirsh Ashkenazi.

"You're here again, you young heathen, are you?" he greets him, and pulls the boy's ear affectionately.

Simcha Meyer sat at the table, playing with Reb Chaim's sons. The boys were older than he, but they attended the same *cheder*, Reb Boruch Wolf's, and they hung on a great deal to Simcha Meyer. They were big, strapping, foolish lads, as good-humoured as their father, and they let themselves be led around by their small, sharp-witted companion. Reb Chaim was glad to have his boys make friends with Simcha Meyer. They might learn something from him. For Simcha Meyer was growing sharper and cleverer from year to year. Not only had he sustained his reputation as a young scholar; he was becoming famous for his grown-up ways and his queer insight into all sorts of problems. On more than one occasion Reb Chaim, unable to make head or tail of an account, had let little Simcha Meyer look at the jumble of figures, and in two or three minutes the lad had brought complete order out of what looked like hopeless chaos. He glanced up and down the columns, he read the ill-written notations in the margin, he sang a little melody to himself while his pen jotted down figures, and, presto, there it was. And Reb Chaim was delighted and astonished. He would

[71]

turn to his sons and say: "Look at him, you loons. He'll lead Lodz by the nose one of these days."

It wasn't only for the sake of his sons that Reb Chaim welcomed Simcha Meyer. He was thinking of his daughter, too. Simcha Meyer was only a youngster, he hadn't reached the confirmation age of thirteen yet. But years pass quickly and, besides, it would be nothing out of the ordinary to reach an arrangement even now. Parents had done that since time immemorial. The wise thing, thought Reb Chaim, was to catch the youngster before the competition had become too keen.

"Dinah, darling," he said to his daughter, "why don't you bring cake and tea for our visitor?"

Dinah obeyed without any enthusiasm. She brought tea and cake for the lad in the silken Chasidic coat, and thought how funny he looked with his flaxen ear-locks and his pious little skull-cap. He had such queer, restless, eager eyes, too. She had never had any liking for him, for she still remembered the days in the courtyard behind the Ashkenazi house, when Simcha Meyer had always been a spoil-sport. Since that time she had spent some years in a German boarding-school, where her head had become filled with romantic stories about kings and knights and heroes. She had picked up the manners, or at least the mannerisms, of the aristocracy; she had learned to curtsy, to dance, and to play the piano.

Blue-eyed and brown-haired, big, spoiled and well developed, she had always been a favourite with her gentile playmates. Not quite thirteen yet, she had read scores of books, in French and German, about romantic lovers, elopements, and duels. The man she would marry would carry her off in the night, as heroines were carried off in the stories she had read. And how funny all the boys who came into her parents' house looked to her, with their pious little gaberdines and their silly, old-fashioned ear-locks. Funniest of them all was Simcha Meyer, who added to all these homely crudities his own queer ways, his restlessness, his nosiness, his cleverness.

The more her dislike of him grew, the greater grew her father's admiration of him, and the more enthusiastically he tried to bring the two of them together. He didn't like the way Dinah put down the tea and cake in front of the visitor.

"Simcha Meyer," he said, "write a German letter for me and show the young lady that a young Jewish scholar can write German too, without having gone to a German boarding-school."

Simcha Meyer took up pen and paper and composed what he thought was a most impressive German letter. He worked hard at the complicated Gothic alphabet and tried to remember the phrases he had learned from Goldlust, his father's head book-keeper.

Little Dinah took one glance over his shoulder and fled from the room. Upstairs she found her mother, threw herself into her arms, and began to scream with laughter. But in the dining-room Reb Chaim thought she had run away out of shyness, and he rubbed his hands with pleasure. The time for action had arrived. The very next day he would send Samuel Zanvil Alexander, the one-time merchant who had lost his money and was now a professional matchmaker, to Reb Abraham Hirsh Ashkenazi, to propose the match officially.

"Samuel Leibish," he said, "you'll go to Samuel Zanvil Alexander tomorrow morning and tell him I want to see him about something important."

"Yes, Reb Chaim, first thing in the morning," answered Samuel Leibish.

"Say: 'God willing,' you heathen," said his employer, "because how do you know you'll be alive tomorrow morning?"

"Yes, Reb Chaim, God willing," added his servant.

$\mathcal{F}$ον the *bar mitzvah,* or confirmation ceremony, of Simcha Meyer and Jacob Bunim, which occurred on the Passover, Reb Abraham Hirsh went to the town of Alexander, taking the two boys along.

The Rabbi of Vorka was dead, and Reb Abraham Hirsh had transferred his allegiance to the Rabbi of Alexander, who lived not very far from Lodz. Reb Abraham Hirsh yielded to his new spiritual leader all the religious loyalty which he had yielded to the old one. On every important Jewish holiday, the Passover included, he left his home, to spend the sacred days in the company of his Rabbi and his Rabbi's followers. As of old, he paid no attention to his wife's feelings on the subject, leaving her always to celebrate the festivals in loneliness, unless she chose to go on a visit to her father. This Passover Reb Abraham Hirsh had several special reasons for going to his Rabbi. His sons were becoming men; they were about to take upon themselves, at the age of thirteen, the full responsibility for their own lives; and Reb Abraham Hirsh wanted the Rabbi to speak with them and impress upon them the tremendous meaning of their Jewish heritage. In the midst of all his business and communal preoccupations Reb Abraham Hirsh had never forgotten that sinister hint which the Rabbi of Vorka, of blessed memory, had let fall concerning his sons—that they would be men of wealth, but not of piety. Whenever he thought of it, he trembled. Reb

[74]

Abraham Hirsh feared God and knew that the things of this world are shadows and vanity. More than once he had prayed that if the wealth of his children was destined to lead them from the path of true Jewishness, God might take their wealth from them if so be that their piety might thereby be saved. Better even that they be removed from the world betimes rather than that they should turn from the faith and practices of their fathers. Now that they were about to take up the burden of their manhood, he would have the Rabbi of Alexander intercede with and for them.

Reb Abraham Hirsh had still another reason for going to the Rabbi. He wanted his advice on Simcha Meyer's education.

Jacob Bunim was no problem. He would be tutored in the Talmud until the time of his marriage, but there was no hope of making a scholar of him. Good enough if he remained a decent Jew, not wholly illiterate in sacred matters, and observant of the ritualistic laws of his people. Very different was it with Simcha Meyer. He had outgrown even Reb Boruch Wolf Lentchitzer, and a special teacher of the highest standing would have to be found for him. Reb Abraham Hirsh would have liked to send him away from home to a Yeshivah, or Talmudical college, where the lad would live with poor students, would perhaps even eat his meals, like the very poorest, with different families in turn, would learn to carry, in poverty and discipline, the heavy yoke of his Jewishness. Such had, indeed, been the boyhood of Reb Abraham Hirsh, and to this training he attributed his own sustained piety.

When Reb Abraham Hirsh's wife heard of her husband's desire to send her oldest son away to live among strangers, she almost fainted with terror. She wept as she had never wept before. But Reb Abraham Hirsh was not over-impressed by her tears. What gave him pause was the advice of his Chasidic friends. Times had changed, they said, and perhaps it was a good thing for a boy to be near his father, especially such a father as Reb Abraham Hirsh. On this very point Reb Abraham Hirsh would also consult the Rabbi of Alexander.

[75]

And there was one more point on which he wanted the Rabbi's advice: a match was about to be arranged for Simcha Meyer.

Reb Chaim Alter had sent word, through Samuel Zanvil, the one-time merchant and present marriage-broker, that he wanted Simcha Meyer for his daughter Dinah. Reb Abraham Hirsh had listened carefully and had sent back word that he did not say yes and he did not say no. He, the father, was not in a hurry. He was not of the hurrying kind. In any case, the boy was still young: he was not yet a *bar mitzvah*, a full-fledged Jew of thirteen years. But Samuel Zanvil became importunate. He was a man of considerable scholarly attainment, and though he had lost all his money, he had lost none of his old impudence. He had the habit of addressing everyone by his first name, and in the second person singular. Learning did not impress him, for he had it; neither did wealth—he had had that too. Therefore Reb Abraham Hirsh's evasiveness failed to put him off, and he returned day after day, demanding an affirmative answer. To get rid of Samuel Zanvil was not easy; to offend him was impossible; to throw him out was dangerous. He knew every Jew in Lodz, as every Jew knew him. He knew, too, a thousand family secrets, and he was capable of coming out with the most disastrous truths right in the presence of a crowd of people.

"Abraham Hirsh," he commanded rather than advised, "I want you to consent to this match. And don't keep me running after you—I'm no errand-boy of yours. Let's have the betrothal soon, and let me collect my fee. I have a daughter of my own to marry off, and I have no time to lose."

Reb Abraham Hirsh could not get away from him. Samuel Zanvil broke into his home, accosted him in the synagogue, and even pursued him to his office. The assistants who tried to hold him back were thrust to one side, and Samuel Zanvil crashed in as though the place belonged to him. "Have you ever heard of such impudence?" he cried to Reb Abraham Hirsh. "They tell me I've got to have an appointment with you, Abraham Hirsh. Who do they think you are—the Governor?"

Reb Abraham Hirsh saw that there was no getting out of

[76]

it. As it happened, the proposed match did not displease him. Reb Chaim Alter was well-to-do, Dinah was an only daughter, and there would undoubtedly be a hansdome dowry, as well as substantial presents and an undertaking to keep the young couple for several years. Besides, Reb Chaim was desperately fond of the boy. There were, of course, certain drawbacks. Reb Chaim Alter's wife was reputed to be lacking in piety. It was rumoured that she had not shorn her head completely before her marriage, as every pious Jewish woman should, and that instead of a full wig she only wore a little covering. She was also accused of being a spendthrift. Still, the house was decently Jewish and always full of Chasidic visitors. Now Reb Abraham Hirsh wanted to hear what his Rabbi would say about the match. Without his Rabbi he would not stir.

So shortly before the Passover he had new alpaca gaberdines and silk caps made for the boys. He packed into three separate coloured kerchiefs a supply of matzos, to last them over the Passover. These were not ordinary matzos. They were made from flour which had been under guard from the growing of the grain until the baking of the cakes; they were less digestible than ordinary matzos, but considerably holier. He also packed his own holiday clothes and a good supply of Passover wine, and a day before Passover he commanded one of the firm's drivers to make ready a roomy cart for himself, his two sons, and the crowd of poor Jews, followers of the same Rabbi, whom he would give a lift as far as Alexander.

Not for one moment during that whole Passover week did he let the boys slip out of his sight. He kept them at his side, listening to the learned disquisitions of the Rabbi and to the conversation of his disciples, most of it given over to recitals of glorious events in the lives of famous Chasidic rabbis. When the Chasidim made a ring and went off into one of their pious dances, Reb Abraham Hirsh had the boys dance with them, just like grown-ups. More particularly he tried to imbue Simcha Meyer with the enthusiastic Jewish and Chasidic spirit of the Rabbi and his followers.

"This is how Jews should worship the Eternal," he said fervently to his sons. "Watch them and be like them."

When Reb Abraham Hirsh made ready to leave, the Rabbi

pinched Jacob Bunim's cheek in friendly fashion, but with Simcha Meyer, the young prodigy, he spoke seriously and at length. He tested him. He put many questions to him, some of them having to do with abstruse problems of ritual; and Simcha Meyer answered every question perfectly. The Rabbi could not refrain from praising the lad to his father even while the lad stood by.

"You've got a fine son, Abraham Hirsh," he said, patting Simcha Meyer on the cheek. "He's got a first-class head. Bring him with you on your visits. And I like the match you mentioned. An excellent match. You needn't send the boy away to a Yeshivah. Put him under Reb Noske, the teacher in Lodz. It's true that Reb Noske doesn't make pilgrimages to any rabbi, but he is a great scholar and a great saint—among the very greatest."

Reb Abraham Hirsh left a handsome gift with the Rabbi and returned to Lodz content with the results of his visit. On the very journey he signalized the coming betrothal by distributing cake and whisky among the poor Chasidim who accompanied him. They drank and congratulated both father and son.

"Good luck, bridegroom!" they cried. "Good luck, father! May the match be a happy one!" And they drank also to Jacob Bunim, the brother of the bridegroom.

Jacob Bunim sat apart, his face overcast. For the first time in his life he tasted the meaning of sorrow, and his big brown eyes, which had always been known to twinkle with happiness, were now darkened with pain.

It had been an uncomfortable Passover for him. The grown-ups, the Chasidim, had neglected him, preferring to talk always with his brilliant brother. The Rabbi, too, had paid little attention to him. He had pinched his cheek now and again, as if he had been a child beginning school, while with Simcha Meyer he had conversed as with a scholar of standing. All this had hurt. This was no courtyard, these were not children he could play with, whose admiration he could win. He felt small, humiliated, and despised. The hour was Simcha Meyer's, and Simcha Meyer had known it. He had treated his twin brother with contempt, had turned away

[78]

from him constantly, as though he did not want it to be known that this overgrown booby was his brother.

All this had depressed him. But he might have recovered his usual spirits on the way, in anticipation of the return home and to his playmates, if the confirmation of the match between Simcha Meyer and Dinah had not been added to all his other miseries. Oh yes, he had heard the rumour of it before. They had hinted at it in the house. But it had seemed so unreal. Now it had happened. The Rabbi himself had ratified the match, and that, of course, meant that it was settled. Here they were, returning to Lodz, and the Chasidim in the cart were drinking merrily to the health and happiness of the bride and bridegroom. Jacob Bunim felt something closing in on his heart and holding it in an agonizing grip.

"Why the long face?" the Chasidim asked him. "Don't be jealous. You'll be a bridegroom too, before long. Shake hands with your brother and congratulate him."

Shamefacedly he stretched out a hand to Simcha Meyer and mumbled: "Good luck to you." The two brothers exchanged a glance which revealed more than they perhaps realized; on the one side the insolence of pride and victory, on the other side bitterness, despair, and hatred.

They were youngsters; yet it was not the prospect of the presents which Simcha Meyer was going to receive, the gold watch and chain, the new set of the Talmud, that stung Jacob Bunim. It was the thought of Dinah, the child he had loved more than all the others, the little girl who had played with him in the courtyard, had ridden pick-a-back on his shoulders, who had clung to him, with her plump warm hands round his neck, like a bird clinging to a friendly hand which takes it out of the harshness of a bitter winter night into the warmth and light of a room. He remembered how glad and proud he had felt when Leah Sarah, the servant, had said to all the neighbours: "They'll make such a sweet bride and bridegroom."

They had gone on playing until a time of separation came for them. Dinah went away to a German boarding-school; she made new friends, the children of aristocratic gentile families. She became too haughty to visit the Ashkenazi girls, who didn't go to such a distinguished school as her own. In all that time Jacob Bunim had remembered her and missed her. For hours he would linger round her house, in the hope that she would pass; and when she did pass, her books under her arm, her brown school-dress half covered by the blue uniform cape, his heart expanded painfully, and he took off his hat to her as if she had been a princess.

Healthy, vigorous, full-grown, Jacob Bunim was, at the age of thirteen, a young man. Unlike the other boys in the schoolroom, he had not diffused and confused his love-impulses in secret conversations about married couples and their practices, or in giggling examination of the sexy passages in the Talmud. He was simple, straightforward, and ripe, and all his impulses strained without guile toward enjoyment and love. He wanted the tenderness of feminine friendship and longed for the touch of girlish hands. He had never let Dinah out of his mind, and he thought of her now, the girl with the brown curls and the soft white fingers; and a fury which he had never known before, a consistent hostility foreign to his nature, unfolded in him, making his brother hateful in his eyes.

Nor was it his brother alone whom he cursed silently. He thought of the favouritism which his parents had always shown toward Simcha Meyer; the father because Simcha Meyer was the prodigy and genius, the mother because Simcha Meyer was the sickly weakling. He, Jacob Bunim, being neither scholarly nor sickly, had received no attention, except from Leah Sarah, the servant. He hated, too, the Chasidim who filled the house and who made such a fuss of the brilliant Simcha Meyer. Then at last he hated himself for his stupidity.

"Blockhead!" he muttered to himself. "Peasant! Idiot!"

The pain in his heart might have been mitigated—or perhaps it might have been sharpened—if he had known how Dinah herself received the news of the betrothal which her father had arranged. No preliminary rumours had reached her ears. Only one evening her father took her on his lap, stroked her cheek, and said softly: "You know, daughter, everybody will be wishing you good luck. You are going to

[80]

be betrothed to Simcha Meyer, the son of Reb Abraham Hirsh Ashkenazi." Ashamed and half-incredulous, she sprang from her father's lap, fled to her mother's room, and burst into such a fit of weeping that her mother turned pale.

"I don't want him!" she screamed. "I don't want him!"

She hated the thought of that funny-looking boy, with the pious Jewish gaberdine and the silly, pious ear-locks. She was ashamed to her inmost being. What would her gentile friends say when they saw this outlandish youth, her husband to be? How often she had talked with them of the kind of man she was going to marry, some nobleman, dark-eyed and knightly! Dinah loved her father and mother, but she did not love her home. She could not stand those ridiculous Chasidic Jews who filled it with the noise of their drawling, pietistic Yiddish. She could not stand her brothers, big, clumsy lummoxes without a touch of grace. She dreamed of leaving them all some day, to live in that glowing, singing world which beckoned to her from the French and German story-books she had swallowed so avidly at school.

These dreams, so remote from the life of her parents and brothers that she had never dared to reveal them, made her proposed bridegroom even more absurd than he might have been otherwise. She knew it was useless to ridicule Simcha Meyer, so she only said, weeping, that she did not want to be a bride. She did not want to marry. Her father looked at her, his big, fat-encircled eyes filled with wonder.

"But it isn't an ordinary bridegroom, Dinah, darling," he said. "It's Simcha Meyer, the prodigy, the genius. There isn't a girl in town who won't envy you."

He had not the remotest idea of what was passing through her mind. Because she was only a girl, who did not need to be learned in Jewish matters, who was not called upon to say the memorial sanctification after her dead parents, he had let her go to a gentile school and pick up all those silly amusements, foreign languages, dancing, and what not. It was all right as long as she was a child. Now that she was becoming a woman and would shortly be a mother in Israel, this nonsense had to be forgotten. It did not occur to him that the nonsense, as he thought it, could become the reality of his daughter's life. And when Dinah turned to her mother in the hope that she at least, she who had read some of the modern books and knew something about civilized life, would understand her better, she was even more bitterly disappointed. Her mother was too lazy or too indifferent to make an effort to understand.

"I cried just like you, Diana," she said, using the girl's non-Jewish name, "when they proposed a husband for me. I was a splendid girl, I could speak excellent French, yet I married your father, and I've never regretted it. If your husband will be as good to you as mine has been to me, you won't regret it, either."

"But I don't like him," cried Dinah, passionately.

"After you're married to him you'll begin to like him," said her mother soothingly.

Dinah felt that the whole world was in conspiracy against her. She made one last, helpless effort to change her fate.

"Mamma," she pleaded, "I'll give in. I'll let myself be betrothed. But not with Simcha Meyer. I hate him." She blushed and began to stammer. "I'll become a bride if—if you'll tell Father that I want Jacob Bunim, not Simcha Meyer."

Her mother, touched at last, made one mild effort to change her husband's mind. She told him of Dinah's predilection. "The girl is in love with the other one, Chaim," she said. "She wants Jacob Bunim."

Reb Chaim leapt out of his chair. "Are you mad, Priveh?" he cried. "Simcha Meyer is the wonder of Lodz! There isn't another like him in the city, for genius and learning and sense. And his brother is a blockhead, a nobody. I don't want him as a son-in-law."

Samuel Zanvil, the marriage-broker, had his say in the matter, too. "You can't marry a younger brother before an older brother," he said, sternly.

"Younger by five minutes!" retorted Priveh.

"It doesn't matter," insisted Samuel Zanvil. "I absolutely refuse to speak to Reb Abraham Hirsh about his younger son. You can't make a fool of a man like that."

There Priveh's efforts on behalf of her daughter came to

[82]

an end. It wasn't only her husband and Samuel Zanvil. As soon as the news of the match leaked out, the house was besieged by uncles, aunts, cousins, brothers- and sisters-in-law, who gabbed so enthusiastically about young Simcha Meyer and congratulated themselves and each other in such a frenzy of pride that Priveh gave way and Dinah stood alone in the midst of a world determined to marry her off to this boy whom she detested. Eight days she held out, and then her opposition collapsed. Red-eyed with weeping, she sat down to perform her first duty as a bride, to sew a silken phylactery-bag for her bridegroom and to adorn it, in gold lettering, with his name and with the Jewish year.

The betrothal was celebrated with great pomp in Reb Chaim's house. Every important Jewish figure of Lodz was there, a host of Chasidim, the cliques of both the fathers, and swarms of relatives. Reb Chaim even sent cake and whisky to his workers and let them take the evening off. On the day of the betrothal the bridegroom received from his father-in-law a big gold watch and a gold chain of heavy double weave. As dowry, Reb Chaim deposited five thousand roubles in the bank and pledged himself to pay another two thousand on the day of the wedding. Reb Abraham Hirsh would not take less, and Reb Chaim had to yield. On his side Reb Abraham Hirsh added, to his son's account, three thousand roubles. The rules called for less—exactly for one third of what the bride's father had given. But Reb Abraham Hirsh liked a round figure, and ten thousand roubles made a respectable start in life for his son. The bride signed her name to the contract in every language she knew—Yiddish, Polish, Russian, German, and French—so as to get a present for each signature. The marriage date was deferred for some years.

As soon as the ceremony was over and the contract had received all the necessary signatures, the furniture was pushed to one side, the flowers and the crockery were taken out of the room, and the assembled Chasidim prepared for a jollification such as Lodz had seldom seen before.

"Dance, Jews!" cried Reb Chaim. "Dance till the steam goes up from the floor!"

Jacob Bunim, grim-faced and silent, moved among the

[83]

guests, hardly feeling the sweaty hands that were thrust into his, hardly hearing the "Good-lucks" that were shouted at him. He did not see the food which the waiters in the silken skull-caps laid before him. He paid no attention to the congratulations of those big, clumsy yokels Dinah's brothers. He only knew one thing: he would try not to look at Dinah, who was just within the line of sight, in the other room, among the women. But in spite of himself he kept turning in her direction, and in spite of himself he caught her glance.

On the very day after the betrothal Reb Abraham Hirsh transferred his son Simcha Meyer from Reb Boruch Wolf Lentchitzer's schoolroom to the care of Reb Noske, who was known simply by the name of "the Teacher." Reb Chaim also withdrew his sons from their former *cheder*, though they had by no means outgrown its possibilities, in order that he might have them study in the company of his prospective son-in-law.

Reb Noske, the Teacher, had his hovel in Balut, in the poorest section, inhabited by weavers, tailors, draymen, and professional beggars. Reb Noske was not primarily a teacher; he was rather a moralist and pietist, but he was temperamentally unfit for the rabbinate and therefore had to make a living as a teacher. The fact that he was equally unfitted to be a teacher did not seem to matter.

In the growing city of Lodz, with its ceaseless business activity, the rabbis did well. They were not only religious leaders; they were likewise the lawyers and courts of justice. Jewish business-men went to them for advice, for the settlement of disputes, the drawing up of partnerships, and even to deposit money in escrow. The rabbis were used by the orthodox Jews in preference to the regular civil courts and thus the rabbinate was a flourishing profession. In Lodz, of all places, Reb Noske would have been hopeless as a rabbi. He knew nothing about bills, percentages, profits, contracts, promissory notes, and all the devices and tricks of the business world, which were held in higher esteem by the rabbis of

Lodz than were the sacred Law and the learning of the sages. He knew nothing about these things, and he refused to learn. He despised them and desired to know only the sanctities of Judaism.

In that field, however, he was a man of prodigious and merited reputation. Unlike the majority of the Polish Jews, he was not a follower of the Chasidic wonder-working rabbis. He was of the school of their opponents. His attainments must therefore have been phenomenal if Chasidic Polish Jews entrusted the education of their sons to him. It was difficult to say where Reb Noske shone more, in piety or in learning, for just as he knew by heart countless volumes of commentaries on the Talmud, so he observed with microscopic exactitude the thousands of ritualistic minutiæ which can be found in the Jewish religion. He was no compromiser, nor would he condone compromise in others. A man was either in the right or in the wrong, and to be partly in the wrong and partly in the right was, to him, to be wholly in the wrong. The accommodations and concessions which merchants must make in their mutual rivalries were to him abominations; he would not listen to them.

On the rare occasions when a case was laid before him, he announced his decision firmly, refusing to yield an inch. "Reuben is right, Simon is wrong. There's nothing more to be said." When the losing side protested that this wasn't the way business was conducted, Reb Noske rapped out: "I don't care how business is conducted. This is the sacred Law," and, ignoring the litigants, picked up a massive volume of the Talmud and continued with his studies. Reb Noske's cases became fewer and fewer, till they ceased altogether. In the same way the Jewish housewives stopped bringing for his judgment cases involving the purity of a chicken or a piece of beef or a utensil. When in doubt Reb Noske always said: "No."

The little Jew with the brown, taut skin and the smooth ear-locks was filled day and night with the fear of God and the vision of the Gehenna of flames in which the world's sinners were undergoing their indescribable torments. Among those sinners none were more severely or more justly punished than those who had been teachers and who had misled their charges. It was theirs to be utterly uncompromising. It was true that even the Law itself made concessions. For instance, if a little milk spills by accident into a meat-pot, but the contents of the meat-pot are sixty times larger than the quantity of milk, then the meat remains ritually pure, or kosher, and may be eaten. Reb Noske knew this of course; but he also knew the weakness of the human will, and he never trusted a woman who told him that the milk had been less than a sixtieth of the contents of the meat-pot. He therefore said, sharply: "Forbidden!" He did not look at the woman's face when he condemned her meal, but added: "Pour it all out in a place where even a dog can't eat it." The woman went away miserably, but she was not more miserable than Reb Noske. For he knew that it is sinful to waste Jewish money and Jewish substance, and he trembled at the thought that perhaps he had unjustly deprived a poor family of its meal. In the end housewives ceased to consult him.

Following the example of Reb Solomon David Preiss, large numbers of Jews erected steam factories, and both they and the owners of hand-looms employed gentile workers in ever greater numbers. They were cheaper than the Jewish workers, and they could be kept at work on the Sabbath. The only thing that was necessary was a fake sale which made the factory the property of a non-Jew. These deeds of sale were drawn up by rabbis and were well paid for. Reb Noske despised this wretched subterfuge. He had never drawn up such a deed, and he never would. The Law was the Law, to be observed in spirit as well as in letter.

Reb Noske's wife, the daughter of a rich Jew who had spent much money to acquire so learned and pious a husband for her, had nothing but contempt for all this frantic piety. A lively, capable, masculine woman, she would have made a first-class Lodz rabbi, for she understood what the litigants and questioners wanted when they came to her husband, and she could have given them just the decisions they sought. But she was forbidden to interfere, and she had to watch her home sink to deeper and deeper levels of poverty. The generous dowry with which she had begun married life had long since been eaten up, and from the handsome home in which her father had settled them she and her husband had been forced to move into a hovel in the poorest section of Balut. She never became reconciled to either her poverty or the vulgar neighbours among whom she was forced to live.

For Reb Noske the change was, if anything, a relief. There was no one to pester him now, none of the old acquaintances and family connections. In poverty he could serve God and the Law without interruption. No business-men came with their dirty disputes, no housewife with her plaintive questions of ritual. In matters which did not entail any sort of loss he was still consulted occasionally. A poor Jew would ask about the right procedure in an obscure question of ritual and, having received the answer, would tender in payment a few copper coins. Reb Noske did not look at the money. He hated to touch it. Without lifting his eyes from the book he would say: "Put it down on the table." Then he would call his wife and say: "Take away that money." His wife, looking at the miserable, greasy ten-kopeck pieces, would cry: "Fool! Do you expect me to feed a family on that?" Reb Noske did not answer. Poverty was the best safeguard of piety and learning. Bread and salt shall a Jew eat, and the bare earth shall be his couch, if he is to be given over completely to the laws of God. What is this life but a brief introduction to the eternal world on the other side of the grave? Reb Noske knew all this and even found no fault with his wife for her ceaseless insults and complaints. She was a woman, and she had not studied; therefore the deeper truths of life were hidden from her.

"Answer me!" his wife shrieked. "Don't you even know when you're being insulted?"

Yes, he knew when he was being insulted, but he wanted to be insulted, and to bear the insult in silence and patience, as an atonement for the sins with which he was covered from head to foot. Perhaps by taking these humiliations on himself he might yet escape the flames of the great torment. When his wife left the room he closed the door, tied the small chain in its place, and returned to his books, in the margins of which he added ceaseless comments on the wisdom of God's law

[88]

and the greatness of the sages of the past.

Shut off from the crying of the children, forgetful of their ragged clothes and tattered shoes, he sank deeper and deeper into his meditations. He left the house only for two purposes: to pray in the little synagogue and to visit the ritual baths. His learning, his rabbinical certificate, brought him in nothing. He had made only one concession to his wife; he would tutor the children of the rich. But he demanded so little in return that no one knew what his wife and children lived on.

On the very first day Simcha Meyer discovered that Reb Noske was not going to be the easy mark that Reb Boruch Wolf had been. All his tricky interpretations, his paradoxes, citations, feats of memory, were wasted on Reb Noske, who despised the barren dialectics of the Polish Jews and of the Chasidim. Reb Noske did not say much. He considered speech wasteful and therefore sinful. He listened to Simcha Meyer, and said: "No acrobatics, boy. Give me the simple truth."

"Of course," chanted Simcha Meyer, "the argument can also be turned round—"

"The argument can't be turned round," interrupted Reb Noske. "Truth is one and eternal. The truth—what is the truth?"

Simcha Meyer's heart sank. He had never been spoken to like this before. Everyone had been delighted by what Reb Noske called his "acrobatics." His teacher's words sounded silly and empty to him; he did not know what the old man wanted.

"He's loony," he told his future brothers-in-law afterwards.

Simcha Meyer was, however, clever enough to realize that it would be useless to try to dazzle Reb Noske as he had dazzled his other teachers. But there were other ways of fooling him. Reb Noske was no teacher. He would become so absorbed in his expositions that he would pay no attention to his pupils, and it did not occur to him that the boys might not be following the text. Sometimes Reb Noske would even break off teaching in order to preach morals—a practice unknown to the Polish teachers, and familiar only among the Jews of Lithuania. Boys stole in and out of the room. Simcha Meyer took a couple of companions with him into a corner,

[89]

drew a pack of cards from his pocket, and proposed a game. Reb Noske rambled on passionately, speaking with ecstatic self-absorption of the pitfalls of this life and the torments of Gehenna.

Reb Noske's pupils were almost all the children of rich parents. They submitted reluctantly to their studies, and Simcha Meyer's daring contempt for Reb Noske made him their leader, though he was the youngest among them. In a few weeks he had picked up all their secrets, was introduced to all their hang-outs, and outdid them in impudence and wickedness. Reb Chaim Alter's sons, who had been put under the same teacher with him in order that they might follow his example, followed it enthusiastically. But it was not the example that their father had expected of him.

In the boyhood days of Simcha Meyer, Lodz was still in a fever of expansion. The city was growing, street by street, old buildings were coming down, new ones going up. There was a continuous stream of settlers and visitors, merchants, agents, buyers, engineers, and experts from Germany, chemists and draughtsmen from England, business-men from remote parts of Russia, outlandish people in long blue cloaks, wide trousers, and short, patent-leather boots. There was a magnetism in Lodz which drew toward it, by the thousand, young Jewish commercial travellers and adventurers, gay fellows who wanted to make money and spend it. The young Jews of Lodz, who had never before come in contact with these worldlings, were quick to yield to their influence; they discarded the traditional Jewish gaberdine in favour of the short coat of the West, they shaved off their beards, they began to look like modern Europeans. Restaurants, hotels, cabarets, gaming-houses sprang up in Lodz, and they were always full. Hungarian dancing-girls smelled from afar the rich odour of the city and came in troops. Actors and circus performers came down from Warsaw, Petersburg, Berlin, and Budapest. Russian officers and officials gathered in a fat harvest of bribes from all sorts of illegalities and joined in the revelry. Lodz danced, drank, sang, applauded in the theatres, rioted in brothels, and played heavily at cards. The demoralization spread to the well-to-do Chasidic Jews. It began with

[90]

visits to the kosher restaurants, which became a habit, so that the home was neglected. The gambling fever spread to pious circles, so that the younger generation used the synagogues for card-games more than for prayers. The study of sacred things declined.

There were special private houses in which these sons of the pious Chasidic families gathered to eat forbidden food, drink schnapps, and occasionally to become intimate with the servant girls who waited at table. Cards were, however, the chief diversion. The most popular of these unofficial resorts was the house of a certain Shillem the "Shark," who was a baker by profession and who was often to be seen in the street in clothes which were dusty with flour, and with his ritual fringes hanging over his trousers. But he baked as little as he prayed: the flour and the fringes were both blinds. He had something more lucrative than either to attend to—the card-games in his house.

The large room above the bakery, one flight up, was always crowded with young Jews of good family, perpetually absorbed in card-games. The stakes were high, and the only steady winner was Shillem. The more they lost, the more passionately the young men played. But they were drawn by more than the fever of gambling. There was something about Shillem himself, his gaiety, his good-fellowship and high spirits, which they found irresistible in contrast with the dour piety of their homes. Besides, Shillem was always ready to play on credit and to take promissory notes. He taught these young men how to dip their fingers into their father's tills, and if they still could not pay off their debts to him he extended credit at innocent-looking interest till the day when they would receive their dowries and be independent householders. Most of all, Shillem liked a promissory note on which some young man had forged his father's name. It was to him a document of great price, independently of the amount.

The walls of the room were covered with pious tapestries showing Abraham taking his son Isaac to the sacrifice on Mount Moriah, Pharaoh's daughter lifting the infant Moses out of the basket, the brothers selling Joseph to the Midianites. At the head of the large table sat Shillem himself, in

[91]

paper cap and blue pants, dealing cards. The money flew into his hands, three-, five-, and ten-rouble notes, which grew dirtier and dirtier as they circulated. Shillem's daughters, big, fleshy girls, served food continually, fat roast duck, chicken giblets, cakes, strudel, and countless bottles of beer. Besides them there were two servant girls, who were assistant waitresses, but who served more than food. A wink, a sign from one of the boys, and they stole down into the storeroom below the bakery, where it was dark even in the middle of the day.

And the pupils of Reb Noske spent more time in the "bakery" of Shillem the shark than in the schoolroom. Reb Chaim's sons were among the most faithful frequenters. The older they grew, the clumsier and the more of lummoxes they became. Their cheeks sprouted pimples mingled with the first growth of hair. They divided their attention between the game-room and the storeroom below the bakery. They learned early to "dip" into their father's till—the more easily as their father never knew how much money he left lying around. They brought money to Shillem always, they never took any away. In this they were like the other pupils of Reb Noske, with the single brilliant exception of Simcha Meyer. Shillem recognized in the sharp-witted youngster an equal and comrade. He tried with him none of the tricks which succeeded with the others, nor did he say a word when Simcha Meyer cut in on his preserves and milked his customers. Better, he thought, a costly ally than a dangerous rival. Within a few months Simcha Meyer had accumulated several hundred roubles, which, following Shillem's example, he lent out at interest, mostly to his future brothers-in-law.

Reb Noske sat at his lessons, the huge folios of the Talmud open before him, not noticing whether a pupil was present or absent. Only on Thursdays, which was the day set aside for revision, were they certain to attend. They were not afraid of Reb Noske; but there was the possibility that on the approaching Sabbath their fathers would take a notion to examine them, and they had to show something for the week. Then there was a feverish cramming and questioning, and Simcha Meyer was in great demand. But his "acrobatics,"

[92]

though they imposed on students and parents, remained as odious as ever to Reb Noske. He would ask Simcha Meyer to read and propound the lesson, let him interpret half a dozen lines, then stop him brusquely.

"No," he would say, sharply. "Nissan," he turned to his son, "you do the lesson."

Nissan, a thirteen-year-old boy, brown-skinned and bony like his father, would open the Talmud, and in a high, clear voice repeat the lesson for the class. Simcha Meyer, sitting next to Nissan, clenched his teeth with rage and kicked Nissan's shins under the desk.

$\mathcal{H}$is pupils were not the only ones who fooled Reb Noske. His own son, Nissan, the thirteen-year-old who seemed on the surface a model of piety and learning, was treading secretly in paths even more sinful than those of his fellow-pupils.

Nissan hated and despised his father. He hated him for the poverty to which he had condemned the family; he despised him for his fanatical and fantastic devotion to the barren study of the Law. Ever since he could remember, Nissan had known only hunger and wretchedness. His mother went about weeping, her head covered with a wet kerchief. His sisters, clothed in rags, cried their eyes out for a decent dress or a presentable pair of shoes. At an age when other children ran around carefree, Nissan had taken upon himself the burden of his wretched family. His boyhood was filled with the sound of bitter complaints, the quarrels of his mother with his father, her hatred of her lot, her reproaches against the memory of her father, who, in the name of scholarship and piety, had consigned her to a life of want, vulgarity, and ugliness. She talked against her husband in the presence of her children, and when he came into the room she would point at him and cry contemptuously: "There goes that father of yours! Look at him! He doesn't know where he's walking. He doesn't know he's alive."

From earliest childhood he was accustomed to the shrill arguments of the shopkeepers who wanted payment and re-

[94]

fused to give any more food on credit. Every Sabbath was reached through a storm of quarrels, every dress was purchased with hysterics and tears. The only one who did not seem to care was his father; Reb Noske could not let the things of this world interfere with his devotion to the eternal values of the Law. In earliest childhood Nissan had learned to go begging from his rich and miserly uncles, to argue on his own account with shopkeepers and workers, to borrow or steal firewood in winter—and all this while his father insisted that he devote himself wholly to the Law and learning. It was a house in which laughter was never heard and to which no visitors ever came except the ragged men and women who had ritual questions to ask of Reb Noske. If his father spoke at all, it was to repeat, grimly, that nothing mattered in his life; joy was a snare, happiness a delusion. "Fear God, Nissan," he said frantically to his son. "Do you hear me? Fear God and no one else."

Dark and wretched as the week-days were in that house, the Sabbaths and high holidays were worse. Prayers without end, and, between prayers, study. Reb Noske reviewed the week's portion of the Pentateuch, studied sections of the Zohar, dug out obscure prayers from thick, ancient books. When everyone else had left the synagogue, he insisted on keeping Nissan behind with him, making him share in his interminable devotions. The child was hungry. The dust and emptiness of the deserted synagogue terrified him. He had to walk back and forth with his father until the middle of the afternoon, when other Jews had long since finished their meals and were taking their Sabbath afternoon sleep.

Such food as was waiting for them at home was cold and tasteless by the time they sat down to it. But food was not made to be enjoyed, according to Reb Noske, and a meal was not a pleasant occasion. He ate without interest, and when the poor meal was done, resumed his prayers. If he permitted himself a short nap later, it was only because law and custom had sanctified the Sabbath rest. He lay down with a book in his hand and studied it until he fell asleep. And he made Nissan do the same.

Nissan hated, together with his father, everything that his

father held sacred; the books, the laws, the customs, the ritual, the very idea of Jewishness, which his father had converted into a terror and torment from which there was no escape. There were so many commandments and prohibitions, so many prayers and adorations, such a pervasiveness and omnipresence of duty and compulsion and harsh self-torture. He hated his father's God, a God of savage vengeance, who demanded of a man senseless sacrifice and undeflecting worship, fasts, prostrations, fulsome praise, a harsh discipline, and devotion without end, without remission or pause. This was the God in whose name and for whose sake his mother and sisters went in rags, the house was dilapidated and cheerless, his own cheap gaberdine was a crazy-quilt of patches. To spite this God, Nissan missed prayers, tore paper on the Sabbath, looked boldly at the cross on the churches, drank milk soon after having eaten meat—which is next door to eating pork—ate secretly on the fast days, and in secret read the forebidden irreligious books which he got from Feivel the rag-dealer.

This Feivel lived in a house near the end of the town, almost where the fields began. In the big yard behind the house girls sat cleaning and scrubbing huge bundles of rags which Feivel collected all over the city, and which he sold again, after they had been cleaned, to manufacturers, who spun them into cheap thread. But Feivel was more interested in the dissemination of enlightenment and irreligion than in the conversion of waste into thread. He was a small, nervous, active Jew, his hat always askew on his curly head, his mocking eyes set deep in his cheerful, puckered, dusty face. Busy though he always seemed to be with his rags, his working-girls, merchants, notes, and bills, his real passion was rationalism, and he would leave everything and walk to the other end of the city if he heard of a new anti-religious book which could be obtained there.

In his large house, which was full of daughters, bundles of rags, papers, bills, and bedding, books predominated over everything. They stood in shelves ranged along the walls of every room, they lay in heaps on the floor, they were scattered in the corridors. He had spent a fortune on them. His pious

[96]

wife and his stupid, awkward daughters detested the books and tore them up or burned them whenever they could. But still the number of books grew. Feivel would drop everything, leave a good customer standing in the house, to go panting excitedly in search of a book which he had heard someone mention. Many of these books were in Hebrew; they belonged to the literature of the modernist revolt which was flourishing at that time, and which went by the name of the Movement of the Enlightenment. They were strictly forbidden in the religious schools and in the homes of pious Jews; and if Feivel was only able to put one into the hands of a Jewish student and persuade him to read it, he felt he had fulfilled his life's mission.

On Sabbaths and holidays, and even on workdays, young people would gather secretly in his house to read the evil books. Feivel would go from one school to another to win proselytes, and his persuasive tongue was equally adept in the religious literature with which his converts were familiar since childhood, and the modernism to which he sought to win them. He was glad to have boys come and live in his house, he fed them and lent them money and gave them shelter, if he could only persuade them to take up the new knowledge; and his heart glowed with pride when he first heard them propounding those dangerous questions which, in his eyes, meant the end of the swindle called religion.

In the middle of the day he would take time out from business to encourage some student who, pale and terrified, sat at table conning one of the modernist books and feeling the foundations of his old life dissolving under him. "Read! Study!" he exclaimed ecstatically. Then he would get up from the table to bring the student something to eat.

Sometimes he conducted classes in philosophy, sitting with his students like an old-fashioned rabbi and chanting the text of a rationalist book with the melody of the Talmudic studies. He brought to his anti-religious faith the devotion of a pietist and preached with the enthusiasm of some perfervid synagogue saint. On Sabbaths and holidays there was always a crowd of young men in silken gaberdines and pious skullcaps. They sat there all afternoon, drinking the tea which

[97]

had been prepared the day before, for neither Feivel's wife nor his daughters would disobey the Law and do any cooking on the Sabbath. Feivel sat at the head of the table, in greasy gaberdine and hat, propounding philosophy and mathematics, history and astronomy, geography and Bible criticism. He took sacred texts from the Bible and Talmud, interpreted them in the light of modern knowledge, exposed the nonsense in them, and taught his students the elements of rationalist thought.

"Boys! Education and free thought—they're the only things. Education and free thought and work. The rest is rubbish."

He passed cigarettes around, on the Sabbath day itself. Students who were still enmeshed in the old ways were horrified at the sacrilegious suggestion, but after a few visits they overcame their scruples, lit up with the others, and, in an ecstasy of revolt, blew the smoke right against the Sabbath candlesticks which stood on the table. And then Feivel's face was illumined with joy; he had won a soul to freedom from superstition.

Among the most eager frequenters of the school of Feivel the rag-dealer was Nissan, the son of Reb Noske the Teacher. Nissan was one of Feivel's happiest discoveries, not only because it was a great achievement to have won over the son of the ultra-pietist Reb Noske, but because the boy's brilliance, restlessness, and unhappiness appealed to him. He foretold a great future for this lad; he would become a mighty figure in the Enlightenment, a leader in the anti-religious revolt. Besides, it was an extraordinary pleasure to teach the lad. His young, swift, rebellious mind caught eagerly at Feivel's words, and he swallowed one after another the books which his enthusiastic teacher passed on to him.

Nissan was in his thirteenth year when he came under the influence of Feivel. His father, Reb Noske, living in a world of his own, did not observe any change in the lad, did not even notice his long absences or the blasphemous Hebrew pamphlets which Nissan spread out on the pages of the Talmud and conned under his father's nose.

"Nissan!" exclaimed Reb Noske from time to time, "fear God! Do you hear me?"

[98]

"I hear you," answered Nissan automatically, his eyes fixed on the pamphlet. Then the boy would come to, and a fierce delight filled him at the thought of the boundless deception which he was practising on his father.

He read day and night, running frequently to Feivel for new material, stealing candles from the synagogue to be able to study when everyone else in the house slept. He read without system whatever Feivel gave him, Mendelssohn's modernist commentary on the Bible, Maimonides's *Guide to the Perplexed,* German translations which he only half understood, articles in the modernist Hebrew periodical *Ha-Shachar,* stories and poems and treatises by Smolenskin, Mapu, and Gordon, rationalist essays by Krochmal and Adam Ha-Cohen, fantastic travel-books, Hebrew treatises on astronomy and higher mathematics, of which he understood nothing, but which attracted and fascinated him because they represented that great brilliant, forbidden world which was opposed to everything held sacred by his father. From Mendelssohn he passed on to Solomon Maimon, and from him to Spinoza and Schopenhauer. He mumbled the German words to himself, caught part of their meaning, tried to guess at the rest, lived in a fever of intellectual effort and wild hope. And with all this he still managed to learn the weekly lesson set by his father, and repeated it to the pupils whose thoughts were with Shillem the baker and his gaming-house.

Reb Noske's pupils disliked intensely their teacher's son. He was not of their world. They might have forgiven him his ability if, like Simcha Meyer, he had joined them at Shillem's, but Nissan's enmity toward his father was of another kind. Simcha Meyer himself could not stand the sight of Nissan, who had so simply and so easily exposed his pretentiousness in class. Nissan returned their hatred with interest, for he could not look without fury on their good clothes and their beefy, well-fed bodies. His was the only cotton gaberdine in the class, and it was a thing of patches. His hat was cheap, and greasy with age. He knew he would never sport a gold watch and chain, as so many of them did. Also, in spite of his contempt for his father, he hated them because of their attitude toward Reb Noske. Obscurely he felt that their derision was low and vulgar. If his father was a fool, they were beasts. Besides, it was his father. He had private and special reasons for hating the old man. What excuse had these pampered, selfish, heartless sons of the well-to-do for making a fool of their teacher?

On one occasion the boys, fearing that Nissan would report their behaviour to Reb Noske, and that their parents would therefore hear of their intimacy with Shillem the shark, persuaded Nissan to come along with them to the gaming-house. But the place had no attraction for him. He sat there bewildered, unable to understand what the others were getting excited about. He slipped out of the room and back to his forbidden books.

In spite of his revulsion against them, he tried to return their advances in his own way. Like his father, and like Feivel the rag-dealer, Nissan was a passionate and instinctive proselytizer. He approached some of his father's pupils with his heretical views, showed them his modernist books, tried to instil in them the first doubts. But these boys were not of the stuff of converts. For a moment they were excited by the novelty and daring of it; then, when they realized that rationalist books meant only more study, though of another kind, they lost interest. Only Simcha Meyer read one of the books right through from beginning to end, and he did not tell Nissan about it. Instead he reported his findings to Reb Noske himself.

He did it in the midst of one of Reb Noske's passionate discourses on the faith and the eternal Law.

"Rabbi," he said suddenly, "the Law was given to the Jews by God Himself on Mount Sinai, wasn't it?"

"What kind of question is that?" gasped Reb Noske.

"Well, I was only asking," said Simcha Meyer, playing the simpleton, "because Nissan says that Moses made it all up out of his own head."

Reb Noske sat like a man smitten with a paralytic stroke. A dreadful hush fell on the boys. After a long pause Reb Noske found his tongue again.

"Nissan," he croaked, "did you say that?"

Nissan did not answer. He would not tell a lie.

[100]

Reb Noske held on to his chair. He tried to get up, but his legs refused to serve him. His eyes remained fixed on his son.

"Jeroboam, son of Nebat, apostate and traitor," he whispered. "You dare not be seen in the company of Jews."

Nissan got up from his place and went silently out of the room.

He went straight to a weaver of his acquaintance and asked to be taken in as an apprentice. He asked for no pay. He would work all hours in exchange for a place to sleep in, enough food to keep body and soul together, and the prospect of learning the trade. The weaver was reluctant; without the father's consent there could be no legal contract. But then Nissan bethought himself of his education and added that, besides working all hours, he would teach the weaver's grown-up daughters how to sign their names, and his sons how to do sums in arithmetic. The weaver yielded and took the boy in on a three-year contract.

Though he was officially an apprentice, Nissan was never taught anything, and whatever he learned was learned by stealth. Most of the day he sat on a low, three-legged stool carding thread, at the same time rocking the cradle of the youngest-born child of the weaver. The low, broad room was jammed with looms, beds, couches, and benches. Apprentices and weavers worked in underwear and trousers. With their little skull-caps shoved back on their perspiring foreheads, they sat singing their synagogue melodies, their hands flying back and forth along the looms. The master weaver, a red-eyed little Jew in greasy clothes which he wore winter and summer, ran up and down the room checking the work and badgering the weavers. "Faster, faster," he kept barking, "a lazy man is like a pickpocket."

The workroom opened on to the big kitchen, where the weaver's wife sat all day in her shabby black wig, through which peeped the strands of her own red hair. With her sat a group of blowzy girls, for ever peeling potatoes and onions. A thick steam of sizzling fat, a harsh smell of frying onions, the softer smells of soups, filled the kitchen and drifted into the workroom.

"What's for dinner today, old woman?" shouted a little

weaver, who, in the midst of the threads running from his fingers to the loom, looked like a spider in a web. "Is it going to be potato soup again?"

"Keep your nose out of the kitchen and put it closer to your work, you black tom-cat," retorted the weaver's wife. "You'll take what you get."

The "black tom-cat" did not answer. Instead, speeding up his work, he began to trill a well-known synagogue melody which went with the text of the Book of Esther. "Cursed be Zeresh, the wicked wife of the wicked Haman," he sang, with many roulades. The workers caught the allusion and burst into loud, mocking laughter. They applauded by stamping on the frames of the looms. The housewife dug her knife viciously into a potato and screamed: "You'll eat potato soup till you burst, all of you, and then you'll know what Zeresh is like." In her rage she cut her finger, and, becoming frantic, she ran over to the beds and benches on which the better workers slept at night—the others usually slept on the floor—and grabbed the dirty, coverless cushions.

"May I never live to see my daughter married," she howled, "if any one of you gets a cushion to sleep on tonight. You can all go to hell and sleep on the floor, not on my feather cushions."

Close to the open door between kitchen and workroom, his hands covered with thread, one foot rocking the cradle, sat Nissan, the son of Reb Noske, the Teacher. Because he was the youngest apprentice, and also because there was something queer about him, he was the butt of the workroom. When he was not carding thread he was sent on countless errands, to bring a piece of bread and herring from the grocery store, to carry a message, to fetch a glass of water—anything, just so long as he was kept busy. They called him "loony," "softy," "half-wit." But he ignored them. He shoved his stool as close as he dared toward the looms, and as he carded the thread, he watched the hands flying over the looms and tried to learn by heart, from a distance, the meanings of the various parts.

During the first months of his apprenticeship his mother came weeping to him, begging him to return to his home.

[102]

She, the daughter of a rich Jew, was horrified at the disgrace of it—a son of hers a manual worker, condemned to the ignorance and vulgarity of a workshop. This, more than Nissan's hungry looks, broke her down.

"Nissan," she wept, "I never thought I'd live to see this— you an apprentice! Come home with me."

Nissan shook his head, let her weep, and remained where he was. He worked all hours of the day; and when there was no work to do, he gave lessons to the master weaver's children. He had very little time for reading now. Sometimes, when he was able to get a piece of candle, he would light it late in the night, and lying on the dirty sack of straw which was his bed, he would study, preparing himself for something, he knew not what.

In Balut, among the pious Jews, the name of Nissan the son of Reb Noske the Teacher became a byword and a warning.

"That," they said in awed tones, "is what happens to an infidel. Neither this world nor the world to come: neither worldly success nor glory in heaven."

In Reb Noske's schoolroom the sons of the rich Chasidic Jews continued to play cards under their teacher's nose. Reb Noske's soul was darker and gloomier than ever; he brooded on the punishment which he, the father, would have to endure in the world to come because of the apostasy of his son. He became less and less aware of what was going on around him.

"Boys," he muttered, keeping his eyes fixed on the Talmud, "be faithful to your Jewish heritage. Fear God, obey His commandments, turn neither to right nor to left from His Law. Do you hear?"

"We hear you, Rabbi," they answered automatically, and continued with their game.

Five Passovers and five Feasts of Tabernacles passed. On each of these holidays there was an official reception for the bride in the bridegroom's house, or vice versa; in the first case the bride received some gift from the bridegroom's family; in the second it was the bridegroom who got the gift. When this cycle of five seasons had passed, the wedding was celebrated, and Dinah, the daughter of Reb Chaim Alter, became the wife of Simcha Meyer, the son of Reb Abraham Hirsh Ashkenazi. Bride and bridegroom were both eighteen years of age.

Mademoiselle Antoinette herself, the half-French, half-German modiste, who made all the dresses for the daughters of Heinz Huntze, prepared the trousseau for Dinah. Reb Chaim Alter opened wide his fat eyes when his wife Priveh told him what that would cost.

"Privishe, darling," he said, horrified, "what are you thinking of? Who ever heard of paying such a sum to a seamstress?" He tugged frantically at his coal-black beard.

Priveh looked at her husband contemptuously. "You know nothing about it," she said, angrily. "Mademoiselle Antoinette is not a seamstress. She is the leading modiste in Lodz, and it's a privilege to have a dress made by her. Do you think she sews for anybody?"

Reb Chaim was so bewildered, both by the exorbitant price demanded by Mademoiselle Antoinette and by the idea that a French modiste was conferring a great privilege on him and his family, that he forgot to be frightened of his wife.

"I'll give her a third," he said. "That's more than enough. There are plenty of modistes in Lodz."

The plump, smooth face of Priveh flushed, her eyes filled with tears, and she clasped her hands. "Mother!" she cried, appealing for heavenly aid, "do you see what I have to put up with?"

During all the years since the betrothal she had lived with this one idea—that the incomparable Mademoiselle Antoinette should make the trousseau for her daughter's wedding. She was not thinking of the clothes themselves and of the quality of the work, for she knew both from her own experience and from observation that the dozens of costly dresses, silk, satin, and velvet, with their laces and flounces, which made up the trousseau of a bride, seldom saw the light of day. They hung in the closets and grew old and outmoded. It was just the idea of Mademoiselle Antoinette, the most expensive and most 'exclusive modiste in Lodz, for whose services the ladies of the aristocracy were glad to pay the highest prices. It had meant months of intrigue and wire-pulling to get an introduction to the famous modiste; it had taken bribes and promises to get Mademoiselle to accept the commission. And here her husband, indifferent to fame and glory, was actually talking of prices, and asking her—she shuddered—to haggle with Mademoiselle Antoinette.

"Mother! Mother!" she wept. "I'll never get over the disgrace. I won't live to see the wedding." And thinking of the dozens of women she had told, loftily and offhandedly, that of course Mademoiselle Antoinette was going to make the trousseau, she redoubled her tears.

At the sight of his wife's tears Reb Chaim collapsed, and his own voice trembled on the verge of tears as he said: "Privishe, darling, bite your tongue off before you utter such words, right on the eve of your daughter's happiness. May they never be heard or remembered! May the wind carry them into the desert, or drop them into the ocean!"

Priveh was so delighted at her husband's about-face that she forewent her usual manœuvres of reconciliation. She flung her arms round her husband and kissed him on both cheeks.

"Privishe, darling!" exclaimed Reb Chaim, terrified and delighted. "In front of Samuel Leibish!"

Samuel Leibish turned as red as his employer and stammered: "It's perfectly all right, it's perfectly all right, I don't mind a bit."

With the same pointless extravagance Priveh spent money right and left on furniture, tea and dinner sets, silver, house ornaments, furs, and lace pieces which the bride would never use. She made Reb Chaim hire the largest wedding hall in town and insisted on the most expensive caterers as well as a huge program of entertainers and professional wedding jesters. Invitations were sent out by the hundred. When it came to the wedding itself Reb Chaim needed less persuading to spend freely. He, too, wanted this wedding to be remembered for many years as one of the grandest in the annals of Polish Jewry. And indeed, the throng that was there assembled was probably the most remarkable that had ever been observed under a single roof in Lodz. There were heavy-bearded Jewish pietists, Chasidim in gaberdine and polished boots, fat-necked manufacturers with shaven faces and with white gloves on their plump hands, religious fanatics in huge fur and velvet skull-caps, with open shirts, their ritual fringes visible to all, anti-Chasidic rabbis in alpaca capotes, Lithuanian commercial travellers in hard hats and conventional Western clothes, blond Germans in frock-coats and immense, starched collars up to their ears, and even a sole and rather bewildered Russian police commissioner, in full uniform and with a breast glittering with medals. Equally incongruous was the feminine half of the rout. There were excited, solid, deep-bosomed, perspiring Jewish housewives in polished black wigs and enormous silk dresses of every colour, ancient crones in the costumes of a forgotten generation, attractive young women in décolleté, and blond German women with long plaits and thick cosmetics on their lips and cheeks. A feminine babbling in Yiddish, Polish, Russian, and German filled the vast hall, with its full-length mirrors, chandeliers, and red plush chairs and settees. Precious stones flashed from end to end of the hall, gold glittered, silk dresses shimmered, compliments danced in the air, eyes looked shrewdly and enviously—a welter of snobbery, pretence, bitterness, and hostile courtesy.

Through the narrow, ill-paved streets of Lodz carriages with white horses brought an interminable stream of guests, and an interminable line of women proceeded down the hall to pay their respects to the bride, who sat on a throne smothered in roses and surrounded by bridesmaids. The bridegroom's sisters had woven a wreath of roses for the bride, and it now adorned the plaits which would have to be shorn the next day, according to the custom of all pious Jewish wives. The bride's brothers, in new clothes, had stolen away from the festivities, and, side by side with one of the hired drivers in a resplendent silk hat made the rounds to pick up guests and bring them to the wedding. They were old enough to be bridegrooms themselves, but they could not resist the temptation to gallop through the streets sitting next to a uniformed coachman. A score of policemen, with curved swords hanging from their belts, kept driving from before the doors of the wedding hall the crowds of the poor who had gathered to feast their hungry eyes on the carriages and dresses of the upper classes of Lodz.

Like all Jewish weddings, this one was marked by violent disputes. According to the terms of the betrothal Reb Chaim was supposed to deposit the last two thousand roubles of the dowry on the eve of the wedding. But Reb Chaim simply hadn't the money. He had been running short even before the fantastic expenses of trousseau and wedding had begun to drain all his resources.

At the very wedding, and shortly before the ceremony, he had pleaded with Reb Abraham Hirsh. "I promise you," he said passionately, "in two days, as I live and am a Jew, I will deposit the two thousand roubles."

Reb Abraham Hirsh was adamant. "I want the money now," he answered, "or I swear that I will take the bridegroom home and there'll be no wedding."

Reb Chaim took Simcha Meyer to one side and implored him, with tears in his eyes, to soften the heart of his father.

[107]

"My son," he wept, "because you are a son to me, and you know how I love you, and how I would do anything for you, I promise you, by everything I hold holy, and by my hopes to see you a great and wealthy man in the community, that as soon as the wedding is over I will get the money together and put it in the bank. Speak to your father."

Simcha Meyer promised to speak to his father, but did nothing of the sort. He knew enough to discount at one hundred per cent the sacred oaths of a Lodz merchant. If the money was not deposited before the wedding ceremony, it would never be paid.

"I've spoken with Father," he told Reb Chaim later. "I've done all I could. But you know when my father makes up his mind. . . . I can't quarrel with him—it's my father."

That same night Samuel Leibish, Reb Chaim's man, was running all over town gathering the two thousand roubles, and they were paid over, in greasy notes of all denominations, before the wedding ceremony began.

When this major quarrel had been adjusted, another claimed the attention of Reb Abraham Hirsh. He was furious with Reb Chaim for having invited a crowd of Germans to this sacred Jewish wedding. He himself had brought along the distinguished Rabbi of Alexander, and he was ashamed, in his presence, of all these shaven faces. He did not know what disgraced him more, though, in the eyes of his Rabbi, these gentiles, or the heathenish Jews, shaved like gentiles, who represented Priveh's idea of the aristocratic Jewish world.

On their side, however, Reb Chaim Alter and his wife had passionate objections to the mob of beggarly followers, without clothes and without manners, who accompanied the great Rabbi of Alexander, and who, in their loud, impudent way, elbowed all the important guests away from the tables. Reb Chaim tore his beard. "Reb Abraham Hirsh," he gasped, "you're killing my wedding. You're driving out of the hall the finest people in Lodz."

"It's my wedding, too," snapped Reb Abraham Hirsh, "and I don't need people with shaved faces at my wedding. They can all go to the devil."

[108]

A little later a report was brought to Reb Abraham Hirsh that men and women were dancing together in the ladies' hall. Reb Abraham leapt up, flew into the ladies' hall, and began to yell at the top of his voice: "Heathens! Sinners! What do you think this is, a gentile wedding? I won't have it! Out of here!"

The bride fainted, the bride's mother went into a fit of hysterics, young people stood around and roared with laughter. Reb Abraham, tall, furious, irresistible, did not rest until every couple had been separated. "Have you no respect for the great Rabbi of Alexander?" he thundered. "Have you no consideration for the congregation of pious Jews assembled here?"

The Chasidic rabble which had come with the Rabbi put out the lamps, poured water on the floor to make it slippery, and prepared to do some of their man-and-man religious dancing.

The old crones in ancient wigs and old-fashioned clothes applauded. "Now we're going to have a real Jewish wedding."

Soon a great ring of pious Chasidim was dancing wildly in the middle of the hall. They crashed into the furniture, overturned tables and chairs, and made the place look like a madhouse, all in honour of the bridegroom and the Rabbi of Alexander.

When he stood under the bridal canopy Simcha Meyer raised himself on his toes, trying to look as tall as the bride. Jacob Bunim, who knew how Simcha Meyer suffered from his lack of height, stationed himself deliberately next to his brother and stood very erect, to accentuate the difference between them. Enraged, Simcha Meyer made haste to step on his bride's foot, before she stepped on his, for custom and superstition said that the one who did this first would be master in the house.

Late that night, before he retired to his bride, Simcha Meyer was led out into a private room by two old men. It was their duty to tell the bridegroom what his duties and privileges were and what he should do with the bride. Simcha Meyer used his handkerchief to hide the grins which he could not suppress. There was something ridiculous about

[109]

the fearful seriousness of the two ancient gaffers who were trying to instruct him in something which he understood better than they.

The very next morning a crowd of his fellow-students, the pupils of Reb Noske, came to him eagerly, to ask him what had happened and to hear all the secrets of a bridal night. But Simcha Meyer had a new status. He was a married man. He looked at his former friends contemptuously and bade them be off.

"I don't talk with little boys," he said, sharply. "Don't pester me."

xii

$\mathcal{D}ina\mathcal{h}$ went through the wedding in a daze of mingled horror and resignation. This was the end of her hopes; this was what she had come to after all her dreams of knightly cavaliers, princely lovers, and a gallant world of adventure. Instead of paladins who, at a word from her, would be ready to leap into the arena full of lions, to retrieve her glove, there had danced at her wedding dirty, noisy, unkempt greasy little Chasidim. Instead of a noble husband, belonging to the aristocracy of birth and manners, she had been given a shrimp of a Talmudist who was supposed to be very, very clever in the comical and loathsome practices which her father held sacred.

She could not help loving her father, he was so generous to her. But when his piety was not revolting, it was just silly. Not that she was overburdened with it. Being a girl, she was not supposed to study. All the arduous labours and preparations of the Jewish boy were spared her. But what there was she found irritating and ridiculous. There were so many don'ts! "Dinah darling," said her father, "don't eat anything without having made the benediction. Dinah, don't forget the little morning prayer when you open your eyes. Dinah, don't eat that piece of milk chocolate. It isn't six hours since you ate meat, and you know that a Jew mustn't put a milk food in his mouth till more than six hours after he's eaten a flesh food. Dinah, you mustn't comb your hair on the Sabbath, you know it's forbidden." Don'ts, don'ts, don'ts. She

[111]

never got anything useful from her father. The studies she pursued he considered the frivolities of a woman. He never helped her with her arithmetic; he could not. Neither could he help her in the study of German and French. The things he knew he considered too sacred for her, and even if he had offered to teach them to her she would have turned away in contempt.

She loathed those pious Jews of his, the Chasidim, the rabbis, the scholars. She loathed their gatherings, their uncouth singing, their noisy feasts and celebrations. Women were, of course, not admitted to these. When a great rabbi was on visit, not even Reb Chaim's wife could come near him. Only now and again little Dinah would be led in, to receive a blessing, which was always to the effect that she might grow up to be what she most hated in her heart.

It was not that Dinah was without religious belief of a sort. She had a great deal of it; but she saw in these practices and companions of her father a ritual of witchcraft and a fellowship of malevolent demons. She feared them just as much as she loathed them. Whenever one of them expressed the hope that she would grow up to be the mother of many pious Chasidic Jews, she remembered the compliments of her schoolmates in the boarding-school, who had always told her that she did not look a bit Jewish.

"Diana, you've got light hair and blue eyes, just like a Christian," they said. "Why don't you become one of us? You'll marry a count, at least."

But that was out of the question, for she was afraid of the Jewish God, to whom, every night and every morning, she mumbled the senseless Hebrew words which her parents had taught her. And yet, unbeknown to her father, she had gone with her friends to services in the church, had listened to the great organ, had looked at the glowing Gothic windows and the figures of the saints in the niches. She had watched the priests in their radiant vestments and had knelt down with the others to be sprinkled with holy water from the censer. How beautiful it all was, how unlike the dirty, noisy gabbling of her father's clique of Chasidim! She had wept tears of envy, sadness, and adoration. But she would never have dared to break with the obscure and vengeful God of her fathers. From her place up in the women's balcony in the synagogue she had seen the men carry out the scrolls of the law, in their velvet coverings, and she had shuddered with fear. That was only once a year, on the Feast of the Rejoicing of the Law; but that once had left a deep impression on her heart. She was afraid, too, of the tall white candles which were lit on the Day of Atonement, to burn for twenty-four hours. She loathed these things, but she feared them too.

She was ashamed of her home and her family. She was ashamed to bring into the house any of her gentile friends, or even Jewish girls whose homes were modernized. She was ashamed of her lummoxy brothers, and when she encountered one of them on the street, she would pretend not to see him, hoping that he would pass on without stopping her. Very rarely did she invite a friend home; and when she did, it was in the hope that neither her father nor her brothers would be there. But she could never be sure. Without warning, her father might burst in with a troop of cronies, and all the ugliness and absurdity of her family would be revealed to her friend.

During the time of her long betrothal she had fallen in love with several teachers in succession; the French-teacher, the piano-teacher, the dancing-master—such handsome, un-Jewish men they were, with such refined manners! But she always loved passionately her schoolmates, who belonged to the world which she could never enter. She tried not to think of her betrothal. She made believe that nothing would come of it, for it seemed incredible that her husband would be this undersized boy in the Chasidic gaberdine, with his crazy darting eyes, his chanted Yiddish, and his odious cleverness.

She had nothing to say to him, and they met seldom enough —twice a year, at the Passover and the Feast of Tabernacles, when official visits were arranged. When the visits were to the house of Reb Chaim, father of the bride, Dinah sat next to her future husband or served him, as the custom was. But she had nothing to say to him. Worse than this was the visit to the bridegroom's house. A strange, cold family it was; her father-in-law-to-be was a harsh, bad-tempered pietist;

[113]

her mother-in-law-to-be was a sickly, old-fashioned woman whose conversation consisted either of fulsome compliments, such as are due to a bride on a visit, or else instructions in the ritual duties of a Jewish wife. Dinah did not know which she detested more. Even the presents which were given her did nothing to atone for the agony of these visits.

Like her father, who was never able to get his accounts straight and therefore avoided facts and realities, Dinah refused to think of the wedding, and during the years of her betrothal she lived more obstinately than before in her world of dreams. Then, when the wedding did come, with frightful suddenness, like a descending sword, she went through it like one bereft of her senses.

But for that she could not have borne it. She saw as in a nightmare the hordes of outlandish creatures who filled the hall; she heard from an infinite distance the jabber, the congratulations, the jokes. In the same way she had put up with the revolting preparations for the marriage, hardly hearing the horrible instructions which were poured into her ears, paying no attention to the pious women who surrounded her and made her ready for the great event. Then at last, when the moment arrived for her first meeting with her husband, when they were alone, she felt that the world had come to an end. She did not know who this miserable creature was who approached her to take possession. She had nothing to say to him. She did not want to be alone with him.

Simcha Meyer, who had been brought up in a world which took no account of a woman's feelings, mistook her terror and loathing for shyness. He tried to open a conversation.

"Was the fast easy for you?" he asked, alluding to the fast which every Jewish bride must observe on the day of her wedding. She did not answer. She cowered in a corner of her bed, trembling at the thought that he was going to touch her.

"No!" she babbled. "Don't come near me. I don't want you."

Simcha Meyer did not think of soothing her, of approaching her gradually. Such things were unknown among the men of his world.

[114]

"Dinah, darling," he said, sternly, "what is the matter with you? This is foolishness."

When he came closer she tried to fight him off, but Simcha Meyer was not the man to relinquish what was his by right. Her reluctance only excited him. Besides, he was thinking of the next day. What a figure he would cut if it became known that his bride had denied herself to him the night of the marriage! He paid no attention to her tears and entreaties, but took her by force, as became a man.

The hatred which she felt for him was confirmed and sealed that night. What her mother had told her—that she would learn to like her husband after she was married to him —was false. This was not the love she had dreamed of; it was something coarse and vulgar and inconsiderate. Her first night with Simcha Meyer was a hideous experience which she never forgot or forgave. She came out of it horrified, dumb, and silent. She had not, the next day, the energy to protest when her mother-in-law came with other pious women to cut off the chestnut locks of which she had been so proud. She submitted in a trance.

According to the letter of the Law, the bride's head must be shaved, and such had been the intention of the wife of Reb Abraham Hirsh. But Dinah's mother would not have it. She tried to persuade the bridegroom's mother to leave the task to her. "Trust me," she said, in a wheedling voice; "you can rely on me to do the right thing." She ordered the pious women to cut off the long plaits, but to leave the rest.

The wife of Reb Abraham Hirsh wrung her hands in horror. "But it's unheard of!" she cried. "You've left all the hair on her head. She's like the wife of a heathen, God save us!"

"I want you to remember," said Priveh, with sudden haughtiness, "that I am the daughter of Rabbi Anshel of Warsaw, and I need no instructions in the ritual of Jewish wifeliness."

Reb Abraham Hirsh's wife was no match for the daughter of Rabbi Anshel of Warsaw. She retreated, heartbroken, When the company of pious women was gone, Priveh made her daughter look into the mirror, saying: "You see, darling,

[115]

it isn't so terrible. If you arrange it like this you can hardly tell the difference."

"Better than that kind of a wig," said the wife of Reb Abraham Hirsh, at home, "is all of one's own hair. At least there's no mockery of sacred things."

Dinah was too far gone to care either way. Let them do with her what they liked. But between the two women, the mother of the bride and the mother of the bridegroom, the enmity which began with the shearing of the bride lasted for the remainder of their lives. The wife of Reb Abraham Hirsh took Dinah to one side and began to repeat in great detail the thousand and one laws of Jewish wifehood. Priveh was enraged by this piece of presumption, which was a reflection upon either her knowledge or her piety. The duty of instructing a new wife belonged to the mother, not to the mother-in-law.

"You may leave all that to me," she said with acidulous courtesy, pursing her lips. "It's true I don't wear a full-blown wig, but, thank God, I know what's proper for a Jewish wife."

During the period immediately following the marriage Simcha Meyer made an effort to awaken some friendship in his young wife. She did not respond. She answered his questions, whenever she was forced to, as curtly as possible. More than ever before, she clung to her novels and romances, and the only partial happiness she knew was in the company of her girlhood friends. Simcha Meyer, though he had been brought up to believe that a wife's feelings are of little account, felt the offence deeply. Once he snatched out of her hands the book from which she would not lift her eyes even while he was talking to her.

"What is this?" he asked.

"A novel," she answered.

He looked hastily at the German text, caught the names of Alfred and Hildegarde, and shrugged his shoulders.

"Drivel," he said, contemptuously. "A waste of time." He handed back the book. "And you prefer to read that rather than talk with me!"

Dinah went on reading. Simcha Meyer rubbed his hands

[116]

violently, as if cleansing them of the contact with the stupid novel. He tried again to start a conversation, gave it up, and left the room angrily. When he closed the door, Dinah burst into tears.

She felt she was utterly alone in the world. She did not dare to uncover the fullness of her shame to her schoolday friends; her mother did, indeed, listen, but only to answer with foolish, unmeant, selfish consolations. Her father would not have understood her at all. Besides, Reb Chaim Alter had other things to think about. For the first time in his life his business worries refused to be abjured by a gesture.

The grand ceremony of the wedding was followed by a host of minor ceremonies, some of them religious, some of them merely social; there were visits, presentations, benedictions, receptions, celebrations—every branch of the family had to be given an opportunity to display its generosity, hospitality, and sense of the importance of the occasion. When it was all over, when the young couple could be considered finally and adequately married, the two principal families were thoroughly exhausted. After all the kisses, handshakes, embraces, and celebrations both the Alters and the Ashkenazis felt as though they never wanted to see a human face again. Even Reb Chaim Alter, usually the most cheerful man in the world, and a great lover of company, felt as though he wanted to retire into a desert.

Yes, the wedding had been a tremendous success. It was the talk of Lodz and the surrounding cities, and rumours of its fame echoed back even from distant Warsaw. But what a hole it had made in his finances! The season had been a poor one for Lodz in general, and Reb Chaim had suffered more than most. Credit was tightened, the banks became cautious, and Reb Chaim was so pressed that the joy of the wedding was swallowed up in the wretchedness of his worries.

Not that he knew exactly what was wrong and how much he was short of. Neither he nor his man Samuel Leibish could have drawn up a balance-sheet for the factory; the queer account-books, with their muddled figures and their annotations in poor German and worse Hebrew, could have been disentangled only by a skilful accountant. All that Reb Chaim knew was that things weren't going right. Notes and bills fell due, and he could not meet them. At the week-end there was not enough cash on hand or obtainable to pay off the workers. Not that the workers dared ask for their pay. That would have been impudence. But they stood around with long faces, sighing, and that was even worse. Reb Chaim could not even pray with the old gusto. Right in the midst of the Prayer of the Eighteen Benedictions, which is supposed to be repeated in motionless absorption, while the body faces east, the faces of his workers and creditors would come bobbing into his mind, and all sorts of accounts danced before his eyes. Reb Chaim lost his appetite, and in the afternoons he could no longer take his pleasant nap on the red-plush-covered ottoman in the dining-room.

Besides, the whole business didn't make sense. The factory was working at full speed, as always. Whether or not they were paid on time, the workers were as busy as ever. On Thursdays they worked until midnight, on Saturdays even later. There was no waste there; the weavers even paid for their own candles. Samuel Leibish was as faithful as a watch-dog. Nothing, then, could be saved in the factory. What was to be done?

Reb Chaim did not know how to think things out; he had never had any practice at it. Ever since he had gone into the business—which was soon after his marriage—he had let the factory run itself. There had been good times and bad times, but always he had muddled through. He had never worried when a customer had gone bankrupt; that was part of the business game. He rescued what he could, and charged the rest to overhead. There couldn't be bankruptcies unless there was business, he argued, and in the same way there couldn't be business unless there were bankruptcies. So he had not bothered to keep a straight account. Superstition fortified his natural laziness and sloppiness. He was always repeating that the more you count, the less you have. "Look at me," he would boast. "I keep as decent a house as any Jew in Lodz. I'm a respectable member of the community, my standing in the banks is good—I always get a cigar from the president when I visit the bank. Other Jews in my position would long ago have gone in for new-fangled devices, steam and accountancy and what not, and would have finished up by shaving off the beard, God forbid. Not Reb Chaim Alter. I stick by the good old ways. And they've done me no harm."

Reb Chaim's weakness was his good nature and his inability to say no. He wanted to be in good humour and therefore had to have everyone around him in good humour. No committee which came collecting a dowry for a poor bride, or Passover expenses for a widow, or a contribution for a gift to the Rabbi, ever went away empty-handed. Besides, Reb Chaim liked spontaneous jollifications, little impromptu feasts with his clique of Chasidim. He hated stinginess, and he considered his contributions as investments in the future world. "This life below isn't everything," he said. "There's a life after death, and I want to take care of my reputation in the world to come. God made this world what it is, with its paupers, its workers, and its upper classes, the takers of charity and the givers. And if in His goodness He made me a giver, not a taker, let me fulfil my function to His glory." And so he handed out gifts right and left, his charities extending even to his own workers.

The house, too, was run extravagantly. Priveh had only to put out her plump, bediamonded hand, and Reb Chaim filled it with banknotes, seldom counting what he gave her. Nor did Priveh ever know what she had received. The money ran out between her fingers; she was as careless with it as she was with her jewellery, which was always getting lost. She had a passion for bargains, and if a thing was being sold for less than it seemed to be worth, the question of its usefulness became secondary. She bought dresses which she never put on, furniture which was stored away in an attic, silver which was never used. And on top of all this she had a great weakness for foreign health-resorts and for expensive physicians. Her bureaux were filled with coloured bottles and boxes of pills which she never took, but which made a grand subject for conversation. Among her other habits, Priveh had the one of trying to smuggle past the customs officials laces and

[120]

jewellery which she had bought on her travels. She was seldom successful, so that her purchases usually cost her double.

Reb Chaim knew all this and could do nothing about it. First because he still loved his wife, though she was the mother of grown-up children, second because he was aware that he himself did not set an example of economy. He, too, loved foreign health-resorts; and if his wife was extravagant in the upkeep of the house, was he any better, with his parties, celebrations, and jollifications? Also—again finding a justification for his weakness—he had always considered it good business to live high. Lodz liked rich men, and the higher he lived, the healthier, he said, was his reputation. And only now, after the wedding of his daughter, when the accumulations of his extravagance were breaking him, did he begin to consider that perhaps ostentation could be overdone.

For after the wedding the tradesmen descended on him like a swarm of locusts on a harvest field: tailors, shoemakers, seamstresses, carpenters, fish-dealers, grocers, butchers. They were innumerable; they were importunate. Samuel Leibish tried to put them off; they refused to be put off. They shouted, they threatened. And on top of that came certain heavy bills from abroad, for raw material.

Samuel Leibish made a long face to his employer. "Reb Chaim," he said, "we're in a tight place."

Reb Chaim would not listen at first. He was too tired. "Don't talk like an idiot," he replied, though he knew that Samuel Leibish was telling the truth.

Samuel Leibish stood his ground. Like his employer he had no idea of the actual state of affairs. He had pored over the books, he had added and subtracted, he had rattled the beads on the old Russian counting-frame, all to no effect. In the end he had asked Reb Chaim to call in a real accountant. And Reb Chaim had answered: "No!" He had done business twenty years without accountants, and he was not going to start now. The more you counted, the less you had. Apart from that, he had a special distaste for the Lithuanian Jews, sinners and anti-Chasidic cynics, who were the accountants of Russian Jewry.

Now Samuel Leibish returned to the charge. "Reb Chaim,"

he groaned, "we'll have to have an accountant."

"All right, all right," answered his employer, with a deep sigh. "Get me one of those fakers."

For a period of eight days the Lithuanian Jew with the pince-nez from which dangled a heavy black cord fiddled around with Reb Chaim's books and accounts. "Debit, credit, paid, due," he kept muttering, "the devil take it—it won't come out." Reb Chaim tried his best to keep away from this learned pauper with the close-cropped beard and the white celluloid collar over his Adam's apple. Reb Chaim could understand it if a rich man, a banker or a manufacturer, turned away from the Jewish tradition, cropped his beard close, and put on the clothes of the heathen. Sin and wealth made at least a congruous combination. But how did a pauper, a penniless employee, dare to indulge in such a luxury? He despised and hated this bony Lithuanian and wanted him out of the factory as soon as possible. And then the fellow had such disrespectful ways about him!

"What's this?" he asked sharply, and pointed to a sort of thicket of figures in a margin. Reb Chaim looked, tried to remember, and could not. He said the first thing that came into his mind. But the Lithuanian meant business. "Expenses aren't income, devil take it," he cried.

At the end of eight days the Lithuanian emerged with a clear balance-sheet. The figures on it stood in straight rows, like soldiers on parade; the totals led them like corporals and sergeants. It was a most inspiring sight. The Lithuanian handed over the document, and, letting fall the pince-nez so that it dangled at the end of the cord, he said: "Mr. Alter, I beg to report that you are bankrupt."

Reb Alter jumped with a violence which surpassed even his convulsive religious enthusiasm on the New Year.

"You damned Lithuanian jackass," he shouted, "you don't know what you're talking about."

The Lithuanian did not take offence. He opened the big new account-book into which he had transferred all the figures, and repeated dryly: "Mr. Alter, you're bankrupt and *konietchno*—that's all there is to it."

The Russian word convinced Reb Chaim. He suddenly

thrust his hands into his trouser pockets, put out his stomach, covered by a coloured silk vest, and said angrily to Samuel Leibish: "Well, what have you to say to that, Samuel Leibish?"

Samuel Leibish coloured, as though it was all his fault, but he had nothing to say. Reb Alter sent the Lithuanian packing and began to consider his position—if a frantic, systemless brooding on the inevitable may be called considering a position. For days he wrestled with himself. He could not eat or sleep or say his prayers. In the midst of the most sacred passages he would suddenly repeat to himself, imitating furiously the intonation of the wretched Lithuanian: "Mr. Alter, you're bankrupt, *konietchno*—that's all there is to it."

For the first time Reb Chaim sought his wife's counsel. But Priveh had no head for figures or for worries. "You know, Chaim, darling, that I have no head for figures," she said. "You'll find a way out, I'm certain."

Seeing that his wife refused to understand, Reb Chaim came down to brass tacks. He told her bluntly that she would have to pawn some of her jewellery. He would send Samuel Leibish secretly with it to a pawnshop at the other end of the town. Priveh turned pale. Was this what bankruptcy meant?

"Mamma!" she cried, appealing, as always, to her mother in heaven.

Reb Chaim soothed her. It would be only for a time. He would meet only the most pressing obligations. But this, too, Priveh refused to understand. She wept, copiously, endlessly. And the flood of tears increased when her husband began to talk about cutting down expenses.

"What I spend!" she blubbered. "Why, I can be happy on bread and water. I never spend anything for myself!"

Reb Chaim saw that it was futile to talk with Priveh. The only thing she wanted to know, at the end of it all, was whether she would still be able to go to Marienbad for the baths. Reb Chaim sighed, said something vaguely comforting, and decided to seek counsel elsewhere. The next day he went out of town to consult his Rabbi, but the latter was no better than Priveh. He took his present, assured Reb Chaim that God was in heaven looking after His children on earth, and everything would be all right. Reb Chaim thought of his sons, but they were hopeless, thick-headed, fond of a good time, looking on their father merely as a source of money. Reb Chaim, in despair, turned to his son-in-law's father, Reb Abraham Hirsh Ashkenazi.

On a Saturday night, immediately after the ceremony of the ushering out of the Sabbath, Reb Chaim went over to Reb Abraham Hirsh and found him in his room, studying the Talmud. Reb Abraham Hirsh put his red pocket-handkerchief on the page, to show that he was merely interrupting his studies, not closing them, and lent an ear to Reb Chaim's story. For a whole hour he listened patiently, never interrupting and asking no questions. Reb Chaim babbled and perspired, though he felt a dreadful cold all around him. The room was cold, with its brown-tapestried walls and its high black bookcases and its huge iron safe. Colder than these, however, was Reb Abraham Hirsh himself. Reb Chaim drank two glasses of tea, described enthusiastically the basic soundness of his business, made light of his passing but urgent difficulties, and came to the point: a substantial loan. Reb Abraham Hirsh passed his hand over his beard and answered quietly with three short words:

"No, Reb Chaim."

The sweat gathered more heavily on Reb Chaim's face.

"Reb Abraham," he gasped, "you won't let me go to the wall! Whom am I to turn to, if not you?"

"The man who lives without reckoning must die without an accounting," said Reb Abraham in a tone of reproof. And when his son's father-in-law began to plead, tried to grab him by the coat, Reb Abraham Hirsh removed the red pocket-handkerchief from the page and resumed his studies of the Talmud in the traditional singsong.

"*Kamah lokin*—how many stripes shall such a sinner receive?" he chanted, paying no attention to Reb Chaim.

Reb Chaim slunk out of the house. When he got home he had not even the heart to sing the last Sabbath songs, which he had always enjoyed so much. The cigar which Samuel Leibish had given him tasted bitter. He spat it out in a rage. He found no pleasure, either, in the fragrant tea which had been prepared for him. "Poisonous stuff," he muttered. "Couldn't you make fresh tea for me?"

Hadassah, the maid, turned red as a beet. "So help me God," she exclaimed, "it's just made. If Reb Chaim will look into the tea-pot—"

But Reb Chaim would not look into the tea-pot. He was looking at his sons, who sat at another table playing cards. He jumped up, snatched the cards from their hands, and tore them across.

"Wastrels! Card-sharps! Gamblers!" he yelled, as though he had never seen them play cards before. "You'll make a beggar of me!"

All night he lay awake, tossing on the thick feather cushions, which had suddenly become as hard as planks. Every face in Lodz passed in review before him, and there was not one that he could think of as a source of help. Only toward morning it occurred to him that, outside of his family, there was one person who stood nearer to him than Reb Abraham Hirsh, and that was Simcha Meyer, his daughter's husband. Simcha Meyer! Why, he had ten thousand roubles lying in the bank, doing nothing! Reb Chaim was astounded at himself for not having thought of him before. Suddenly all his worries vanished. He saw salvation before him. The cushions became soft and inviting again, and he fell into deep, happy slumber.

Very different from his father's was the manner in which Simcha Meyer received his father-in-law's desperate appeal for help. Simcha Meyer was living with his in-laws, for according to the terms of the marriage contract he was to be kept, together with his wife, for five years, while he devoted himself to the study of the Talmud—this according to an ancient Jewish custom. Simcha Meyer listened to his father-in-law's plea with the utmost sympathy. He nodded repeatedly while the other explained the situation in much detail, mingling his story with fulsome compliments and excited reiterations of the basic soundness of his position. He returned over and over again to one burden:

"I tell you, darling Simcha Meyer, you'll get much better returns from me than from the bank. And you can sleep peacefully with your money in my hands; I wouldn't, God forbid, harm one of my own children."

"Why, of course, Father-in-law," said Simcha Meyer, simply.

Reb Chaim was beside himself with joy at the pliancy of his son-in-law.

"Your capital will grow weekly, Simcha Meyer. You'll be getting compound interest on it from me. And no worries. In any case, you're living with me, and you have no expenses. You understand, dearest Simcha Meyer, don't you?"

"Why, of course I understand," said Simcha Meyer, nodding.

But when it came to the point, when he had to go to the

bank to draw out the money, Simcha Meyer developed the most honourable scruples. "You know, I've got to ask Father. It wouldn't be decent to do it without advising him, don't you think?"

"You're a silly boy," answered his father-in-law, trembling with impatience and fear. "What do you want to bother your father for. After all, you're not a child. You know what you're doing."

"It just wouldn't be decent," repeated Simcha Meyer, like a pious simpleton. "I must ask him."

For hours Reb Chaim, dreading Reb Abraham Hirsh's advice to his son, walked with Simcha Meyer, holding him by the arm, patting him affectionately on the shoulder, persuading him that it was superfluous to seek his father's advice. "You've got the best head in Lodz," he said, in a wheedling voice. "There isn't a smarter man of any age in the city. You don't need to ask your father."

"It's a matter of decency," answered Simcha Meyer, obstinately.

But he kept Reb Chaim waiting for several days, with one pretext after another. Father wasn't in. Father hadn't had time to go into the matter.

As a matter of fact, he had never made an attempt to speak to his father. He was waiting until Reb Chaim became frantic.

"Believe me, Father-in-law," he kept telling Reb Chaim, "I'd trust you with my life. So would Father. Only it wouldn't be decent of me to do such a thing without his knowing."

The idea of consulting his father was ridiculous to Simcha Meyer. How many years had he not waited in order to free himself from the yoke of his father's authority! And now, when the first important matter of his married life was to be decided, he would act as the independent adult and husband that he was. Besides, he knew that his father would answer with a blunt no. At the end of a few days, sitting at table with Reb Chaim, Simcha Meyer gave him the answer. He talked slowly, simply, calmly, as though he was not particularly interested in the business. He buttered a roll, took a bite, and said, chewing: "Father said I have to get collateral from you."

[127]

"Why, certainly," almost sang Reb Chaim. He was amazed and delighted. "All the collateral in the world. My own personal notes of hand."

Simcha Meyer put a piece of cheese on the tip of the knife, transferred it to the roll, took a hearty bite, and said: "Father told me to get nothing but a mortgage. He said I wasn't to take any promissory notes."

Reb Chaim's face dropped. "A mortgage!" he stuttered. "What's the favour in that? I can get a mortgage anywhere.

"Well, why don't you do it, Father-in-law?" asked Simcha Meyer, looking naïve.

All day long Reb Chaim argued with Simcha Meyer, explaining how solvent the business was, how ungenerous it was of a son-in-law to make such difficulties about the matter of a loan. Reb Chaim did not dare to apply again to Reb Abraham Hirsh—as Simcha Meyer well knew. And therefore Simcha Meyer refused to budge. "I can't disobey my own father. It wouldn't be decent."

And then, when Reb Chaim finally agreed to a mortgage, Simcha Meyer delayed his answer until his father-in-law was almost out of his head with worry. "I'll tell Father," he said.

"Tell Father again!" exploded Reb Chaim. "You ask for a mortgage, I'm ready to give it." But Simcha Meyer was patient and quiet. Long ago, in the days when he used to play cards in Shillem the shark's gambling-house, he had learned that when others are excited and frantic you must be calmer than ever. He let several days pass, watching his father-in-law approaching a breakdown.

Then he brought the answer. "Father says it has to be a first mortgage," he announced.

Reb Chaim felt his heart contract. He couldn't give his son-in-law a first mortgage, for he had already given a first mortgage on his home to meet the expenses of the wedding. He did not know that Simcha Meyer was perfectly aware of this fact—had, indeed, informed himself thoroughly on the condition of his father-in-law's affairs. Simcha Meyer did not want a mortgage on the house. He wanted something very different.

Ever since he had set eyes on his father-in-law's factory—

and that was long before there had been talk of a match between him and Dinah—he had dreamed of becoming the
owner, if not precisely of this factory, then of another like it.
It was a preliminary or preparatory dream. Simcha Meyer,
small, physically insignificant, had Napoleonic visions. Steam
was the real thing, as he knew. But he also knew that one
does not lay hands so easily on a steam factory. There was
the intermediate step, of a small factory of hand-looms, the
transition to one of those mighty barracks, with their chimneys spitting smoke into the hearts of the clouds and sending
out the scream of their sirens across the whole city. The in-
termediary step was unavoidable, but it should be as short as
possible, for he hated not only the pettiness of the hand-
looms, but the character of the workers and merchants which
they represented, the little Jews with their gaberdines and
ear-locks and noise and excitability. He knew the history of
every industrialist in Lodz, and there was not one who had
not started small, with a limited number of hand-looms.
What they had done, he would repeat—but on a vaster scale.

Nor would it take him as long as it had taken others. Lodz
was not the primitive town that it had been when the first
factories had been built. The tempo was another and faster
one. Besides, he had a start; he was the son of Reb Abraham
Hirsh Ashkenazi, the son-in-law of Reb Chaim Alter, the
possessor, in his own right, of ten thousand roubles and accumulated interest. Also, he was himself, not another. He
would not begin with two or three hand-looms, as the others
had done. He would begin with an entire factory.

It had not taken him long to discover that his father-in-law
had prospered by sheer accident, had been carried with the
general wave of prosperity. For he understood Reb Chaim
only too well—saw through his laziness, his inefficiency, his
extravagance and recklessness. This was not the man for
the new Lodz; sooner or later he would be trampled under
foot; sooner or later he would be shoved out of the factory,
and a new owner would come in. Who would that new man
be?

And so when his father-in-law came to him with his pitiful
plea for the loan of his dowry, Simcha Meyer knew that his

hour had struck. He laughed inwardly at the offer of promissory notes; not the question of their value, but of their irrelevance, amused him. He laughed at the idea of a mortgage on the house. Reb Chaim no doubt thought that, having taken his son-in-law's money, the latter would quietly go on studying the Talmud, according to the arrangements in the marriage contract. Simcha Meyer did not want to study the Talmud. He wanted the world of affairs, reality, power. True, his father would be furious with him, asking him how he dared to give up his studies so early and occupy himself with the things of this world. But that was of no consequence. Let him be furious. It was the business of fathers to be furious with their sons. Meanwhile he already saw, in his mind's eye, the new shingle outside the factory: "Chaim Alter and Simcha Meyer Ashkenazi."

Sitting at his Talmud he repeated: "Alter and Ashkenazi." It sounded good. It had a business-like ring about it. He wrote it out several times in big, flowing letters. It looked as good as it sounded. There was a lilt in the names. Then it occurred to him to invert the order: "Ashkenazi and Alter." A decided improvement. It was snappier. It came sharper off the tongue. Best of all, however, was the brief, unqualified title: "S. M. Ashkenazi." That had an incomparable neatness about it. It smacked one in the eye. It was the kind of name which carried conviction, needed no explanation or introduction. "Factory of S. M. Ashkenazi."

Knowing, then, that his hour had struck, Simcha Meyer waited calmly while his father-in-law ranted, perspired, and screamed. Clearly, he thought, the more excited a man gets, the more he resembles a stupid animal. His father-in-law made him think, in fact, of an infuriated bull, surrounded and doomed. For there was no escape. Money was scarce in Lodz. Business was poor. Firms were failing right and left. Meanwhile note after note was falling due in Reb Chaim's factory. Let the old man yell, let him carry on, let him reproach, weep, insult. He would come to terms.

And come to terms Reb Chaim did.

He found that arguing with his son-in-law was like battering one's head against a stone wall. Simcha Meyer suddenly developed a great passion for study. Whenever his father-in-law came to speak to him, Simcha Meyer sat swaying back and forth over the pages of the Talmud. His father-in-law asked him furiously how he could be so hard-hearted, so indifferent to the agony of so near a relative. Simcha Meyer had nothing to say. He was studying. Then Reb Chaim mastered himself and for several days avoided his son-in-law, hoping the other would revert to the subject. No such thing happened. Meanwhile the notes pressed heavier and heavier. When actual bankruptcy threatened, Reb Chaim gave in. For the ten thousand roubles cash Simcha Meyer became a one-third partner; but even at this last moment there was a delay. Simcha Meyer wanted the agreement to be drawn up by reliable lawyers. He wanted to understand all the terms of the contract. He wanted protection. Reb Chaim was on his last legs when he got the money.

"You're a hard man, Simcha Meyer," he said heavily, when they left the airless office of the lawyer and shook hands on the new partnership. "But everything is fixed now."

He meant by this last remark that now Simcha Meyer could go back to his studies and forget all about the partnership. And since Simcha Meyer didn't seem to understand at once, Reb Chaim added: "You know, I'm a man of my word. Partner or no partner, you're still entitled to live in my house, at my charge, and continue your studies."

"Why, no, Father-in-law," answered Simcha Meyer, piously. "If I'm a partner I expect to carry my share of the burden. I'm no parasite."

Reb Abraham Hirsh did not hear direct from Simcha Meyer of the new situation. Reports were brought to him by outsiders, and Reb Abraham Hirsh sent Jacob Bunim for Simcha Meyer.

Jacob Bunim was not a frequent visitor in the Alter house. He was afraid to go there; and when his father sent him he approached the house with beating heart, glad of the excuse which made it impossible for him to turn back.

In the dining-room he found Dinah, sitting, as always, with her feet under her on the couch, reading one of her novels.

She did not look up when Jacob Bunim entered.

"Good evening," he said in a voice that did not sound to him like his own.

She started and cried out. Jacob Bunim put his hand up to his hat, forgetting that he was not in the street. Dinah blushed.

"How is Jacob?" she asked, oddly, addressing him neither by the formal "you" nor by the informal second person singular.

"How is Dinah?" asked Jacob Bunim, following her lead automatically. Neither of them answered the other's question. Their eyes dropped and they were silent.

Simcha Meyer came in and greeted his brother curtly. He knew that nothing good could have brought him to the house unexpectedly, and he received coldly the message that his father wanted to see him without delay. But he obeyed at once; he would get the matter over with.

He found his father seated before the Talmud. The red pocket-handkerchief had been laid on the page. Reb Abraham Hirsh let his son remain standing.

"Simcha Meyer," he said in the calm, ominous voice which indicated great anger, "did you ask me whether you ought to take your money out of the bank?"

"No, Father."

"Why did you take it out without letting me know?"

"Father-in-law was hard-pressed," said Simcha Meyer, an expression of pity on his face. "I couldn't bear to see it."

"Just your charitable character, what?" said Reb Abraham Hirsh.

"Yes, Father."

"But isn't obedience to one's father just as important as charity?"

Simcha Meyer did not answer.

Reb Abraham Hirsh shoved the skull-cap back on his head and looked long and earnestly at his son. He wanted to see the boy—he was hardly more than that—drop his eyes, show some sort of respect or fear, some consciousness of shame. But Simcha Meyer returned his gaze steadfastly. He retained the look of pity which he had put on when mentioning his father-in-law's difficulties. Simcha Meyer's brazen falseness made his father's blood boil.

"Listen, you saint," he said sharply, "I command you to give up this business arrangement and go back to your studies."

"I'll study as often as I can get away from business, I promise you that," said Simcha Meyer.

"Nothing of the sort. You'll continue your studies for five years, while your father-in-law keeps you, according to the terms of the marriage contract."

"I can't let Father-in-law carry the burden alone," said Simcha Meyer. "It is written: 'Thou shalt help carry thy brother's burden.'"

Reb Abraham Hirsh felt his rage rising to his throat, threatening to choke him. The pious quotations were more than he could bear.

"Liar and hypocrite!" he gasped. "I forbid you to set foot in the factory before your five years of study are finished. And I demand that you take an oath on that, that you swear it now and shake hands on it."

The old man stretched out his hairy hand. Simcha Meyer let it stay there untouched.

There was such deathly silence in the room that the sound of Jacob Bunim's breathing could be heard distinctly. For about half a minute Reb Abraham Hirsh remained thus, his hand stretched out to his son, waiting, enduring the insult of his son's rebuff. When he could bear it no longer he rose and, lifting his hand again, smacked Simcha Meyer's face with all his strength.

"Out of my house, ingrate and scoundrel!" he shouted.

Without a word Simcha Meyer picked up the silk cap which had flown off his head, rubbed his inflamed cheek, and went out of the room.

Except for the pain of the blow he felt no discomfort whatsoever. Going homeward through the streets, he even smiled to himself.

What did a slap in the face from his father matter to him, Simcha Meyer Ashkenazi, member of the firm of Alter and Ashkenazi? What difference did an empty, angry gesture

[133]

make to the man who had taken the first step toward the conquest of the city of Lodz, who, at eighteen, already had fifty
hand-looms working for him, thrusting him forward on the
path of victory?

His wide, eager nostrils vibrated as he strode through the
streets, breathing in the smoke and dust of Lodz. His footsteps were firm and certain on the irregular and broken
pavements.

*I*t was with a furious release of long-pent-up energies that Simcha Meyer flung himself into the work. It was as if he wanted to swallow the factory at a single gulp. His pointed, hare-like ears heard everything; his restless eyes, changing from a mild grey to a hard, rapacious green, were everywhere. But what looked like an unrestrained, wasteful assault, was, in reality, a systematic process of conquest, thought out well in advance.

He began with the account-books, those complicated, primitive records which had served Reb Chaim and Samuel Leibish for so many years. Simcha Meyer knew nothing about scientific book-keeping, and the Lithuanian who had prepared the balance-sheet would probably have laughed at his methods; but Simcha Meyer had a head for figures. He might make superfluous entries and duplicate much of the work, but he knew what he was after, and he did not let go until the accounts balanced. After that he appointed himself official book-keeper, permitting neither his father-in-law nor Samuel Leibish to touch the books. Next he attacked the office records, which were in the wildest disorder. Unpaid bills and cancelled promissory notes were piled on uncollected accounts and unfilled orders. Simcha Meyer made it his business to prevent his father-in-law from stuffing letters and telegrams into his pockets, where they were liable to remain until the end of the week. He took over the correspondence. His German was poor; he had picked up a few phrases from his father's chief accountant, Goldlust; he had copied out some of the correspondence in the German ready letter-writer, with its pompous interchange of messages between the High-Born Herr Solomon Goldman of Leipzig and the Extremely High-Born Herr Rabinowitz of Odessa. He knew even less Russian—just a smattering gathered from the Lithuanian Jews he had met in his father's house. But he had an instinct for languages. If he knew three words in a sentence he could guess at the rest. More than instinct, he had nerve and boundless self-confidence. In his comically faulty German he answered the correspondents, amusing them by his grammar, but startling them by his acumen and imagination.

Even while he was working on the books, records, and correspondence, Simcha Meyer turned his attention to Samuel Leibish, his father-in-law's man. The first thing he did was to ask for the keys of the safe, which had been entrusted to Samuel Leibish years before by his employer. Samuel Leibish did not yield easily. He had so long been boss in the factory, with more effective authority than Reb Chaim himself, that the idea of demotion never occurred to him; and at first he simply did not understand what this impudent boy with the new-sprouting beard, this restless, inquisitive, sneaking snotty-nose was driving at.

"I'll give the boss whatever money he needs," he said loftily to Simcha Meyer, when the latter asked him for the keys. Reb Chaim, standing by, smiled furtively. He hoped his son-in-law understood. Samuel Leibish had referred to him, Reb Chaim, as the boss. The junior partner did not count. Reb Chaim hoped it would come to a show-down. But Simcha Meyer did not dream of a direct assault. He smiled and let the incident pass. He had time. The most important thing was to undermine the standing of Samuel Leibish; then the symbols of his authority would drop naturally from his hands.

Simcha Meyer made it his practice to appear in the factory before Samuel Leibish and to poke his nose into the distribution of the work. He had a feeling for merchandise, and, unlike Samuel Leibish, he thought of the factory as a unit. He began to issue his own instructions, taking workers

[136]

off one order and putting them on another; and he would wait until Samuel Leibish appeared, to see if the latter would dare to challenge his authority openly. But Samuel Leibish was afraid of a public clash, and when the cheeky youngster said: "You can go, Samuel Leibish; I'm looking after things here," he turned and walked out. The workers gaped. Here was a new boss who not only had a way with him, but who also understood the work itself.

With the same tacit and insolent ability Simcha Meyer took over the interviews with important buyers. Here he found the going even easier than in the factory; for Samuel Leibish had for years accepted bribes, and the buyers were only too eager to do business direct with one of the partners. Besides, young Simcha Meyer did not waste their time. He got the point of a conversation before it was half over, and when he assured a customer that his order would receive immediate attention, it sounded as though he meant it. Samuel Leibish might be present at such conversations, but fewer and fewer remarks were addressed to him; also he discovered that more and more of the customers and agents did not want to see him, but preferred to speak with Simcha Meyer. A dreadful feeling of insecurity, a sense of his essential superfluity, assailed him, and at last, when Simcha Meyer began to give him orders, curtly, he could only stammer: "Now look here, Simcha Meyer—you can't treat me like an errand-boy. I've been foreman here—"

Simcha Meyer stuck his hands into his trouser pockets, rose on his toes, looked Samuel Leibish straight in the eye, and said coldly: "If you don't like this position, you can find yourself another. Furthermore, be good enough, Samuel Leibish, not to address me as Simcha Meyer. I don't remember having been a close pal of yours."

Samuel Leibish turned pale. "Why, Reb Simcha," he stammered, "I didn't mean anything by it."

As Simcha Meyer had foreseen, Samuel Leibish yielded everything, once his position had been undermined. The keys of the safe dropped into Simcha Meyer's hands. Samuel Leibish could not fight back because he had neither the energy nor the will nor the ability of Simcha Meyer. He was de-

[137]

moralized and routed. Reb Chaim Alter tried to be offended on behalf of his own foreman, but he was even less of a fighter than Samuel Leibish. Besides, there was something soothing and reassuring about his son-in-law. Reb Chaim might resent this resistless authoritativeness, but it gave him a peculiar and restful feeling of confidence. He could lie down for a nap in the afternoon unharassed by the thought that he must get up in time to put in an appearance in the factory. On Saturday nights he could sit at a little feast with his clique of Chasidim, safe in the thought that Simcha Meyer was in charge. All his natural laziness rose up gratefully in him when Simcha Meyer said to him: "You can go take a nap, Father-in-law; I'll look after things." Frightened and yet soothed, Reb Chaim held Simcha Meyer up as an example to his sons. "That's what I call a worker, you good-for-nothing card-players," he grunted, settling on the ottoman. "He's at it day and night."

Simcha Meyer was seen less and less in the little Chasidic synagogue, more and more frequently in the restaurants where agents, buyers, contractors, money-lenders, and loafers generally had their hang-out. These restaurants were the primitive stock-exchanges and markets of Lodz; all day long they buzzed with the sound of bargaining; wool was bought and sold there, loans negotiated, contracts sub-let, bills discounted. At the dirty little tables, wet with beer and covered with chalk markings, reputations were discussed, bankruptcies foretold, credits established. All the labour of Lodz converged on these noisy restaurants. Here prices were fixed, crops bought up in advance, shipments ordered and cancelled. In the midst of the smoke and tumult, across a barrage of Chasidic stories, dirty jokes, scandal, lies, and conspiracies, the labour of tens of thousands of lean weavers and red-eyed seamstresses was disposed of; the ingenuity of engineers and chemists, the inventiveness of draughtsmen and designers, all was bought and sold here. And in the midst of it Simcha Meyer moved eagerly, sniffing up information, getting his bearings.

He drank it all in with passionate thirst, saying little, letting nothing pass. He was unknown to the crowd at first,

[138]

and they paid no attention to this queer young fellow who moved among them, pulling impatiently at the hairs on his chin, as though he wanted to force the beard out before its time. Impatient he was in his ambitions, but patient in his methods. He needed first to catch the lingo of these Lodz restaurants, so that his greenness would not be noticed. He needed to understand the idiom of the conversations here, what was phraseology and what was substance, the art of the bazaar, the trick of evading a direct question, of saying nothing in many words, of forcing the other man's hand, of being silent when necessary. And it did not take him long to master it all. Something about him attracted attention and inspired a vague, almost superstitious respect. He himself was unknown, but his father-in-law's name meant something, and his father's name a great deal.

"That's Simcha Meyer, son of Abraham Hirsh Ashkenazi and son-in-law of Chaim Alter!"

He heard that behind him more than once. He also heard, occasionally, the complimentary remarks of those with whom he had exchanged a few words: "Say, that young snippet knows what he's after. You watch him."

He picked up their argot, their manner, to such good effect that within a few months he was accepted as one of them. He joked with them, snapped back the current catchwords, showed the right degree of cynicism, was as good as the next man at capping a story, taking a hint, and sneering at an offer. Moreover, it soon got abroad that this odd-looking, under-sized, half-beardless youngster was a one-third partner in the firm of Reb Chaim Alter, had ten thousand cash in the business, had quit the study of the Talmud, and knew more about the factory than his father-in-law. It was remembered, too, that this boy had once given promise of being a mighty scholar. He was accepted, then, not as a son, and not as a son-in-law, but as Simcha Meyer, the coming young man.

"He's the real stuff."

What was he looking for, Simcha Meyer? He did not know exactly. Somewhere, somehow, in this welter, he would pick up information which he could put to account. What kind of information? He had no idea. But it was there, waiting for him; that much he was sure of. He was also sure that he would recognize it when it came along, the particular idea which he could turn into money. So, one day, he heard someone remark that the women's kerchiefs made by the firm of Chaim Alter were wider and longer by a whole inch than they needed to be. Needed to be? Did they need to be anything, Simcha Meyer asked himself. They needed only to be sold. Would the Jewesses and the peasant women who bought these kerchiefs notice if an inch were taken off? What was an inch? To the customer, nothing. To the manufacturer, turning out tens of thousands of kerchiefs, a great deal. Simcha Meyer had contracted the habit of carrying a pencil behind his ear and writing with it on anything that lay to hand— table-cloths, odd pieces of paper, the wall, or even a scrap of fabric. Simcha Meyer no sooner heard the offhand remark than he began to figure. His workers made three kerchiefs a day each, one hundred and fifty a day for the factory, less than a thousand a week, nearly fifty thousand a year. One inch each way on the kerchiefs meant, then—he figured closely and rapidly—yes, it meant a very decent saving in wool.

The very next morning he issued instructions to the weavers to drop an inch each way on the kerchiefs.

Tevyeh the-world-isn't-coming-to-an-end-yet repeated the order loudly: "Hey, boys, the old man wants you to graft an inch each way."

Simcha Meyer turned on Tevyeh savagely. "Hold your tongue," he snapped. "There's no graft in that. The kerchiefs are too long and too broad, and it's nobody's business what goes on in the factory. Do as you're told and keep your mouth shut."

The weavers did as they were told, pulling the kerchiefs out a little longer to make up for the missing material, and the first orders went out. Simcha Meyer waited eagerly for complaints, and none came back. Neither the consumers nor the merchants noticed the difference, and Simcha Meyer rubbed his hands joyously. The success of his first trick tempted him to a second. Using the old designs, he wove a kerchief with a second-grade thread, the kind that was spun from old rags. There were spinneries enough in Lodz turning out these inferior threads. When new, they could be distinguished from the better kind only by an expert, who would unravel the thread between his fingers. Orders went out made with the second-grade thread, and again Simcha Meyer was successful. He became a big buyer of the cheap, home-made threads.

He made a third experiment. Instead of an all-wool kerchief, he tried out one which was wool at the ends and half cotton in the middle. As an offset he introduced brighter colours into the designs, working on the pattern with Tevyeh the-world-isn't-coming-to-an-end-yet, who was an adept at putting designs into the fabric. The new kerchief took, orders came in, and Simcha Meyer had to hire additional workers. Before long the two-piece kerchief was being copied by half a dozen firms, but in the meantime Simcha Meyer had earned a substantial sum.

He turned next to the cheapest grade of goods, a flimsy, all-cotton kerchief which could be sold at a price within the reach of the poorest classes of women. The colours were gaudy, the material inferior. The weavers turned them out at the rate of seven and eight a day. Instinct told Simcha Meyer, who only a few months before had still been a Talmud student, that money lay in quantity, and that quantity meant cheapness, and that cheapness had to be counteracted by superficial attractiveness. His father-in-law had other ideas; he had been proud of the reputation of his factory for good, solid, reliable work. He was ashamed of these rags which Simcha Meyer wanted to turn out in such huge quantities. There were arguments.

"I should like to know," chanted Simcha Meyer to his father-in-law, using the old Talmudic singsong, "in what verse of the Pentateuch you will find the command to manufacture only woollen kerchiefs of a certain grade, and what particular reward in heaven is reserved for the manufacturer of woollen goods."

Reb Chaim replied with something about reputation, decency, standards of the craft. Simcha Meyer laughed openly. "Leave all that to me, Father-in-law." And when the old customers came, asking for the better goods which the factory

[141]

had at one time produced, Simcha Meyer saw to it that they did not get at his father-in-law.

The old mixture of cowardice, inefficiency, and the longing for a peaceful life kept Reb Chaim from putting up a fight. He did not like what was happening to his factory; he did not like the too-obvious diminution of his own importance; he did not like his son-in-law's kindly, soothing way of sending him packing. But his rebellious moments were few and weak and disorganized. Every now and again he promised himself to take the situation in hand and put the upstart in his place. He would suddenly appear in the factory and start giving orders; he would insist on interviewing the customers himself; but both the weavers and the customers could see at a glance that he was no longer in control, that he did not even know what he was talking about. Indeed, he had never known too much about the business. He had always relied on Samuel Leibish, and his feeling that he had once been in control was illusory. His rebellions always collapsed within a few hours. He stormed into the factory and stormed out of it, the same futile, incompetent figure.

And when he came to think of it, it occurred to him that, after all, his son-in-law was not behaving badly toward him. He still brought all papers to him to be signed, as Samuel Leibish had done in the old days. Again as in the old days Reb Chaim did not read too closely the documents he put his name to. Whenever he asked for money he got it, just as in the days when Samuel Leibish had had the keys of the safe. The bad times seemed to have passed, and the old scale of living was maintained. Priveh did not change any of her habits; neither did Reb Chaim. There were the old visits to the watering places abroad, the old purchases of useless things, the old parties and jollifications with his cronies. The only difference was that Simcha Meyer, unlike Samuel Leibish, and unlike Reb Chaim himself, kept accounts. He did not believe, apparently, that the more you counted, the less you had. And he made Reb Chaim sign a receipt for every rouble, every kopeck, which he withdrew from the safe.

It was Samuel Leibish who suffered most for the dignity

[142]

and authority of his employer and who suspected that be-hind Simcha Meyer's efficiency and thoughtfulness there was something that needed to be watched.

He kept muttering to Reb Chaim: "I don't like it. There's something too smart about him, Reb Chaim. He's too good to you. I'm telling you, keep your eye on him."

But Reb Chaim followed the line of least resistance and slid without any special reluctance into his new and comfortable status. Everything would come out all right! What else could he believe, if he was to go on enjoying his afternoon naps, his feasts with the Chasidim, his cheerful humour and his thick, delicious cigars? Besides, to carry on the struggle with the ubiquitous and irresistible Simcha Meyer for the control of the business would have meant letting his good, lovable Priveh go to the foreign health-resorts all alone, an unthinkable privation for him. And there were dangers in Marienbad and Karlsbad and the other *Bads:* men who hung around the fountains of Sprudel water and ogled the women. Priveh was the mother of a married daughter, but she was still a plump and pleasant armful. No, it was impossible to let her go alone. So, all in all, Reb Chaim thought it best to praise God from day to day, to enjoy His gifts, and to hope for the best.

Simcha Meyer encouraged the pious cheerfulness of his father-in-law.

"There's really no sense in your staying in Lodz for the summer," he said, in that queer kindly way that so ill became him. "All the smoke and dirt and noise. You and Mother-in-law have a good time at Marienbad."

And Reb Chaim went, his heart full of confidence.

At the end of a year, when Simcha Meyer prepared his first annual balance-sheet, Reb Chaim beamed, feeling that his faith in the goodness of God was justified. The ten-thousand-rouble cash investment had pulled the factory past the critical period, and the year showed a solid upward movement. These new policies of Simcha's, the saving in material, the switch to low-grade goods, plus the efficiency he had brought into the operation of the factory, the attention to detail, had proved what Reb Chaim had always

[143]

believed—that the business was sound. There was also something that Reb Chaim knew nothing of. Simcha Meyer's nosy interest in the restaurants of Lodz had borne fruit. He had made three heavy purchases of cotton, on credit, and had sold at a profit without investing more than option money. But this was not entered on the books. True, he might never have been able to swing these deals if not for his status as junior partner in the firm of Chaim Alter; but on the other hand, he told himself, he had carried everything out by himself and had made use of none of the facilities of the firm. Why, he had never even seen the bales of cotton. He had no idea what they looked like. What right could Chaim Alter have to a share of the profits? However, to make sure there would be no dispute, he said nothing to his father-in-law.

Simcha Meyer might have been happy, for he had found himself; he was in his element, calculating day and night, writing on walls, pieces of paper, table-cloths, whatever came to hand, foreseeing profits, outwitting competitors—he might have been happy, if not for his brother, Jacob Bunim. Just as in their childhood days, Jacob Bunim, younger by a few minutes, but in the matter of ability separated from Simcha Meyer by an unbridgeable gulf, was getting the best of everything, not by merit, but by the blind, stupid luck which had made him tall, handsome, and beloved. And again, as in childhood days, Simcha Meyer felt that his triumphs and achievements were being overshadowed by the one person who was least entitled to priority of reputation. The extraordinary good fortune which had come to Jacob Bunim poisoned Simcha Meyer's nights and days; and there was nothing he could do, in the face of a malevolent fate, to redress the balance.

Not long after Simcha Meyer's wedding, Samuel Zanvil, the marriage-broker, called on Jacob Bunim's father, and proposed for the boy a match so brilliant and so unexpected that Reb Abraham Hirsh Ashkenazi was stupefied.

"Reb Samuel Zanvil," he said, "do you mean to tell me that you are trying to pair off my son with a grand-daughter of Reb Kalman Eisen?"

"With the grand-daughter of Reb Kalman Eisen himself," answered the marriage-broker, chanting the words triumphantly. "Exactly as I told you, Abraham Hirsh."

Like everyone else, Reb Abraham Hirsh had grown accustomed to Samuel Zanvil's impudent way of dropping the title Reb, and of addressing everyone in the second person singular.

"But how did you have the—I mean, how did you get the idea?" asked Reb Abraham Hirsh.

"I happened to be in Warsaw," answered Samuel Zanvil. "So one day I just went in to Kalman Eisen and I said to him: 'Listen Kalman Eisen: I want you to give your grand-daughter to one of the sons of Abraham Hirsh of Lodz.' That was all."

Reb Abraham Hirsh looked with dour suspicion at the marriage-broker. "I don't care what you said to him. I want to know whether you thought it up yourself or whether someone told you to propose the match."

"*Told* me?" shouted Samuel Zanvil, offended. "I'm not

that kind of marriage-broker. I don't wait to be told. Besides, it's none of your business. All you need to know is that the bride's family is willing. And it is."

Reb Abraham Hirsh was not a modest man, but in the complicated hierarchy of the Jewish families of Poland he knew his place. "I just don't understand it," he muttered, and thrust a large pinch of snuff into his nostrils to clear his head.

For though Reb Kalman Eisen lived in Warsaw, there was not a Jew in Lodz, or for that matter in any other city or village of Poland, who did not know that name. His fortune was popularly computed in millions only, and his pride was equal to both his possessions and his family standing. What was queerest of all to Reb Abraham Hirsh was the fact that Reb Kalman Eisen was a passionate adherent of the Rabbi of Ger and therefore a bitter opponent of the Rabbi of Alexander, Reb Abraham Hirsh's Rabbi. What, then, was the meaning of this offer of a marriage alliance? And with whom? With Jacob Bunim. An offer for Simcha Meyer would have been barely conceivable—such young prodigies of scholarship were rare. But Jacob Bunim! There were a thousand boys like him in Warsaw.

The only one in Lodz who was in on the secret, and therefore knew that Samuel Zanvil was lying in his throat when he boasted that he had taken the initiative, was Jacob Bunim himself.

At his brother's wedding he had exchanged a few words with a girl he had never seen before. She was not especially attractive; she was lean, and her face had a greenish tinge, accentuated by her white silk dress. The conversation began in the courtyard of the marriage hall, where the bridal canopy had been erected. It was the girl who spoke first.

"If you don't mind, young sir," Jacob Bunim heard a mocking voice behind him say, "just step a little to one side. I'd like to see the ceremony and you're just a trifle too tall." The voice and the language were equally affected; the girl spoke the Germanified Yiddish which passed among the Polish Jews as the symbol of culture.

He stepped aside without looking round, but the girl still could not see.

"Would it be asking you too much, sir," she asked, while she and her companion burst into a giggle, "to lift me just a little? And please don't shake that candle; it's dripping on my nice silk dress."

Jacob Bunim blushed furiously.

"You seem to be afraid of me," the girl said. "You needn't be. I promise you I don't bite."

Jacob Bunim answered, in his Chasidic Yiddish: "I'm not afraid."

"But bless my soul," the girl said, "you're dressed like one of the real Chasidim, you speak like one of them, and yet I don't believe you're such a terrible fanatic as to be afraid of a girl." She stood closer to him, so that the length of her tightly clad body pressed against his, and somehow, before he knew what had happened, they were holding hands.

"How is it that you let your brother get married before you?" she asked softly. "You're bigger than he."

"He's older," answered Jacob Bunim.

"Really?" she exclaimed, astonished. "And aren't you thinking of getting a bride, too?"

Jacob Bunim did not answer. He was ashamed and uncomfortable. The girl pressed his hand.

"Do you think you'd like me as a bride?" she asked, daringly, and covered the remark with a thin, ironic laugh.

The blush deepened on Jacob Bunim's face. He seemed to be on fire.

"You're not bad-looking," she went on. "But I'd like you better if you'd change those Chasidic clothes for civilized dress. Tell me, do you think I'm pretty?"

Jacob Bunim was scandalized. He was afraid that, in spite of the thick crowd, someone would notice he was holding the girl's hand. But he did know how to let go. The girl did not seem to care who saw or what might be said.

"You've got to answer that," she insisted. "Do you think I'm pretty? But be truthful; no compliments."

Jacob Bunim glanced at her hastily. "Yes," he gabbled, "I

think you're very pretty." But he thought nothing of the sort.

"Then I'll tell you my name," she answered, proudly. "Pearl Eisen, of Warsaw." She waited, to let the revelation take effect. "We're relatives, in a way, now that your brother is marrying Dinah. We're connected with the family, on her mother's side. That's why we came to the wedding."

The conversation ended there, and Jacob Bunim did not see the girl again. When the ceremony was over and the crowd began to disperse from about the canopy, she disappeared, leaving Jacob Bunim astonished and restless. It was the first time that a girl had spoken to him so boldly, big-city fashion, and not in the manner of the provincials of Lodz. He had remembered her, wondering whether she had been talking nonsense or whether she had been serious.

He might have been terrified if he had known how serious she had been. The moment she had set eyes on this magnificently built, dark-eyed boy in the Chasidic clothes, Pearl had felt her young, slender, sickly body yielding toward him. Her language had been pert, but she had been so dreadfully moved that she had not dared to speak to him a second time. From that moment on, and until she returned with her father to Warsaw, she was in a fever of impatience; and scarcely had they unpacked before she told him sharply that she wanted this Lodz boy, Jacob Bunim, the son of Reb Abraham Hirsh Ashkenazi, and he was to send a marriage-broker to the father without delay.

Her father turned pale.

"Pearl, darling, have you taken leave of your senses? Can you imagine what will happen if Grandfather hears of this?"

Grandfather Kalman, though close to eighty years of age, ruled his family with detailed and ruthless severity, and his sons, middle-aged and grey-bearded, trembled in his presence like small boys. In the eyes of their father they had, in fact, never grown up, and he kept them in utter dependence on himself. He had not admitted them to a share in the administration of the business, and the extent of his possessions was still unknown to them. Like the public at large, they could only guess that he was enormously wealthy. He owned

[148]

several streets in Warsaw, one of them actually known as Kalman Eisen Street. He had figured in the newspapers as an important Government contractor, supplying from his forests in Russia and Poland millions of telegraph poles and railroad sleepers for the newly expanding system of communications. But ever since the early days of his poverty when he had begun with a little wood store on a back street in Warsaw, he had been an absolute and uncommunicative autocrat in business. He did not believe in stock companies and boards of directors. He had made his fortune alone; he would administer it alone. To his sons and daughters he apportioned spacious houses and apartments in the courtyard of his house, maintaining them in a style becoming to his reputation; but as long as he lived he would not admit a single one of them to the secrets of his business. Helpless, they submitted their lives to his rule. He arranged the marriages of their children, provided the girls with dowries, took upon himself the upkeep of young couples for a number of years while the new husbands continued their studies. With the addition of a couple to the circle of the family, Reb Kalman added a new building to the family courtyard or added another storey to an old building. On Sabbaths and festivals no son of Reb Kalman could conduct services round his own table; the entire family, sons and daughters, sons-in-law and daughters-in-law, grandsons and grand-daughters and their wives and husbands, gathered at the long table in the enormous dining-room of old Reb Kalman. And besides the clan itself there was invariably present a considerable number of guests—travellers, pious Jews, wandering scholars, and rabbis.

A strict tradition of precedence ruled in the seating. At the head of the table, on a vast, high-cushioned armchair, sat the patriarch himself, tall, handsome, and white-bearded. On either side the family and guests stretched away, their closeness to Reb Kalman being in proportion to their years, their distinction, and their scholarship. No one put hand to knife or fork until Reb Kalman had picked up his implement; no one uttered a word unless addressed by Reb Kalman. The oldest sons of Reb Kalman, themselves grandfathers, were as obedient and timid as the youngest child admitted to the

[149]

foot of the table. In this, however, they did not differ from thousands of Jews—some of them belonging to important families—in their attitude to Reb Kalman, for he had imposed himself on the community as a natural ruler. When his brilliant carriage, drawn by two snow-white mares, passed through the streets, people glanced at him with awe, as at the passing of a king. It was in this same carriage that he travelled through the country to pay his respects to the great Rabbi of Ger. When he went abroad, to the health-resorts, he had with him a retinue of servants, his own cook, and his own utensils, for ritual purity. Though a Chasid and extremely pious, he did not wear the traditional Jewish hat, but one of his own invention, a silk cap with a shiny black peak, which looked very un-Jewish; heathenish, in fact. But he would permit no member of his household to wear anything but the traditional Jewish hat. His own piety was, by virtue of his position and possessions, so securely established that he could permit himself this minor digression without incurring the suspicion of laxity; but no one else could thus symbolize his incorruptibility. It was whispered in the city that he used only silver spittoons in his home, and that when he travelled a servant carried a silver spittoon for his personal use.

Among his sons none feared him more than did Reb Solomon, the father of Pearl. The youngest among them, he was also the most stupid, and the accumulated repressions of so many superiors had filled him with a sense of helplessness. He knew he was not clever, and he made a point of it whenever a decision was put up to him. "You know I'm no good," he would say, shaking his head, and he would turn away, praying to be left alone.

His status, such as it was, had suffered its final collapse when he became a widower. It was regarded as something belonging to the fitness of things that his children, with the one exception of Pearl, should have died early and that his wife should have followed them. For he was a natural born *schlimihl,* with whom nothing could prosper. The one child left to him, Pearl, was too much for him, and he was afraid of this sharp-tongued, imperious child, with her authoritative

ways and her sickly body, as he was afraid of his father and
brothers. Now, when she commanded him to send a marriage-
broker at once to Lodz, to negotiate for Jacob Bunim, he
trembled in every limb.

"Bite your tongue off," he stammered. "I didn't hear a
word. God help us if Grandfather hears of this, or Reb
Ezrael Cohen."

Reb Ezrael Cohen was the accredited marriage-broker of
the Kalman Eisen clan; that is, he was the official plenipo-
tentiary of Reb Kalman himself. Reb Ezrael's qualifications
were unchallenged: he was the nosiest person in Warsaw,
knew the genealogy of every family, and its financial standing;
was privy to every scandal in Polish Jewry, and, like his com-
peer Samuel Zanvil of Lodz, was dreaded for his impudence
and vindictiveness. He lived in one of the apartments in the
Kalman Eisen courtyard, as if he were a member of the clan.
It was not known whether marriages originated with him
or with Reb Kalman himself, but in any case no marriage
negotiations were started without the consent of Reb Kalman and Reb Ezrael and without the active participation of
the latter. The suggestion that he, Solomon, the youngest
and most stupid of the sons of Reb Kalman, should propose
a marriage on his own initiative was dreadful enough to
Pearl's father; the additional suggestion that he send *a* marriage-broker to the father of Jacob Bunim demoralized him
completely.

"I can't do it, Pearl, darling," he stammered. "Forget it.
I didn't even hear it."

Pearl cast one contemptuous, impatient look at her father
and swept out of the apartment. She was going to see Grandmother Tertza, Reb Kalman Eisen's old wife.

In that immense family Grandmother Tertza was the only
one who could stand up to Reb Kalman. They had married
in childhood and had worked their way together through
early poverty to their present immense wealth and prestige.
Clever, ambitious, and strong-willed, she had been Reb
Kalman's only adviser. Now, close to eighty herself, and con-
fined to her bed by partial paralysis, she still influenced him
both in business and in family affairs, and her alert old mind

kept as close a watch as his on all that went on in the office and home.

She lay in an immense bed, bedecked with silks and lace; this was her throne, as Reb Kalman's was the high-cushioned armchair at the head of the table. Once a morning every member of the family came to greet her and to kiss the withered old hand which she stretched from under the cover. On Sabbaths and holidays there was a more ceremonial visit, from which no one was exempted. From her bed Grandmother Tertza still directed the affairs of the enormous household, supervised the daily buying, and kept the keys of the silver on the little table near by. On Sabbaths and holidays ten poor Jews—the religious quorum—conducted prayers in an adjoining room, so that she might be able to hear and to put in the amens.

The stupidity and misfortunes of Solomon Eisen, which had made him the butt of the family, had given him a special place in his mother's heart; but the affection and pity she felt for him she concentrated on his daughter, the motherless one. The double circumstance that she was an only child, one survivor among many children, and that her grandmother loved her for her own and for her father's sake, had moulded Pearl's character. She had long been accustomed to getting her way, whatever her father or even her grandfather thought. Now she did not bother to convince her father. She went straight to her source of power and spoke to her grandmother as frankly and shamelessly as she had spoken to her father.

"In love, you little heathen, eh?" said the old woman, shaking her head.

Pearl threw her arms round her grandmother and began to kiss her passionately.

"Grandma, darling, sweetheart, you don't know."

The old woman summoned all her strength and with a trembling hand stroked her grand-daughter's head.

"You wouldn't trust your grandfather, eh? You had to make your own choice." She waited awhile. "I'll see what I can do. But, little Pearl, I don't like your looks. You're all green, and if you're in love you ought to be all red. Go. I'll

[152]

speak with your grandfather."

That same day she sent for Reb Kalman, and when he came in she bade him sit down on the bed, as she always did when she had something momentous to impart. Slowly and impressively she told him of the visit of her grand-daughter. Reb Kalman had no sooner grasped the point than he leapt off the bed as though some one had touched him with a red-hot iron.

"What is this, Tertza? A girl in my house falls in love, like a gypsy? I won't hear of it."

"Kalman," she said, "sit down."

"I won't have it," he repeated. "Love! The kind of talk you hear among fiddlers and beggars."

"Kalman, sit down."

The old man seated himself on the bed.

"Listen to me," his wife said. "You're playing with fire. She's a sick child, one left of many. Do you know how many tears of mine purchased her life? A sick child, and an orphan. You can't deal with her as with the others."

Reb Kalman was silent. His face retained its hardness, but the old woman had a way of talking which touched unsuspected weaknesses in him.

She went on: "I want to see her standing under the bridal canopy before I die. And there isn't much time, Kalman. Just a little while."

Reb Kalman got off the bed again, but this time to reach down for his handkerchief, into which he blew his nose fiercely. "Terrible," he muttered. His hard hand rested for a moment on the old woman's wrinkled cheek. "I suppose it's destined. Disgraced in my old age."

He went out of the room and sent for Ezrael Cohen.

"Tell me, Ezrael," he asked, abruptly, "do you know anything about a certain Abraham Hirsh Ashkenazi, of Lodz?"

"Do I know?" replied Reb Ezrael Cohen, offended. "Who should if not I?" And he read off from memory the generations of Reb Abraham Hirsh, their possessions and marriages, their achievements and affiliations.

"Lodz, Lodz," the old man growled to himself.

He had a low opinion of Lodz. Why, he remembered it

when it was nothing but a village, and its inhabitants, now such braggarts, nothing but beggars.

"What rabbi does this Abraham Hirsh follow?" he asked.

"When the Rabbi of Vorka was alive, he attended his court; now that he's dead, he goes to the Rabbi of Alexander."

The look of disgust deepened on Reb Kalman's face. "Vorka—Alexander," he muttered. "No good." A true follower of the Rabbi of Ger, he despised all others, and the thought that a grand-daughter of his would ultimately abandon the rabbinic dynasty to which he and his family were pledged galled him not less than the scandalous irregularity of the whole procedure. But he had given his word to the old woman, and there was no going back on that.

When Ezrael Cohen understood what his patron was driving at, he stared as though he had been presented with a monstrosity. The mere impudence of the girl was bad enough; but it faded before the fact that he, Ezrael Cohen, had been ignored; and this fact was itself eclipsed by another —he had practically made up his mind whom the girl was going to marry. He had picked a bridegroom for her, he had made the first indirect approaches, and he considered the business settled. A much better match it was, much more in keeping with the splendour of the house of Kalman Eisen, than the one offered by the obscure provincial.

"Reb Kalman," he said, ponderously, "it is utterly impossible."

He had several hundred reasons: the standing of the Ashkenazis, their heretical rabbinical allegiance, the scandal that had occurred in a certain branch of the wife's family some thirty years back, the obscure alliance contract by a fourth cousin—he went on interminably. It was utterly impossible. But this time his poisonous tongue ran on to no effect.

"Leave all that, Ezrael," said Reb Kalman, sternly. "Go about the business."

But that was easier said than done, for it was quite unthinkable that the first steps should come from Reb Kalman's side. The reverse had to be made to appear the case. Ezrael Cohen took the train to Lodz, giving it out that he had business of his own, not connected with the Eisens, to attend to there. In Lodz he went, as always, to visit Samuel Zanvil, whom he loathed from the bottom of his heart because he was so much like himself. As always, again, their talk was of marriages, past and future, of prospects, fees, dowries, precedence, genealogy, and reputation.

It took some time to get Samuel Zanvil to the subject of Jacob Bunim, who was not among the most brilliant offers in his stock, and when Ezrael Cohen asked who was in prospect for the boy, Samuel Zanvil pretended that he had kept the best for the last. "*He* is the least of my worries," he said, waving his hand. "Will you be going out of town for him?" asked Ezrael Cohen, carelessly, but not carelessly enough. Samuel Zanvil sniffed suddenly, like a charger taking his bearings. So? Ezrael Cohen was interested in Jacob Bunim. Ezrael Cohen was the official marriage-broker of Reb Kalman Eisen. Was it possible? Was there a hope—? Samuel Zanvil put out a feeler, did not meet with a rebuff, put out a second, still encountered encouragement—and before long proposed boldly—Jacob Bunim and Pearl Eisen. Ezrael Cohen shrugged his shoulders. "Ridiculous," he said. "But there's no harm in trying."

Then Samuel Zanvil knew he had his man. There was no doubt about it now: the other side was dead set on the match. Yes, it was incredible, but the house of Kalman Eisen had actually made the first approach toward the provincial family of Reb Abraham Hirsh Ashkenazi.

Ezrael Cohen, caught between humiliation and fear, yielded to the latter. "Reb Samuel Zanvil," he said, "discretion, you understand. We won't quarrel about the fee, and no one has to know."

He meant: no one had to know who had taken the initiative.

"Trust me, Reb Ezrael," answered Samuel Zanvil smugly.

Yes, he could be trusted, for nothing filled him with greater happiness than to inform all and sundry that he, Samuel Zanvil, had paid a visit to the city of Warsaw, had marched in on Reb Kalman Eisen, and had laid down the law: "It is written in heaven that there shall be a marriage between Jacob Bunim Ashkenazi and Pearl Eisen."

[155]

Only Reb Abraham Hirsh himself did not believe. He sent for his son and looked him over from head to foot.

"Tell me, Jacob Bunim," he said, sharply, "what's been between you and Reb Kalman Eisen's grand-daughter?"

Jacob Bunim blushed. "I saw her once," he said, "near the canopy at Simcha Meyer's wedding."

Reb Abraham Hirsh sighed deeply and dismissed his son. An unseemly business this—open talk between Jacob Bunim and a girl he had never set eyes on before. A bad generation; first Simcha Meyer, now Jacob Bunim. The words of the dead Rabbi of Vorka, uttered nearly twenty years before, recurred to him. But against the match Reb Abraham Hirsh had nothing to say. By whatever means it had come to pass, it was infinitely better than he had ever dreamed of.

The betrothal was carried through quietly. Reb Kalman, wounded in his pride, wanted the news of the marriage to filter through to the public rather than be proclaimed. The marriage, which took place on the Pentecost of the following year, was, however, in full keeping with the reputation of the Eisens. It was celebrated, like all family weddings, in the great house in Warsaw. The mighty Rabbi of Ger, the most illustrious of all the Chasidic prelates, officiated. The exact amount of the dowry was not known, but Simcha Meyer guessed that it ran into many tens of thousands. Besides, the bride was rich in her own right, by inheritance from her mother. And then Jacob Bunim received countless presents, among which not the least valuable was the one from Simcha Meyer himself. For the latter understood that his brother had landed in the very highest and most influential circles in Polish Jewry, and it would be well to keep on the right side of him.

But he could not forgive him his stupid, incredible luck. What he, Simcha Meyer, had acquired by his gifts and infinite labour was overshadowed and made to appear contemptible by the miserable accident of a handsome figure and a silly, obstinate girl. What were his, Simcha Meyer's, ten thousand roubles compared with that honey-pot, that money-bag, that barrel of fat, in which Jacob Bunim had landed with both feet? And even if he added the earnings of

[156]

his first year, and his partnership in the factory, he was still a pauper compared with his brother.

He returned from the magnificent wedding feverish with envy and restlessness. His habit of calculating, of scribbling on whatever came to his hand, became a mania. He was getting ahead too slowly! "Faster!" he said to himself. Everything was too slow for him: his deals, his calculations, the factory. Slowest of all were those wretched hand-looms. They still made money, of course. They would always have their place. But that place would always be second. The big money was in steam. All those clever ideas of his, the cutting down of the kerchiefs, the introduction of cheaper material, the half-cotton kerchiefs, the bright colours—what were they worth? His hand-looms produced so slowly that in a month other manufacturers could steal his ideas and flood the market with the patterns and models he had thought out.

No! He was through with hand-looms. But before he gave up this factory, he would have to squeeze the last bit of blood out of it. He needed every rouble he could lay his hands on. During the last period of the Alter hand-loom factory Simcha Meyer worked like a demon. He dismissed several of his salesmen and maintained direct contact with the customers. He found, in near-by villages, a number of subcontractors who, working with the cheapest labour, were able to turn out material for him below his own costs. And finally he decided to take half a rouble per week off the pay of his weavers. That would bring in about twenty-five roubles a week, or over a thousand roubles a year.

He wrote out, in his best hand, two copies of the notice concerning the decrease in pay and gave them to Samuel Leibish to post on the walls of the factory.

"And if anybody doesn't like it," he said, putting his hands in his pockets and rising on his toes, "he is free to go and work for someone else. I'm thinking of changing to steam, anyway."

The little synagogue of the weavers, in Balut, jammed in among shapeless houses and coal- and wood-yards, was packed with worshippers.

The weavers had long since finished their Sabbath prayers. They had uttered the last song of praise, and had spat out on every side to indicate their contempt for the worshippers of idols, who pray to gods which cannot help them in the hour of need. They had rolled up their prayer shawls and shoved them into the cheap bags which had been made for them on their betrothal. The young men had dropped the prayer books into the pockets of their flimsy Sabbath gaberdines. Yet not a man had stirred from the place.

There on the pulpit, from which the reading of the Pentateuch was conducted on the Sabbath, stood Tevyeh, whose nickname was The-world-isn't-coming-to-an-end-yet; he banged on the worn velvet cover of the pulpit, shouting: "Quiet! Order! Let me say something!"

Tevyeh was the official reader in this synagogue of the weavers, but everyone knew that it was not to announce some preacher, or to give instructions for forthcoming services, that he had mounted the pulpit. Nor was it to appeal for a new velvet mantle for a scroll of the Law, or to call forth the name of some weaver who, having been blessed with the increase of a son, was treating the congregants to whisky and cake. For some such purpose it would have been easy to obtain silence. But everyone in the synagogue knew what secular matters agitated Tevyeh now, as they agitated every man and boy in the synagogue; and therefore it took much banging and pleading to obtain some sort of order. For every man wanted to have his say, and every man felt that his own life was threatened by the turn things had taken in the factory.

For these lean, hungry weavers, assembled in the shabby synagogue, with its crazy benches, it rickety Ark, its dirty, cracked windows, life had been hard enough even before Simcha Meyer announced his drastic cut in pay. Out of their meagre wages the weavers paid for the candles which lit their work at night, and what with the winter days, and the overtime which lasted beyond midnight on Thursdays and Saturdays, this was a considerable item. Employment and pay were not steady. A week was dropped now and again; sometimes a month. Yet it was impossible to save anything in times of full employment. Their chief dishes were barley soup and potatoes, the latter fried, not in meat fat, but in a cheap, sour oil which gave the weavers heartburn. Meat was eaten, if at all, only on the Sabbath, and then it consisted of the cheapest cuts or parings, a leg-bone, liver and lungs, and the like. Fish they ate only in the summer, when the heat made it impossible for the women in the markets to keep their goods for more than a day, and they had to sell at any price before the stink became too oppressive. In other months a piece of salt herring did service for a piece of fresh fish; this was eaten with onion and followed by a thin beet soup. Very frequently pious weavers were even unable to get a small glass of raisin wine for the Sabbath benediction, and the prayer was therefore said in default over a piece of white bread. What was worse, certain wives were unable to get candles for the Friday night benediction, the most sacred duty of a Jewish woman; and when they could, they went to their mothers' homes, so that one set of candles did service for several families.

The children's schools of the weavers, in which the rudiments of the faith and of Hebrew lore were taught, were tiny, filthy, and dark. No father who could scrape the money together would send his son to these charitable institutions, which were treated with contempt by the children of the

[159]

well-to-do. The teachers, unqualified and ill paid, vented their wretchedness on the children, beating them unmercifully, so that it was nothing unusual for a boy to come home with his face black and blue or his hands bleeding. Just as these schools were wretched and inadequate, the hospital maintained for Balut weavers was never able to accommodate more than a fraction of the number of the sick. Children suffered from rickets, fathers from tuberculosis, mothers from the strain of frequent childbirth, all from undernourishment and malnutrition. The streets were almost as thick as the factories with the wool and cotton dust which came out of the looms, or, more heavily, from the rags which were being reconverted into thread. Medical service of a sort was, when obtainable, free; but medicines cost money; and the weavers dreaded having to go into the clean, shiny apothecary's, with its picture of the Madonna and its glittering carboys. Here they could not haggle; they had to come in, hat in hand, take what was given, pay humbly, and crawl out. But for that matter Sender, the Jewish healer, was almost as bad. For almost every sickness he prescribed leeches; when that failed, he administered an enema. And he never charged less than a rouble.

Fathers were compelled to put their sons out as apprentices before they had reached their teens. The child brought nothing in, but it was one mouth less to feed, and if this meant that the boy got no schooling, there was no help for it. Mothers hired out their daughters as servants at the same age; and in strange houses, where they were treated as inferior creatures, these little girls lugged pails of water, scrubbed floors, and carried babies in their thin, weak arms. The weavers' wives were in a constant torment, trying to manage on the pay their husbands brought home. The first consideration was the rent. Every week a rouble was taken off and put into a broken pot, which was tied with rags. The most desperate want could not persuade them to touch this money, for unless the rent was paid on time, the family found itself in the street. Few and far between were the families—they were the ones with several bread-winners—which had a whole house to live in; for the most part one or two rooms, sub-let, had to suffice. Food came after rent, and after that, a long way behind, clothes, so that the population of Balut went round in rags, and it was hard to tell the original part of a coat from the patches.

And now, like a thunderbolt, there came this cut of half a rouble, fifty whole kopecks, in the factory of Reb Chaim Alter.

The women, hearing it, cursed furiously, put down their iron cooking-pots in front of their husbands, and screamed: "Here! Take it! You do the cooking for that money!"

The older weavers, tired men with bent limbs and glazed eyes, received the ukase in silence, as they had received all the other burdens of their life. It was the younger group that broke into rebellion, and in the front stood Tevyeh, the-world-isn't-coming-to-an-end-yet.

Three days had elapsed since the notice had been up in the factory. In the interval Tevyeh had been working at fever heat bringing the resentment to a head. Seated at his loom, he had sung loudly and boldly that little song of his, which came no one knew whence and the sound of which had become a symbol of revolt. The other weavers did not dare to sing the words with him at first, but as they took heart, the melody was heard from other looms. The melody, not the words. Samuel Leibish shoved his bony finger under Tevyeh's nose and croaked: "Wait till the boss comes in! You'll sing another tune then." But Tevyeh looked at Samuel Leibish contemptuously and went on singing and weaving. At night he ran from house to house in Balut, arguing with weavers, encouraging them to action, preparing them for the great demonstration on the Sabbath.

His wife, a big, bony woman, aged before her time and surrounded always by a host of children, cursed him loudly and bitterly.

"Tevyeh," she screamed, "may your bones be as dry and withered, so help me God, as the bit of food that's drying up! May the soul be blown out of you as I've blown my breath out, keeping the fire going to give you a warm meal!" And with children hanging on to her skirt, she ran through the Balut streets, looking for her husband.

[161]

But when she found him he had no time for her or for his meals. Hungry and thirsty, consumed by an inner fire, Tevyeh went from house to house, pleading, calling for united action.

"Stand together," he shouted. "We'll bring them to their knees, the dirty thieves. Only stand together."

They were all afraid, even the young men who agreed with him. They had to face not only the rage of their employers, but the discouragement of their parents. Long, exhausting years had beaten the older men to their knees. They were pious people, convinced of their own unimportance, terrified by the chimneys of the steam factories, in which they could never work because they would have to desecrate the Sabbath; they were enslaved to their wives, chronically tired, longing for nothing more than a little peace, a little sleep. They were dumbfounded by Tevyeh's words. They murmured, in reply: "Let be! It's God's will."

But something else made Tevyeh's task difficult. Where the pressure of parents did not dissuade the young men from open action, their individual, blind selfishness tempted them to forget the common cause. Every man dreamed of the time when he, amongst all the workers in the factory, would be able to save up enough to get himself a couple of looms and be a little boss. It might come—such things had been!—by way of an unexpected dowry. It might come through promotion. And meanwhile there were little hierarchies which afforded some satisfaction to the emotions. The more skilful workers bullied the weaker ones, the accepted weavers tormented the apprentices in their charge, and even the apprentices turned on the unfortunate workers who were hired by the week. Every worker who had passed through the hell of an apprenticeship relished the idea of inflicting these sufferings on another. "I went through it; let him do the same."

There was only one man who understood Tevyeh, stood openly with him, and worked side by side with him. This was Nissan, the son of Noske the Teacher.

He had long since passed through his apprenticeship, and he was now a full-fledged worker, not attached to any factory, but hiring himself out by the season. He had dreamed in his boyhood of finding liberation through work. He would be free to live for himself, released from the tyranny of his father, who wanted to marry him off as soon as possible and make a Jewish scholar of him. He would work and at the same time pursue his liberating studies. But it had all fallen out otherwise. The work had swallowed him up. His studies had not liberated him. He lived the life of the poorest, most despised of the weavers, the season and week worker. And he was usually employed, not by a factory-owner, but by a sub-contractor.

He had made his peace with his father. The latter had come to him, not cursing or reproaching, but moaning softly. And Nissan had suffered more from this than from blows or curses. With all his contempt for his father, he felt, somewhere, a deep kinship with the old man. And because his father made him indescribably miserable, he accepted his fate as a season worker and sank deeper and deeper into the slavery of the subcontractors' workrooms.

The subcontractors, the little master weavers, were the scum of the employers. These subcontractors were themselves at the mercy of both the factory-owners and their foremen or agents. The latter were free to distribute the work where they liked, and the system was unclean with bribery. If a subcontractor dared to complain to a factory-owner, he still remained at the mercy of the foreman, who would either give him inferior material, wool which was dry and brittle, so that the weavers spent more time binding up broken threads than weaving, or would find fault with the delivered orders, rejecting them for faults which would otherwise have been ignored. Sometimes the foreman would steal for himself a quantity of the distributed material. The subcontractor had to keep quiet and make good the loss, and often enough, between that and the poverty of the wool, he would find himself a loser at the end of the week. Apart from the wretched insecurity of the work, there was attached to it the most miserable humiliation. The subcontractor had to cringe for the bundle of work as though he were a beggar receiving charity, and the bitterness which accumulated in his heart he poured out on his own wretched employees.

[163]

Like the factory-owners, the subcontractors kept apprentices and employees whom they fed and lodged, but the bed was the filthy floor, and the food consisted mostly of bread, which the wives of the subcontractors bought cheap from the army stores—black bread, heavy and sour, which was sometimes washed down with thin, unsugared coffee. Workers who were shameless, or skilful in thievery, got the larger share; the others suffered hunger in silence. They sat, all of them, in the dark, low rooms, working by the light of oil wicks or smoky candles, their eyes watering, their limbs trembling with exhaustion. At night they put their heads on bundles of work and slept uncovered, freezing in the winter, choking in the hot summers, eaten by the bugs and fleas.

Sometimes the bundles on which the workers slept were wet, not by accident, but for a special reason. Just as the distributors of work had their special tricks, so the subcontractors had their ways of pilfering. Wool and cotton thread were distributed to them by weight, and the finished work was likewise returned by weight. Subcontractors learned to sprinkle water and sand into the thread, so that it took on weight. When workers slept on such bundles, the damp ate into their bones, and sometimes the colours on cheap material ran, so that when the workers rose in the morning their faces were black, like those of chimney-sweepers.

The workers had to help the subcontractors in the pilfering. They "pulled" on the loom, so that a length was produced with less than the prescribed material, the weight being made up by sand and water. The pieces on top and at the bottom of a pile were usually up to specification; the dishonest pieces were in the middle. The workers had to follow the subcontractors' instructions or be thrown out. Then, when a bundle was ready, a worker had to put it on his back and trudge to the other end of the town to deliver, for a subcontractor would not have dreamed of hiring a droshky, with so many human packhorses at his command.

Miserable slaves themselves, the subcontractors showed the cruelty and meanness of slaves toward their workers. It might happen that, at the end of an entire season of work, starvation, and sleeplessness, a weaver would not receive a kopeck in the way of wages. Then he sued his employer, and in the presence of the Rabbi judge, the subcontractor would rip open his greasy vest and howl: "All right, take the heart out of me. I haven't a kopeck. I'm as poor as you."

It was among these and their like that Tevyeh preached the gospel of rebellion and unity, in the face of warnings that came from every side.

"Tevyeh! It's none of your business! Tevyeh! Keep your ideas to yourself! Tevyeh, you'll be the first one to be thrown out."

There was only one person who understood him: Nissan. The bitter life of the seasonal worker—the end of his dreams of advancement—had made him receptive to the idea of rebellion. He was sick of the pointless labour and starvation, and sick of the name by which he had been known ever since he left his father, Nissan the Wicked. The utter insanity of the life around him, the filth and poverty and oppression, had become intolerable. Nights he followed Tevyeh around, listening eagerly as the latter argued, quoted verses from the Bible and Talmud, appealed to reason and justice, and promised liberty if there was only unity.

"Stand together!" he kept repeating, in his hoarse, exhausted voice.

This was not the first sympathetic contact between Nissan and Tevyeh; it was only the first occasion on which they worked together openly for common action among the weavers. Nissan, who to his employers was a worker among others, to be starved and robbed like the rest, was a well-known figure in Balut. It had never been forgotten that he had given up the possibility of a great future to become a weaver, and while respectable folk still alluded to him as Nissan the Wicked, the workers were proud of him. They were grateful when he came on the Sabbath into the little weavers' synagogue. They respected him for his Jewish learning, as well as for his studious habits. They liked him, too, because he was helpful. He would write letters for parents whose sons were with the army in far-off parts of Russia, or for girls whose sweethearts lived in another town. He taught the illiterate at least how to sign their names. He read and ex-

[165]

plained to them the contents of documents which they received from the prefecture or police headquarters. Besides, he was clever, quick-witted, always ready with some quotation or parable. Brought up in poverty, he knew the lives of the weavers; but he knew also, from his early contact with the children of the well-to-do, the outlook of the upper classes.

Even Tevyeh's wife, the embittered, screaming virago, moderated her language to her husband when Nissan was by, and Nissan was with Tevyeh a great deal during the days when they worked together to rouse the weavers against the cut in Chaim Alter's factory. It was widely known that the order had come from Simcha Meyer, and him Nissan remembered only too well. In the years that had passed, the gulf between them had grown wider than ever. Simcha Meyer was now a manufacturer, who issued edicts of starvation against the Jews of Balut; Nissan was a seasonal worker, and though he was not employed by Simcha Meyer, Nissan felt that this was peculiarly his affair. The old hatred which he had felt for the well-to-do youngster who had played cards contemptuously under the nose of Reb Noske the Teacher rose in him again. He threw himself into the work with a fury which delighted Tevyeh, but his plans ranged wider than Tevyeh's. He called to the Sabbath service in the weavers' synagogue not only the workers in Chaim Alter's factory, but all workers, whoever lived and sweated in Balut.

They came. There was no danger in coming to the synagogue; that might be merely for the services. But they knew that after the services there would be something else, and whether or not they were ready for action, they wanted to be in on the excitement. And now the synagogue was jammed to the point of asphyxiation, and on the pulpit stood Tevyeh, not to read the week's portion from the Pentateuch, which he always did with great skill, but to initiate the great rebellion.

When he had at last obtained order, Tevyeh called up Nissan to read forth the manifesto. Nissan stepped up to the pulpit and unrolled a long document covered with fine script. The language was a highly Hebraized Yiddish, with a strong Biblical background.

"Improvements demanded by the brotherhood of weavers, in the city called Balut.

" (a) The weavers who pray in the synagogue Ahavath Re-im, as well as all the other weavers of Balut, will not permit any reduction in their miserable wages. Such reduction may be likened to robbery, and therefore the weavers hereby resolve that they will not go to work; moreover they resolve that no man here will take another man's work, for this action may be likened to murder, as if a man were to rise up in the field against his brother and slay him.

" (b) It is the will of the weavers of Balut that there shall not be any more work beyond midnight on Thursdays and Saturdays. On Thursdays they shall work until midnight, and on Saturdays they shall work in the summer from the time of the ushering out of the Sabbath until midnight, and in the winter from the time of the ushering out of the Sabbath until ten o'clock.

" (c) On week-days a weaver shall not work more than fourteen hours a day, from the hour of six in the morning until the hour of eight in the evening. The time taken out for afternoon and evening prayers shall be counted in the hours of work; and in winter, when it is too dark in the morning, the morning prayer shall be said in the factory, and that too shall be counted with the hours of work.

" (d) On Fridays and on the days preceding festivals the work shall stop two hours before the lighting of the candles in the first instance, and two hours before sunset in the second instance, so that the weaver shall be able to go home and wash himself and prepare for the Sabbath and the festival.

" (e) The pay of the weaver shall not be delayed from one week to the next. Henceforth the pay for the week shall be given out regularly on Thursdays, so that on Friday the weaver's wife may make preparations for the Sabbath. Likewise payment shall be rendered the weaver betimes for festivals, for he that does not pay his worker in time may be likened to a robber.

" (f) Candles for work shall be bought by the employer, not by the worker.

" (g) It is forbidden for employers to call their workers

by abusive names, for it is written that no man shall shame his brother. Likewise employers shall not strike their workers, for the man that lifts his hand against his brother is wicked. Nor shall the weavers abuse the apprentices, nor the apprentices the seasonal workers, but they must remember how they themselves have been tormented and not do likewise to another. If any weaver fail to obey this law, he shall be expelled from the brotherhood.

" (h) On feast-days the weaver shall work only till midday.

" (i) In the middle days of the Passover and the Feast of Tabernacles, the weaver shall work only till the time of the later afternoon prayer.

" (j) The workers, apprentices, and seasonal workers who are lodged by their employers must be given food that is properly fried; likewise the coffee shall have milk and sugar in it. For if the workers are ill fed, and yet work is demanded of them, they are like the slaves in Egypt, who were bidden make bricks but were not given clay or straw.

"These improvements have been put forth by the weavers of Balut, assembled in the synagogue Ahavath Re-im, on the Sabbath when that portion of the Pentateuch is read forth which is called the Law of the Lepers."

When Nissan had done reading, a great tumult arose in the synagogue.

"Simple justice," shouted many. "Holy words those are."

"We'll never get it!" one despairing voice was heard.

"We will if we stand together!" came the cry from others.

Tevyeh banged on the pulpit till order had been restored again, and launched into a long harangue in which, taking his text from the manifesto, he compared the workers to the Jews in Egypt, and the employers to their taskmasters. He spoke passionately and at length, using words and figures with which they were all familiar, homely quotations and parables from the Bible. He spoke of the foremen and subcontractors as the overseers in Egypt, Jews themselves, but sworn to do the bidding of the tyrants. As the ancient Egyptians had forced the Jews to build their children as living sacrifices into the walls of Pithom and Ramses, so did the employers of Lodz force the weavers to build their children, too, into the system of slavery. For either the fathers, slaving day and night, were not able to feed their own children, or else the young ones were handed over at a tender age to the taskmasters.

"It's true! It's true!" they cried. "As true as it is the Sabbath today in God's world!"

As a peroration Tevyeh demanded that this same night the bosses of Balut be presented with the ten conditions of the weavers, and that the weavers refuse to go to work until the conditions had been granted.

There was silence for a moment, then again doubting voices.

"We shall be left without a bite of bread!"

"They'll never yield!"

"No threats! Let's go to them peacefully, not to anger them!"

"Nobody will go to the bosses! The first man to present the demands will be thrown out."

Tevyeh banged again on the pulpit and shouted hoarsely: "You speak like the slaves of Egypt. 'We remember the fleshpots,' they cried. You are worse than they, for you receive no flesh. You do not even receive enough dry bread to still your hunger. But Moses did not listen to the muttering of the slaves, and went to Pharaoh. Shall we be slaves of Pharaoh for ever?"

The voices sank into a shamed silence. Tevyeh glared triumphantly at the assembly and lifted his hand. "I will go to our Pharaohs and speak in the name of all. But let no man go with cunning, behind my back, to the bosses. Let no man go to work until our demands are granted."

"No one will sell you out, Tevyeh," someone screamed.

"I want an oath," shouted Tevyeh. "From all of you. Here, in this sacred place, before the Ark of the Law, I want each one of you to swear that he will not take his brother's place at work."

An old weaver, with a tangled grey beard which looked like a mass of uncombed cottonwool, with eyes reddened by many years of work by smoky candles, struggled through to the pulpit and, with trembling hand uplifted, cried to the

[169]

weavers: "Jews, hear me! It is forbidden to take an oath on the Sabbath, even for a true thing! It is a sin against heaven!"

But Nissan thrust him aside, shrilling: "That is a lie! When there is danger to life it is specifically permitted even to break the laws of the Sabbath. And the lives of your wives and children are in danger. Therefore you may take the oath, even though it were on the very Day of Atonement."

Without waiting another moment Tevyeh flung toward the Ark, took out the scroll in its shabby velvet mantle, and laid it before him on the pulpit.

"By the Law of God, and in this holy place, we swear that we will not return to work except by the consent of all. I swear it for all who are here!" He turned to the assembly. "Answer me!"

"We swear it!" came back a roar of voices.

xviii

Word of the strike reached Simcha Meyer that same afternoon, and he took up the challenge of the workers in his
factory with bitter resolution.

Reb Chaim Alter was not in the city. This was the time
of the year—the period following the Pentecost—when he
went to the Austrian resorts with his Priveh. Shortly before
Simcha Meyer had announced the pay-cut, Reb Chaim had
packed his heavy leather valises, remembering above all to
include his shining silk hat, which he put on the moment
they crossed the border, so that his wife, who looked like an
operatic star, should not be ashamed of her husband. Simcha
Meyer had been glad to see him go, for he had anticipated
trouble, and his father-in-law was not the man to have around.
He had not been so glad to see his Dinah go with them.

But he asked himself, as he strode excitedly up and down
the dining-room, what good would it do him to have her
near him. What encouragement could he have drawn from
her presence? In this past year and more, while he had been
making a place for himself among the manufacturers of Lodz,
she had not shown a glimmer of interest in his achievements.
The clever dodges which had wrung from hundreds of merchants reluctant expressions of admiration had left her un-
impressed. Sitting with her at table, eating feverishly, he had
more than once tried to explain how cleverly he had overreached his competitors, how neatly he had trapped a buyer,

[171]

how ingeniously he was squeezing the maximum from the factory.

"Do you get the idea, Dinah?" he would ask, chanting the words as if he were explaining an obscure text in the Talmud.

She did not understand. She did not want to understand. She looked at him and saw, instead of the brilliant merchant which he believed himself to be, only an outlandish young Chasid, whose eyes were feverish with impatience, who ate with big gulps, who dipped his buttered roll into the coffee, and let the food dribble on to his sparse beard.

"Clever, wasn't it, Dinah darling?" he crowed.

"Wipe the food off your beard," she answered, "and don't scribble on the table-cloth."

This, or something like this, was always her answer, and the words stung so cruelly that he took an oath never to try to interest her again. But the oath was taken in vain, for he could not help himself. He hungered for her admiration; and, even more, he wanted to know that she was his. His darting, slightly insane eyes would pass over her, telling him that she was beautiful. He longed to feel her soft white flesh warming to him, to be a recipient and not only a giver of caresses; but the greater his longing grew, the more coldly she withdrew from him.

There was no formal complaint he could have brought against her. She did her duty as a wife. She saw to it that meals were always ready on time; she had clean linen ready for him on Fridays; she saw to it that he had a fresh handkerchief every morning, and before he went out she reminded him to brush the cigarette ashes off his gaberdine. All this she did faithfully; but he had never seen her smile at him, except in scorn, and in the fulfilment of her duties there was always a suggestion of contempt. Sometimes she seemed to feel as much contempt for herself as for him, but this, too, was a reflection on him.

It was incredible to him. He was a somebody in Lodz! He had done more in one year than older men had done in ten. Aside from business matters, too, scholars still came to him, to talk of Jewish learning, and found in him an equal. A whole world admired him; only his own wife treated him as if he were not even worth spitting at. He asked himself a hundred times what one was supposed to do in order to win a woman's admiration and love, and he found no answer. He knew only two worlds: that of the Chasidim, with their scholarship, their Rabbinic disputes and scandals, and the business world, with its profits and losses, its bales of goods and its accounts. The world in which she had locked herself, that of knights and princes and courtly lovers, was utterly mad to him.

"What's that you're reading?" he would break in on her for the hundredth time, though he knew perfectly well what kind of book it was.

"God, how you frightened me!" she answered.

Again he would snatch the book from her hands, read through half a dozen lines, catch a couple of gentile names and the word "love," and fling the volume back at her.

"If you were to pay me for it," he said, furiously, "I couldn't read that trash."

It was worse than trash; it was the symbol of the insuperable barrier between them. It was the wall of ice with which she surrounded herself whenever he drew near her. Not that he permitted this coldness to rob him of his rights. He was not the man to relinquish what was his, and he took it in the nights, whether she was willing or not. But it left him bitter and dissatisfied. He felt that he had the right to more, to some tenderness, to a kindness which would soothe him after his furious days, with their quarrels, competition, and hostilities.

And not even when, a few months after the wedding, it became known that Dinah was pregnant was there any change in her attitude toward him. The very manner in which the news reached him was a blow to his pride and a rebuff to his longings. When Dinah first suspected that certain alarming changes in her body portended a child, she ran to her mother and, bursting into tears, told her of the symptoms. Priveh stroked her daughter's hair, kissed her, laughed, and bade her go and tell Simcha Meyer.

"Never, Mamma," she sobbed, and clung to her mother;

[173]

and nothing that Priveh said could persuade her daughter that it was the wife's place, and no one else's, to break to a husband the news of her pregnancy.

So it was that Simcha Meyer learned from a third person that he might soon be a father. The thrill of masculine pride which was his first response died quickly, and with it the momentary hope that with the coming of a child Dinah would change in her general bearing, and above all in her bearing toward him. Often he had thought that this would make all the difference, this serious business of having a child; then Dinah would throw away her foolish books, give up her silly day-dreaming, and turn to her husband with the affection which he merited. He had seen it in other young matrons; the child made them more tender toward the husband. With all his contempt for woman, partly instilled in him, partly the result of his own character, Simcha Meyer could not bear Dinah's coldness. He could not bear, to be more exact, that a person should escape him, defying his mastery.

A change did come over Dinah, but it did not affect her attitude toward Simcha Meyer. It was as though the fruit she bore about in her body absorbed her completely, to the exclusion of the man who had planted it there, and this new joy of hers locked her off from Simcha Meyer even more effectively than the world of fancy which had till then been her refuge. Long before the unborn child could have given such signs, Dinah was telling her mother rapturously that she felt it stirring about in her, and she would lie for hours on the ottoman, waiting, suspended, for the flutter in her body.

"I feel it, Mamma, I feel it," she cried rapturously.

"You're a goose," her mother said. "It's much too early. It's just your imagination."

"I don't care if it is too early," cried Dinah, her face radiant. "I do feel it."

During her pregnancy she was lovelier than ever. The outward changes in her body were slight, and throughout all the period her skin retained its freshness and smoothness. Her blue eyes took on a new warmth, unknown to her before, and when she smiled—as she did more frequently now—they shone as if with their own light. Her mother, looking at her, murmured again and again the exorcism against the evil eye; and Simcha Meyer felt his hunger for her becoming intolerably sharp.

He would come into her room hastily, and in his nervous, unbalanced way ask her how she was.

"Tell me, Dinah, how do you feel?" His voice had in it a mixture of his baffled desire toward her and the queer, slightly insane restlessness which was part of him.

"I'm tired," she answered, and turned to the wall so that she might not see him.

When the Pentecost was over and she prepared to go abroad with her parents, she showed a complete indifference to Simcha Meyer. She had not asked him whether she might go, and parting, she did not offer to kiss him. Without looking at him, without calling him by his name, she held out her hand and said, coldly: "Good-bye."

In the loneliness of the empty house he asked himself repeatedly what good it would do him if in this crisis Dinah were with him. But the question did not drive the bitterness from his heart. During the day he threw himself furiously into his work, but for all his exhaustion the nights brought no sleep. Worst of all were the Sabbaths, when he could not go to the factory or run around in the city restaurants or even scribble figures. Long Sabbaths they were, of the late spring, hot and oppressive. He tried once or twice to take up again his studies of the Talmud, but after a few minutes he pushed the volume away from him. Those queer, ancient laws of a dead world did not interest him. He wanted work; he wanted the factory; he wanted Dinah.

On such a Sabbath the two emissaries of the weavers came to him, Nissan, the Teacher's son, and Tevyeh, the-world-isn't-coming-to-an-end-yet. It was evening. Impatiently Simcha Meyer had awaited the ending of the day and the emergence of three stars in the smoky Lodz sky, that he might light a cigarette and hurry over to the factory. But before he left the house, the two men had arrived, bringing with them the ten demands, written out on a sheet torn from a notebook.

"A good week to you," they said quietly.

Simcha Meyer looked at them, withholding answer for a

[175]

few moments. Poverty-stricken workers, in their Sabbath gaberdines. It was the first time that workers had ever come to his house.

"I'll see you down there," he answered curtly, pointing toward the factory.

But Tevyeh thrust the paper toward Simcha Meyer and said: "We can't go into the factory. Be good enough to read this first."

Simcha Meyer snatched the sheet, glanced through it hastily, and smiled.

"Let me see," he said, looking up, "you're Nissan, the Teacher's son, aren't you? What have you got to do with this man?" and he indicated Tevyeh.

"I am a weaver," answered Nissan.

"So?" answered Simcha Meyer, as if this were news to him. He pulled at his little beard and grinned. "You've become a worker. And what does your father think of it?"

Nissan did not answer. Simcha Meyer thrust his hands into the pockets of his silk gaberdine, and the grin died on his face. "It seems to me," he said sharply, "that you don't work in my factory."

"I come in the name of the weavers," answered Nissan. "They've sent us to talk with you."

"But suppose I don't want to talk with you?" asked Simcha Meyer angrily. "I don't propose to treat you as an equal."

Nissan was confused. He did not know how to answer Simcha Meyer. The other had addressed him by his first name, and in the familiar second person singular. He could not say "Mr." to Simcha Meyer after that; at the same time he could not bring himself to be rude. Besides, this rich house, which reminded him of the homes of his uncles, to whom he used to go miserably in his childhood to beg a loan for his mother, awakened old terrors in him. The sheet with the demands had fallen to the floor, and Nissan did not know whether or not to pick it up. Simcha Meyer decided for him, by picking it up himself. Smoothing it out, he read it through again.

"Well, well," he said, in a singing, Talmudic voice, "you're all united now, are you?"

"Yes," answered Tevyeh.

"And what you want, in brief," he continued in the same hateful, mocking voice, "is more money and less work."

"Exactly," answered Tevyeh. "More money and less work."

"And suppose I refuse? What dreadful things do you propose to do to me?"

"We won't go to work," answered Tevyeh.

"Bless me! And what will you eat in the meantime?"

"What's the difference?" asked Tevyeh. "We starve when we work; we might as well starve without working. We have no more strength to work."

Simcha Meyer lifted his hand and shook his finger under Tevyeh's nose. "This is your doing, Tevyeh," he snarled. "Yours and this young fool's here. You gabble and gabble to the workers until you turn their heads and rob them of their last piece of bread."

He meant it. He could not understand why people should want to work less. Ever since his childhood he had been accustomed to seeing the workers give up all their energies at the looms. What else should workers do?

"They'll change their minds," he said, shrugging his shoulders. "Just wait till Thursday, when the wives begin asking for the week's pay. That'll make quite a difference. They'll all be here, at my feet, begging to be taken in."

But Simcha Meyer was wrong. Thursday came round, and none of his workers showed up. All week long he had walked up and down the factory, biting his lips. He had sent Samuel Leibish through the city to find workers, but there were none to be had. As if to taunt him, things had taken an upward turn. There was work for everyone, and he himself received many orders. Leibish found a few old Germans and one or two drunkards. They worked slowly, they were thievish, they were inefficient. Simcha Meyer missed the sound of the factory working at full speed. He calculated his losses, and cursed Tevyeh and Nissan. On Friday he sent for the teacher who on the Sabbath taught the Ethics of the Fathers to the weavers in the synagogue Ahavath Re-im, and instructed him to scold the workers bitterly for rising in rebellion against their masters.

It had been a dreadful week for the weavers. The wives who had thrown down their pots and refused to go on cooking when the pay-cut was announced, were now the first to turn on their husbands, reproaching them furiously for their obstinacy, and recalling the good old days when the end of the week brought some pay into the house.

"Murderers!" they shrieked at their husbands. "Do you want us to die of hunger, us and the children?"

But the workers did not budge. On the Sabbath, when they assembled in the synagogue, they were in no mood to listen to the moralizings of the teacher. They howled him down and would not be quiet until Tevyeh had mounted the pulpit. He exhorted them again to stand fast.

"I had to pawn my cushions for bread," one weaver groaned.

"I pawned my prayer shawl and phylacteries," another countered.

"But it's worth it!" cried Tevyeh, hoarsely. "Another few days, I tell you, and the boss will send for you. Listen to what I tell you. He's being ruined by the strike. He can't stand it."

He explained to the workers: it was not only the orders which Simcha Meyer could not meet at the moment. It was the terror of the steam factories, which encroached more and more on the work of the hand-looms. A customer once lost might never be regained.

Tevyeh, a skilled worker, knew what was happening in Simcha Meyer's mind and did not need to be told that the latter was genuinely frightened. In his first enthusiasm, believing that in a day or two the strike would collapse, he had welcomed the test joyously. Now the extraordinary and unexpected obstinacy of the weavers put another complexion on the matter. Simcha Meyer scribbled continually. He calculated how much he was losing each day; he calculated what were likely to be his permanent losses. True, he would not stick to hand-looms. But the very fact that he wanted to go

[178]

over to steam made his present losses the more dangerous. It was the critical transitional period, when he needed every rouble he could lay hands on.

It was a bad business. But on the other hand, if he gave way, there was, first of all, an immediate loss; and second, perhaps worse, the prospect of further demands. The immediate loss was heavy enough for a small manufacturer, over a thousand roubles a year, not to mention the interest; then the cost of candles; then the shorter hours. Prospective losses were incalculable. "Those filthy paupers!" he thought. "One concession and they'll be after me like a pack of dogs. Whereas if I hold out, if I make them come to me, crawling on their bellies, I can squeeze out my losses from them."

He pulled at his beard, calculated, cursed, and waited. In the restaurants, where he met merchants and agents, he put on a cheerful face.

"I'm in no hurry, gentlemen. I'll take my time," he said. "Let those paupers get a good taste of the whip."

And the whip was felt in Balut, as Samuel Leibish, who made the rounds of the streets every day, could testify to his master. In the dirty little groceries, in which flies buzzed thickly all day long round the sacks of sugar and boxes of candy, the women of the weavers pleaded in vain for a little more credit. The shopkeepers hung on grimly to their loaves, answering angrily: "The books are swollen with your debts. How do you expect me to get bread from the baker if you don't pay?"

The wives brought to the grocers their household possessions which they could not pawn: pillow-slips, an old-fashioned wedding dress, which could never be sold, but which was precious to the owner, a winter hat, even a woman's Bible. Then the shopkeepers wearied of these tokens and would give no more. But the children at home hung on to their mothers' aprons and still cried: "Bread! Mamma, bread!"

At street-corners the workers of the Alter factory assembled in little groups, still wearing their Sabbath gaberdines. There was a tug of war between the older weavers and the young men.

[179]

"Tevyeh is right," the latter cried. "Keep it up just a little while longer and we win."

"It's easy for you!" the old men answered, bitterly. "You're not married. You don't have half a dozen children hanging on and screaming for bread. If you had to face that every time you went home, you'd talk different. Simcha Meyer will get other workers, and, God help us, where will we be?"

Others added: "We've been fools. Let's go to Simcha Meyer before it's too late and tell him that we didn't want to do it, only that precious couple, Tevyeh and Nissan, got us into the mess, scared us into it. I tell you, let's do it, because if we don't, there'll be nothing left for us but to go begging from door to door."

"We swore an oath in the synagogue!" another reminded them.

"We'll go to the Rabbi. He'll release us from the oath. It's a matter of life and death. The Rabbi will see that and release us."

Without the knowledge of their husbands, the wives of some of the weavers went to Simcha Meyer, to beg the loan of a few roubles. "My husband will come to work soon," they pleaded. "I'll see to that. Only please lend me a couple of roubles."

Simcha Meyer gave them no money. He gave them a sermon instead to take back to their homes. "Those two hooligans," he said sternly, "Teyveh and Nissan, will ruin your husbands, and you too. I won't forgive them, and God won't forgive them either."

"Don't say that, master," the women implored. "May God take those two and twist their mouths round to the back of their ears, for the sake of the false, sweet words they misled our husbands with."

"I tell you those two will finish by baptizing your husbands," said Simcha Meyer indignantly. "Your husbands will leave you, and it's your fault."

"Master, master," the women pleaded, stretching out their lean, calloused hands, "don't say such things. Lend us a little, only a little. We'll chase those two out of the city like scabby dogs if you'll only help us."

[180]

Simcha Meyer did not help them, but the women began to make scenes in the streets whenever they met Tevyeh or Nissan. Bitterest among them was Tevyeh's own wife. She went running through the streets in search of her husband, a baby at her open dress, through which her black breast showed, children clinging to her skirts.

"Idiot!" she screamed. "Everybody's business is yours. You've got a heart big enough for the city, but not big enough for your wife and children. May it grow too small for you, may it wither inside you! What do you think you are? I'll tell you. You're a dirty old broom; everybody sweeps with you, then they throw you out. Fool! Look after your own wife and children, and let others look after theirs."

The children clinging to her skirts wailed with their mother.

Even Nissan had lost his status in her eyes, and she cursed him publicly as she cursed her husband.

"You too, with your clever little head, may God screw it off your shoulders! Don't you dare to come to my house again, if you don't want me to throw a potful of boiling water over you. Nissan the Wicked! Nissan the Wicked! That's your name!"

Tevyeh bore it stolidly and went on with his work. "A few days more," he said to the workers wherever he met them. "No cowardice, no weakness. Victory is in sight." His frantic obstinacy, backed by Nissan's sharp, clever phrases, held the workers together.

The second Thursday came, and still no one returned to the factory. Simcha Meyer was appalled. Who would have thought that this vermin would hold out so long? He began to think seriously of retreat, for more than one customer had openly threatened to leave him for good. He remembered how in the old days he had learned at cards to take a loss in time and not to throw good money after bad. If the luck was against him, he knew how to quit. With all his rage against the workers, his mind still worked coolly. "I'm beaten, blast them," he thought. "The sooner I give in, the better."

It was only at the end of the second week, when he had almost decided to send for his workers, that the brilliant

[181]

winning idea came to him in a flash. Walking furiously up and down the factory, he burst suddenly into a loud, yelping laugh.

"Samuel Leibish!" he shouted. "Where's Samuel Leibish?"

Samuel Leibish came running, startled.

"Can you find me Lippe Chalfan?" asked Simcha Meyer. "Certainly Reb Simcha," answered the other.

"Bring him here, at once. Tell him it's something important."

Lippe Chalfan, an undersized Lithuanian Jew with a close-cropped beard and a lisp, was a well-known character in Lodz, extremely useful to a certain class of people. He had come to the city many years before, in rags, bringing with him a stock of needles, packages of thread, shoe-laces, collars, and pins, which he peddled in the street. But he was not born to remain a pedlar. He had an ingratiating way about him, spoke and wrote Russian well—a rarity among the Jews of Lodz—and even while he was peddling he was learning to render the kind of service which later made him notorious in the city. At first he carried messages, wrote Russian letters, interpreted documents. Then he worked his way in among lower Russian officials and found out who took graft easiest and where it went furthest. Within a few months he had given up peddling, had taken a house and hung out a shingle: "Lippe Chalfan, Interpreter and Commissioner." He was an unofficial notary, a negotiator, an under-cover man, a writer of petitions, all in one. He found himself without difficulty in Lodz, and higher officials began to pay attention to him not less than important Jewish merchants. Regular lawyers and advocates sneered at him and proclaimed him an illiterate meddler. But Lippe Chalfan had what they had not —the connections which made him much more useful than they. Dressed now in smart European fashion, a derby hat on his head, a heavy brief-case under his arm, he strode through the streets, saluting with a great flourish every policeman and official he met.

"Your Excellency!" he called out loudly, so that everyone might hear.

"What do I care for those lawyers, with their diplomas and

[182]

degrees?" he sneered. "I've got the police here where I want them"—and he slapped his pocket—"and that's what counts."

Lippe Chalfan did everything: be bought up bad bills and promissory notes, acted as bailiff, advanced money, sued the railroads when deliveries were misplaced, hung around the courtrooms, sending messages to judges and lawyers, and, whenever necessary, was ready to expose a Jew to the rigours of the law for doing what everybody else was doing. For this last he took a special fee from the man's rival.

"Leave it to me!" he assured his client. "Your rival will be out of the way one-two-three. All you have to do is pay."

This was the man for whom Simcha Meyer now sent. The Lithuanian listened with the utmost attention to Simcha Meyer's long story, delivered rapidly in singsong Lodz Yiddish and filled with invective against the two authors of the rebellion. Lippe Chalfan did not interrupt save when Simcha Meyer addressed him as "Reb Lippe," and then only to murmur: "*Gospodin* Lippe, if you please." When Simcha Meyer had finished the recital, Lippe Chalfan drew a sheet of paper out of his portfolio, asked for the exact names of the culprits, and wrote them out carefully in Russian script.

"Consider it fixed!" he exclaimed. "They're as good as out of the way. That is—of course—"

Simcha Meyer took out his pocketbook, and the eyes of the Lithuanian brightened.

"You see, my dear *Gospodin* Ashkenazi," he said, "the behaviour of those two tramps is in direct contravention of Article Seven, Chapter One Hundred and Eighty One of the Russian Criminal Code. And if it isn't, it's going to be, get me? They're in prison already."

"No one is going to know about this, you understand," said Simcha Meyer.

"*Konietchno!* Of course! Not a soul!" said the other. "I understand you perfectly."

Late that night the police thundered at the doors of the houses where Tevyeh and Nissan lived. The same scene took place in each case. The arrested man asked in amazement what he was charged with. The answer was: "You'll find out at the station."

[183]

Neighbours gave the alarm, and in ten minutes all Balut was awake. Before the police had reached the station, they were surrounded by a curious and frightened crowd, through which they made a way with the flat of their swords.

Tevyeh's wife, in her shift, wailed as if her husband were in a coffin and being taken to the cemetery. "Jews," she wept aloud, "what will I do now, left alone in the world?"

For more than thirty-six hours Tevyeh and Nissan sat in a filthy cell, among drunkards, pickpockets, and travellers who had no passports.

"Hey, how did you get into stir?" the pickpockets asked them.

"We don't know, we haven't done anything," answered Nissan.

"God-damn boobs," said the pickpockets, pushing them about the cell. Neither they nor the drunkards liked these newcomers. They would not let them sleep at night. During the day they forced them to do the filthiest work. On the morning of the second day the two men, exhausted and grimy, were taken before the chief of police himself.

"Attention!" yelled the chief of police in Russian. His yellow sideburns trembled with discipline and indignation. "Stand up straight and don't dare to move."

Neither Nissan nor Tevyeh understood more than a few words of Russian. They muttered that they had done nothing and their passports were in order. But the chief of police would not listen. He insisted that all prisoners stand at attention in his presence. At a sign from him two policemen taught Nissan and Tevyeh how to stand at attention by hitting them in the stomach to straighten them out and striking them under the chin to make them lift their heads. *"Tak!"* they said. "That's how." The chief of police, satisfied, combed his sideburns with his fingers. Then he got up from his chair and went up to each of them in turn, shoving his face close to them and almost stepping on their toes.

"So!" he began, sneeringly. "Conspirators! Want to overthrow the Government, do you?"

Tevyeh and Nissan got a glimmering of his meaning, and in a mixture of faulty Polish and Yiddish, interspersed with

[184]

fragments of Russian, they tried to tell the chief of police something about the wretched lives of the weavers and about the half-rouble cut at the Alter factory. The chief of police was not interested. He walked up and down before them blustering.

"We'll teach you to mislead innocent workers!" he said, working himself up into a passion. "There are hundreds of your kind rotting in chains; and that's what you'll be doing before long, with a touch of the nagaika to keep you awake."

And striding up and down, he dictated to his secretary a long indictment, full of heavy legal terms, in which the two men were charged with a variety of state crimes ranging from secret conspiracy to open, armed rebellion. When he was through he asked the secretary to read it back, then turned on Tevyeh and Nissan and roared: "Sign that! And if you can't sign your name, make a cross."

The two men looked at each other in horror. The two policemen who stood ranged, one to the right, one to the left of them, slapped them on the legs with their scabbards. "Didn't you hear?" they snapped. "Sign!"

One after the other they signed: Tevyeh Melech Mendeleiev Meyerev Buchbinder, and Nissan Nusinev Schlomovitch Eibeschutz. The secretary read the names over laboriously.

"Take them back," ordered the chief of police.

That afternoon the chief of police sent in a detailed report to the Governor at Piotrkov, in which he described how, after much investigation and effort, he had apprehended two dangerous conspirators, who were responsible for the unrest among the workers of Lodz. The gravity of the case impelled him, the chief of police of Lodz, to beg His Excellency to have the two men removed without delay from the vicinity; if he could be permitted to suggest, it would be well to send the two men to St. Petersburg, far from the ten states of the Polish Kingdom, without trial and merely on an administrative order. While waiting for the permit from St. Petersburg, he, the chief of police, would keep the two men under provisional arrest.

All this was duly reported to Simcha Meyer by Lippe Chalfan, who added: "You can rely on me—it'll take a good year

[185]

or more to get that permit revoked. Maybe more. And by that time your two strike-leaders will have learned a lesson that will last them the rest of their lives."

In Balut the arrest of Nissan and Tevyeh was treated as a public calamity. The women who had cursed the two men in the streets now ran from one Rabbi to another, asking them to intervene. But the answer was always the same. "If it were a matter of theft, we could ask for clemency. But you can't do anything for conspirators. It's dangerous to try; the police will think you're one of the conspirators."

Within a few days the strike was broken, and Simcha Meyer's factory was working under full pressure. The hungry strikers threw themselves into the work with such enthusiasm that they promised soon to make good the loss incurred by Simcha Meyer during the period of idleness. On Thursday, when they received one half-rouble less than in the past, there was not a murmur. Simcha Meyer, encouraged by his victory, figured out new economies. He decided that the teacher paid by his father-in-law to lecture in the synagogue to the weavers was a superfluity and therefore dismissed him.

In the restaurants of Lodz there was only a vague suspicion that the arrest of Tevyeh and Nissan had not been a spontaneous act on the part of the police. But whatever the reason for the collapse of the strike, Simcha Meyer's reputation was tremendously enhanced by it. He had clashed with the workers and won.

"Watch that young fellow. He's as smart as a pickpocket," they said; and higher praise than this was unknown in Lodz.

Never had Reb Chaim Alter lived through such a year of mingled happiness and wretchedness.

The year began happily. His only daughter Dinah, after an easy confinement, presented him with his first grandchild —and a boy at that. Reb Chaim considered the occasion only less inferior in importance to the wedding and celebrated the circumcision in grand and expensive style. If he had been less enthusiastic, his wife Priveh would have made up for it.

"Money, Chaim darling," she said to him, stretching out to him those soft fingers through which money ran so easily.

"Simcha Meyer, my son, money," said Reb Chaim to his son-in-law.

Simcha Meyer gave freely, made out notes, and presented them to his father-in-law to sign. Reb Chaim signed and took the money. The celebration drew a great throng of pious and important Jews; both groups of Chasidim came, those that followed Reb Chaim's Rabbi, and those that followed the Rabbi of Alexander, to whom the family of Simcha Meyer belonged. The attendance might have been smaller, in view of Simcha Meyer's gradual defection from the ways of the Law. But the fact that his first child was a boy made up for much.

"Just your luck, Simcha Meyer," the young Chasidim told him. "Your first child can be circumcised. If it couldn't have been, we wouldn't have come."

Even Reb Abraham Hirsh, who had not exchanged a word

[187]

with Simcha Meyer since he had slapped his face as if he had been a little boy, decided on a reconciliation and came in skull-cap and silken gaberdine to the ceremony. Nothing was missing from the celebration—not even the regulation squabble. For Reb Chaim wanted the boy named after his Rabbi, and Reb Abraham Hirsh after his.

"Reb Chaim," said Reb Abraham Hirsh sternly, "you contributed the mother, but I contributed the father. The girls belong to you, the boys belong to me."

Reb Chaim pleaded for a division: one name from his Rabbi, one name from Reb Abraham Hirsh's. Reb Abraham Hirsh was obstinate. One name only, he said, and that Isaac, in memory of the beloved Rabbi of Vorka. Reb Abraham himself performed the circumcision; after it he and his clique danced so boisterously that Priveh protested.

"Reb Chaim, you're taking the house to pieces! Reb Chaim, my daughter is still weak. She can't stand it!"

"Louder, Jews, faster!" shouted Reb Abraham Hirsh, in a ring with his Chasidim.

Dinah, lying in her room, wept over her baby and threw angry glances at the door, through which the noise of the celebration penetrated. "Murderers!" she cried. "My baby wants to sleep!"

"Hush!" said her mother-in-law severely. "When your husband was born they danced like this too, and it did him no harm."

The other women sniggered. "It certainly didn't. And, Dinah, darling, if your little Isaac is as good as your husband, you'll have lots of grandsons before long."

Reb Chaim was deeply hurt by his defeat in the matter of the name. Reb Abraham Hirsh and his clique had triumphed. But Reb Chaim consoled himself by the magnificence of the ceremony and swore loudly that his second grandson—who would certainly be born soon—would carry the name of his, Reb Chaim's, great Rabbi. "Watch me!" he shouted, drinking. "I'll give the Alexander Rabbi the fight of his life."

Reb Chaim had scarcely digested the happy experience of the celebration when the first blow fell. Hadassah, the maid who had served the family for many years, observed that the young servant who had been taken into the house when Dinah became pregnant was behaving in a suspicious manner. She had developed a habit of wearing her stays tight and parallel with that a habit of stealing little delicacies, and dipping her spoon into tasty dishes. Likewise she had spells of faintness, and brought up. Hadassah took the girl into a room and began to question her closely. The girl tried to escape, whereupon Hadassah seized her and with skilful hands felt her body.

"Tfui!" she spat out. "So that's what it is, eh? And you thought you'd fool me, a mother of nine children, five of them dead, may their light be bright in paradise! You unclean little goat! Who gave you this?"

"Reb Chaim's sons," the girl wept. "They wouldn't leave me alone. They kept on talking and talking and talking—"

Reb Chaim's sons, the clumsy louts with the pimply faces, denied everything, but Reb Chaim, no less than Priveh, knew that the maid was telling the truth. However, they decided that it would be stupid to pretend to believe her.

"A whore's word," shouted Reb Chaim at the girl, "is taken only by a fool. Don't you dare to drag my sons into this."

"You will leave this house at once!" said Priveh. "Filth and impudence."

But they were afraid that the girl would make a public scandal. They therefore gave her a hundred roubles and sent her back, in the company of Samuel Leibish, to her father, a village innkeeper. Shortly thereafter Reb Chaim spoke with Samuel Zanvil, the marriage-broker, for his two sons.

"Get me wives for them, Reb Samuel," he said. "I want to have the boys off my hands. The sooner the better, and the two of them at once."

"Trust me, Chaim," said Reb Samuel. "You're satisfied with Simcha Meyer, aren't you? I'll do just as well by your sons."

And Reb Samuel Zanvil worked fast. Within a few weeks both boys were betrothed; within a few months both were married off. Again there was a mighty celebration. Again

[189]

Priveh stretched out her hand, crying: "Money, Chaim darling." Again Reb Chaim stretched out his hand to his son-in-law. "Money, Simcha Meyer." Simcha Meyer gave, wrote down everything, took notes, put them away. It had the regularity of a ritual.

The joy of the double wedding almost wiped out in Reb Chaim's mind the bitter incident of the servant girl, but with the coming of the winter new vexations descended upon him. Nor were they easier to bear because they were shared by thousands of others.

In Lodz, as in every other city and village in Poland, Jewish fathers and mothers went about with heavy hearts, their faces clouded with care. This was the time of the year when recruits were called up into the army, and every man of twenty-one—with certain closely guarded exceptions—was liable to service. The prospect of five years' duty in some remote Russian province, among soldiers and officers who made the Jews the butt of every brutality they could devise, appalled everyone. Many of the prospective soldiers were already married. They, like others, looked forward with horror to the ordeal. They did their best to break down their health before the examination. They went in for long fasts; they drank salt water and ate herring, in order to lose weight, hoping to be rejected. Sons of rich parents bought their way out, bribing either the official who checked up on their names or, failing that, the examining doctor. Healthy young Jews of the villages, knowing there was no escape for them, prepared regulation wooden boxes for their kit. In the city young apprentices, knowing that they, too, could not buy their way out, resorted to prayer. At least, they pretended to do that. They gave up work weeks before the time for the examinations and, encouraged by their parents, sat day and night in the synagogues. Actually, they knew if they hadn't the money to buy their way out, they had little to expect from above. They therefore gathered round the synagogue stove, roasted potatoes, and played cards. Occasionally they got drunk, marched round the synagogue with sticks at their shoulders, and fought with each other.

A spirit of despair, of mingled indifference and self-contempt, descended on them. They paraded in groups through the streets, in the dead of night, banged at doors, woke up householders, and sang Yiddish songs which mocked the service of the Tsar.

> Better be born without legs, my son,
> Than wear brass buttons and carry a gun.
> Or better never be born at all
> Than into the hands of the army fall.

Reb Chaim's sons were not in danger, for the children of the rich never served. But there was worry enough. The boys were well grown and so obviously healthy that it would need a fat sum to enable a doctor to find that they suffered from tuberculosis or diabetes or some other disqualifying sickness. The parents of the young men's wives refused to contribute anything. It was Reb Chaim's business, they said. He was rich—witness the magnificent celebrations which took place so frequently in his house. Besides, he had promised faithfully that he would look after this matter of the army. Reb Chaim raised the money—from Simcha Meyer, as usual. He was frightened by the amount he took, but as soon as the boys were released, he was so overjoyed that he forgot his fright and asked for more money with which to celebrate the escape. He did not give a second thought to the wretched young workers who, physically unfit, would be dragged into the army to make up the local quota.

These last, driven to desperation, complained to the authorities and gave the names of rich young men whom they accused of buying their way out of the service. Lippe Chalfan was the man who wrote out the official complaints on the one hand and then helped the guilty to bribe their way through on the other. The tactics of the workers did not succeed; they had only kopecks where the others had hundreds of roubles. The largest number of complaints was made against Simcha Meyer, whom the workers hated, and in his case something like a concerted effort was made to compel him into the service. Three separate examinations, each more expensive than the last, were the result. Simcha Meyer was not afraid, but it was a wrench to part with so much money. He made his father-in-law contribute some of it; not in cash, but in the form of the notes which were accumulating in the safe.

At the end of the year Reb Chaim experienced one great joy before the final disaster. Within one month his daughters-in-law presented him with two grandchildren, and both of them sons. Reb Chaim felt that God was good to him. He would have names enough and to spare; a name for his Rabbi, and another even for his own grandfather of blessed memory. He forgot the tribulations of the year; he decided that things had taken a decisive turn for the good. And he celebrated once more, with money which he obtained from Simcha Meyer.

And now the time had come, Simcha Meyer felt, to show his hand. The Sabbath after the last circumcision ceremony had drawn to a close. Reb Chaim was in an exalted mood, and he had ushered out the day of rest with joyous songs of praise and gratitude, when Simcha Meyer presented a long slip of paper on which was written an appalling number of figures.

"Father-in-law," said Simcha Meyer dryly, "I've got to ask you to meet these notes. I can't wait any longer."

Reb Chaim did not quite understand. "Notes?" he asked blankly. "What notes?"

Simcha Meyer went to the safe and came back with a large envelope out of which he took several account-books and slips of paper.

"On the 10th of the first," he said, "you took. . . . On the 18th of the second. . . . On the 7th of the third . . ."

Reb Chaim listened impatiently. He did not want these details. He hated figures.

"All right, all right," he said, "don't bother me with those details. What's the total?"

"Wait a moment," said Simcha Meyer calmly. He went on calling off dates and figures, checking and adding. "Let me see. That makes three thousand, seven thousand, eleven thousand . . ."

Reb Chaim listened and his breath came short.

"What the devil are you babbling about?" he asked. "You

[192]

mean to tell me I took all that money? It's ridiculous."

"Father-in-law," answered Simcha Meyer, "I've got your name on every one of these notes."

"Let me see them," said Reb Chaim brusquely, and stretched out his hand. He had barely touched them when Simcha Meyer, seeing the intention in his father-in-law's mind, snatched the package back.

"They're all signed," he said calmly. "That is, unless you want to deny your own signature."

Reb Chaim turned pale. There was something in Simcha Meyer's voice and manner, a coldness, a viciousness, which sent chills down his spine. This was no longer the young man who had advanced those sums in such friendly fashion; this was a stranger.

"You've trapped me, eh?" he asked in a cracked voice.

"I lent Father-in-law money. I want it back," said Simcha Meyer coolly.

"And suppose I won't pay," asked the other. "Eh? Suppose I won't pay. What will you do about it?"

"Father-in-law knows what one does with promissory notes."

"What do you want to do? Ruin me? You know I can't meet those notes. Do you want to kill your own father-in-law?"

"Business is one thing," answered Simcha Meyer, "family another."

Reb Chaim found his voice again. "Robber!" he shouted. "Murderer!"

Priveh came running into the room, and after her Dinah. Even Hadassah was so frightened by Reb Chaim's yells that she burst in to see what was happening.

"Kill me!" howled Reb Chaim, tearing open his silk gaberdine and presenting his throat to Simcha Meyer. "Stick a knife into me! Don't stand there looking at me! Give him a knife, somebody!"

Pale and bewildered, Priveh and Dinah led Reb Chaim to a chair and made him sit down. "For God's sake," cried Priveh, "what are you doing to him?"

Reb Chaim only continued to shout. Simcha Meyer rose from the table, put the envelope under his arm, and left the

[193]

room. He did not go to the factory, where he would easily be found, but to the little synagogue of his father's Chasidic clique, where he had not been seen for many months, and he did not return to the house till late in the night.

The next day there began between Simcha Meyer and his father-in-law a long-drawn-out legal battle. Reb Chaim ran from Rabbi to Rabbi, from court to court, seeking redress against the son-in-law whom he had purchased for seven thousand roubles. He even went to Reb Abraham Hirsh, the father of his son-in-law, though he knew in his heart that no help would be coming from that quarter.

Reb Abraham suspended his study of the Talmud and asked in a singsong voice: "Who asked you to take my son into partnership? You knew, didn't you, that I wanted my son to go on with his studies for another five years? You got yourself into this mess. Get yourself out of it. I have nothing to say to my son."

Reb Chaim banged on the table, screamed, pleaded; Reb Abraham Hirsh took the red handkerchief off the Talmud and went on with his studies. He did not hear Reb Chaim.

Reb Chaim tried the Chasidic clique, the followers of the Rabbi of Alexander, to which Reb Abraham Hirsh and his son belonged. But no one would interfere. Reb Chaim went out of town to the Rabbi himself. The Rabbi replied that he was not the kind to interfere in money quarrels. He advised Reb Chaim to call together a special court of rabbis.

Reb Chaim obeyed and, in the prescribed fashion, sent a messenger to his son-in-law to appear against him before a Rabbinical court. Simcha Meyer accepted the call. He was not afraid of Rabbinical courts. He knew the Talmud, he was more adept in it than most rabbis; and he knew what kind of rabbis he had to deal with in Lodz. He held his own in the court. He proved that he had lent the money honestly, his own money. He proved that Reb Chaim had known, or should have known, what he was doing. His position was unassailable. He demanded his rights.

Months of private quarrelling and public litigation followed. The upshot of it was that Reb Chaim saw himself stripped of the factory, his last asset being the wooden looms, which were of little value. There was nothing left for him but to accept whatever terms Simcha Meyer chose to dictate. He did not yield easily. He shouted, swore, brought down curses on Simcha Meyer's head, and called him by every ugly name he could think of. Simcha Meyer took it calmly. He remained calm even when his mother-in-law, forgetting that she was a great lady, threw a cup of hot tea into her son-in-law's face. Simcha Meyer took out a handkerchief and wiped his face and his streaming gaberdine. Childish things these were. Curses and insults are uttered and are forgotten, he thought. Even a father's slap in the face is forgotten. Money stays.

He had only one vulnerable spot, and that was Dinah. He knew that Dinah needed no prompting from her parents to think the worst of him, and he could easily imagine what they said about him to her. He waited for a word from her. If she had only been willing to interfere, if she herself had come to him with a request to soften his demands, or if she had given a sign of interest in his plans and hopes. . . . No. She turned on him the same cold, silent looks. If she suspected that she had the power to wring some concession from him, she gave no sign of it.

The house became hateful to Simcha Meyer. He felt all round him, even in the manner in which Hadassah served him his meals, only contempt. He would have been glad to move out, though according to the marriage contract he was still entitled to three years' free board. But that very contract would have prevented him from taking his Dinah with him, and he knew she would not go of her own free will.

He both feared and desired to have Dinah use her power over him; feared it because he himself did not know how much she could have wrung out of him, desired it because her hatred of him only increased his hunger for her. Often on an obviously silly pretext he would come into her room; he wanted to see the child; he wanted a handkerchief; he had forgotten to ask her something. She did not look up at him. She was busy with the baby or she was reading; and Simcha Meyer blundered about the room, biting his lips, knowing he was making a fool of himself, and not having the self-control to go out, banging the door behind him, as his self-respect bade him do.

It began to dawn on him that he had never understood how deep was her aversion toward him. Her parents were entirely in his power; he could, if he liked, throw Reb Chaim out of the factory and even sue him for unpaid debts. He could, on the other hand, leave Reb Chaim in as a minor partner. And Dinah would not put in a single word for them. Then it occurred to Simcha Meyer that if he took the first step, if he showed himself unexpectedly generous, that would make it easier for her. She would perceive that her husband was not merely a money-making machine. She would soften toward him; she would perhaps reproach herself for her harshness in the past; and the mere thought that Dinah would perhaps come to him, her arms open, to give herself to him as she had not done once in their married life, sent a wave of weakness through Simcha Meyer and made his flesh hot and cold by turns.

But still he waited, in the hope that she would take the first step.

Priveh, too, was unable to understand her daughter. She herself had been accustomed, during all her married life, to trading on the weakness of her husband. She had learned early—if such a lesson was necessary—that a smile, a caress, an unexpected tenderness, could get anything out of a doting husband; and that Simcha Meyer, for all his meanness, doted on Dinah was clear to the mother.

"You're as foolish as a little girl," she told her daughter. "You forget that you're a mother now. You're supposed to manage for yourself. Go and talk to your husband, for your parents' sake. We've done enough for you."

"Mamma, don't torment me," Dinah wept. "I can't go. I hate him."

Her father interfered. "All right," he said, heavily. "Suppose your mother and I had fallen into the hands of a bandit and you had to go and beg for our lives. Wouldn't you do it?"

"I won't go," cried Dinah, desperate. "Take everything I've got, my jewels, my silk dresses, but don't ask me to go to him."

[196]

Then, when her parents pleaded that it was for her sake, and in order to get her a brilliant husband, that they had ruined themselves, Dinah became hysterical and screamed that it was all a lie.

"It wasn't for my sake," she screamed. "You weren't thinking of me. You were thinking of yourselves and your pride. You wanted a prodigy to show off with. . . . I didn't want him. . . . You forced me . . . I always hated him. . . . You did it. . . ."

She recovered and, still sobbing, threw her arms round her mother. "I'll do anything, Mamma, but I won't lower myself before him. I can't do it."

"Let it go, then," her father said gloomily. "We won't force you."

Their daughter's fierce pride gave the parents back some of their self-respect, but it did nothing to improve their position.

Simcha Meyer waited, thinking with beating heart of the moment when Dinah would come to him, her eyes lowered, her posture one of humility, to beg mercy for her parents. But she did not come. It was as though she were blind and deaf to all that was happening in the house. Quietly she served him his meals, gave him his fresh laundry on Fridays, and did all her housewifely duties.

In this one instance, it was Simcha Meyer who yielded. The waiting became intolerable, and the fear that he would wait too long and lose even the opportunity of making the first concession broke down his resistance. One day, finding her alone in her room, he shut the door and told her, with a slight breathlessness in his speech, that he wanted to make peace with her father. She wasn't to think that he, Simcha Meyer, was quite heartless. He was going to—and just when he was about to say that he would return the promissory notes to her father, he saw the look which she deigned to throw at him from her book. It was a look so contemptuous, so full of revulsion, that he stopped short. "Fool!" he thought to himself, "I nearly gave away the work of years. Life and death in the power of a word, and I almost uttered the word which would have undone me."

"I see you're not interested," he said sharply, and left the room.

Outside he breathed as if he had escaped from some dreadful danger, as if he had almost committed a ghastly folly, from which his guardian angel had saved him at the last moment. "I must be mad," he thought. One word more and he would have given up his possession of the Alter factory, and for the sake of what? A childish weakness for a woman. He spat out in disgust with himself. He would be done with all that.

And what if Dinah despised him? What if his father-in-law and mother-in-law and all his own and Dinah's relatives called him foul names behind his back? The noisy insults of the weak, meaningless to the man of power! Let them talk! Let all Lodz talk! Let them say, in the restaurants, in homes, in the synagogues: "But you can't do that sort of thing! You can't throw your own father-in-law out of his business!" Simcha Meyer would show them that it could be done. And he would do it so skilfully that even the envious would come to his defence, out of sheer admiration. For though there were some to condemn (oh, out of spite, he was certain, for they were no better themselves), there were already others to justify him. "Idiots!" they answered. "Business is business. You can throw anybody out of anything if you're strong enough."

"And I'm strong enough," said Simcha Meyer to himself.

The palace which Heinz Huntze had built himself hard by his factory, the palace which was the talk of Lodz, with its huge iron palings dividing it off from surrounding houses, and its massive watch-dogs at the gate, was anything but a palace of peace. Day and night its rooms were filled with the noise of squabbles between the older and the younger generation, between the multimillionaire factory-owner on the one side and his sons and daughters on the other.

Well on in the seventies, old Heinz Huntze was still vigorous and active. He was perhaps more active than in the past, as though in frightened anticipation of the time, not far off now, when he would have to stretch himself out in the darkness and give up all work. He went to the factory as early as the first worker and left it after the last worker was gone. He kept in his own hands the threads of all the departments and was as interested in trifling details involving two or three roubles as in a transaction involving hundreds of thousands. No new machines were bought or installed unless the engineers had consulted with him first; no new designs introduced into a fabric unless he had approved them; no new accounts opened without his advice. He was everywhere, in the machine-rooms, the stockrooms, the offices, asking, checking, countermanding the orders of others, making himself felt by everyone.

The one sign of old age which he did show was an increasing deafness, which only served to make him more alert and suspicious. He resented, naturally, being shouted out. When Albrecht, his chief assistant, the general director of the factory, brought his mouth close to his ear and in a loud voice repeated what the old man had not heard before, Heinz Huntze would start back with a snarl: "Don't yell at me, you damned beer-barrel. I hear you perfectly." And the huge director, his face streaming perspiration, would get back into the chair, which almost broke under his weight, and hitch it a few inches nearer to his employer.

Heinz Huntze had a deep-rooted aversion for all persons in authority, especially if they had any education. It pleased him to speak to them familiarly and brutally, calling them by their first names, smoking his big porcelain pipe into their faces, and spitting near their feet when he spoke to them. It was not enough that the workers should tremble in his presence; he wanted no man to feel so important as to approach him without trepidation. Seated upright in his chair, his short snow-white hair bristling on the top of his head, he looked sternly and yet cunningly at everyone who approached him, sniffing for any sign of independence or rebellion.

He was compensating himself in the factory for the lack of authority which he felt in his home. There he was not master; or, if master in the technical sense, he knew he did not inspire the fear and respect which filled every one of his employees from Albrecht, the chief, down to the most timid young apprentice. Quite openly his sons and daughters expressed their disapproval of his manners and behaviour. They did not like, first, his ridiculous absorption in his work, so unbecoming to the leading industrialist of Lodz. They liked still less his vulgar bearing, his perpetual pipe with its cheap, rank tobacco, his spitting, his gross Saxon accent, his clothes, his noisy way of eating—in fact, there was nothing about him that they could say they liked, unless it was the millions which he had accumulated for them. And even these were embittered for them. Some day Heinz Huntze would leave them all that he possessed, and that, unfortunately, included his own heritage of a plebeian name and some of the characteristics of the peasant-weaver stock from which he had sprung.

[200]

His daughters were painfully if obscurely aware of these natural handicaps. Tall, blonde, with straw-coloured hair, watery eyes, and vulgar, turn-up noses, they looked not a whit more distinguished than the common factory girls who worked for their father. The stigmata which they had not taken over from their father they had from their mother, who had come from the same lowly stock as their father. As if this natural curse were not enough, they had to listen to their parents still speaking the ugly dialect of their childhood years; and looking on their mother, with her wrinkled face, her potato-shaped nose, her high cheek-bones, and the big, protrusive teeth, they felt that the same undistinguished old age lay in store for them if they did not change themselves betimes. Not that they had thought this out; there was only an angry impulse to get away as far as possible from the family records and family manners; and the first step was a change of the family name through the purchase of a patent of nobility.

In the city of Lodz the name Huntze meant much, and the addition of a title would have done nothing to improve it, while a complete change would have been a dead loss. But outside of Lodz the name Huntze did not, except to some merchants and manufacturers, suggest power and millions; it suggested precisely nothing. It was the name of any Tom, Dick, or Harry, any Heinz or Wilhelm, peasant boy or factory worker. Old Huntze was never out of Lodz and did not care. His sons and daughters were abroad a great deal, and their family name was loathsome to them.

When they were told that in Lodz the name Huntze was synonymous with the title of emperor, they asked who, in the civilized world, cared about Lodz, with its dirt and filth and commerce. And who wanted to live in Lodz, where hundreds of old folk still remembered Heinz Huntze as he had arrived with his creaky cart carrying his two hand-looms? Over there, in Germany, with its aristocratic estates and clubs, its magnificent hotels and homes, it was impossible to make decent headway with a name like Huntze—not even a *von* in front of it. Over there a mere nobody was at least a baron.

Old Heinz's ambition had been to marry his daughters to

the sons of Lodz industrialists; theirs was to get out of Lodz for good as soon as possible. He dreamed of a powerful industrial dynasty perpetuating his name; they dreamed of a world of counts and princes where industry was never mentioned and the name Huntze would never be heard. For the sake of his dream old Heinz was prepared to give away most of what he had accumulated with his own two hands in a long, turbulent life of labour; for the sake of theirs his daughters were ready to give away everything.

But on the able young men whom he invited into the house, hoping to make a match for his daughters, the latter did not even cast a glance. They praised God daily for the fact that, if it came to the worst and they could not persuade their father to buy himself a title, they could at least get rid of the name by marriage. And to exchange Huntze for some equally plebeian Lodz name was not their intention. They would rather not marry at all; they would rather remain old maids. This was what they shouted at their father whenever he asked them, in his blunt, hateful Saxon German, why they couldn't show a little more friendliness to the scions of industrial families whom he brought to the house. During such quarrels the girls threatened hysterically to run away with the first gypsy or actor they met rather than let themselves be fastened for ever into the life of the hated city. They would choose their own husbands or else disgrace the family.

For years the struggle had gone on. The old woman, worn out with the perpetual bickering, and feeling that her daughters meant every word they said, begged Heinz on her knees to give way, lest he bring shame on her and on himself. In the end he gave way, and the two girls brought back with them from one of their periodic visits to Germany the husbands of their choice. One was an elderly aristocrat with a long name and a longer string of debts: Baron Conrad Wolfgang von Heidel-Heidellau. He had—or had had—estates in Prussia, near the Russian frontier. They were heavily mortgaged, and Count Conrad saw his only hope in a rich marriage. He arrived one day with a manservant, several hunting dogs, and a case of guns, and at the table of the Huntzes he turned up his long, lean nose and asked how the devil one could live in "this filthy Polish-Jewish pigsty." Later he told his bride that the sooner they got out of the stinking city, the better; he could not stand factories; he could not stand smoke; and above all, he added significantly, he could not stand people who spoke like vulgar peasants.

He stayed long enough to collect every kopeck of his dowry, then left, with his manservant, his hunting dogs, his guns, and his wife, for his Prussian estates. Parting with them, he was kind enough to shake old Heinz by the hand and even to touch with his lips the gnarled old hand of his mother-in-law. He was through with them. He never wrote to them, never even added a postscript to one of his wife's letters to them. He did have one-sided transactions with them, but these he conducted through his wife. When new debts accumulated he told her to write to her father for money. When the money did not come he made life so miserable for his wife that she was compelled to return to Lodz and to stay there until she had wrung the needed sum out of her father.

The second daughter, Gertrude, had better luck with her husband—that is, to the extent that he was young and handsome. His name was Baron Otto von Taube; he belonged to the Baltic aristocracy, was an officer of the Imperial Guard in St. Petersburg, and sported the magnificent mustachios of a hussar. He, too, received a handsome dowry, and if he had not the debts of Baron Conrad Wolfgang von Heidel-Heidellau, he was a better spender. After a brief honeymoon he returned to his old life, gathered around him his boon companions, and ran through the money rapidly at cards and wine. He ran so fast, however, that when there was no more money, he could not stop, and before long he told his wife that unless he could pay his debts of honour he would be thrown out of the regiment, and then nothing would remain for him, as an aristocrat, an officer, and a gentleman, but to put a bullet through his head.

Thus it came about that the girls, after their marriage, were with their parents as frequently as before. Old Heinz did not part with money easily, and it needed a siege of weeks and sometimes of months to get the required sums out of him. But his daughters had the satisfaction of their aristocratic titles, and they were able to snub their old friends or to make them envious with tales of high life in the European capitals.

This was not the end of Heinz Huntze's troubles. His three sons, Wilhelm, Friedrich, and Johann, sickened by the snobbery of their sisters, demanded justice: the girls had titles by marriage, they wanted a title by purchase. They pointed out that it was ridiculous for them to be the brothers of titled ladies and have to present themselves by the unadorned name of Huntze. Had the girls married commoners, it might have been tolerable; the present situation was not.

Many governors had come and gone at Piotrkov since the far-off days when Heinz Huntze had purchased his Cross of St. Anna, and all of them had been anxious to serve him further by obtaining for him a patent of nobility. The title of baron, they all told him, was the lowest he could aspire to in view of his services to the industrial development of the country. Not that he didn't merit a much more distinguished reward. It was only a question of presenting his case properly at court. They were eager to do that for him. Of course there were certain expenses connected with that: visits to the capital, little presents to a few officials, reminders. They themselves, these governors, wanted nothing. All the expenses would be lost at the other end.

The three sons of Huntze had been intended by their father for business and industrial careers. He had sent them to German academies to study engineering, chemistry, and administration; but they had spent their time making aristocratic connections and picking up aristocratic vices. They returned to Lodz determined to do anything rather than give up their lives to the stupid ambitions of their father. They were good drinkers, eager hunters, feverish card-players; they kept stables of their own and—what they considered much in the same light—mistresses. They were for ever in debt and, like their sisters, for ever pumping their father for money. They waited with ill-concealed impatience for their father's death and among themselves cursed openly his extraordinary vigour and his apparent intention of living till the age of a hundred.

[204]

"Nothing seems to get the old fool," they said. "He's made of cast iron."

On the other hand, they did want their father to live long enough to get a title. That was almost as important to them now as his money. They were three and he was one; it would cost them three times as much, then, to get separate titles—if they could get them at all. Long before their father had agreed to it, the three sons had already come to terms with the Governor at Piotrkov, and after the marriage of the second daughter they made a determined assault on their father.

"I don't want it," old Huntze shouted, *"Ich pfeife darauf.* My name is Huntze; I'm sticking to it; and I won't give a rusty pfennig for the highest title in the land."

He raged not only at the prospective expense, but at the contempt which his children showed for a name which he had covered with glory. He felt, too, how all that he loved and stood for was, to his sons and daughters, as well as to his sons-in-law, matter for mockery. He disliked the upper classes, he despised education, he had no use for aristocrats. More than one impoverished Polish nobleman had come to him for help, and it was always his delight to speak to such persons not in Polish or in Russian, but in good, homely Saxon German. And he asked himself what sort of honour it would be for him, Heinz Huntze, the master of men, to have the same title as these cringing and refined paupers.

But his sons gave him no rest.

"When I'm dead," he roared, "you can change the name if it isn't good enough for you. But as long as I live you're Huntzes, like me, whether you like it or not."

In his rage he exaggerated his plebeian manners. He came to table, when his sons and daughters were seated there with friends, in shirt-sleeves. He picked up pieces of meat in his gnarled hands, gnawing noisily and smacking his lips with pleasure. He spat on the carpets. And a few times, in an ecstasy of rebellion, he actually went into low-down beer-saloons and sat down with common weavers, to drink beer with them as he had done fifty years before. The weavers were astonished and terrified; they could not reply to his *prosit,* but from sheer fright sat there staring at him, their old toothless mouths agape. Huntze had no pleasure in their company. He rose, leaving his drink unfinished, and returned to the place of his torment—his home.

Old Frau Huntze, bewildered by the perpetual quarrelling, lost among the heavy carpets, the massive furniture, the hunting trophies, was essentially as simple as her husband. But she suffered more, for the brutal things which her sons and daughters dared not say to their father they flung at her. They mocked her clumsiness; they sneered at her timidity in the presence of strangers; they even told her that she had not the manners of her lackeys, who were ten times more distinguished in their behaviour. She had never wanted to live in this enormous palace. She remembered as the happiest time in her life the days when she had cooked huge pots of food for her husband and his workers and had felt herself part of his life. In those days she had had friends, too, the wives of other master weavers, who understood her language and had worries like her own. Now she had no one to exchange a friendly word with. There were only haughty guests, and servants who stood in awe of her, as she stood in awe of them. Whenever a gentleman kissed her hand, she was covered with confusion, and she recalled the time when she, a simple peasant girl, had used to kiss the doctor's hand.

She was at peace only when the children were gone and she was left alone with her old Heinz. She loved then to have him stuff his pipe to the brim, throw off his coat, lie down on the sofa—boots and all—and talk to her in his Saxon German, while she darned a stocking. But these were rare occasions. Much more frequently she sat cowering in her chair, listening to the gross insults which her sons and daughters levelled at her and her husband.

For herself she did not care. She felt that she did not fit into this magnificent world to which her children belonged. But it wounded her to hear her husband spoken of contemptuously, and she would wring her hands and implore her children to stop. "Ah, God, ah, dear Jesus, children, don't speak like that about your father. Only stop, and I'll do whatever I can to persuade him to buy the title."

[206]

She did not quite know what this "title" meant. She did not understand how they would cease to be Huntzes, the children of their father, if someone in St. Petersburg sent them a certain document. What bewildered her most was the fact that somehow, in the process, she would have to become a baroness. It was fantastic. They might as well have told her that she would have to become the Holy Virgin. But for the sake of peace she yielded to her sons, and when she was alone with old Huntze, implored him to give way.

"Do it, Heinzel," she begged, "do it for your old wife's sake."

"They want everything," the old man growled, "everything. Why can't they do one thing for themselves, instead of having it all thrown ready-made into their laps?"

Feeling that his resistance was breaking down, old Heinz consulted his principal agent, Reb Abraham Hirsh. He had, as a matter of fact, no one else he could go to; for he had no friends, and his employees only took orders, replying with a military *"Ja wohl."* At best they tried to guess what the old man wanted and to anticipate his wishes.

"How much is it going to cost you, Herr Heinz?" was the first question Reb Abraham Hirsh replied with.

"Plenty," answered Huntze. "Tens of thousands of roubles."

"And what is it worth to you?"

"Nix. Nothing."

"Then what's the sense of it?" asked Reb Abraham Hirsh in a singsong voice.

"There isn't any sense in it," roared Huntze, and he left Reb Abraham Hirsh's office determined, once for all, to have nothing to do with titles. And when he came home, he banged the table and shouted: *"Kein Wort darüber.* I won't hear another word."

Very different from his father's was Simcha Meyer's feeling with regard to the baronetcy which the sons of Heinz Huntze were panting for.

He was not a frequent visitor in his father's house; indeed, one interval had elapsed, between the evening when his father had slapped his face and the night of the circumcision of his son, during which they had not spoken a word to each other. Even after the so-called reconciliation Simcha Meyer's visits were few and short. But he knew everything that went on in Reb Abraham Hirsh's home and office. He got his information from his father's employees, from the servants, from Goldlust, and from his own sisters, whom he invited to the house for the purpose of pumping them. But for this need for information he might never have maintained the contact with them, for he had nothing in common with them. From words which their father let fall, however, from conversations overheard between their father and his business acquaintances, they were often able to make up a picture of general conditions. Between the fragments they brought him and those he picked up as it were casually from the others, Simcha Meyer reconstructed in fairly accurate detail the state of his father's business. He knew when there had been a good season and when a bad one. He knew when there had been bankruptcies and when there had been more orders than could be filled. His interest in the Huntze business was almost sentimental. In childhood days he had loved to play in the stockrooms and offices of the agency on Piotrkov Street, and even now he had the obscure feeling that somehow the agency belonged to him, too, and that what happened there was his business.

He had prospered greatly—always within the limits of the second rank—since he had become sole owner of the factory. He had never had a slack season, and he had kept all his looms going at full speed. But he had made more out of side lines than out of his own factory. He had an instinct for buying and selling as well as for production-organization. He was generally able to guess what fabrics would be in demand, though, with all his luck, he was always careful to leave himself a loop-hole of escape, never committing himself to a purchase until he was practically certain that he had found a buyer. The ten thousand roubles with which he had started business had grown to more than ten times the original amount, and another than Simcha Meyer might have been content with his progress. But content was something which he had never known and never would know.

Years had passed since he had made up his mind that he would not remain among the hand-loom owners, and by this time he had capital and standing enough to erect a small steam factory; but the obviously possible was not his line. Yes, he could, in a quiet, respectable, humdrum way, open a small steam factory, compete with the big factories, grow moderately from year to year, and find himself, when he was approaching old age, a fairly wealthy man. The prospect repelled him. He would be first or nothing, and to be first he had to find short cuts, for the distance between him and the top was, in spite of his comparative success, enormous. The direct route, which lay across countless towering obstacles, was not for him. He would find the straight line—the one which led, like a tunnel, under the foundations of the lives of others.

Far off in the distance, towering above all the other fortresses which he would have to carry or undermine, was the factory of Heinz Huntze, for him the climax of his ambitions. Entry to it lay, in the first instance, through the chief agency, which Simcha Meyer's father controlled. The idea of displacing his father by demonstrating to old Huntze his own

[209]

superior ability occurred to Simcha Meyer and was dismissed at once. Reb Abraham Hirsh conducted affairs in a solid, reliable way which gibed well with old Huntze's conceptions of business. Huntze was thoroughly satisfied with his agent, and even if Simcha Meyer had been able to show him ways of making more money, he would have turned the offer down. As to asking his father for a share of the agency, that, too, was out of the question. His father disliked his methods and disliked him.

But with that combination of eagerness, impatience, and far-sightedness which was his peculiar gift, Simcha Meyer kept in touch as well as he could with the affairs of his father and the Heinz Huntze factory. He knew—as everyone else did —that in the Huntze family there was a bitter division on the question of the purchase of a title; but it was only when one of his sisters—who had overheard her father when he told a friend of the incident—recounted how old Huntze had come to seek her father's advice, and what her father had answered, that his great idea came to him.

Simcha Meyer saw everything from one point of view— that which meant the furthering of his ambitions—and in the present constellation of circumstances he suddenly perceived a glorious opportunity. Heinz Huntze was an old man. He was active and sturdy, to be sure, but with old people one never knew. They had a habit of collapsing suddenly, especially when, like old Huntze, they persistently overworked, refusing to acknowledge the fact that they no longer had the nervous and physical reserves of younger men. When old Heinz went he would leave behind him—whom? Wastrels, spoiled, foolish young men who had no intention of carrying on their father's work. The future of the factory lay, then, in their hands. It was stupid of his father not to understand that one always played to the future. But then, Abraham Hirsh himself was an elderly man and as obstinate and set as Huntze himself. He had no use for Huntze's sons and heirs; he made no effort to win them to him. Well, so much the worse for him, thought Simcha Meyer. What the father was too proud and obstinate to do, the son would do for him.

Besides, in a general way, Reb Abraham Hirsh did not fit

into the new Lodz, the Lodz of rapid combinations, hasty turnovers, and financial-commercial manipulation as opposed to workaday manufacturing. Simcha Meyer was dizzy when he thought of the marvellous things he could do with the control of a vast organization like Heinz Huntze's, things his father would not dream of and, if told about, would never agree with. But then, his father would not always be there. When Huntze died his heirs would most assuredly find a new general agent, more pliable to their wishes, more like themselves in outlook; and that day was not far off.

Simcha Meyer had, more than once, considered the question of establishing a connection with Heinz Huntze's sons, but they were not less remote from him than the control of the factory which they would, before the passing of many years, sell to the highest bidder. He had never met them. How should he? They were seldom at home. And even if they had lived always in Lodz, what had he, the funny little Chasidic Jew, to do with them? He never met them in the way of business; they had no interest in it. He did not speak their language. He came from another world, one which they despised. Also, if he had met them, he had nothing to propose. And it was not till he heard his sister recount how old Huntze had been driven by the importunity of his sons to seek Reb Abraham Hirsh's advice that he perceived a sudden pathway created for him.

For two or three days Simcha Meyer revolved the matter, at the same time preparing himself for an interview by looking up in a Polish-German dictionary the key words of the conversation which he anticipated. It was a tremendous gamble. He would have to risk, he foresaw, not only all his free capital, but a good deal more besides. He would have to borrow. If he lost, he would suffer a set-back which it would take him years to overcome. But if he won! If he won, if he tied the sons to him with manifold obligations, then he would achieve at a single leap what others had not achieved in a lifetime of effort.

The first step was to write to the Huntze sons. Simcha Meyer took out the old German ready letter-writer and combined sentence with sentence, inserting his own meaning. He

[211]

offered the young men money, on notes; as much as they wanted, for as long as they wanted. He offered them enough (this he did not mention in the letter) to buy the services of the Governor at Piotrkov and the title which their father would not pay for out of his own pocket. He wrote the letter over five or six times. He wanted to strike the right note between strength and humility. He wanted them to understand on the one hand that he had means, and on the other that he considered it a signal honour to be allowed to serve such distinguished clients. He wanted to inspire confidence in himself; he also wanted to make them feel that he was theirs to command. He could have found any number of correspondents who would have written a perfect German letter for him, but it was important for him that this business should remain a secret between him and the sons of Heinz Huntze. Business and cards, he said to himself, one held close to one's chest, so that no one could peep.

Twenty-four hours of feverish impatience elapsed between the dispatch of the letter by private messenger and the receipt of the reply. In the meantime Simcha Meyer had been calculating the extent of his resources—cash in hand, money he could release from transactions, money he could borrow. It represented a great deal more than he was actually worth, but his name was good. He was known, among the second-rank business-men of Lodz as a sharp, shrewd, brilliant manipulator, a man to be watched, but a man who could be relied on.

When the answer came, he snatched it from the lackey's hand and so far forgot himself as to give the carrier a rouble note before he knew whether the letter brought good or bad news. He retired to his room, and when he had glanced through the few lines scrawled on the expensive note-paper, he trembled with joy. The letter was short and discourteous. It began without a formal introduction. He was not addressed as *Herr* anybody. But it was to the point. He was invited to call on the brothers, at their home, the next day, at four o'clock in the afternoon.

For the first time in many years Simcha Meyer paid some attention to his appearance. He looked in the mirror and did not like the looks of his beard. He tried pressing it back against his collar, but it would not stay. He took scissors and cut away the lop-sided strands on one side, and when he had finished he discovered that now the other side was lop-sided by comparison. He tried to redress the balance and again went too far. By the time he had finished, his beard had shrunk to dimensions which in his father's circle were considered a disgrace to a pious Jewish face: it was the beard of a heathen or an apostate. But Simcha Meyer was too excited to care. He even cut off the greater part of his ear-locks, those signs and symbols of Jewish orthodox conformity, leaving just a bare reminder, a rudimentary wisp, which in the eyes of a pious Jew would have appeared worse than no ear-lock at all. He put on his best suit of clothes and stole out of the house. At a distance from his house he went into a haberdashery store and bought himself a stiff collar and a black tie and put them on. Then he looked at himself again. Not bad! It was almost a new Simcha Meyer. The short gaberdine—it was almost a regular coat—the tie, the polished shoes, the silver-tipped walking-stick, the tiny beard—this was no Chasidic Jew of Balut! It was a regular worldly man of affairs.

He went hastily out of the shop, waited until a closed droshky passed, leapt in, and asked to be driven to the Huntze palace.

The three Huntze brothers had only just got out of bed, after a night of wild roistering and a day of heavy, brutish sleep, when Simcha Meyer presented himself at the palace promptly at four o'clock.

"Wait," commanded rather than asked the lackey who admitted him, looking with not a little astonishment at this queer young Jew, and went back to report to his masters.

They were in evil humour, the Huntze brothers, all three of them. They had drunk heavily the night before, they had had a wild time at the Renaissance cabaret, they had played cards afterwards, and they had gone to bed after sunrise. Now their mouths were dry, they had heartburn, and there was not even the recollection of a joyous and pleasurable night to make it worth while.

In fact, it had been, from every point of view, a most disastrous night. There was, first, the astounding incident at the Renaissance.

For some weeks Lodz had been buzzing with the exciting news of the young Hungarian dancer at the Renaissance cabaret. Her like had not been seen in the city before. She was of the big world, who had blazed a career through the most famous places of entertainment in the great European capitals. Provincial cities had to content themselves with stars of the third and fourth magnitude, and only the enterprise of the owner of the Renaissance had been able to procure this dazzling entertainer for Lodz. Within two or three

[214]

nights of her first appearance she had the gilded youth of the city at her feet. Manufacturers, young aristocrats, sons of industrialists, army officers, came in droves, and a fantastic public competition began for her favour. Huge bouquets of flowers were presented to her at every performance or sent to her dressing-room, with little cards attached. The flowers were accepted, the cards were ignored. Guests ordered large quantities of champagne and invited her to drink with them. The champagne was delivered; the dancer did not come to help drink it. The door of her dressing-room was guarded by an elderly lady with flashing, penetrating eyes. To everyone who came knocking at it she said, in a mixture of Hungarian, French, German, and Russian, that they were not to disturb the artist.

"My daughter is tired. She has to rest between turns. Please leave her alone."

If the suitors became insistent, the elderly lady sent a waiter for a tall, dark, sickly-looking young man in evening dress. This mysterious person said, in a quiet, impressive voice: "Messieurs! Be kind enough to let my wife take her rest." The excited suitors retired for the moment, but the rebuff had only a temporary effect. They waited till the dancer appeared in the cabaret again, and renewed their attentions. They were uniformly unsuccessful.

Her inaccessibility no less than her beauty made the dancer the talk of Lodz. Heavy bribes slipped into the hand of the cabaret-owner did no good. He said sadly to his customers: "Gentlemen, I would do anything for you, but you see she doesn't stir without her mother and her husband." The manager of the hotel where the dancer lived returned a similar reply, and when offered a bribe to let visitors go up to her suite, said regretfully: "I'm sorry. I have strict instructions to admit no one. They receive no one."

There were all sorts of speculations as to the identity of this mysterious trio.

Romantic young Germans shook their heads and surmised that there was a fascinating history behind the dancer's chastity. "She's an escaped nun. The man is her brother, not her husband. She's really a saint."

"She's the daughter of a Rabbi," said the young Jews, half-seriously, half-ironically.

Others proclaimed for certain that she was a genuine Hungarian countess who had run away from her husband for the sake of the tall, thin young man. The elderly lady in black was the young man's mother. Others had it that she was the wife of a pious Jew of Galicia, married to a Rabbi against her will. She had run away with the dark young man, and he had made an artist of her. Still others laughed at all these stories and believed that the whole business was fake; they were just ordinary cabaret artists who were putting on an act to get the girl talked about and to mulct boobies. But if it was nothing more than an act, the three principals sustained it consistently. No one was able to boast that he had broken into the mysterious circle.

News of the fascinating and unobtainable dancer finally reached the Huntze boys, who as a rule had no interest in the entertainments of their home town. They considered the universal failure a personal challenge.

"*Quatsch!*" they said. "How do you expect a gang of peasants to make an impression on a big city artist? This is a job for us."

However, they did not intend to compete publicly with the yokels of the locality. They sent for the cabaret-owner and took over his establishment for one night. No one was to be admitted but themselves and a select group of aristocrats and Russian officers. The party was to be private; the young woman was to dance for them alone. Each one of the three brothers prepared a present for the dancer, and they set out for the cabaret convinced that at least one of themselves would carry off the prize.

Everything went swimmingly up to a certain point. The food and the wines were excellent, and the dancer was in fine form. For the first time she consented to sit down at the table of one of the guests, and by common consent that table belonged to the hosts of the evening, the three Huntze brothers.

This concession convinced them at once that the dancer had recognized at a glance the difference between the higher world which they represented and the middle-class rabble

[216]

which filled the cabaret on ordinary nights. They considered it quite unnecessary to advance by degrees. Besides, it was unbecoming to the Huntze brothers to beg for anything. It was theirs to command.

"Girlie," said one of them, "one hundred roubles for the first kiss."

"Two hundred," said his brother promptly.

"Three hundred!" shouted the third.

The dancer smiled and did not move. The dark young man who passed for her husband sat next to her, his face expressionless.

The indifference which the dancer showed to these large sums was both imposing and provocative.

"Listen, honey," said one of the brothers; "I've got a little present for you here. I'm not asking anything for it. I just want to put it round your neck." He did not wait for her permission; he did not wait for his brothers to produce their presents. He bent over and with clumsy, fumbling fingers tried to fasten a glittering necklace round the dancer's neck. His hot, reeking face was close to hers.

The dark young man rose, and snapped: "Monsieur, take your hands off my wife!"

"Don't be a fool," the young Huntze hiccuped. "I'll give her a hundred roubles on top of it. She's worth it, by God!"

The young man took a step forward. "Monsieur, apologize at once to my wife!"

The young German took his hands away, looked the other in the face, and said, drunkenly: "Well, two hundred more, if you think she's worth that much. You ought to know."

Here the young man leaned forward, lifted his hand, and smacked the other across the face.

There were several moments of dead silence. No one knew exactly what had happened, and when the Huntzes and their guests had come to, the dancer and her husband were no longer in the cabaret. Howling with rage, the young Huntze who had been slapped began to smash the furniture, and when the cabaret-owner tried to interfere, held him down on a table and poured a bottle of champagne over him. Finally, to show that he was a gentleman just the same, he drew out a handful of notes, flung them in the owner's face, and yelled: "Let's get out of this pigsty. It's no place for people like us."

To get the sour taste of this experience out of their mouths, the Huntzes went with their guests to the officers' quarters in the barracks at the other end of the town. There, until morning, they drank and played cards. They fared as badly at cards as they had fared in the cabaret. When they went home they had nothing in their pockets; or rather less than nothing, for they left behind them notes for considerable sums.

They were taken home, after sunrise, and they flung themselves down on couches and slept with their clothes on until the afternoon. When they awoke they got their wits together slowly, tried to remember their losses, and above all cursed the cabaret-owner and his dancing-girl. They knew that by this time the story of the failure and the slap was all over Lodz, and this burned more than the thousands they had lost at cards.

When one of the servants, breaking in on them, announced that the Jew was downstairs, waiting to speak to them, they looked at each other puzzled.

"We don't see Jews," said one of them. "Throw him out."

The servant happened to be the one who had carried the note to Simcha Meyer the day before. Timidly he reminded them that they had themselves asked the Jew to come at four o'clock. Then the Huntzes remembered; and remembering also that they had new debts to the extent of several thousand roubles, they told the servant to show the Jewish swine in.

Simcha Meyer advanced uneasily across the heavy rugs and carpets, looking with frightened eyes at the magnificent furniture and squirming away from the enormous dog which followed him silently, sniffing at his Jewish gaberdine as though it was still not short enough. To his horror and astonishment he was ushered into a vast bathroom, where the three Huntzes, still naked, were drying themselves. Simcha Meyer blushed violently and did not dare to look.

"You there," said one of the Huntzes, "are you the son of our father's general agent?"

"Yes, gentlemen, I am," answered Simcha Meyer, his heart beating fast.

[218]

"And you want to be our—what do you call it—our court Jew?"

"I'm willing to deposit my money with you gentlemen," said Simcha Meyer.

"Have you got a lot of it?" asked another of the brothers eagerly.

"As much as you gentlemen need," answered Simcha Meyer boldly.

"Oh!" came simultaneously from the three of them.

"But we don't know when we can pay you back."

"I can wait," said Simcha Meyer.

"Our father must know nothing about this."

"I can keep a secret."

"Understand one thing. We shan't be able to pay you a pfennig till the old man kicks off. And we don't know when that'll be."

"You'll find me patient," said Simcha Meyer.

"Well, we need a good lump sum right now—twenty thousand at least. We'll need more than that—but not for a few weeks."

"I'm completely at your service," answered Simcha Meyer promptly. "Will you gentlemen always be kind enough to give me a week's notice when you need money?"

"Yes, we can do that—but not this first time," answered the oldest brother, who, still naked, but now dry, was performing his gymnastics. "This first twenty thousand we've got to have at once. Tomorrow morning at the latest. Good-bye."

Simcha Meyer went out in a confused state of mind. The raw, brutal reception had frightened him, but the complete success of his manœuvre had produced a counter-effect. It had been amazingly easy! They, the Huntze brothers, the most snobbish and most insolent set in Lodz, had received him and had accepted his services. Well, what did it matter if they had, at the same time, practically spat on him? He had broken in! Or rather he had crawled in on all fours. It didn't matter how he had got in. He was on the inside! Gradually his elation grew, so that even the problem of raising the huge sums which he foresaw would be needed seemed to become trivial. He was too excited to take a droshky. He wanted to walk and to feel the power that streamed through his limbs. He strode along the railing of the palace and made his way to the Huntze factory. He felt drawn to it. He wanted to be near it, for he had taken his first step toward the conquest of it.

A group of workmen coming from the factory saw the excitable little Jew with the radiant face striding toward them and burst into loud laughter. "Hey, Ikey Mo, any old clo'?" they shouted as he passed. He did not hear them. His mind was in a whirl. Now that he had taken the plunge, he foresaw that his entire mode of work would have to change.

Before he reached his house he had taken his fateful decision. He would sell the factory! He was through with that. His game was too big. He would sell the factory, provide himself with cash, borrow, beg, and throw everything into the gamble. And sitting down in his room, he began to scribble names and amounts, the people he could turn to and talk into helping him through this period of investment.

He brought to this new enterprise all the energy and inventiveness that he had once brought to the exploitation of Reb Chaim Alter's factory. It was work of a different sort. It meant, not the driving of workers, but the persuading and winning over of people with money. Simcha Meyer suddenly developed many friendships. He became mightily interested in the future and welfare of his brothers-in-law, of his sisters' husbands, and of sundry other young people who, having married recently, had dowries salted away in the bank. He talked to them vaguely but persuasively of the big game he was after, of the foolishness of letting money rot in the bank at a ridiculously low rate of interest, of the returns which he, Simcha Meyer, could get for them. He awakened in them an appetite for big money, so that they itched with impatience to become his partners, though they had no idea of the nature of the enterprise.

He went further afield. He had to prepare large sources for later demands, for he knew that the Huntze sons, having once tasted easy money, would borrow to the limit. Having covered the ground in Lodz, he took the train for Warsaw and visited Jacob Bunim, who, like all the sons- and daughters-in-law of the great Reb Kalman Eisen, lived in the patriarchal family house.

It was quite a different Simcha Meyer now. He had set himself a definite task—to please, and to inspire confidence in his character and intentions—and he organized that, too, as if it were a factory job. To the older people he talked piety and scholarship; to the younger people business and world affairs; to the women, whenever he was in their company, family gossip. He took the Eisen family by storm.

"He's brilliant, brilliant," said the older men. "He's good at everything. Scholarship and business combined."

Even Reb Solomon, Jacob Bunim's father-in-law, was captivated. "I know I'm no good," he said, "and my opinion doesn't count, but I tell you I just love that Simcha Meyer."

Jacob Bunim himself, incapable of sustained enmities, was delighted with him and was proud to be singled out for special attention by the lion of the family. He was proud, too, to be taken into Simcha Meyer's business, and promised him every rouble he possessed or could lay hands on. Simcha Meyer returned to Lodz feeling that, unless the Huntze sons went completely out of their minds, he would be able to meet their requests.

He could, of course, have discounted the promissory notes of the young Huntzes. There were any number of merchants and loan-sharks in Lodz who would have been glad to get hold of the paper. But here, precisely, lay the point: no one had to know of the loans, and it was out of the question to put the signature of the young men in circulation in Lodz. Simcha Meyer's service was not just money; it was, equally, secrecy. Besides, once the notes left his possession, he might as well throw up the game.

He delivered the first twenty thousand roubles, which the Huntzes needed mostly to cover their debts of honour, on the very day after his visit.

"*Sehr nett!*" they exclaimed when he presented himself with the cash. "We like that kind of service!"

Within a few days they sent for him again, for it dawned upon them that now they could push forward with the purchase of the title for their father. It did not matter to them

whether their father spent the money direct or they anticipated their inheritance; it all came out of the same pocket.
Within a week after their first interview with Simcha Meyer
they had interviewed the Governor of Piotrkov, and shortly
thereafter the latter set out for St. Petersburg, his pocketbook
stuffed with persuasive arguments to present to the officials
at court.

When old Heinz received from the Governor official notification that His Imperial Majesty the Autocrat of the Russias and King of Poland had been pleased to bestow a baronetcy on him, Heinz Huntze of Lodz, in recognition of his services to the industrial development of the fatherland, he knew at once that his sons had somehow raised the money which he had refused them. How much it had cost and where the money had come from he did not know. But he did know that he was trapped. It was one thing to refuse to apply for a title; it was another to refuse a title that had been offered. In vain did he bang on the table and shout that he had not asked for a title and would not assume one. In vain did he yell that he would not trade his good old Saxon name for the most imposing patent of nobility in the keeping of the Tsar. The only concession he dared plead for was a partial retention of identity. Henceforth, then, Heinz Huntze was to be Baron Huntze-Schwarzwald of Schwarzwald, with the right to display a coat of arms showing a naked bear standing on his hind legs and resting his two front paws on a crooked cross.

If a simple acceptance had been all! Unskilled though he was in the ways of the aristocracy and the court, Heinz Huntze knew only too well that the sums expended by his sons in the procuring of the title represented the smallest part of the expense involved; for it was incumbent on him now to demonstrate his gratitude, loyalty, and patriotism by an appropriate reception of the title. The Governor himself had been delegated to make the presentation; the ceremony would have to take place in the Huntze palace; and for the kind of guests who would be present, the palace itself would have to be renovated from top to bottom. A niggardly reception would be interpreted in the highest circles as evidence of an indifference amounting to lèse-majesté.

An interval of several months was set between the announcement by the Governor and the date of the official presentation, and during this interval Huntze's sons and daughters took charge of the renovation of the palace. An architect was imported from Munich, but the structural changes were dictated by the young Huntzes, who had their own ideas as to what the residence of a baron should look like. The simple, massive home was, in their eyes, stupidly plebeian. They wanted turrets on the corners, crenellations on the roof, and lots of statues—all kinds of statues: Germanic and classic, ancient heroes and mediæval warriors, saints and nymphs, cupids and harp-players, eagles, serpents, Bacchuses and bacchantes, lions and goat-footed satyrs. Whatever they had seen anywhere in the homes of friends in Germany, whatever they had envied, they wanted reproduced in the walls and niches and gardens of their baronial residence.

The new coat of arms was everywhere, on the gates of the palace, on the oaken doors, the carriages, the crockery, the silver, the liveries of the servants, and the high silk hats of the coachmen. All the old equipment was thrown out. The vast rooms were furnished anew in rosewood, walnut, and mahogany, and the ornaments and bric-à-brac, like the architecture and statues, brought together under a single roof, and often in a single room, everything that the young Huntzes had ever longed to possess. In one room the knights and ladies on the costly Gobelin tapestries looked down on a collection of Japanese vases and Chinese plates. In another the heroes of Greek legend were ranged round a collection of Venetian glass and modern Bohemian chandeliers. And, everywhere, gilt; on the cornices, the door-posts, the door-knobs, the picture-frames, the furniture. The rooms screamed money, and the hearts of the young Huntzes expanded with pride. There was not another palace like this within a radius of a hundred miles.

The installation ceremony took the form of a grand ball, to which were invited whoever was anybody in Lodz and the vicinity; the Polish provincial nobility, industrialists, Russian officials and army officers, and bankers, Jewish and gentile. The sons and daughters of Huntze considered nine-tenths of the guests riff-raff, a compliment which was returned by nine-tenths of the guests; but the advantage was on the side of the Huntzes, for they knew that what drew the guests was largely envy. They came, the broken-down Polish aristocrats, the bearded Russians, the pot-bellied Germans with the double necks and double chins, the flashy Jewish bankers who felt uneasy in the midst of so much un-Jewishness. There were, among the industrialists, Germans who had arrived in Lodz, like Heinz Huntze, with a small cart and a hand-loom or two; in homely German they told each other that old Heinz was a stupid show-off. The Polish aristocrats, whose titles went back several centuries, twirled their mustachios, looked with astonishment on the tasteless decorations, drank the costly wines with much relish, and poured their scorn out not only on their hosts, but on everyone else, the Russian conquerors who paraded in uniforms, the Germans who had elbowed them out, the Jews who controlled finance. The first were brutes, the second barbarians, the third swindlers. But they shook hands delicately with old Heinz and his wife, saying: "Congratulations, Baron! Congratulations, Baroness."

The younger Huntzes were present in full force. The sons-in-law had been bribed, by payment of their last batches of debts, to lend their presence to the occasion and to remind the guests that titles were extremely common in the Huntze family. They were needed, too, to help carry off the occasion, for sons and daughters alike were on edge for fear the father or mother should disgrace them with some unexpected peasant turn of speech or behaviour.

The climax of the evening, and the most ticklish point in the proceedings, was the actual presentation of the patent of nobility by the Governor. The moment he entered, sur-

[225]

rounded by his uniformed aides-de-camp, the orchestra burst
into the Russian national hymn. Men and women stood up,
officers saluted, and a tremor of anticipation passed down the
hall. The Governor advanced slowly toward Heinz and his
wife, carrying in his arm the parchment scroll with the Imperial decree. When he reached the couple he stopped, unrolled the parchment, and read forth solemnly the title which
had been conferred on Heinz Huntze by the ruler of All the
Russias for his incomparable services to the fatherland. Old
Heinz, who had an idea of the amount which the Governor
must have received for *his* services, was, in spite of himself,
so deeply moved by the mention of his merits that the tears
came into his eyes, and when it came his turn to reply, he
forgot the prepared address which his sons had been drumming into his head for weeks, forgot that he had to speak
nothing but pure German, and lapsed into dialect, so that
his sons and daughters and sons-in-law ground their teeth
and cursed him under their breath, while the assembled
guests bit their lips in an effort to restrain their laughter. Old
Heinz tried to go on, but was lost. Count von Heidel-Heidellau saved the situation—or what was left of it—by interrupting and calling for three cheers for the Baron and Baroness of Huntze-Schwarzwald.

"He'd feel more at home in a beer-saloon with his other
weavers," said one of the Polish noblemen to his neighbour.

"That affectionate smile on his daughter's face doesn't
seem quite natural," said the other.

"Give the poor man a good piece of sausage and a plate of
sauerkraut," said a third; "he'll be happy."

"Thick-headed gentile," murmured a Jewish banker contemptuously. Why, every Jewish boy of thirteen had to learn
a speech for his confirmation ceremony, and the most stupid
did better than the Herr Baron.

After the presentation there was a superb supper, followed
by dancing. The windows of the Huntze palace shone out
into the night, and four deep around the iron railings stood
the poor of Lodz and stared and wondered, and envied the
people inside. But inside the palace, in the midst of the
drinking and jesting, the singing and dancing, there was

[226]

little that those outside need have envied. The impoverished Poles felt themselves humiliated, for here, in the heart of Poland, Russian and German were spoken, and one hardly heard a word of Polish. The Russian officers looked down on the conquered race. The Jewish bankers despised the pretentiousness of officials and officers and aristocracy. The German industrialists smiled ironically at the Russians, Poles, and Jews. And everyone snickered secretly at the wretched taste which the vast, glowing rooms showed, and most of all at the incongruity between the pompous title and the old German couple upon whom it had been bestowed.

The sons and daughters of Baron Huntze-Schwarzwald hustled their parents off to bed as early as possible, so as to be able to spend a couple of hours with their guests free from the perpetual terror of some dreadful blunder. But old Heinz and his wife were glad to get out of it. After his one emotional outburst the newly made Baron felt forlorn and ill at ease. He was thinking of the cost of all this; he was thinking of the sheer waste of it. He had no taste for ostentation, and he could not understand why he should be envied. Long after he had retired, he lay awake, murmuring from time to time: "Matilda—are you sleeping?" and getting always the mournful answer: "No, Heinzchen, I can't." To which he replied: "Neither can I."

Old Heinz, Baron Huntze-Schwarzwald, slept little that night. He would not have slept at all if he had been able to foresee the course of events. For it turned out that this incident of the elevation to the peerage became a landmark in his life. It was as if fate had set a definite term to the period of his success. The baronetcy was the pinnacle of his career, unsought and unappreciated; but he was not to remain on the heights long, and the descent was much more rapid than the ascent.

There was, first of all, the expense attached to the title. The preliminary cost, which his sons had met without consulting him, was by far the smallest item. The renovation of the palace, into which old Heinz had gone reluctantly, had swallowed up an enormous sum. From the preliminary estimates given him by his sons and daughters he had ima gined that the cost would be trifling, but before he knew it he was involved in an outlay which exceeded the original cost of the building. There was a fatality about it: either he would be compelled to celebrate his accession to the peerage in an unfinished house, with half the rooms empty or demolished, or he would meet the expense of the complete renovation; and there was only one choice really open to him. Then there was the matter of the celebration itself. His sons and daughters had made up their minds that this would be a function without a parallel in the annals of the Polish nobility, and they spent more on wines, on fruits brought from tropical countries, on roses sent by special courier from the Riviera, on musicians and singers, than Heinz Huntze had earned in his first ten years in Lodz. The bills were staggering. Baron Huntze-Schwarzwald was not only stripped of all his available cash; he had to dip heavily into the firm's reserves.

His chief assistant, Albrecht, the huge German for whom special chairs had to be built, watched the proceedings with increasing alarm and was at last compelled to draw his employer's attention to the dangerous state of affairs.

"Herr Baron," he shouted into the old man's ear, "I have to advise you that we are getting into difficulties. Every time you withdraw a sum from the funds, Herr Goetzke does the same, and we're in very low water."

"What does Goetzke need all that money for?" asked the Herr Baron angrily.

"I don't know," answered Albrecht. "He says if you withdraw money, he has the right to do the same."

This was true. As far as financial participation was concerned, Goetzke stood, in this partnership, on the same footing as Huntze. Originally this equality had extended into the field of management too, but the superior ability and standing of Heinz Huntze, as well as his obstinacy and furious will to rule, had pushed Goetzke into second position and had ultimately reduced him to a figurehead. Popular instinct was right in still alluding to the firm, which bore on its letterheads the double name of "Huntze and Goetzke" as "Huntze." Goetzke had seen himself retreat steadily, and his efforts to hold his ground had been futile. Somehow department heads, chemists, engineers, foremen, and designers showed more respect toward old Huntze. They went to him oftener. They recognized in him the master; in Goetzke only the employer. As far as the management of the firm was concerned, Goetzke had become a supernumerary.

He therefore clung all the more desperately to those more specific contractual rights out of which he could not be manœuvred by the superior prestige and abilities of his partner. He had long since regretted the partnership, which had obliterated him; he had long since learned to look on Huntze as a ruthless, scheming, selfish power-seeker who, through his Jew, Reb Abraham Ashkenazi, had invited him, Goetzke, into the partnership, for the sole purpose of getting rid of him. All the glory was Huntze's; his was the name which grew in standing from year to year, while that of Goetzke sank more and more into obscurity, as if he were a dead partner. And now, as if to point the distinction between them, came this elevation to the peerage. Goetzke was immeasurably embittered. He considered himself as able as Huntze; he had done as much for industry in Lodz—consider the fact, for instance, that Huntze had had to approach him for a partnership on equal terms; he was half-owner of the firm of Huntze and Goetzke. Huntze became a baron; Goetzke remained a nobody. It was galling.

Goetzke was the only one among the German industrialists of Lodz who did not go to the inauguration ball. He was the only one in the factory who refused to use the title Herr Baron in speaking either to or of his partner. When somebody mentioned to him the wishes or instructions of the Herr Baron, Goetzke would look a little puzzled, would sniff the air as if trying to locate something by its smell, and would say: "*Ach, ja,* you mean Heinz; of course."

During the years of the partnership Goetzke, puzzled by the inexplicable way in which authority flowed always toward Huntze, had even imitated the other in the matter of public display. He had spent as much money as Huntze on his residence; he had driven carriages every bit as magnificent; he had even tried to speak in the same brusque imperious way

[229]

as old Huntze. All to no effect. There was something about the other—something. Goetzke believed it was a gift for intrigue and bribery, which bought applause and created a false aura of greatness. But whatever it was, it had succeeded.

Even if his equal right to the funds had not been the last citadel of his authority, Goetzke would still have refused to leave his money with the firm; out of spite and envy and impotent resentment, he would have demanded his share, whether he needed it or not—and he did not need it—whatever the consequences to the factory. "The old bastard's the manager, isn't he?" he muttered. "Let him manage. He's withdrawing money, isn't he? I have the same right to it. He expects me to leave the money in so he can buy himself baronetcies. He'll be stinking in the grave before I do that for him."

It was barely possible that if Baron Huntze-Schwarzwald had himself requested this help from Goetzke, the latter would have yielded, for the satisfaction of helping his old employer out of a tight place. But old Heinz would sooner have shot himself than beg a favour of the former apprentice to whom he still alluded as a *"Lausbub."* It was Albrecht who asked Goetzke to leave his money lying in the firm, and Goetzke had told him to go to hell.

Albrecht, who perspired even when he sat still and was inwardly at peace, had felt rivers of sweat bursting from his body. He was at a loss. The only step he could propose to Huntze was—the raising of money on notes. But that would never do. It would be the first time that Huntze had borrowed, and besides fearing the effect on his reputation, pride forbade him to apply for a loan. And yet new money had to be found. Where could he get it?

At home the demands grew continuously. That wretched title had involved him in subsequent obligations he had never dreamed of. He was always being approached by charitable organizations and patriotic societies which, headed by the highest aristocracy, and sometimes by a member of the royal family, simply could not be turned down. And if he did turn some of them down with the angry reply: "I pay taxes enough; let the state build hospitals for the damned paupers," his sons and daughters would announce a contribution for him, and he would pay. Then there were five active and insatiable leeches, three sons and two sons-in-law, always sucking at his blood. Debts always; old debts and new debts, for cards, for clothes, for holidays, for parties. It was all very well for him to scream that he would let them go bankrupt. He could not; he dared not. It was not of them that he thought; it was of his own name. And they, knowing where his weakness and their strength lay, pushed their advantage for all they were worth.

It was Albrecht who finally worked out a plan.

"Herr Baron," he shouted into the old man's ear, "the factory is sick."

"I know it," growled Huntze.

"The best cure for a sick body," went on Albrecht, "comes from within. The body must cure itself. It must call as little as possible on outside help, because that becomes a habit."

"Right, Albrecht."

"Herr Baron, we will look for help within the factory itself, then."

Huntze spat. "You're not going to change the quality of the goods," he said, fiercely.

"No, Herr Baron. God forbid!" That would, indeed, have been worse than borrowing money. For nearly two generations the name Huntze had been synonymous with quality. Millions bought Huntze fabrics on trust, and the loss of this public confidence would put the Huntze factory in the same class as dozens of others which still had to plead and argue with customers. "Not the goods, Herr Baron," said Albrecht; "the workers."

"Ha, the workers." Huntze saw it at once.

"Thousands of workers, Herr Baron. They're overpaid. And we use too many men. Women are just as good at the machines. They ask for less. They'll do the same work for less than one half the money. Fifteen per cent off the men's pay will make a big difference," and Albrecht produced a sheet of paper with calculations. Within less than a year Huntze could make back, on this item alone, a good share of the cost of the remodelling of the palace.

[231]

"Right, Albrecht," exclaimed the old man excitedly. "It's the only sensible way." He got up from his chair and slapped his director on the back. "Albrecht, you're good. Listen: I've had a new carriage made; I mean my sons insisted that I have to have a new carriage, though the old one is as good as new. But you can have the old one."

A vast smile of gratitude spread over Albrecht's face and rippled downward over his body. "Thank you, Herr Baron. Herr Baron is too generous."

"Only be careful that you don't break the springs with that big fat behind of yours, Albrecht."

"Oh, I wouldn't do that, Herr Baron."

The changes were introduced into the factory immediately. That same week-end several dozen men were dismissed from the looms and, the word having been passed round that the Huntze factory was going to engage women, a long row of these, materializing as if by magic, already besieged the doors. The dismissed weavers, who had received their last pay, stood outside the factory twisting their peasant caps nervously in their hands, looking at each other and the women, and asking blankly what they were going to do with themselves now. Following Albrecht's instructions, the foremen had turned away only Poles, villagers who had up-rooted themselves from their homes, who were helpless in the city and were unable to return to the country.

"Jesus," they muttered, "he might as well drown us."

The following Monday a notice was posted up in the factory announcing an all-round fifteen per cent cut in pay. Only foremen and directors were exempt. Albrecht had explained to Huntze that it would be a sensible move to keep the foremen satisfied and loyal; also to make them feel that they were a privileged class, whom their employer did not confuse with the rabble. Huntze had agreed and had again congratulated Albrecht on his cleverness. And in fact the better-paid employees rose eagerly to the bait, as the gulf between them and the ordinary workers was emphasized; but these last, helpless in the grip of their employer, living in the barracks which he owned, cursed savagely and silently while their hands flew over the looms. Not one word of resentment was uttered aloud, for day after day male workers were dismissed, their places being given to peasant girls from near-by villages who had never worked for wages before and were glad to accept something like a third of the pay which the men had received. They were eager and willing, in more ways than one. The foremen discovered that village wenches, besides being industrious and obedient, were too scared to complain when, caught in a dark corner or in one of the stockrooms, they were put to other than strictly industrial uses. In fact, what with the feeling of security in their superior pay, the power to dismiss male workers, and the control of an increasing number of subservient girls, the foremen were having the time of their lives.

Happiest among the higher officials were Melchior, the red-haired doorkeeper in the green huntsman's uniform, and his bosom friend Yostel, the old watchman. Officially speaking, they were very humble employees, but they were placed in a strategic position which brought them in contact with all the workers. Both had developed to a pitch of perfection the arts of the small usurer. Workers who found themselves short at the end of the week, either because they had chalked up too many drinks at the inn or because they were faced with unexpected expenses, came to them for help. The system was simple. On Saturday night Melchior or Yostel would lend a worker a rouble, but give him only ninety kopecks of it; the following Saturday the amount had to be repaid in full. The workers thought it quite reasonable: the actual percentage was eleven for the week, or nearly six hundred per annum.

Melchior and Yostel had saved up large amounts, especially the former, for he had, besides his weekly pay and his usury, an important source of income in the form of tips from merchants and agents who bribed him to announce them out of their turn to his master. He had a fourth source, too, when the new system was installed. It was his business to find good-looking working-women who would take care of Albrecht's bachelor quarters, and as these women were changed frequently, Melchior's income from this source was

[233]

steady. Albrecht liked the services of fresh young women from the country, and Melchior was an expert in choosing the most willing. But he was more than a mere provider for Albrecht. He had a healthy and changeable appetite of his own. He also played the clarinet and kept a good stock of wine in his quarters. He was successful with the women.

Yostel took no tips from customers and agents eager to see Huntze. His specialty was the management of the buyers of waste products. He could arrange that one man got the pick of these, another the last remnants; so it paid to bribe him. Old Yostel kept a large sum in a special iron safe of his own, on which was inscribed, in religious Gothic lettering, the motto: "God's grace shines on him who rises early to work." He lent out money as readily as Melchior, but he preferred to deal with women, and particularly with mothers of very young daughters. He was too old for grown-up girls and women, and he needed little ones who didn't know what it was about, and who for a couple of kopecks or a piece of candy let their nice old grand-daddy play funny games with them. The mothers, who owed Yostel money, had to submit their daughters or pay up. Some objected; but there were many who remembered that they too, when they were little girls, had played at such games with some old grand-daddy or "uncle" in the village, the teacher or the doctor or the pharmacist, and it hadn't done them any harm; they had grown up and married just the same. So they sent their little girls to old Yostel's lodge at the back of the factory, asking for loans which they never intended to repay except through their daughters.

The new policy of Albrecht and Huntze meant a great increase in business for Melchior and Yostel. Housewives were unable to cook satisfying meals for their hungry workers on the new wages; husbands whose habit it was to steal into the inn for a drink found it necessary to make larger loans at the end of the week. Besides, as money became more scarce the drinking actually increased, for the wretchedness in the homes, the perpetual complaints and quarrels, drove the men out, and they sought consolation in drink. The women, in turn, were driven by the two motives of want and

[234]

neglect to make whatever money they could on the side, and to many it did not matter if it was their own or their children's bodies they sold; for small change, for a piece of silver, they gave themselves to unmarried young working-men with a little money to spare, or winked if their young daughters earned something at the game.

A rapid demoralization set in among the workers in the Huntze barracks. The pastor was a more frequent visitor than ever before as the mortality among the children rose. The police, too, found that an increasing number of trails led from petty thefts to the workers' quarters. From the small farms which neighboured on these barracks chickens and young pigs were always disappearing; and even dogs that went astray were sometimes traced to a worker's family which had slaughtered it and boiled the most eatable parts.

Applications for loans from Melchior and Yostel became so numerous that they felt the time had come to raise the rates; they now took fifteen per cent off each rouble for a week's loan. Melchior played joyously on his clarinet and passed the winebottle to the latest arrival from the village; old Yostel found, to his infinite delight, that there was an inexhaustible supply of little girls whose mothers needed money badly enough to wink at what happened in the lodge at the back of the factory.

While all this rot ate at the human material of the Huntze factory, the looms worked as fast as ever, the sales were as large, the orders as steady. The factory was, in Albrecht's language, "curing itself" without the dangerous use of artificial injections of new blood. For while the prices to the customer were maintained, the wage bill had decreased by several thousand roubles a week, and in spite of the continuous drain of his children, Baron Huntze-Schwarzwald was slowly replacing the moneys he had withdrawn and thereby compelling Goetzke to replace his share too.

"Albrecht," said the Baron contentedly, "things look a bit better now."

"*Ja wohl, Herr Baron.* By the end of the year we'll have the situation in control again."

"You made a good job of it, Albrechtchen," grunted his

employer, becoming almost affectionate in his satisfaction. He took out a thick cigar and handed it to his employee.

"Thank you, Herr Baron."

"And listen, is that carriage breaking up yet under that big fat behind of yours?"

"Not yet, Herr Baron," shouted Albrecht, grinning with joy at his master's familiarity.

xxiv

As long as old Heinz had spent his days in the factory, running from department to department, putting his nose into every operation, checking the designers, the chemists, the engineers, the foremen, and even the book-keepers, as long as he had worked from early morning till late at night, he had seemed to be made of cast iron. Except for the touch of deafness he might have been thirty or forty years younger. He was alert, vigorous, and as imperious as of old. Sickness had no power over him; and at the end of a long day's work he was as energetic as in the morning.

Doctors warned him that he was abusing his strength. It was absurd for a man of his age to walk for hours up and down the cold, hard stone floors of the factory; he would come down with rheumatism any day. The thick air, laden with wool and cotton dust, was bad for his lungs; so were the chemical fumes of the dyes. The constant noise and tumult of the factory did his nerves no good. He had no business to be on his feet for the greater part of the day. He ought to take a holiday on one of his farms or, better still, visit the warm springs abroad.

Old Heinz spat, and grinned at the doctors. *"Quatsch!"* And when their backs were turned he growled: "What do those damned fools know?"

And the older he got, the more strength he seemed to derive from his devotion to the factory—as long as that devotion was whole-hearted and uninterrupted. It was only when that

[237]

accursed title, which he had never wanted, began to interfere with his work that his resistance broke, and when the first crack appeared in his powerful physique, all the accumulated abuses of the years descended on him and exacted the deferred payment.

It was the baronetcy that did it all, the new duties and obligations in which it involved him, the time and energy it wasted, the frequent absences from the factory to which it led. Apart from that, too, his children raged at him continually for his ridiculous absorption in the work. It was unbecoming to a baron. It made them ashamed to have a father who went into work when the first whistle blew, and left after all the workers. "You've got employees, haven't you?" they said. "Why must you behave like one of your own foremen? Why can't you think of the reputation of your family?" Besides, they interfered with his habits. They refused to let him smoke his old porcelain pipe and insisted that he become accustomed to cigars. They scolded him for spitting on the floor. They surrounded him with doctors who pestered him with their advice and only made him nervous.

Before the year was out, old Heinz had collapsed. His limbs had become weak, and his joints ached. His legs swelled up, his skin became dry and hot, his mouth burned always with thirst. He complained of pains in the head. Very often, while seated at his desk and talking with people, he would fall into a coma and, coming suddenly out of it, would forget what had been said and accuse the others of having interrupted him.

He became abusive. "Idiots!" he snarled. "Why don't you let me finish talking?"

"But, Herr Baron," they protested, horrified, "no one interrupted you."

"Damn it, you did. You're always interrupting me."

At home his behaviour became intolerable. He made the servants miserable and even spoke harshly to his wife. He had fits of rage during which he flung glasses and plates about the room and spat furiously on the carpets and skins which covered the floors. During the first period of sickness he made an effort to master himself. He refused to admit his condition and with aching limbs and unsteady feet crawled from floor to floor of the factory. He still interfered everywhere, insisted on controlling every operation, and demanded that all plans be submitted to him. Albrecht, seeing his condition, tried to persuade him to go home. "Herr Baron," he said into the old man's ear, "let me look after things today. Herr Baron should be in bed."

"Shut your damned jaw," shouted the other. "I'm as healthy as you are. And you don't have to hold me up. I can stand by myself."

But there came days when his children and the attending doctors forced him physically into bed. He was too weak to fight them off. He lay panting, refusing to listen to advice, and flinging the medicines which were offered him to the other end of the room. He shouted that if they insisted on keeping him in bed, they might at least let the department heads come to him, so that he could know what was going on in the factory. The doctors had to yield, and the department heads brought their reports and recommendations to the old man's bedside. Most of the time he talked wild, changing the subject frequently and confusing the departments. Then suddenly he would come to and issue swift, intelligent orders which astounded and frightened the listeners. At such moments some of his physical strength would return, too. He would get out of bed, thrust the white-robed nurses to one side, put on his dressing-gown, and, taking his heavy walking-stick, shuffle from the palace to the factory. His appearance there threw the workers into a panic. It was clear that he was not in his right mind, but the habit of obedience was so deep-rooted in them that they were afraid to ignore his orders.

He would stand at the door of a huge room, lift up his stick, and yell: "Stop the machines! Who gave you permission to put these machines on today? I don't want anything done without my orders."

He was taken back to the palace and put into bed again. He began to rave that there was a conspiracy to keep people away from him. He wanted everyone round his bed.

[239]

The fact was that his sons, taking advantage of the doctors' orders, did their best to keep him in isolation. They knew that the end was approaching, and they were afraid of him. At the last moment he might do something to ruin their prospects, perhaps in order to punish them, perhaps merely to stage a last exhibition of authority.

"Murderers!" the old man shouted. "You want me to die here alone." When they brought him medicine, he pushed it away, crying: "Poison! You want to poison me, but I won't let you."

"Heinzchen!" his old wife pleaded, "Heinzchen! Why don't you rest? Where do you want to go?"

"I want to go to the factory! I want to set fire to it. I won't have it remain standing after me. I want to leave nothing behind."

But as the end came nearer, he lapsed into long fits of complete apathy. He did not lose consciousness; he lay there awake and so indifferent to what was taking place that he soiled himself in the bed, let himself be washed, and said nothing. It was in such a fit that he died. A few minutes before his death he started suddenly and said: "I don't hear the factory! What's the matter? Today isn't a holiday. The factory isn't working."

It was true. The doctors had ordered the machines stopped, so that there might be complete quiet in the near-by palace. They explained to the dying man that his condition was very grave.

"All right, I'm ready to die. But I want to hear the factory working," said old Heinz. "Set the machines going, and the whistles. Everything."

Orders were sent to the factory to start the machines and blow the sirens. In the middle of the day Lodz heard a tremendous blowing and whistling from the Huntze factory, and the report spread rapidly that the old Baron was dying. Old Heinz himself lay listening contentedly, until he started convulsively, stretched out, and died.

The sons, who stood around the bed, looked at each other, their relieved looks betraying what they did not dare to utter. Without a moment's delay they sent for Albrecht and

[240]

told him to take in hand the arrangements for the interment of the Herr Baron. The day after the funeral, they added significantly, they would consult with the director on the future management of the factory.

Albrecht understood them perfectly. The old order was ended. The men who had worked with the dead founder of the factory were to go. Youth was wanted now, and a new type, conformable to the ideas of the heirs of Heinz Huntze-Schwarzwald. And the young noblemen were brutally outspoken. "Herr Albrecht," they said, "the factory's beginning to look like a home for the aged. We're going to change all that."

Among the first changes was the removal of Reb Abraham Hirsh Ashkenazi from the general offices on Piotrkov Street, and the installation in his place of his son Simcha Meyer. This was Simcha Meyer's first reward for his services to the young Huntze-Schwarzwalds. Albrecht himself took the news of his dismissal to Reb Abraham Hirsh and told him who his successor was. Reb Abraham Hirsh did not react to the treachery of his son as Reb Chaim Alter had done. He listened quietly to the end and nodded.

"I'm sorry, Herr Ashkenazi," said Albrecht sincerely. "The young gentlemen want their own kind. They think your son will do better."

"Koheleth, who was King Solomon," answered Reb Abraham Hirsh in his Yiddish German, "has told us that there is a time to plant and a time to pluck up that which is planted, a time to build up and a time to break down. Nothing happens, Herr Director, without the will of God, not even the breaking of a little finger."

"*Ja*, Herr Ashkenazi, then it must be His will that I be broken too, for I am next in line. There's no help for me, either."

For the first time in all the years they had known each other, the two old men shook hands.

Reb Abraham Hirsh had no intention of disputing the place with his son. There would be no trials, no appeals to courts, rabbis, or business-men. Quietly and systematically he brought his office into perfect order, so that it could be

[241]

taken over without the slightest difficulty. He carried nothing away with him except the heavy volume of the Talmud which he had always kept there for odd moments of study and relaxation. With the volume under his arm he went to the door and handed the keys over to the watchman. Then he turned, aware of the sad eyes and frightened faces which were fixed on him.

"Good-bye," he said quietly, and turned again.

The next day Simcha Meyer took over the office as if it were the most natural thing in the world to oust a father from the place which he had occupied half a lifetime. He walked around the place, looked at the various rooms, and expressed dissatisfaction with the furniture and equipment. "This place looks old," he said, "and shabby. I want it to look fresh."

He changed everything. He installed gas lighting, which in those days was known only in the richest homes in Lodz. He took down his father's sign outside and put back the old trade-mark of the firm, which his father had refused to have there—the two naked Germans with the fig-leaves and the spears. Underneath he painted his own name, Max Ashkenazi, General Agent. This same de-Judaized name he had printed on all the office stationery.

Within two days Jacob Bunim, in Warsaw, heard how his brother Simcha Meyer had thrown their father out of his office. He took the train for Lodz, and went straight from the station to the offices on Piotrkov Street.

A uniformed lackey barred his way. "Herr Ashkenazi is busy," he said. "He sees no one without an appointment."

"Get out," said Jacob Bunim, and flung the lackey to one side. He smashed open the door of the office and found Simcha Meyer alone. The latter rose, exclaiming: "Jacob Bunim! How are you?" and stretched out his hand.

Jacob Bunim stood towering over him.

"Where's Father?" he asked.

Simcha Meyer looked up at him as if puzzled. "Am I my father's keeper?" he answered.

Jacob Bunim did not answer. He only drew closer to Simcha Meyer, and Simcha Meyer retreated steadily before him till he was brought up against the wall.

[242]

"Is that what you wanted my money for—to throw Father out of his job in his old age?" asked Jacob Bunim, spitting the words into Simcha Meyer's face.

Simcha Meyer was pale. He began to stammer. "You can have your money whenever you like. I've got cash—"

Jacob Bunim lifted his hands and began to slap his brother, first the right cheek, then the left, then the right again, then the left again, steadily. "That's for Father!" he said with every slap. Simcha Meyer stood as if paralysed. He did not try to defend himself. Only when Jacob Bunim stopped, he bent down and picked up his hat, and when he straightened up, the other was already at the door.

"You'll remember this," he called quietly after his brother. That was all. To the office-workers who now came crowding the door in astonishment he said, brusquely: "Get back to your work!" And, as if nothing had happened, he sat down again at his desk and resumed the calculations which Jacob Bunim had interrupted.

For Simcha Meyer Ashkenazi the final break had come with the old life, and the modernization of his name symbolized the interment of the one-time Chasidic Jew and the birth of the liberated European. The day after his installation in the offices of Huntze and Goetzke he shaved off his beard, leaving only a tiny spot on his chin; he threw away his Jewish clothes, putting on, not a longish coat which would be a sort of shamefaced transition from the full-length Jewish gaberdine to the dress of a gentile, but a suit which proclaimed him an apostate. He gave notice to the crowd of pious Chasidic Jews who had worked for his father, and engaged in their place young, modern, German-speaking assistants. Instead of the Yiddish which had always been heard here, the rooms were filled with a queer Polish-Jewish variety of German. Simcha Meyer himself never again used Yiddish, except when counting money and adding columns of figures.

Reb Abraham Hirsh Ashkenazi received the news that his son Simcha Meyer had forsaken the true path of Jewishness as quietly as he had received the news of his own dismissal. He heard that his son had shaved off his beard, had put on

[243]

the clothes of the gentiles, and had torn down from the doors of the offices the mezuzahs, those tiny scrolls which, on every door-post in every Jewish house, are the literal fulfilment of the command of God: "And these words ye shall bind for a sign upon thy hands . . . and upon the door-posts of thy house." Henceforth Reb Abraham Hirsh considered his oldest son dead in the flesh as he had died in the spirit. He therefore tore the lapel of his coat in sign of mourning and instructed Leah Sarah, the servant, to bring him a low stool, on which he sat for the seven prescribed days which follow the death of a member of one's family. During these seven days he read the book of the afflictions of Job.

Book Two

In the Tsar's court in St. Petersburg a furious struggle was being waged for the control of the new Emperor and the Imperial policy.

After the assassination, by a group of terrorist students, of the Emperor Alexander II, the liberator of the Russian serfs and the initiator of a liberal policy in the Empire, the division between liberals and reactionaries sharpened, and with it the struggle for the control of Alexander III. In the opinion of the liberals, a continuation and intensification of the old policy of liberalism would cut the ground from under the feet of the revolutionaries. The reactionaries, headed by Pobyedonostsev, asserted that it was precisely the liberalism of Alexander II that had encouraged the revolutionaries and led to his assassination. The latter stood for the stern repression of all liberal tendencies and the elimination from Russian life of every element which did not fit into their pan-Slavic program. In particular this meant a violent anti-Jewish policy. The Tsar's chief minister, Ignatiev, was a liberal, but he was a high liver, perpetually in debt, and when he was in danger of losing his estates he opened negotiations with a number of Jewish millionaires of St. Petersburg and demanded half a million roubles, failing the receipt of which he threatened to join the reactionary forces.

The sum was a large one, but the leading Jews of St. Petersburg could have raised it. What deterred them was the fear that this was only a beginning. Ignatiev himself would

[247]

certainly come for more, and as soon as it leaked out that he was being subsidized by the Jews, a host of parasites would follow his example, and the court was filled with impecunious noblemen. The rabbis of St. Petersburg, too, advised against the step, and Count Ignatiev joined Pobyedonostsev and with him prevailed on the Tsar to issue an edict of expulsion against the Jews of Moscow.

Within a few days thousands of Jews, of all ages and conditions, were expelled from the ancient Russian capital. Some of them uprooted themselves completely from the Old World and made for America; the majority clung to the land, or at least the Government, of their birth and moved over into Poland. Warsaw and Lodz received the main stream of immigrants, with Lodz, as a centre of commerce and industry, strongly in the lead.

They came, the refugees, with their furniture, their bedding, their Sabbath candlesticks, their samovars, and their Russian abacuses, or counting-frames. They were by no means of the poorest class, and they moved at once into the better business and residential streets and brought a new stream of life into the city. They maintained their old connections in the interior of Russia, and before long they became new distributors of local products, breaking into sections of the country which till then had purchased little from Lodz. The newcomers were all called "Litvacks," or Lithuanian Jews, for the Jews of Lodz classed most Russian Jews, even if they came from the interior, with the Lithuanians, as being queer, irreligious and anti-Chasidic. The heavy influx drove prices of rent and commodities to unprecedented levels. Landlords and shopkeepers discovered that these "Lithuanians" were free with their money and wanted the best. Local business-men who went looking for offices, local housewives who had been accustomed to good service, found themselves relegated to the second class of customers. Grocers, butchers, and fish-dealers got an itch for easy money, fawned on the newcomers, and treated their old clientele in very cavalier fashion.

These were the first grounds for bad blood between the Jews of Lodz and the Jewish refugees from Moscow. The second were based on the un-Jewish appearance and manners of the Muscovite Jews. Their boys did not wear the gaberdine and the ear-locks of the pious Polish-Jewish boys; they were dressed in blue semi-military high-school uniforms with bright brass buttons; the girls, too, wore the regulation brown Gymnasia or high-school dresses. All of them spoke pure Russian, like officials and army officers. The youth of Lodz disliked them for their standoffishness, but envied them their smart appearance and their mastery of the language of the conquerors.

"They're half-baptized," they said, spitting. "When they grow up they'll be wholly baptized."

Even the older Muscovite Jews, who spoke Yiddish, were disliked. In the first place their Yiddish sounded outlandish in the ears of the Lodz Jews; when a Muscovite Jew spoke rapidly, he was quite unintelligible. Their Hebrew pronunciation was also different. They all came to the synagogues; in fact, they crowded the old worshippers out, and prayers had to be said in relays, so that by the time the morning prayers were finished, the first afternoon prayers were due. But they had their own way of praying. They did not sway backwards and forwards, they did not make excited gestures, like the Polish Jews. They stood stock still. They said the Amens not fervently, but in high, sharp, clear voices. Very odd indeed they looked, in their short gaberdines, their half-bearded or wholly beardless faces, and their hard, un-Jewish derby hats, standing stiffly at prayer, showing not a bit of fervour or enthusiasm. Prayers indeed! And in almost unrecognizable Hebrew. The Polish Jews were certain that these prayers got no hearing in heaven. In particular, these Muscovite Jews said the Sanctification, which mourners must repeat once a day for a year, and one day a year for ever, very slowly and coldly. Now, what good did that sort of Sanctification do the dead person? The Polish Jews, hearing a Muscovite Jew repeat this prayer, responded with grudging Amens. A real, hearty, passionate Amen would not have fitted such chilly devotions.

In the evenings, after the last prayer, Muscovite Jews would take out copies of the Talmud and begin studying. This was amazing, for the Polish Jews hardly expected the foreigners to be so Jewish. And yet . . . again there was this remoteness and strangeness about it all. The chant was not the same, nor the pronunciation, nor the accompanying gesticulations. It made the Polish Jews think of non-Jews studying Hebrew and the Talmud, only for the purpose of being able to confound Jews in argument and lead them off the right path.

Because of their strangeness, the Muscovite Jews became the subjects of many legends. They were reported to be extraordinarily clever and able. They were dangerous business competitors. They were as cunning as gypsies, and the truth was not in them. They were to be avoided under all circumstances, left severely to themselves. Socially the two groups, the Muscovite Jews and the Polish Jews, remained divided. Chasidic Jews moved out of houses in which "Lithuanians" began to appear; in the courtyards round which dwellings were grouped, Polish fashion, housewives avoided lending any utensils to new, Muscovite neighbours; in the synagogues the groups remained apart. On the streets the Polish-Jewish children ran after the Muscovite children singing offensive songs.

But business developed rapidly between the two groups, for the Muscovites had new and important connections to place at the disposal of the Lodz factories. In the autumn and spring seasons large numbers of Russians, big-bearded and clad in vast, wide trousers, came into the city to make purchases of Lodz textiles through these Muscovite Jews. The new homes and apartments were filled with Russians sitting round samovars, perspiring as they drank countless cups of hot tea or played cards or crunched chicken giblets in between their calculations and transactions. They came from remote governments, from the Persian and Chinese frontiers, and even from beyond. Yes, these Muscovite Jews brought a new wave of prosperity to Lodz, but they were not received the more intimately for that. They were regarded as standing half-way between Jews and gentiles, being neither here nor there. Polish parents forbade their daughters to have anything to do with young Muscovite Jews; Muscovite parents were equally cautious. For the Muscovites did not take the insults lying down; they in turn mocked the Polish Jews, with their whining pronunciation and provincial manners.

"Hi-yi, yiddle," they imitated the others, "give me a forty-piece!"

The Polish Jews did not count their money in kopecks, like the Russian Jews, though the currency, even in Poland, was the rouble and the kopeck; they called a kopeck two groschen, and a twenty-kopeck piece a forty-groschen piece.

Not long after the Muscovite invasion there came a second, this time of real Lithuanian Jews, refugees from the adjacent Lithuanian territory. The Muscovite Jews, with all their un-Jewishness, had at least their money to recommend them. The real Lithuanian Jews had not even that. They came from one of the notoriously poverty-stricken sections of Russia. They came like hungry locusts, bringing nothing, needing everything. Their baggage consisted of a tea-kettle and a razor. They shaved as shamelessly as the Muscovite Jews. They brought no income to the city, like the others. They lived on it. They peddled needles, shoe-laces, soap, cheap shoes. They bought up and resold the junk, waste, and garbage of the factories. They filled the streets with their raucous voices and offensive Lithuanian pronunciation. They earned little and they lived on less. They slept in a corner of a kitchen in some Polish family. They ate bread and herring and were amazed by the extravagance—as it appeared to them—of even the poorer Polish Jews. As to the middle and upper classes of Lodz, these were almost monstrosities in the eyes of the wretched Lithuanians. They simply did not understand how a grown-up man could go into a restaurant and spend an enormous sum on a meal, when he could sit peacefully at home and eat a piece of salt herring for one fiftieth of that amount of money.

"Polish hogs!" they said. "Grease-bellies!"

"Litvack garlick-eaters!" the others responded. "Beets and herring!"

These Lithuanians from Vilna and the villages did not remain pedlars and junk-merchants long. Far more dangerous than the Muscovite Jews, they worked their way

[251]

rapidly into the life of the city. They were clever, industrious, quick-witted, frugal, and well educated. They had the advantage of knowing Russian well. Many of them were excellent book-keepers. The Chasidic Jews disliked them, but found them useful; in the same way they disliked the Muscovite Jews, but did business with them. The Litvacks slowly filled the offices of the Lodz Jewish merchants, pushing out local employees. A Litvack never thought of going to work in a hand-loom factory or any other. He considered that fit only for the ignorant Polish Jews. His aim was higher. He would do business for himself, or at least enter a profession.

These Litvacks came in larger and larger numbers, like a conquering army. The men did not intermarry with Jewish girls of Lodz. They waited until they had accumulated a little money and then sent for the sweethearts they had left behind in Lithuania. Before long they had become an enormous colony in Lodz, with a great influence on the life of the city. They began to build their own synagogues and their own Hebrew schools. In the former they had their own customs and modes of prayer; in the latter they taught the Bible and Hebrew in the modern fashion, with a systematic grammar which Polish Jews considered impious, fit only for the seminars of gentile priests. The teachers in these schools were short-bearded modernists, too, who taught their pupils all kinds of superfluous things connected with mathematics and geography and other dangerous, worldly sciences.

Finally the Lithuanian Jews brought down their own chief Rabbi, who looked more like a Church dignitary than a Jew. His ear-locks were so small as to be practically invisible, his beard was neatly trimmed, and his first sermon, which drew a great crowd of Polish as well as of Lithuanian Jews, was packed full of Biblical citations, with little emphasis on Talmudic subtleties such as Polish Jews considered the only true learning. There was a great scandal, and the Jews of Lodz asserted loudly that they would not submit any problems or disputes to this half-apostate. But the standing and influence of the Lithuanian Rabbi grew from day to day. He was liked by the wealthy Jews who were tired of their own local Rabbinate. He was taken up at once by Maximilian

Flederbaum, the millionaire textile industrialist and President of the Jewish Community. Flederbaum had long desired to be connected with a rabbi who was presentable to the gentiles, and this Lithuanian Rabbi spoke excellent Russian and—what was more remarkable—learned Polish very quickly, so that he was at home in all circles. Flederbaum's Rabbi had been a Jew of the old type, with a huge tangle of a beard and fantastically pious Jewish clothes. Flederbaum had been secretly ashamed of him. He indicated his preference for the new, modern Rabbi by inviting him—to the scandal and astonishment of the Polish Jews—to officiate at the wedding of a daughter in the Flederbaum palace. But the scandal and the astonishment passed, and the Lithuanian Rabbi became the leading Rabbi of Lodz and symbol of the conquest of the community by the Lithuanian Jews.

This new Rabbi had the immense advantage of having won early the favour of the Governor. It was said that when he was still in his Lithuanian village, he had delivered so brilliant a sermon on the occasion of the coronation of Alexander III, and had composed so moving a prayer for the health and long life of the new ruler, that the court had rewarded him with a medal. Some said that the Tsar had sent him a golden sword. They had not seen this sword; indeed, no one had; but the fact, they insisted, was indisputable. But sword or no sword, the Rabbi's reputation among the gentiles had preceded him to Poland, and the local Governor had received him in audience and expressed the most friendly sentiments toward him. Flederbaum, too, stood well with the Governor, and he was proud to have a Rabbi who could represent him and his community worthily in the eyes of officialdom. Thus it came about that Flederbaum joined himself with the Lithuanian Jews, though he liked them as little as did his fellow-Jews of Lodz.

Lodz, a Polish-Jewish community, stood henceforth under the sign of its Lithuanian community. The Litvacks increased in number and power and crept upward toward domination of the business and professional life of the city. Litvack teachers and book-keepers among the men, dentists and midwives among the women, became commonplace in Lodz. In the new synagogues Lithuanian rabbis and preachers set the tone, with their modernist sermons, their Biblical quotations, their secular Hebrew and general spirit of enlightenment. Lodz was passing through a new phase of expansion, changing as it grew, losing its purely Polish and provincial character, becoming noisier than ever, and moving up into the rank of the world's great cities.

Among the stream of wanderers there appeared one day two persons who created a tremendous sensation in Balut. It was on a frosty winter evening, when Jews, bent double, were hurrying home from afternoon and evening prayers, that the two strangers were first observed. They wore short coats; on their heads were thick fur busbies, and round their throats thick military scarves. They carried kit-boxes and kettles, and they looked like ex-soldiers returning from many years of service in distant parts of Russia. But when curious passers-by stopped and looked at them more closely, it soon became clear that these were not soldiers, either in appearance or in bearing. One of them was an elderly man, who could not have been a returning soldier; the other was, indeed, young enough, but too frail and sickly.

The elderly man stood under a lantern, examining a piece of paper.

"Are you looking for someone?" asked one of the Jews who had stopped to observe the two.

"Yes. Perhaps you can tell me where Keile Buchbinder lives." His speech was half Polish-Jewish, half Lithuanian-Jewish.

No one in the little crowd knew.

"Keile," repeated the elderly stranger, "the wife of Tevyeh the weaver."

Still no one knew. The stranger tried a third time.

"I mean Keile, the wife of Tevyeh the-world-isn't-coming-to-an-end-yet."

"For heaven's sake!" several Jews exclaimed simultaneously. "Why didn't you say that in the first place? Certainly. Everybody knows where she lives. It's not far from here, in a celler underneath a bakery." And a babel of voices instructed the two men.

[254]

The strangers stopped and picked up their boxes. They had hardly taken a step when one of the Jews who had advised them started and, turning round, exclaimed: "But aren't you Tevyeh the-world-isn't-coming-to-an-end-yet?"

"Tevyeh!"

There was a general cry in the little crowd. "Tevyeh! It's Tevyeh come back!"

Long before Tevyeh himself reached his wife's cellar a group of boys had arrived there, breathless, to announce the news of his coming.

"Keile! Your husband's here! Keile!"

She did not believe it. And even when Tevyeh appeared she did not recognize him as easily as the others had done. Confused and helpless, she stood staring first at him and then at his companion, and the blood flowed into her face and ebbed from it. Still confused, she shoved a corner of her apron into her mouth, then took it out hastily and wiped one of the chairs to let the stranger sit down.

When all but Nissan and himself had withdrawn, Tevyeh took off his huge scarf. Keile still did not trust her eyes.

"Keile," he asked, "how are you?"

The voice, too, was strange. Tevyeh no longer drawled, like a Polish Jew. He spoke sharply and clearly, like a Lithuanian. Even when Tevyeh opened his box and took out the scarf which he had brought Keile, she still could not say a word. She only stood there, silent, her hands folded on her breast. She could not believe this was her husband. Still less could she believe that the other man was Nissan, the son of Reb Noske, Nissan the Wicked.

The one-time Balut apprentice had changed greatly. He was taller and much older-looking, with a tan on his sallow skin and a heavy down on his cheeks. He resembled his father now. Like his father's, his face was bony and ascetic, his big black eyes wide open, staring beyond the person addressed to some remote point where something important but invisible to others always seemed to be happening. His tall gaunt frame was thrust into clothes which Polish Jews considered fantastic; black trousers, over which hung a Russian blouse embroidered at the collar and fastened round with a belt.

His thick black hair, with a bluish glint in it, covered his head completely. His eyebrows were heavy, but sharply marked, meeting above his thin, stern nose. Keile and her children stared at this strange young man even more than at Tevyeh.

"I can't believe it," she said at last, when she had begun to believe it, and she spat out in sheer astonishment.

Not less astonished were the Jewish weavers of Balut when they met this strange pair, and particularly Nissan. He was the same, and yet not the same. The kit-box which he had brought back with him contained mostly books—heavy, close-printed Russian books, which he unpacked tenderly, looking at them as reverently as a pious Jew would on volumes of the Talmud. This passion of his he had more than kept; it had grown deeper and more purposeful. He was in everything the old Nissan so intensified as to be almost another. A similar change, though not to anything like the same degree, was observable in Tevyeh.

On the following Sabbath the weavers' congregation of the synagogue Ahavath Re-im expected Nissan and Tevyeh, and it had been agreed that the latter should once again be honoured with the reading of the week's portion of the Pentateuch, a duty he had fulfilled every Sabbath for many years. But the congregation waited in vain. Tevyeh did not appear. They assumed then that he had elected to say his Sabbath prayers at home; so when their prayers were done they went to him in a body, to invite him to drink the benediction with them. But Tevyeh had said no prayers at all!

"He says no prayers!" Keile told them, horrified. "He puts on no phylacteries or prayer shawl. He makes no blessing over food. He does not say grace after meals. He walks about with uncovered head, like a heathen! And all day long he sits reading those thick, black books."

"He has forgotten God!" said the weavers, shaking their heads. "He's become like one of the worst Litvacks."

For a time it was believed that the two men had brought money back with them. It often happened that swindlers, counterfeiters, and incendiaries sent to Siberia returned with plenty of money; and for the sake of their money the un-

Jewish habits they had picked up in exile were ignored or condoned. But before long Tevyeh was working again as a weaver, and Nissan was giving Russian lessons in poor homes; whereupon it became clear that these men had no status at all, having forfeited the regard of Heaven and the fortunes of this world. They were just two ungodly paupers.

Had they been only this, however, they would soon have sunk into complete obscurity. Shortly after Tevyeh's return, rumours began to spread through Balut concerning the books in his cellar and the people who came to read them. The latter were a new type in Balut and had never been seen there before the great Muscovite and Lithuanian invasion. Young men with long hair, with spectacles on their noses, with stooped shoulders enclosed in Russian blouses, and on their heads student caps or wide-brimmed hats. The women who accompanied them were queer, too; they were dressed very simply; they had short hair; they smoked almost as much as the men; and they had an air of mannish independence.

What these young men and women were doing in Tevyeh's cellar, no one knew. It was clear, however, that they did not gather to chant psalms. The curious began to inquire from Keile what went on. Keile herself did not know. "They talk!" she said. "They keep on talking and talking and talking, and I don't understand a word of it. Or else they read and read and read."

It was noticed that after the return of Tevyeh and Nissan the Sabbath services at the weavers' synagogue drew fewer and fewer of the young apprentices and workers. It was not difficult to trace them. They were attending services of another kind, in Tevyeh's cellar. There they listened, not to the praise of God and dissertations on the Talmud, but to extraordinary tales of a workers' movement, of the progress it had made in other parts of Russia, particularly in Lithuania, of the constant fights with the bosses, of the funds which they accumulated, week by week, to aid them in the fight. The workers, in their Sabbath gaberdines, listened with open mouths to these recitals about things at once remote and intimate. They felt themselves caught up in a vague, exciting impulse.

"We'll do that too," they said. "We'll pay dues, every week. We'll take an oath on it."

Nissan opened up wider vistas to them. He spoke of the life of workers in other countries, told them about the French Revolution, about the international Socialist movement, about the heroism of the Russian leaders. Into these descriptions he wove a little theory regarding the relations of capital to labour, adding occasional digressions into the sciences and history. He spoke simply and straightforwardly, as his father had taught him in childhood years, addressing himself to the heart as well as the mind, his own faith and warmth infecting his listeners. The workers were astounded.

"How true it all sounds!" they said. "It's simple truth."

All the wretchedness and meanness of their lives seemed to vanish when they were caught up in these discourses of Nissan's. This was the first time they had heard someone speak to them, not of their worthlessness and unimportance, as the rabbis and preachers in the synagogues did, but of their dignity and strength. Something like a meaning appeared in their lives. That meaning became sharper and more definite when Nissan boldly taught them "revolutionary conspiracy." The very word "conspiracy," mysterious, attractive, and full of promise, gave direction to their miserable days.

They carried away from Tevyeh's cellar pamphlets and little books which they read in secret after the long day's work. They lit candles at their heads when they lay down to sleep on the bales of goods, and in whispers argued about the lessons in the books. This was something new, and it caught, it spread rapidly. Young workers who had been wearied of the synagogue, but had found nothing better to do with their time than take girls to the woods on the Sabbath, now frequented Tevyeh's cellar. Circles were formed throughout Balut, and groups were organized, with every member paying his ten kopecks a week. Even women came in; elderly women, housewives, who had never in their lives heard of a workers' movement. They wanted to be part of this curious and exciting activity.

Feivel the rag-dealer, who in years past had initiated Nissan into modern books, heard of the movement. Feivel had no interest in workers. As of old, he was consumed by one passion: he was against God and religion. Nothing else mattered. Workers were no good in his eyes; they were thickheaded, they had no education, they didn't want education. They therefore had no value in the struggle against obscurantism. Therefore the first question that Feivel asked Nissan when he met him again was: "Nissan, are you spreading irreligion?"

"Why, yes, Reb Feivel."

"Good. In that case I'll keep open house for you and your friends." And Feivel's wrinkled face, and even his beard, sewn with woollen threads, were illumined by a happy smile.

The big house of the rag-dealer became a branch of the school. On Sabbaths it was filled with workers and with Talmud students who had been attracted primarily not by the idea of a workers' movement but by the fascinating and dangerous literature of irreligion which Feivel distributed. To Talmud students Nissan, the one-time brilliant Talmudist, could speak in their own language. He knew what doubts tormented them. He knew how many of them hungered for the secular knowledge which their teachers and parents forbade them to so much as taste. He approached them, therefore, through education at large, directing them in their first contact with the natural sciences, with mathematics and history. But always, while spreading secular knowledge, he wove in his revolutionary views, so that imperceptibly the Talmud students were won over to his vision of the future, and their passion was transferred to the workers' movement.

He was a brilliant teacher, for he remembered how, both in his childhood and in the years of his political exile, he had had to struggle through, with his imperfect equipment, to an understanding of the modern world. He had picked up his training from students who had been expelled from their universities for revolutionary activities. Most of all, Nissan had been attracted by Marxist theories, which were only just penetrating into Russia in those days. But while learning the theories, he had also learned how to teach, how to transmit to others his own fiery joy in the vastness of the Marxian outlook, its irresistible logic and architectural magnificence. Whatever Nissan taught led back to Marxism. Among the weavers of Lodz, as among the workers of Lithuania, the new doctrine spread like wildfire; and Nissan did his best to guard them against a romantic interpretation of the working-class struggle. He spoke with the utmost scorn of the Narodniks, with their idyllic idealism, with their silly faith in mere talk. There was only one truth: the Marxian truth; the rest was stupidity or deliberate falsehood.

The Talmud students who frequented the house of Feivel the rag-dealer made even better material for the movement than the workers themselves. They were mostly poverty-stricken and oppressed. Their brains had been sharpened by Talmudic exercises, and they were eager to learn. Their old faith was gone; they needed a new one; they were open and receptive. There were also workers who had once been Talmud students and who had been forced, by sheer hunger, to apprentice themselves to weavers. Among the workers they were the most wretched. They had nothing in common with the majority of their fellow-workers. They did not share the same pleasures. They did not spend Saturday afternoons and evenings in the woods outside the city, picking up young seamstresses. Besides, they were the perpetual butt of the other workers, who sneered at them for their education.

Feivel was not interested in the revolutionary aspect of Nissan's lessons. He did not care for the talk about higher pay, workers' organizations, and a just social system. What delighted him was the anti-religious crusade that went along with it all. He measured his successes by the number of former Talmud students whom he could persuade to light the forbidden cigarette on the Sabbath; and every sentence which was aimed at the rabbis, at the Torah, at the faith taught in the synagogues, brought a grin of happiness to his features.

"Light up, boys," he cried, distributing cigarettes. "The Sabbath is a good day for a smoke."

A spirit of unrest made itself felt among the workers and apprentices of Balut. New songs were heard, which gradually replaced the old synagogue melodies which used to accom-

[260]

pany the humming of the looms. At first they were songs which made fun of the Tsar and the Government, so that the overseers and employers were terrified lest the authorities arrest them too.

"Hooligans!" they shouted at the workers. "Walls have ears! Do you want us all to be sent to Siberia in chains?"

But these songs were followed by others, in which they themselves, the employers, were derided, and this was even worse.

"May your mouths be twisted round to the backs of your necks!" the foremen and employers yelled. "You spit on the bread which you eat."

The songs became louder and more frequent. The employers threatened to hale the offenders before the Rabbi; but the workers laughed and went on singing.

"We're our own masters," they answered. "We'll sing whatever we like."

Words like these had never been heard before in the workshops of Balut. The employers were paralysed with astonishment.

Worse followed. The workers and apprentices began to assert their rights. Apprentices refused to lug bundles of completed work to the other end of the city after working-hours.

"Hire a droshky," they said angrily to their employers. "We're not packhorses. We've done a day's work, and that's enough."

The younger apprentices, who had from time immemorial been used as errand-boys by the employers' wives and set to all sorts of housework, refused to sweep the kitchens, to go to the grocery store, or to carry to the baker's the Sabbath meal which was to be kept warm in the oven overnight. "We're learning to be weavers," they said, "not housemaids."

In the synagogues terror-stricken parents complained about the young generation.

"Nothing is sacred to them any more," they said. "They speak openly against God and the Tsar." But they did not dare to voice their anger openly; they were afraid for their own children.

[261]

"It's the fault of the Litvacks," others answered. "Ever since they came to Lodz, the town hasn't been the same. One sick sheep can infect the whole flock."

The police appeared in ever greater numbers in the streets of Balut. They poked their faces into the factories, listened, understood nothing, and suspected everything.

"Sheenies!" they called out, shaking their fists at the workers. "We'll get you yet."

The prophecy of the Rabbi of Vorka concerning the sons of Reb Abraham Hirsh Ashkenazi was fulfilled to the letter when Jacob Bunim, following in the footsteps of his brother, Simcha Meyer, openly sundered himself from Jewish ways and traditions.

Jacob Bunim did it more neatly than his brother. He waited until Reb Abraham Hirsh died. As long as the old man lived, Jacob Bunim pretended to cling to the faith; and certainly whenever he visited Lodz he always wore the long gaberdine, the hat, and the ear-locks of a pious Jew. In Warsaw, the capital, he permitted himself a few liberties, wore shorter coats, dropped in at certain restaurants, and in general tasted the pleasant ways of the gentiles. All this he did quietly, lest word of it should reach his father. In Lodz he was even more careful; but the moment his father died he passed over, without hesitation, to the extreme of un-Jewishness. He threw out for ever his Jewish gaberdines and hats. He shaved the sides of his cheeks and trimmed his beard, so that it looked extremely elegant and extremely gentile. He put on a lustrous silk hat, which was most becoming; and he changed his double, Jewish name from Jacob Bunim to the single Polish name Yakob. Overnight the young Jew blossomed into the brilliant European.

Simcha Meyer had indeed tried to get rid of his Jewishness, but he was not successful. He worked hard at transforming himself—changed his clothes, trimmed his beard, got himself

[263]

a new name—all in vain. He still looked like the excitable, slightly insane Talmudic student who had first visited the house of Reb Chaim Alter. He spoke German of a sort—and spoke it with a singsong intonation which proclaimed the Chasid. His beard was short, but he could not rid himself of the habit of tugging it and plucking at it, like some rabbi bending over his Talmud. He wore a silk hat or a derby, but whatever he wore, it always slipped back and perched itself on the crown of his head like a Chasidic skull-cap. His collar always worked its way round his neck; his lapels were always covered with cigarette ash.

Jacob Bunim, or Yakob, without any effort, and as if he had been a changeling, slipped into the easy grace of the modern; Simcha Meyer, or Max, as he now called himself, sweated over it and still remained the little Jew that he loathed being. When Yakob Ashkenazi slipped on his cape, put on his silk hat, and took his cane in his hand, he could be taken for a nobleman educated in the universities and courts; Max Ashkenazi looked like a misplaced pedlar.

But then, all things that came hard to Max came easy to Yakob. Even money. Yakob did not have to work. He only had to be himself and wait. So, for instance, when old Abraham Hirsh Ashkenazi died suddenly, of a stroke, and the will was opened, it was discovered that Simcha Meyer had been cut off without a kopeck, and the very considerable fortune was divided equally between Yakob and his sisters. Max might have expected this, but he had not permitted himself to believe that his father would take his resentment with him beyond the grave. He was infuriated and made several efforts to break the will, citing his brothers and sisters before the Rabbinic courts. It did him no good. There could be no mistake as to the intentions of the father, who had proclaimed his son as dead when he abandoned the tradition.

Max was still more furious when he learned of his brother's sudden change to a gentile life. It was amazing.

"The things I sweat for and pay for, that brainless oaf carries off just like that!" he said to himself. "Blind, idiotic luck, always. You can't fight that."

No, it was not cleverness on Jacob Bunim's part, for he
[264]

had no brains. He had pretended to his father to remain a pious Jew, not as a matter of policy, but because he had been too lazy, too indifferent, too frightened, to make a fight of it. And the result? Something like fifty thousand roubles, his share of the cash value of the inheritance. Without intelligence or education, but just because a nit-wit of a girl went crazy over him, he had picked up a rich wife, and a dowry that made Max's look like a gift thrown to a beggar.

"And blast him," muttered Max, whenever he thought of his brother, "he doesn't even work! He's a damned wastrel."

It was true. Jacob Bunim, who now called himself Yakob, had never been a worker. In his father-in-law's house in Warsaw he had had nothing to work at; old Eisen had seen to that. After Abraham Hirsh Ashkenazi died, Yakob spent much more time in Lodz than in Warsaw. He rented a bachelor's apartment in the newly built Rex hotel, furnished it with great elegance, and lived the life of a man about town. He preferred Lodz to Warsaw for several reasons. First, he was at a good distance from his wife. Second, he could not live as freely in Warsaw as in Lodz because of his father-in-law. Third, Dinah, his brother's wife, lived in Lodz. And there were other reasons, bound up with the excitement and liveliness which reigned in the great industrial centre of Poland.

The theatres, restaurants, cafés, and cabarets soon learned to know him and to value his patronage. He came always with a group of guests, idle sons of the wealthy who were irresistibly attracted to him. When he passed through the streets in his flashy, rubber-tired carriage, hands saluted him and hats were raised from all sides. He was liked. There was a natural, infectious joy about him which it did one good to feel. Everything about him was hearty: his laughter, his eating and drinking, his greetings, his gestures, his speech. It was this difference in health and temperament between him and his wife which made it inevitable that they should drift apart. Pearl, with her sickly body and her pallor, could not have kept pace with him even if he had desired to take her with him everywhere. He wearied her. She found his very company, when others were around, exhausting. He compelled others to live as exuberantly as himself, and she had not the strength for it. Yet she loved him and was jealous of his friendships. She nagged him. She could not bear to see the gusto with which he ate. His full laughter irritated her. In the night she would listen to his deep, steady, happy breathing until she could bear it no more, and she would wake him up.

"Jacob," she cried, "how can you sleep like that when I can't even close my eyes?"

When he did happen to invite her out, she refused to go. "I can't bear those friends of yours," she said.

She hardly knew why this was so; but the fact was that when she saw Jacob Bunim among them, when she saw the back-slapping and the handshaking, when she felt the universal joviality which he inspired and which always surrounded him, she felt sick. And whenever a woman greeted Jacob Bunim, Pearl would look with narrow, sharp eyes, and ask afterwards: "Who was that cocotte you shook hands with?"

He felt better in Lodz, far away from Pearl. He did not have to apologize for every pretty woman who greeted him at a party or on the street. There were dozens of them, hundreds, who made eyes at him. Nor were they all of them of the demi-monde. The wives of the rich manufacturers, with nothing to do all day long, without hobbies or employment, neglected women—for their husbands were entirely absorbed by their work—found Yakob extraordinarily charming. They invented occasions to meet him; they went to the restaurants and cabarets which he frequented; they had themselves invited to the houses of his friends. They were proud when, passing them in the street, he took off his shining silk hat with a great flourish and bestowed a smile on them.

They meant little to him as individuals. There was only one woman who had the power to move him, and her house he could not visit. This was Dinah, his brother's wife. He was astonished by the power she still had over him. Just as in his boyhood days, when he had lingered in the streets along which she would pass on her way to school, he found himself passing and repassing the shops which she frequented with her mother, and if he managed to catch her eye, he felt the blood coming into his face as he saluted her at a distance. She never went without her mother. The two of them made a most attractive pair. Priveh, already a grandmother, looked more like Dinah's sister. Her cheeks were still fresh, her form plump and erect. She dressed elegantly. She was the right companion for her pretty daughter. Jacob Bunim thought bitterly of the insanity of it. Dinah would have been the right wife for him, instead of which his ridiculous brother, who hadn't the slightest idea how to treat a woman, had married her. And whenever he remembered the time when the chubby little hands of Dinah had been fastened round his neck, in the days when he used to carry her pick-a-back, a new rush of hatred for his brother overcame him. Perhaps it was as well for him not to know that more than once Dinah went walking with her mother on Piotrkov Street only in the hope that she could encounter Jacob Bunim.

Dinah no longer lived with her parents. The year he became general agent for the Huntzes, Simcha Meyer rented a new, large apartment and set up house for himself. He wanted a place of his own to which he could bring his new friends and business acquaintances without having to present his parents-in-law and without the fear of finding the house crowded with noisy pietists. He did his best to modernize and Germanize himself. He had taken to calling his wife by her German name, Diana. He spoke German with the children. He invited wealthy merchants to his table and tried to imitate the grand style. But his manners were as uncouth as ever. He ate quickly and noisily. He still scribbled on odd pieces of paper and on the table-cloth. He muttered to himself. And when in the middle of a meal he remembered an important engagement, he would gobble his food at double speed and rise from the table like a distracted man.

"Where are you running like that?" Dinah asked him. "You haven't had your dessert."

"No time," he gabbled.

"Don't you think you might stay and talk a little with your children?"

"What? The children?" He looked at her blankly. "Oh, yes, the children. Certainly. When I get back."

He seldom remembered that he had children. He did not know how to talk to them, much less to play games with them. "I'm dreadfully busy," he said, whenever they approached him. *"Furchtbar beschäftigt."*

He only wanted to see their school reports.

"Bring me your card, Ignatz," he said to the boy, who had been put into a German school.

The boy brought it reluctantly. His father glanced at it and frowned. It was not a good report at all. The worst marks were in mathematics.

"Absolutely incomprehensible," he said, angrily, and looked up at his wife, as if to intimate that it was from her and from her family that the boy had inherited his slow-wittedness. The boy hated his father more for the way he looked at his mother than for the reproach to himself.

Little Gertrude's school reports were better, but they did not interest her father. He looked at the card, saw that she was considered gifted at embroidery and art, said: *"Sehr net"* coldly, and handed the card back.

They were strangers to him, these children, and they found their father a strange man, too. There was no point of contact between them. Often, sitting at table with him, they observed his manners and grinned to each other when they saw their father pick up a piece of meat with his fingers or, right in the middle of his meal, start scratching his beard meditatively. They laughed aloud when he forgot himself and sucked his teeth. Max had no idea why they were amused, but his wife understood, and she was angry with the children. She disliked her husband; she thought him impossible. But she felt that this attitude of hers was her business and no one else's. She felt that it was a reflection upon her that her husband should be laughed at. It was for this reason, rather than out of thoughtfulness for him, that she would stop him when he was getting ready to rush out of the house, and make him brush the cigarette or cigar ash off his coat.

"Simcha Meyer," she said, "you can't go out looking like that."

He made a grimace. He hated to have her call him by that

old name of his, that Chasidic Yiddish name which he was doing his best to forget.

"What's the matter with me?" he asked, singing his German like a true Polish Jew.

"You're covered with ashes, and your tie is coming apart."

"Tie it for me, please, Diana," he said. She tied it with quick, skilful fingers, but when he tried to put his arm round her waist she slipped away from him.

"Please don't make yourself ridiculous, Simcha Meyer."

He dropped his hands as if she had hit them. Why was she so unfriendly? Why did she insist on calling him Simcha Meyer? And why would she never speak to him in German, though she knew the language better than he? Nothing about him seemed to impress or please her. Even the guests he brought to the house, modern people who should have been to her liking, failed to rouse her interest. And her conversation with him consisted of nothing but curt admonitions.

"Simcha Meyer, don't drop your ashes on the rug! Simcha Meyer, stop scribbling on the table-cloth! Simcha Meyer, use that ash-tray!"

It was just her contrariness, he said to himself. She refused to become a social figure, merely because he wanted her to. She even continued to wear the wig which, after her marriage, had replaced her natural hair.

"But you don't have to, Diana," he pleaded. "Nobody forces you to wear that silly thing."

"I like it," she said.

She did not bother to explain to him that if she refused to become one of the great ladies of Lodz, it was because she was ashamed to have to appear as the wife of the graceless little Jew who thought he had become an important and imposing personality.

"You're very pious all of a sudden," he said, sarcastically. She did not answer.

The less she had to do with him, she thought, the better. She kept house for him, she looked after the children, and her free time she divided between her eternal novels and her mother. She made no friends among the modern young wives

[269]

of the manufacturers who visited Simcha Meyer. She forgot herself in romantic stories of great loves. She was still able to live half her life in the adventures of impossible heroes and heroines with noble names and lofty sentiments. If she was not reading in her free time, she was with her mother, either sitting at home with her or, as was more frequently the case since Yakob had practically settled in Lodz, walking in the streets and staring into the shop windows.

Simcha Meyer could not understand what drew his wife so much to her parents. He accused the latter of deliberately stealing his wife from him. He suspected, too, that she gave them much more money than she told him, for he knew their habits, their extravagance, and their lack of discipline. It infuriated him to think that they were still carrying on as in the old days, at his expense, while they interfered in his family life. Wherever he looked around him, Simcha Meyer felt and saw only hostility: his wife, his parents-in-law, his sisters, and his brother, who was making such a stir in Lodz. The last was the hardest to bear with.

"He'll finish up a beggar," said Simcha Meyer viciously to himself. "His luck can't last. We'll be seeing him going round for hand-outs."

Contemplating all these people who hated him, feeling a conspiracy of unfriendliness in those who should have been nearest to him, Simcha Meyer worked all the more furiously, determined to show them that he could get along without their friendship. Above all he waited for the day when Jacob Bunim would collapse and he, Simcha Meyer, would come into his own and be able to prove that work and brains told in the end.

Only meanwhile Jacob Bunim showed no signs of collapsing. On the contrary, he was growing stronger and stronger. Shortly after his arrival in Lodz, Jacob Bunim became a frequent visitor in the mansion of Maximilian Flederbaum, the leading rival of the Huntzes, and within a few months had been appointed their general agent. No one knew how it happened, whether at the dinner-table or at cards or over a glass of wine; it just happened, as things of that kind happened to Jacob Bunim.

[270]

When the news was brought to Simcha Meyer, in his office, he turned white.

"It's a filthy lie," he exclaimed in Yiddish, forgetting his German in his agitation.

But if he had wanted to believe that it was a lie, Jacob Bunim prevented it by opening magnificent offices on the opposite side of the street. The trade-mark of Flederbaum, an anchor and key crossed, stared into Simcha Meyer's window. Below the trade-mark was his brother's name. At the door of the offices stood a lackey in uniform. It was much more elegant than anything Simcha Meyer had ever permitted himself. To shut out the sight he ordered curtains put on the windows of his office.

But he could not shut his ears to the talk which went on around him. He could not shut his eyes in the street when he saw his brother pass in his dazzling carriage. Nor could he refuse to open a newspaper because he saw there, day after day, the full-page advertisements which carried his brother's name. He essayed a sickly consolation by repeating that all this was brainless and systemless. The collapse was due. It would come any day. Extravagance could not prosper. One needed calculation, hard work, watchfulness. He would prove it.

As if to mock him, Jacob Bunim carried off another triumph for himself and his firm, proving within a few weeks of his appointment that Flederbaum had made no mistake. It was a triumph which, moreover, was a direct blow at the firm of the Huntze brothers. When Simcha Meyer heard of it he turned not merely pale, but slightly green, so that his face took on the tinge of the curtains which he had had put on his window to shut out the sight of his enemy on the other side of the street.

Flederbaum's triumph, engineered by Jacob Bunim, was symbolic rather than substantial, but not the less dangerous to the Huntzes for that reason. A new Governor had arrived in Piotrkov, direct from St. Petersburg, and the first private invitation he accepted from the local notables was that of Maximilian Flederbaum, who arranged a ball in honour of the new official. Until that year it had been a tradition that the Huntzes were the first to entertain a new governor. When von Miller turned down the Huntzes, the blow to their prestige, not less than to their vanity, was a painful one. It meant ultimately loss of business, too.

Maximilian Flederbaum, now the most dangerous competitor of the Huntzes, had, like old Heinz, worked his way up from utter poverty. He, too, had arrived in Lodz, many years before, with little more than his bare hands. Mendel Flederbaum he had been in those days. He came, a bronzed, broad-shouldered village boy, in a shabby gaberdine and heavy boots, walking all the way from his native village, to seek his fortune in the rising townlet of Lodz.

His father was a village innkeeper who lost his livelihood when a wealthier rival bought out from the local landowner the rights to the inn. There were twelve brothers and sisters in the family. The day after he was thrown out of his inn, the older Flederbaum tied up a fresh cheese in a bag, filled a bottle with pure honey, and set out with his son to Kazmir, to consult the Rabbi. The Rabbi told old Flederbaum to take the cheese and honey into the kitchen and to come back. He then blessed the father and son and gave each of them a three-kopeck copper piece, which he told them to carry with them always, for good luck, except on Sabbaths and holy days, when Jews must not have money about their persons.

Greatly encouraged, Flederbaum returned with his son to their native village and took up the flax and wool business. He went from farm to farm buying up raw material to send to Lodz. But he could not persuade his son to stay with him. The latter, a powerful boy who felt that somewhere great things awaited him, said that the place for him was Lodz itself, the little town that was drawing hundreds of others like him into the maelstrom of its activities. He therefore put into a bundle his crumbling, greasy phylacteries, a few patched shirts, a loaf of bread and a piece of hard cheese, a few spring onions, a little bag of salt and a pen-knife which a peasant had left at the inn for payment and which Mendel's mother had stuck into the soil for a few days to cleanse it of its unkosher contacts. With this, and a few coins in his pocket, Mendel set out for Lodz. The three-kopeck piece given him by the Rabbi he kept apart.

He spent no money on the road and did not eat all of his food. He dug up potatoes from fields and roasted them. He slept in barns or in the woods. And he arrived in Lodz, the strange, magnetic town, to fulfil the destiny which he felt burning within him. He was twenty years old.

Huntze had been in Lodz several years when the boy Mendel Flederbaum arrived, and the first successes of the young Jew had only filled Huntze with scorn. And, indeed, as long as old Heinz lived, Flederbaum had not been the dangerous rival that he had become since. It was Goetzke who absorbed old Heinz's attention until the founding of the partnership. Flederbaum merely irritated him by a degree of success which was undeniable and which might become a threat to the primacy of the Huntze firm.

Old Heinz was immensely amused by Flederbaum's eagerness to shine socially. When Flederbaum changed his name from Mendel to Maximilian, Huntze made a mental note that the new name did not exist for him. Meeting the other on the street, he would cry out loudly: "Hi, Mendel, how's business? Come round some time. I've got a lot of rags and waste to sell."

"Thank you, Huntze. I've got some good horses you might be interested in. They're more in your line than woollen goods." This was Flederbaum's answer, uttered as it were good-humouredly, but veiling a profound envy and contempt.

Huntze's elevation to a baronetcy had filled Flederbaum with wretchedness. In all other things, in the standard of living, in the scope of his business enterprises, he might hope to outshine the German. But a baronetcy was beyond the reach of a Jew, and no matter how much money was poured into the bottomless pockets of the Governor at Piotrkov, a title would never be forthcoming. A Cross of St. Anna, such as Heinz Huntze had, was to be obtained, and Maximilian Flederbaum obtained it. He wore it proudly on his waistcoat, while directly under it, beneath his shirt, reposed the smooth three-kopeck piece which the Rabbi of Kazmir had given him for good luck. He had also managed to obtain from St. Petersburg the title of Worthy Citizen, or Honourable, which would pass to his children. He also had many bronze, silver, and gold medals. But he had no baronetcy, and he never would have one.

As far as elegant living was concerned, he outshone Huntze, who had no taste for it and who was only driven to expenditures by his sons and daughters. Flederbaum's mansion was not as imposing as Huntze's, but it was handsomer, and those who had been in both asserted that Flederbaum's appointments and ornaments were far superior to Huntze's. Flederbaum, though he laughed at Huntze as a miscast horse-dealer, dealt in horses himself: but they were racehorses. He kept several stables and carried off some of the best racing-trophies in Poland. He hated dogs, for in his boyhood he had been chased off more than one estate by the dogs of the landowners; but since it was the thing for a rich man to possess thoroughbred dogs, he went in for these too. He also kept a good pack of hunting dogs. He learned to shoot, and though the sight of blood naturally made him sick, he schooled himself to go out hunting with Polish noblemen and Russian officials. He

[274]

taught himself, too, how to speak to servants, calling to mind the manner in which the Polish gentry had spoken to him and his father when they went, hat in hand, to sell something. The Governor himself had visited Flederbaum's country estates and had hunted with him. In all these things Flederbaum was ahead of old Huntze. But the baronetcy killed it all.

The man Flederbaum was symbolized by the glittering cross of St. Anna which he wore on his waistcoat and the copper coin amulet which he wore next to his skin. With all his love of finery and social prestige, with all his worldly success, Mendel Flederbaum lived in the fear of God. His good luck came to him from the Rabbi's coin; but he wore it hidden, and trembled lest the sins of his outward, un-Jewish life destroy the efficacy of the charm. More than once he thought that he would be punished. He had not done well by the Rabbi and the God whom the Rabbi had invoked to help him. He had fallen into evil habits. He ate unkosher foods freely; he smoked and rode and wrote on the Sabbath; he shaved his beard; he sinned with strange women—and all these things were surely displeasing to God. Lying awake in his broad, soft, comfortable bed, Maximilian Flederbaum had more than once resolved to do the right thing by the God who had been so generous to him at the Rabbi's special request. Good merchant that he was, Flederbaum knew that credit could be stretched just so far and no farther; one of these days God would call for an accounting, and it would be too late to pay up.

But Maximilian Flederbaum knew that it was quite impossible for him to change his mode of life, and revert to the piety of his ancestors. God loved pious Jews, and those who studied Jewish lore. Maximilian Flederbaum had no learning, and his position made it impossible for him to observe all the ritual minutiæ that are pleasing in the eyes of God. But there was at least a partial substitute in charity, was there not? God was also pleased with those who fed the hungry and clothed the naked and healed the sick. Certainly it would be best if a man could combine all three, piety, learning, and charity. Perhaps, reflected Maximilian Flederbaum, a man might get by if his charities were so big as to make up for the absence of the other virtues.

In this hope—an uneasy one, it is true—Maximilian Flederbaum spent great sums for charitable and religious purposes. He had endowed the Rabbi of Kazmir, the Rabbi whose intervention had been the beginning of his fortune. Neither the Rabbi nor his children nor his grandchildren would ever have to worry about a livelihood. True, he never invited this Rabbi, or other queer pietists of his kind, to the Flederbaum mansion. The lackeys would have been scandalized. For that matter, so would the Rabbi, for there were no mezuzah scrolls on the door-posts, and Jews ate at table without hats on. "Well," reflected Maximilian Flederbaum, "what good would it do the Rabbi to visit me? As long as he's looked after. . . ." Instead of a rabbi, Maximilian Flederbaum kept an almoner in the house, a Jew well versed in all the ways of Jewish life, and an expert in apportioning gifts to wandering rabbis and preachers, fathers collecting dowries for their daughters, visitors from the Holy Land, heads of Talmudic colleges, and the thousand and one others who came knocking at the back door of the Flederbaum mansion.

As against this, though, Flederbaum had also found himself compelled to contribute heavily to Christian institutions and had even helped to erect several churches. On one occasion he found it impossible to refuse the honour of laying the foundation stone of a church, and there his name was, together with that of his wife, built into a Christian edifice. He thought with much distress of this circumstance. If he remembered rightly, it seemed to him that the Jewish God was a jealous God, who did not like to have Jews contributing to the religious edifices of other gods. Maximilian Flederbaum sought to redress the balance by ordering ten scrolls of the law to be made at his expense, covered with the finest velvet mantles and crowns and ornaments, and to be delivered to certain Jewish synagogues. Fearing this was not enough, he had a new synagogue built, and in the nights calculated whether he had managed to placate the jealous deity.

His ideas concerning the next world were rather confused, but he remembered distinctly that the village Hebrew-teacher had given him one definite picture. There were scales up there. When a man came knocking for admission to heaven, his sins were put into one pan of the scales, his good deeds into the other pan. If the good deeds outweighed the sins, the man was saved. Well, then, it was clearly a matter of having more good deeds than sins. Therefore for every sin one committed, one must hasten to do a good deed of at least equal weight. On this theory Maximilian Flederbaum ordered his life.

Of late Flederbaum had been troubled because, as far as he could calculate in this difficult sphere, his sins had been very weighty, and it was no easy matter to find corresponding good deeds to set off against them. There were his own sins, and there were those of his children, for which he felt partly responsible. Two of his daughters had married Jewish apostates and had themselves been baptized in order to conform to the faith of their husbands. This was a very bad business. Flederbaum had not even interfered, in part because he would have alienated so many modernized Jews and liberal-minded gentiles, who would have regarded his opposition to the matches as old-fashioned and offensive; in part, also, because the matches were extremely advantageous to him and his reputation. The young men belonged to the wealthiest and most powerful Jewish families of Lodz. What would it have looked like if Maximilian Flederbaum had obeyed the Jewish Law, had torn the lapel of his coat in sign of mourning, proclaimed his apostatizing daughters as dead, and sat on the floor for seven days? He had to give his fatherly blessing, turn up his moustaches proudly, and express great satisfaction. The worst of it was that he did feel satisfaction. This threw him into such confusion that he passed many sleepless nights in his wide, soft French bed wondering what his next step ought to be vis-à-vis the Jewish God.

He was afraid. He knew that of all sins the greatest, the most unforgivable, was this of apostasy. Nothing angered God more or provoked Him to sterner measures. And God could be very stern; that much he remembered out of his childhood lessons. His anger was a terrible thing; it smote not only the sinner, but the father of the sinner, and the children to the third and fourth generation. Maximilian Flederbaum

[277]

had ghastly visions of white-hot coals and flames of sulphur and vast kettles full of boiling pitch. He groaned in the nights so that his wife, Elizabeth, forgetting her Polish and her social standing and her husband's new name, cried out in good, homely Yiddish: "Mendel, darling, wake up! You're frightening me!"

There was worse to follow in the tale of transgressions. It is bad enough for a daughter of a Jewish house to leave the faith; it is infinitely worse for a son, who after a father's death is supposed to remember him in the sanctification prayer once a day for a year, and one day every year for ever, to pass over to the creed of unbelievers. This was what threatened now in Maximilian Flederbaum's home. His sons had become altogether too intimate with Christian priests. Here again the father was to blame. His sons had been brought up by Christian governesses, who had often taken the children with them to church and taught them to kneel before the sacred images. Maximilian Flederbaum had not interfered, not conceiving that the matter was serious. It seemed to him that such experiences were necessary to the complete modern education of his children, and he never dreamed that his sons would acquire a permanent taste for the church. True, he should have stopped this church-going betimes. The boys had long ago shown a complete disinclination for Jewish things. They had refused to learn the Kaddish, or sanctification prayer; they had refused to set foot inside a synagogue, even on the dread Day of Atonement. But Maximilian Flederbaum had let all this pass, and now he saw disaster looming; he would never, never be able to set this right with the Jewish God. For not only would God thrust him, for such neglect, into the deepest pits of Gehenna, but there would not even be a son on earth who would recite the Sanctification for him and thus help to rescue him from torment.

And the day of reckoning could not be far off. Maximilian Flederbaum's hair was black, not with youth, but with dyes. He was still strong for a man of his years, but the years were many, and the count was getting close. Soon he would have to set out on that dreadful dark journey at the end of which was the inevitable weighing in the balance. And Maximilian

Flederbaum perspired with terror in the nights.

The older he grew, the more frantically did he try to heap up good deeds on the pan of the heavenly scales. Seeing that his sons would not say the Kaddish after him, he hired, not one Kaddish, but ten. Ten good and faithful Jews were endowed to start saying the saving prayer for him when he died, and to keep it up for the rest of their lives. After all, he reflected, ten pious Jews ought to be more effective than a couple of indifferent sons. He increased his contributions to the Hebrew schools and founded new ones; if the Flederbaum sons did not win merit in heaven by the study of sacred things, the father would make up for it by paying for the instruction of hundreds of sons of the poor. If he himself did few pious deeds, he would at least be the occasion of pious deeds in others, which ought to amount to the same thing.

What, indeed, were the poor for if not to provide the rich with an opportunity to pile up good deeds? God had made the world so, workers and employers, paupers and magnates, so that the employers and magnates could practice piety by means of the workers and paupers. Maximilian Flederbaum would not admit Jewish workers to employment in his factory. That would have been sinful, because the factories were kept going on the Sabbath, and to be the cause of a Jew desecrating the Sabbath was far from Flederbaum's intentions. There did happen to be other reasons. Gentile workmen were more obedient and respectful and less ambitious. Also, they were healthier, and their standard of living was lower. They did not have to eat kosher meat, send their children to Hebrew schools, and make special expenditures for the Sabbath and the holy days. Obviously it would have been sinful to employ Jews and pay them so little that they would not be able to observe the Jewish laws. Only in his offices did did Flederbaum employ Jews. They were more intelligent and they had some education; gentiles were mostly useless there.

Yet, though he did not employ Jewish weavers, he looked after the Jewish workers of Balut like a father. Apart from the Hebrew schools which he provided for them, he also contributed to their hospital, their burial society, and their fund for poor brides. When the Passover came round, Flederbaum bought great quantities of matzos and other necessaries and had them distributed in Balut. In times of unemployment he opened cheap kitchens, where weavers could get a pot of soup and a piece of bread below cost.

After the apostasy of his daughters Flederbaum cast about for some tremendous good deed which would send the pan of the heavenly scales down with a great thump on the credit side, and he decided to build a new hospital and to equip it in a fashion which would dazzle the accountants in heaven. He would have mezuzah scrolls on every door-post in the building; every sick man would be made to wear ritual fringes; there would be a special little synagogue for patients; a congregational quorum of ten Jews would always be on hand to say psalms for anyone who died, and candles would burn alongside every corpse.

The synagogue was built, and the dedication of it was one of the grandest public affairs ever seen in Lodz. The most important Jews and gentiles of the city and suburbs were there, and some even came from Warsaw. The Chief Rabbi of Lodz officiated. The building was crowded and the streets surrounding it jammed with workmen and their wives and children. The boys were let out of Hebrew school for the occasion, and they came in the hope of seeing the Rabbi's golden sword that everyone spoke about, though no one had seen it. A troop of mounted police kept order among the crowd, and Maximilian Flederbaum's firemen's band played for hours on end. To crown it all, the new Governor himself came down with his entourage from Piotrkov. Maximilian Flederbaum felt that the eyes of Heaven were fixed on him, and that he had made an impression which would stand him in good stead on the day of reckoning.

This was the brilliant occasion which Jacob Bunim utilized in order to get the new Governor to make his first private appearance at the Flederbaum's rather than at the Huntzes'. Von Miller had come to the dedication of the hospital as part of his public duties. But he was treated with such skill that he was won over at once to Jacob Bunim and Maximilian

Flederbaum. Besides, on Jacob Bunim's advise, Flederbaum turned the opening into a great patriotic demonstration. Two of the wards were named after members of the Imperial family, the Emperor and the Empress. In each ward a splendid portrait of the rulers of Russia looked down upon the beds. The Governor was charmed, and when Flederbaum petitioned him humbly to honour his house with a visit, he set a date at once.

The Huntzes had had every right to expect that the first private visit of the new Governor would be to them, but they had done nothing to make sure of it. They had relied on precedence and on their titles. The result was a set-back which was a blow to them and to their firm.

Among the Jews of Lodz the mark of honour which had fallen to the Jew Flederbaum caused much rejoicing. When one Jew was treated with distinction by the Government, the status of all the Jews was lifted. In workshops and groceries, in homes and synagogues, they spoke with pride of their Maximilian Flederbaum and his influence with the Government. Jews felt safe.

But one dreadful incident took place, the Friday night before the great reception at the Flederbaum mansion, which threw the population of Balut into a panic.

Through most of Thursday night two men, Tevyeh and Nissan, worked by the light of a small lamp on a proclamation to the workers of Lodz. Together they polished the phrases, with their bitter allusions to Flederbaum, the Governor, and the ruling powers at large; in simple language they appealed to the workers not to permit themselves to be fooled by the trickery of the rich, whom from the fortunes they had squeezed out of the exploited and starving masses detached an infinitesimal part and threw it back at those who were the producers of all wealth. On Friday Nissan did not go to work; he remained in the cellar making copies of the proclamation in his neat handwriting. Just before evening came, and the synagogues were still empty, because Jews were either at home or in the baths, Nissan sent out a few of his fellow-conspirators, and they stole into the syna-

[281]

gogues and posted up the proclamations on the notice-boards at the front, among the appeals and exhortations which Jews always found there.

When the congregations came to the services and began to read the proclamation, a shudder of dread passed through them. Such words had never been published in Lodz before. There was first the attack on Flederbaum, the blood-sucker, who would not employ Jews in his factory, but who had made millions from the sweat of others and who thought he was doing a noble thing because he provided hospitals for the exhausted and exploited workers; next was the attack on the Governor, who was no better than Flederbaum, since he represented the might which enabled Flederbaum to go on oppressing the masses; last, and most dreadful of all, was an attack on the Tsar and the court, the arch-enemies of the people.

It was Friday evening, and for twenty-four hours it was forbidden to Jews to tear paper. But how could one leave such a proclamation there? Might not word reach gentile ears? The police would come. The entire Jewish population of Balut would be involved.

Messengers were sent hastily to the Rabbi, and word came back from him that inasmuch as the situation practically involved danger to life, the laws of the Sabbath might be ignored. The proclamations were thereupon torn down, and the incident passed off safely.

The following night the Flederbaum mansion was ablaze with lights, and the great reception attracted all the leaders of Lodz's industrial and social life. Von Miller and his officers were the lions of the event, and never had Maximilian Flederbaum worked harder to please. Among the guests Yakob Ashkenazi, the new general agent of the firm, seconded the efforts of his employer. Resplendent in evening dress, with a rose in his buttonhole, he was everywhere, jesting, complimenting, and raising the mood of the evening.

He danced with Flederbaum's daughters, who found nothing better to say to him than that he didn't look a bit like a Jew. He could easily be taken for one of the Russian aristocrats. He sat down at the card-table with the officers of the

[282]

Governor's suite and, following the skilful example of his employer, managed to lose gracefully without seeming to have intended it. Before the night was over, he had confirmed his position as the most charming man in Lodz.

Flederbaum clung close to the Governor and finally drew him, too, into the card-games. It was the most convenient way of handing that important official a big bribe. The Governor appreciated the delicacy and generosity of the act and, warmed with wine and adulation, finally took Flederbaum to one side and told him that, in view of the way the latter was acting, he deserved to be let in on something important. The Governor happened to know that the plans for the new railroad line from St. Petersburg to Lodz had been completed, and the site for the station in Lodz had been decided on.

"You have shown, my dear Flederbaum," he hinted, "that you are the kind of man who can be trusted with such information."

"Your Excellency," said Flederbaum, flustered, "I hope to prove that to you again and again in the future."

The Governor smiled. It was a pleasure to do business with a man of this sort. A hint was enough. He indicated the location of the new station to be built, and returned to the card-table. Flederbaum saw to it that the money flowed even more freely in the direction of the Governor.

Before the reception ended he called over Yakob Ashkenazi, and gave him the information he had received. "This is a job for you," he said. "I expect you to handle it tactfully."

"I'll begin tomorrow morning," said Jacob Bunim.

"And now, Herr Ashkenazi, you can go back to your ladies."

Simcha Meyer Max Ashkenazi took the incident of the Governor and Flederbaum much more to heart than did the Huntze brothers. At table, trying in vain to interest Dinah, he inveighed against the stupidity and negligence of his employers.

"Their mind isn't on the business," he snarled. "They're busy with dances, chasing animals, fencing, and running after women. They hang out with people who can't do them any good. How do they expect the factory to hold its ground?"

Strictly speaking, it had nothing to do with the factory; but it had to do with the standing of the firm, and it had to do, as Max Ashkenazi expected, with money. He did not need to wait until Lodz found out about the new station and about the adjacent plots, as well as many along the line, which Yakob Ashkenazi bought up for Flederbaum. Whether it was a new station or an order for army supplies, the first local man to know about it would be the Governor; and if he intended to sell his information, it would be to the man who reached him first. Flederbaum resold his newly purchased lots to the Government, and even those which the Government did not buy up for the line rose enormously in value. The peasants who had sold the land in the country, the merchants who had sold it in the city, cursed Flederbaum and Yakob Ashkenazi when they learned what they had missed. Their curses were neither so deep nor so ingenuous as Simcha Meyer's. He calculated feverishly the

[284]

money his firm and he had lost, the money which Fleder-baum and his brother had probably earned. He plucked at his little beard and chanted the figures.

"Should have been mine, blast those peasant-headed Huntzes," he moaned.

As bad as the money loss was the personal insult he suffered. Lodz was talking about Yakob Ashkenazi. He, and not his brother, was the hero of the hour; and this poisoned Simcha Meyer's days and nights. If an Ashkenazi was talked about, admired, envied, or even hated, it had to be himself. Least of all should it be that empty-headed, smirking brother of his. If any firm was considered first among the factories of Lodz, it had to be the one he, Simcha Meyer Max Ashkenazi, represented.

True, he was only its general agent and not the first or largest beneficiary of its progress. But Max Ashkenazi had already learned to look on the Huntze factory with that prehensile proprietorial interest which he had displayed long ago in Chaim Alter's little hand-loom factory. When he increased the sales he thought of something more than the commissions that came his way. He thought of the future of the firm with which he would ultimately be connected in a more significant capacity.

In the first year of his connection with the Huntze brothers he revolutionized the sales system. Until his coming the firm of Huntze had sold goods on its slowly acquired reputation. It did not deign to compete. Its agents were sober, steady, old-fashioned men who did not run after business. This was not Max Ashkenazi's way. Sales were good; they had to be better. They always had to be better. He called in the agents and explained that a new order was about to be instituted. The old, quiet ways would no longer suffice. Looking at these elderly men he decided swiftly which of them would go first, for he realized that after their many years of service under the old régime they would resist, or be incapable of following, the new régime. And shortly after he had made the preliminary changes, he determined to set an example by going out on a big sales tour himself.

His knowledge of Russian was fragmentary. His habits were

not social. He hated drink and despised drinkers. He did not care for the average Russian merchant's idea of "a good time." But knowing what was expected of him, he schooled himself to passing nights in cabarets and brothels, drinking as little as possible, avoiding the use of the women, while he entertained his customers. Russian merchants were high livers, their tastes were gross, and they expected to celebrate every business deal with a riotous night. Max Ashkenazi was lavish for them, cautious with himself. He let them lose their heads; he kept his own. He returned from his first tour with a batch of orders which almost frightened Albrecht, the general director.

The factory was not Max Ashkenazi's business; in theory he had not even the right to put his nose in. But theories did not bother him. He knew that the Huntze brothers were learning to look on him as a sort of miracle man. If he wanted to help in the reorganization of the factory, so much the better. Besides, Max Ashkenazi made no frontal attack on Albrecht's status, but went about the supplanting of the enormous lazy and inefficient German as he had gone about the supplanting of Samuel Leibish. First undermine the man's standing; then fighting is unnecessary. He collapses of himself.

Albrecht had been good enough in the old days. He could drive the workers and he could keep up production. But he was utterly without ingenuity. He had no inventiveness. He did not co-ordinate the various departments and save power and labour by timely distribution of orders. He simply handed over the orders to the foreman. Simcha Meyer saw at once that this stiff, unadaptive system was costing the factory enormous sums, and, in transmitting orders, he began to instruct department heads himself, so that as the turnover increased, the productivity of the factory increased with it.

Albrecht felt his authority diminishing from day to day and could do nothing about it, for the worst of it was that this confounded interfering Jew knew what he was doing. Even the Huntzes could see that. Not that they had the slightest idea of the technical ingenuity of Simcha Meyer's arrangements, but even they could appreciate that at the end of the month the orders that had been filled were larger and more numerous, and the profits correspondingly greater. They asked Simcha Meyer in astonishment where he had learned all this.

"I learned it," said Simcha Meyer proudly, "in the old Talmudic university, under the special guidance of the famous experts Akiba and Gamaliel." The Huntzes took the statement seriously and were profoundly impressed.

Perhaps it was as well, reflected Max Ashkenazi, that the Huntze brothers were what they were, thick-witted, sensuous, without ambition, and eager for a good time. It would not have been easy to carry out his far-sighted program against a group of men who had a genuine interest in the factory, backed by intelligence and the will to control. For there began, with the Huntzes, the old story which had lost Reb Chaim Alter *his* factory. The Huntze boys wanted money—much money—money without accounting. Max Ashkenazi was the man to get it for them. Old Albrecht, asked for cash from the firm's reserves, would pull faces, would reply that it was difficult to withdraw liquid money. Max Ashkenazi told the brothers that there was money enough on hand, always, if one only knew how to manage. Here again Albrecht lost standing with the brothers and he began to tremble at the thought that before long he would be sent packing with all the other elderly employees. Timid by nature, lazy, easily consoled for the loss of prestige by the women Melchior provided for him with faithful regularity, he decided to meet the situation by submission, and Max Ashkenazi found that the actual control of the factory was passing into his hands more rapidly than he had expected.

All this was internal; it was felt in the factory; Simcha Meyer felt it. But in the city of Lodz his name had suffered eclipse, and it was his brother at whom fingers were pointed as the coming man. Even in Max Ashkenazi's own house he had to listen to the fulsome admiration which the handsome and stupid and lucky Yakob so easily provoked. Max Ashkenazi's mother-in-law took special delight in gurgling enthusiastically about Yakob Ashkenazi.

"You should have seen him today, my dear," she exclaimed

[287]

ecstatically, addressing her daughter, Dinah, "riding in his carriage down Piotrkov Street. He looked like a prince. All the people stared after him. It was positively impressive." She spoke as if Dinah had, in fact, never seen Yakob Ashkenazi since the quarrel between the two brothers. Simcha Meyer could feel how she enjoyed singing the praises of the other. What could he reply? He set his teeth, thinking to himself: "Wait, you fools. He has the luck, but time is with me. He must wait for things to fall into his lap; I make my own progress. The day will surely come when I, and not the Huntze sons, will control and own the greatest factory in Lodz. I will have done it for myself. When that day comes, Yakob Ashkenazi will be a nobody, as he deserves to be. My name, not his, will be mentioned respectfully in every home in Poland."

Whatever he did was always pointed, directly and indirectly, toward this end. If he changed the sales system and interfered with the production, it was not simply to increase his percentage of profits; it was, at least as much, to bring larger areas under his control. Before the day of open assumption of power came, he would have everyone connected with the firm—workers, foremen, experts, salesmen, and customers—feel that the master was Max Ashkenazi. So, later on, the transition to public acknowledgment of the private fact would be simple. The most important single step which Max Ashkenazi took toward the ultimate acquisition of the factory was the transformation of the form of ownership into that of a corporation. He persuaded the Huntze brothers to this decision by pointing out that, first, they could always realize cash on their stocks; second, they could push Goetzke out of the business by getting control of a majority of stocks. That the same could be done to them, by their *homme de confiance,* Max Ashkenazi, never occurred to the Huntze brothers. The suggestion would have sounded fantastic to them. Yet it was not to get rid of old Goetzke, who was no problem, that Max Ashkenazi worked so hard to bring about the change in the form of ownership. It was with the view to acquiring ultimately the majority control for himself. Indeed, his reward for effecting the change was a block of stocks.

[288]

He refused a cash bonus—thereby again impressing the Huntze brothers with his loyalty and devotion.

Shortly after this change Max Ashkenazi recaptured the leadership which he had lost to his brother in the public opinion of Lodz, by bringing off an extraordinary business coup.

It began very trivially, if not foolishly. Walking distractedly one day along the street, his mind running over a hundred confused duties, he was suddenly aware of a woman walking in front of him, a woman who had startled him into the most alert and excited attention.

It was not the woman herself. Max Ashkenazi was not given that way; and if he had been, this woman would hardly have interested him. No, it was not the woman; it was her dress. An astonishing dress it was, of a brilliant and alluring red, which Max Ashkenazi recognized at once as not having been produced in Poland. Others besides him had noticed the woman; but while they merely glanced on her with the passing curiosity of laymen, Max Ashkenazi had fixed on her the wolfish, concentrated gaze of the specialist. The dress thrilled him. It was *the* dress he had been looking for. He followed the woman, forgetting in his excited joy that his interest would most certainly be misconstrued and might lead to ludicrous and perhaps unpleasant consequences. After a while the woman noticed that he was following her. She turned off the busy streets and proceeded into a quieter section of the town. Near a garden railing she stopped, let the man catch up with her, and spoke to him.

"What are you following me for?" she asked.

"I'm interested in your dress," said Max Ashkenazi.

She shook her head. "It's no good," she said, obviously not believing him. "You'd better stop following me. I'm a decent woman."

"Where did you buy that dress?" asked Max Ashkenazi.

The woman laughed suddenly, a hearty peasant laugh. Apparently the man was determined to keep up the pretence. She looked at him again, saw that he was well dressed and belonged apparently to the upper classes, and was complimented, insulted, and amused all in one.

"But I'm not a streetwalker," she said. "It's silly to follow me. I have a husband."

"Will you sell me that dress?" asked Max Ashkenazi sharply. "I'll pay a good price for it."

"I didn't buy it in this country," said the woman, puzzled. "I got it in Germany."

"I'll pay whatever price you ask for it," said Max Ashkenazi, and drew out a crisp ten-rouble bill.

The woman stared. She had heard queer things about city people. There were men, she had been told, who didn't care for women, not in the ordinary way. They had odd desires; sometimes just for a woman's dress. She became slightly frightened. This man was obviously a Jew. The Jews, she had heard, also liked to fool Christians into quiet places, then kill them and use their blood for their own Jewish Easter services.

"What do you want my dress for?" she asked. "You're trying to fool me. You want something else."

But the sight of the ten-rouble note was too much for her, and she agreed to go with this queer man. She thought he would take her to some quiet house, instead of which he directed her to his offices. The employees gaped when he came walking in with her. He ordered one of them to go out and buy a good dress that would fit the lady, and when the dress was brought, sent her into an empty office to change. He gave her, besides the ten-rouble bill, a golden Imperial and sent her away, an utterly bewildered person.

He sat looking a long time at the dress, feeling the fabric and contemplating the colour. He knew quite well that the Huntze chemists could not duplicate it, but to make sure, he sent for the head chemist. The latter shook his head.

"It's a secret process," he said. "The Germans control that."

Max Ashkenazi nodded, and dismissed the man. He would find someone to duplicate the colour; if not in Poland, then in Germany.

A few days later Max Ashkenazi left for Frankfurt am Main. He arrived there a complete stranger, having his own reasons for not availing himself of the firm's connections. It was not at all difficult for him to make connections. He attended Sabbath services in one of the leading orthodox synagogues and became friendly with some of the worshippers. He knew that Frankfurt was one of the strongholds of German Jewish orthodoxy. It was a city in which it was no uncommon thing to find university professors, modern scholars, scientists, and doctors who wore skull-caps and studied the Talmud, ate only kosher food, and obeyed all the laws of Jewish ritual with the same fervid enthusiasm as the most religious Jews of Poland. Among such Jews Simcha Meyer Max Ashkenazi made a great impression, the more easily as, unlike most of the Polish Jews who visited Frankfurt, he was not on a money-raising mission and had not come to look for a way of earning a living. At the Sabbath service he announced a generous contribution for the upkeep of the synagogue, a gesture which attracted much attention. Thus he established contact with some of the best orthodox Jewish families and through them began to extend his inquiries for the kind of man he needed —a gifted chemist who could do a job quickly and quietly. He found his man: an orthodox Jew who was reputed to be one of the rising young scientists of Germany, but who nevertheless clung to traditional Jewish life in a manner that would have satisfied the most pious Chasid. This chemist returned with Simcha Meyer Ashkenazi to Lodz—and did not forget to put his phylacteries on in the morning, even on the train, in order to say his prayers in form. Simcha Meyer told no one about the chemist. He provided him with lodgings and a laboratory, giving him a piece of the red dress, and saying: "Get me that colour and you'll be well paid. And not a word to anyone."

For two months the chemist worked in secret and at the beginning of the third came to Max Ashkenazi with the formula. Then Max Ashkenazi gambled. He put half of the factory on the production of the new cloth, and when the new season opened, sent out every salesman with the material. It took instantly. The colour became the rage throughout Poland and Russia, and there was no one to compete with the Huntze firm. Orders declined among the competitors of Huntze, while the Huntze factory could not keep pace with

[291]

the demand. By letter, telegram, and special messenger the repeat orders came in. Max Ashkenazi raised the price and still could not keep pace with the orders. The Huntze factory had the best season of its career.

Max Ashkenazi's portion of the profits was considerable. He spent every rouble he made on stocks of the Huntze factory. He was as nearly satisfied with his coup as it was in his nature to be. But it was not the money and not the stock that gave him ultimate satisfaction; it was the fact that Lodz was talking once more about him, while his brother was almost forgotten. When he passed through the ill-paved streets in his carriage, he saw the significant glances which were thrown his way, and he could almost hear the respectful murmurs: "That's Max Ashkenazi, who used to be Simcha Meyer; he's the smartest man in Lodz. He's young, and he'll go far. He'll be the first man in the industry before long."

They did say such things; but they also said other things, which Simcha Meyer Max Ashkenazi did not guess at. They commented on his odd appearance, on the queer impression he made riding in a flashing carriage, of the incongruity of that nervous, excitable little Jew pulling abstractedly at his beard, trying to look as if he belonged in that handsome equipage. Max Ashkenazi seldom went on foot now, and yet he always sat in a carriage as though he had never climbed into one before—on the edge of the seat, or flung to one side, or holding on with both hands as if he were afraid of being pitched out on to the sidewalk.

That alone would have been reason enough to prompt Dinah to refuse to ride with him. Often he would say to her: "Diana, if you're going into town, I'll take you along in the carriage. I'm going there, too." Invariably she would reply: "Thank you, Simcha Meyer, I'd rather walk," or: "I'm not going to town. I'm going over to Mamma's"—although ten minutes before she had let fall the remark that she had to go into town.

Then Max Ashkenazi would climb furiously into the carriage and revenge himself on the world by ignoring the greetings of the less important people who saluted him from the sidewalk.

[292]

And then Lodz was suddenly at a standstill.

The city was like a hoggish gormandizer who goes on stuffing himself with food long after he has eaten all he needs, who goes on eating with the aid of artificial stimulants to his appetite, till he reaches the point of exhaustion and immobility and can go no further before the stomach-pump has done its work. Lodz had the indigestion of over-production.

There were not only the great factories, with their two steady shifts; there were the smaller mills, the tiny ones, the hole-in-the-wall and hand-loom factories, the subcontractors and sub-subcontractors, all of them turning out textiles steadily. And everything was done on credit, by means of promissory notes.

Notes provided the dowry when the son and daughter of two manufacturing families were led under the canopy. The young man simply endorsed his father-in-law's note, and so obtained his first supplies of cotton and wool. He gave the cotton and wool to some contractor to turn into fabrics and paid for the work with more notes. The contractor endorsed the notes and issued little notes of his own to the workers. The workers put their unreadable signatures on the little notes and used them for bread, potatoes, clothes, and rent.

In the same way there came from the villages local shopkeepers, business-men, sons-in-law just starting out on their own, and bought bales of goods for which they left behind their notes. The sellers did not ask for cash, for while the merry-go-round worked, notes were not examined; they were regarded as the equivalent of currency. And so workers, servants, teachers, all, were accustomed to the Lodz habit of notes. Contributions to charities, pledges in the synagogue, payments for big parties in the expensive restaurants—all notes. And there was no control. No one knew how much Lodz needed, whether in the way of factories or restaurants, of workers or of gay ladies in cabarets. There was an insane unreality and baselessness in the activity of the city. Whoever was clever, glib, and shameless, whoever could catch the mood of frantic and uncalculating paper-exchanging, set processes in motion, got his rake-off, and let the rest go to the devil. There was only one class which took no part in this lunatic hunt for quick riches, one class which went on grinding steadily at its task, the only class in touch with ultimate reality, with substance destined for use. This was the class of the workers. On their shoulders rested the platform on which the others danced the frenzied dance of unmerited and unearned profits.

And then suddenly everything stopped. A large bite stuck in the throat of the hoggish city. The mad eating and guzzling was at an end. The cleansing process was about to begin.

To make matters worse, a great drought struck the country at the same time. The Russian Orthodox priests carried their gold- and silver-embroidered banners and images in processions through the fields, and peasants knelt in prayer for rain, lest man and beast and grain perish. But no rain fell. The blazing sun rose morning after morning in a copper sky, and went through the round of heaven undimmed by the shadow of a cloud. The cornfields withered, the cattle dropped by thousands. Then when the harvest came and the peasants made ready to cut down the meagre sheaves which had escaped the heat, tremendous, belated rains began to fall, and what the drought had not destroyed was ruined by the rains. The land stank with the rotting bodies of unburied animals, and cholera and typhoid and scarlet-fever epidemics broke out. The peasants drove the Jews out of many of the villages, accusing them of having poisoned the wells. In other

[294]

villages the doctors and students who came down to stop the epidemics with quicklime, pitch, and carbolic acid were set upon as godless instruments of Satan.

No peasants came to the cities or to the country fairs. The goods bought in Lodz for that autumn season remained moveless on the shelves. And suddenly, for reasons which no one understood, notes ceased to be currency. Cash was wanted, and there was no cash. The notes were called in, protested, and discovered to be worthless. The paralysis crept slowly upward, from the shops to the wholesalers, from the wholesalers to the factories, from the factories to the banks. Banks began to close.

First went the little banks and the little manufacturers, the small, fly-by-night enterprises of recent growth: merchants who had never had any cash, subcontractors who had never owned their own looms, shopkeepers for piece goods, agents and commission men. They burned up very quickly, like dry stubble in an autumn field. Or else they put one in mind of poisoned mice running round convulsively. But they could not escape destruction, for the poison was in their veins, the poison of their unreal existence and purposelessness. They tried to sell whatever assets they had, but there were no buyers. Their notes were equally valueless.

The big fish withstood the shock somewhat better, though among these, too, there were heavy casualties. But for the most part they came through, battered but still alive. One after the other they laid off their workers and decided to wait for better times. There was no demand for finished goods. Also, there was no desire to get rid of the huge supplies of raw materials which filled the warehouses. The large factories worked one day in the week. Tens of thousands of workmen wandered the streets of the city.

Balut was silent. The looms stood still; tailors, stocking-weavers, shoemakers, seamstresses, embroidery-workers, covered their machines, so that they looked like corpses in a pestilence waiting for the hearse. Every worker ran around with notes which he had received for past work, trying to get something substantial for them.

"You can take that paper and use it you know what for,"

[295]

said the shopkeepers angrily when the workers tried to buy provisions with their notes.

The middle group, those between the big manufacturers and the tiniest business-men, wriggled hard and in part saved themselves. Wives had jewellery, bought in the happy paper-days, and stocks of goods or of raw material might be got rid of at a very low price. Others turned to more dubious means. Although it was late autumn and the days were cold and wet, an astonishing number of fires broke out in the city of Lodz. Night after night the sky reddened in various parts of the city. The buglers who gave the alarm woke up the population, and the powerful horses of the fire-brigades thundered through a thousand dreams. Those that woke up looked for the red patch in the sky and tried to guess who had succeeded that night in balancing his accounts, or, as some put it, "had lit Sabbath candles in the middle of the week."

If the insurance companies lost in the epidemic of fires, lawyers did not. There were civil and criminal processes on every hand; the courts were cluttered with cases. Judges and other officials took bribes from insurance companies and from factory-owners. Those who saw that the game was up got together their last possessions, slipped across the German frontier, and fled to America.

There was only one class which had no recourse in those days, one class which knew no tricks, lit no fires, offered no bribes, had nothing to turn to—the class of the workers. They had to stand and let the storm break on them. Worst of all was the lot of the Jewish and German workers who could not escape from the city. Most of the Polish workers went back to their farms, where, wretched though conditions were, one might at least find a husk to gnaw on. The women weavers returned to their parents' homes. A few of the young Jews had homes in the country to return to, but the majority were fastened in Lodz. They had no connections, no haven. The shops gave them no credit, the landlords would not wait. Hundreds and then thousands had to sleep in cellars and lofts and in the open. Some went to the woods outside the city and dug caves for themselves. Mothers took their children to factory foremen and asked them to take the young ones and give them nothing more than bread and water in exchange for a day's work. Women and girls wandered in the streets ready to sell their bodies for a bite of food or a night's lodging. Then the epidemic came to Lodz, and scarlet fever, diphtheria, and typhoid fever began to fill the hospitals.

The big Jewish manufacturers, those whom the storm had shaken but not uprooted, organized for philanthropic work. It was Maximilian Flederbaum who took the lead. He used his mansion as headquarters for meetings and enrolled the foremost figures of Lodz society, chiefly the elderly ladies. Kitchens were opened in Balut, doctors were engaged, burials arranged. Flederbaum's factory was practically closed, and he was losing money steadily, but he gave large sums to the charities and rescued the Jewish workers who were not permitted to enter his mills. He also set an example in the field. His carriage was seen every day in Balut. Children ran after it, and Flederbaum in person threw handfuls of copper and silver coins to them. He made the rounds of the kitchens and health-stations. He did more: he went into some of the wretched homes and spoke with unemployed weavers and their wives and children. On one occasion he even took off his overcoat and coat, rolled up his sleeves, and with his own hands—the hands of Flederbaum the multimillionaire—administered an alcohol rub to a weaver sick with typhoid! And on that same day he helped to lay out and wrap in cerements a dead worker. Lodz buzzed with the fame of Flederbaum's piety. The original incidents were multiplied many times and adorned with many pathetic details. The Jews mentioned Flederbaum's name with awe, and hearts were filled with gratitude and inspiration by the recital of his generosities and sacrifices. They forgave Flederbaum his unJewish ways; they even forgave him the apostasy of his daughters. For such a saint there was a special measure.

There was only one house in Balut where the name of Flederbaum was mentioned without awe and the story of his devotion to the poor was treated with bitter derision. This was the house of Tevyeh.

Like other weavers, Tevyeh was unemployed. All day long

[297]

his wife stood at a street-corner with a pailful of pickled cucumbers. In the evening she returned with a few greasy copper coins and a heart full of curses. The smaller children roamed the streets with little boxes of candy. The older children had left the house, each one to find some corner for himself or herself. The house was more miserable than ever; it was damp, cold, and lightless. There was no food or comfort in it. But Tevyeh seemed to notice nothing. Ill-dressed, with his military scarf wrapped tight round his throat, hungry—but not aware of it—he sat at his table, writing, or ran about the streets propagandizing and organizing, distributing the proclamations which he and Nissan had composed, slipping pamphlets secretly into willing hands, heartening new proselytes, promising better times, keeping resentment at white heat, pouring forth scorn on the givers of charity, attacking the Government and in a hundred ways preparing the revolution.

He carried on his work in the very soup-kitchens which the millionaire Flederbaum and his committees had provided for the starving workers of Balut. At the ugly tables where the workers sat before the thick bowls of watery soup and the heavy hunks of hard, black bread, Tevyeh argued with the victims and beneficiaries of the manufacturers. He directed himself in particular to the older weavers, who, as they gnawed the bread and drained the thin soup, blessed the name of Flederbaum, who was saving them from death by starvation. Tevyeh could not stand the pitiful gratitude of these workers. He pleaded with them passionately for their own sake, tried to get them to understand that the charity was a device, that at best it represented a tiny fragment of what was due the workers, that the rich distributed it only out of fear, that, whatever they did, the manufacturers were the enemies of the workers, and not their friends.

But Tevyeh and Nissan were not alone now, as in those remote days when they organized the first strike in Lodz. Their work had borne fruit, and among young workers and former Talmud students there had grown up groups of propagandists and organizers. They worked not only among the weavers, seamstresses, and stocking-workers, but among shop-clerks and book-keepers, who had until that time considered themselves the upper classes among the workers and who had at last discovered that they shared the same fate as the lowliest and most menial employees.

Proclamations began to blossom on Lodz walls, in Lodz synagogues, and even—so daring had the revolutionaries become—on the police and railway stations of the city. Crowds gathered round them and read them, until the police appeared and tore them down. Nissan and his fellow-conspirators worked steadily at turning out new proclamations. They copied out pamphlets. They smuggled in literature from other cities. The demand grew from day to day. The workers of Lodz were eager for enlightenment.

It came to such a point that in the very soup-kitchens the entrance of one of the big manufacturers or one of the wealthy ladies who fussed around the organization would be the signal for a demonstration, and from among the eaters of the charity bread would be heard loud cries: "Down with the bosses! Down with the exploiters!" On one occasion a great lady was so frightened that she sent for the police.

On the outskirts of the city, in the Constantine woods, masses of the workers collected, debated, discussed, and sang revolutionary songs. It seemed to them that their hunger had suddenly acquired significance and, instead of being mere brute suffering, pointed in a direction.

Nissan worked furiously, but under great handicaps. He could get, through underground channels, large enough quantities of Russian revolutionary literature, pamphlets, booklets, and leaflets. But he needed Yiddish material and could not get any. In despair he organized a group of copyists, and a dozen young men and women sat day and night making copies, by hand, of the translations which he prepared. But there were also the German workers to look after.

These were at once easier and more difficult to handle than the Jews. In recent years there had come into Lodz from across the German frontier a new type of German worker— the Social Democratic type, driven from the country by the anti-Lassalle enactments of Bismarck. These were wholly unlike the first kind of German weavers; they did not sing homeland songs or hymns; they did not go to church and listen to sermons glorifying the Kaiser. They read forbidden books, and evenings they sat in the inns and drank enormous quantities of beer and smoked countless cheap cigars. The beer and cigars made the work miserable for Nissan; but if he managed to accustom himself to the acrid atmosphere of one of these saloons and to put down at least one drink— though he loathed the stuff—he found a sympathetic and intelligent audience. Nissan revived the German which he had learned in his boyhood from Moses Dessauer's commentary and the philosophic books he had read without understanding. He was glad to hear the revolutionary songs of these weavers and to listen to their stories of Lassalle and the Social Democratic movement. His task was to waken them to action in the new land, to make them part of the revolutionary movement in Poland. In spite of his awkward and halting German, he transmitted some of his enthusiasm to the big-bodied Germans who sat smoking and drinking hour after hour in the saloons.

Like his one-time schoolmate Simcha Meyer Max Ashkenazi, Nissan had no faith in the future of the hand-looms. Sooner or later they would go. But it was from his own point of view that he laid the emphasis of the future on the steam factories. Nissan did not deceive himself. He saw that the hand-loom workers, particularly the Jewish ones, were not a genuine proletariat. Hand-looms made possible little capitalist enterprises on slender beginnings, and therefore every hand-loom worker looked on himself as a potential employer. It was only in the steam factories that the workers realized how impassable was the gulf between them and the owning classes. From the revolutionary point of view, then, Nissan hoped for little from Balut and its workers. The true proletariat was among the non-Jews who worked in the steam factories, the thousands that he saw every morning clattering in their wooden clogs through the streets in response to the shrilling of the sirens, every one with his lunch-basket, the hosts that never dreamed of redemption through individual success and the exploitation of others.

Yes, while the depression lasted, while the Jewish workers
[300]

in Balut hungered and suffered cold, they would be with the revolution. Let better times come, and each man would be for himself, thinking of his own future. Nissan heard the promise of the revolution, not in the noisy cries of the Balut weavers, but in the rattling of clogs which came from the feet of the thousands who tramped every morning into the steam factories. Here the process of centralization and concentration of wealth was going on, according to Marxist law, while in Balut there was perpetual decentralization, which led to demoralization. The employers were not bourgeois, the workers were not a proletariat. He therefore preferred his work among the German workers, especially those of the post-Bismarck period, who had brought with them a readiness to listen to his propaganda. In the darkest days of the crisis he put his faith in them, so that from opposite corners, and for opposing reasons, both he and Max Ashkenazi looked for a future to the great steam factories.

Meanwhile there had been growing up into the revolutionary movement someone whom Nissan had hardly ever noticed and whom he used now for all sorts of odd jobs—and chiefly for running errands and carrying revolutionary literature—without noticing that something more was involved than service to the cause. This was Bashke, the fifteen-year-old daughter of Tevyeh. Among his children she was the only one who had ever shown an inclination to side with her father. At a tender age she had been put out to work in the mills, and when she came home from work, exhausted and sick, her first thought was to prepare something for her father. She had never known what it was to be proud of a good dress or a new pair of shoes, but, still a child, had begun to feel, rather than understand, how true and honest were her father's arguments.

She even tried to influence her mother, and when the latter poured out curses on the head of her husband, Bashke, trembling with unhappiness, would say: "Mamma, you mustn't talk like that about Father. You ought to be proud of having such a husband."

"I'm just bursting with pride," her mother screamed, and she shook her finger under her daughter's nose. "Bashke, don't let that father of yours mislead you or, as I stand here, you'll finish up in prison with him."

Bashke did her best to see that her father was dressed in something better than rags. She mended his shirts and, while her mother stood at the street-corner with her pail of pickles, prepared a sort of meal for her father. She made his bed for him, so that he might be able to sleep comfortably after the long, weary day of furious argument and propaganda. It was her kindness and devotion which made of that wretched cellar, with its poverty, its darkness, and its curses, a home for Tevyeh. Sometimes in the night she would creep into her daddy's bed, to lie near him and make him feel that he was not utterly alone in his struggle.

Deeper and more fearsome was her love for Nissan, to whom she never dared to show any tenderness, to whom, in fact, she hardly dared to speak at all before he had spoken to her. In the nights, when he sat at the table copying manifestos and pamphlets, she would lie on the wooden bench which served for her bed, pretending to sleep, but unable to close her eyes because of him. She watched the long, bony fingers flying over the paper, she looked intently at the pale, ascetic face, marvelling at him who, so young, had already suffered so much, in distant places, for the sake of the liberation of the workers, and who in the midst of privation and persecution had gone on studying and teaching himself, so that he might be a leader in the coming revolution. During the day she trembled with happiness when he asked her for some service, and as he grew into the habit of using her as his regular messenger, she began to feel that she had become his partner in the great work. She was glad that there was no work for her in the factory. She hoped that the unemployment would last a long time, so that she might be at Nissan's beck and call. Herself uneducated, barely able to write a poor Yiddish letter or struggle through a simple book, she did not let herself dream of anything more than these humble services in connection with Nissan. Scarcely daring to breathe, lest he might notice her and be disturbed, she sat on the edge of the chair, waiting for him to finish the letter which he would ask her to carry secretly to one of his men in another part of the town.

She carried his messages and pamphlets in a food-basket, covering them with rags. She understood as well as he how important secrecy was.

"Take this, Bashke," he said, briefly. "And remember, if you get caught, not a word as to where you got the books from."

She nodded. She wanted to tell him that she would let the police cut her open before she would say anything, but she did not trust herself to speak, and without a word she picked up the basket and went up the stairs into the street.

XXX

Martin Kuchinsky, former student of the Veterinary Institute, lived on the outskirts of Lodz. Expelled from the university for belonging to a branch of the Polish Social Revolutionary "Proletariat," he had given up all prospect of a career, and devoted himself entirely to the movement. It was in his room that one of the first secret hand-presses of the revolutionaries was set up, and from this little house near the woods a steady stream of proclamations and leaflets flowed out to the workers.

Kuchinsky sat, pen in hand, at his desk, looking impatiently at his comrade, who stood at the press, with dissatisfaction on his face.

"What is it, Felix?" he asked, pushing back the shock of blond hair which had a habit of falling over his eyes.

"These first copies are smudged," answered Felix, a tall young Jew with eye-glasses on his sharp, hooked nose, with a thick head of curly hair and a tiny, pointed beard. "The next will be better, I think. Let me have some paper, Martin."

Near the kitchenette in the workroom sat two young women, one of them a bright blonde, with a golden cross at her throat. She was the school-teacher Wanda Chmiel, who was living in free love with the expelled student Kuchinsky. The other, small, dark, with the black hair and black eyes of a gypsy, was the biology student Maria Licht. The two girls took the sheets as Felix lifted them off the press, dried them, and piled them in neat stacks.

[304]

"I don't care what you tell me, Felix," said Kuchinsky, suddenly. "I say this proclamation is no good. It won't appeal to the workers."

Felix put down the hard rubber roller and fixed his eyes on his comrade.

"Remember, Martin," he said, and his voice sounded frightened, "you're talking about the Tseka—the Central Committee."

"My dear Felix," said the other, laughing, "you really remind me of the Talmudists. You talk about the Tseka with the same awe as Jews mentioning their Rabbinic lawgivers. If I had my way, I'd draw up a proclamation which would lift the workers out of their skins. Something hot—and dripping. . . ."

"It's always blood with you, Martin, blood, blood, blood," said Felix, grimacing. "Always violence and murder. It's no good, I tell you. When you talk to a man, appeal to his intelligence, not to his instincts."

"I happen to be a veterinary," said Kuchinsky, "and I know that the only thing you can do with the carcass of a horse is skin it. You don't talk logic and sweet words to it. You're too much the lawyer; you can't get out of your legalities and documents."

"I believe in the power of the word," answered Felix, passing the roller over the paper.

"Above all," said Kuchinsky, dryly, "you're a Jew, and you're afraid of the sight of blood. Your methods may be all right among the little tailors and hand-loom workers and pedlars in Balut. They're no good for our kind. Our kind like something hot, and dripping. The Tseka doesn't understand our people, can't get next to it. And no wonder; just a bunch of intellectuals, that's all it is. They've never been in contact with our workers, they don't know the language, so all they do is moralize at them, preach sermons, like a damn rabbi. . . ."

Felix put down the roller and wiped his hands on a piece of paper.

"Martin," he said, restlessly, "this isn't the first time I've heard you speak like this. And I don't like it. There's an

[305]

anti-Semitic stink about it, and you know that doesn't belong in our movement."

Martin leaned back and laughed uproariously. "There it is!" he shouted. "You just can't keep down the Jew in you! The Jew who smells anti-Semitism everywhere. It's impossible to talk with one of you sensitive Semites. . . . Go ahead, you moralist, you, with the printing. It's getting late and we've got another proclamation to turn out. Give me the roller and you go back to the cases."

Felix cleaned his hands again and slowly, unskilfully, began to pick the letters from the cases with his fingers.

Felix Feldblum had not been intended to be a printer. Actually he was an ungraduated law student who, like his friend Martin Kuchinsky, had given up his career. Unlike Kuchinsky, however, he had not been expelled from the university, but had left of his own free will, for like all young Russian revolutionaries of that epoch he had considered the pursuit of private studies and a personal career unethical and anti-revolutionary. He had broken off his studies in order to go forth and work among the masses.

Felix Feldblum belonged by birth to the higher bourgeoisie. His father was the owner of several glass-factories and brick-kilns, and his opposition to the class into which he was born began even before his father's death. He had openly declared himself on the side of his father's workers, had agitated among them and urged them to strike for better pay and shorter hours. When his father died and the property reverted to Felix, who was an only son, the latter sold out all his interests and turned over every rouble to the Proletariat organization, so that it might be enabled to extend its propaganda among the Polish workers and peasants, the victims of Tsaristic oppression.

Himself the son of a Jew, Feldblum knew that the Jewish masses suffered under severer repressions than the Polish masses; nevertheless it was not to the Jewish masses that he devoted his revolutionary activities.

He had had no contact with the Jews. In the village where his father's glass-factories and brick-kilns stood, he had seen only Poles, and the language of the Jews, their life, their

[306]

manners, and their problems, were strange to him. In his
father's house the servants, the guests, and even the nurse
had been Polish. His teachers, too, had been non-Jewish. The
local priest had been a frequent visitor. Feldblum the elder
had considered himself a Pole, not a Jew. The only Jews
Felix had seen had been merchants who came into his father's
office, and pedlars and junk-buyers who passed through the
village. He had nothing in common with these queer persons who stood humbly before his father, hat in hand, and
spoke a strange, singsong Polish jargon.

Shortly after he entered his teens, he had been sent by his
father to an uncle in Moscow, and there Felix went through
the Gymnasium, or high school, and entered the university.
There too, in his uncle's house, there had been no sign or
memory of a Jewish life. The language was Russian, the manners, interests, and culture were Russian. Not that Felix was
ever permitted to forget that he was a Jew. There were frequent reminders, in the high school and at the university.
But this Jewishness which was thrown in his face was something quite negative; it was a disease; it was a sick growth
which he could not cut out, but which meant only discomfort and misunderstanding.

The only thing he had in common with Jews was this mis-
fortune, this entry in his passport. Their language, literature,
and tradition meant nothing to him and could not have appealed to him. The entry in the passport said: "Of the Jewish
religion." But as far as he knew, Felix had never belonged to
any religion. He had never had any religious impulses, and
when he was attracted to the revolutionary movement, he
soon stifled any inclinations in that direction. He had not the
faintest interest in the collection of laws which had been
given to some wandering Hebrew tribes at the foot of a
mountain called Sinai, in the interior of Asia.

Yes, he knew that the Jews were more severely repressed
and oppressed than the Poles; but then Felix had learned from
his non-Jewish teachers and comrades that the Jews consisted
mostly of merchants, shopkeepers, pedlars, agents, and smugglers; it was an unproductive class which never did any work
itself, but lived on the work of others, of proletarians and

[307]

peasants. Therefore Felix Feldblum the revolutionary could have nothing to do with Jews. In any case, the revolution would not be made by Jews, for even if they were inclined that way, they were few and without power. The liberation would come through the million-headed mass of peasants, and then Jews, too, would learn the meaning of freedom. The revolution made no distinction between races and nations; it would bring freedom to Poland, too. The Jewish student Feldblum became an enthusiastic member of the Narodnik party. Later, when the Polish revolutionary organization Proletariat was founded and Polish students formed their own circles, Feldblum went over to them. He left the university, despising the thought of becoming a member of the privileged classes, and returned to Poland. There he threw himself into the underground revolutionary movement, working at first in his father's village, and passing later to Lodz, the great industrial centre. There were many Jewish workers in Lodz, hand-loom weavers, shoemakers, tailors, and others. But they were concentrated in Balut, and to Felix Feldblum they were all one with the bankers, the small merchants, the pedlars and agents who filled the streets of Lodz with their excited chaffering and money-chasing. Most of them were dressed in those funny, long gaberdines which helped to fuse them into a single class, and they all behaved alike too; they were all nervous and restless, they all gesticulated, and they all spoke singsong. In the cafés, on the sidewalks, in the dirty little shops into which he peeped, they were everywhere the same.

And as against them there were the thousands of non-Jewish workers who streamed into the factories every morning, peasants from the country, massive, steadfast, reliable types, true sons of the proletariat. Feldblum was drawn to them rather than to that suspicious mixture of worker and bourgeois which swarmed in Balut. It was for the Polish workers that Feldblum had given up his university career; for them he had refused to touch one rouble of the fortune which his father had left him, and for them he lived the hard and dangerous life of a conspirator. For them, too, he was standing now at the type-case of the press and with unskilled fingers

[308]

putting together the proclamation for the workers.

His reward from Polish workers and peasants had not always been proportionate to his devotion. More than once he had encountered suspicious looks and heard strange, unfriendly words from those to whose liberation his life and energies were dedicated. Those suspicious looks proclaimed him a stranger. He spoke Polish without a trace of a Jewish or other accent; his use of the language was often purer and more correct than that of many a full-blooded Pole. But there was little of the Pole in his face; the thick mop of curly hair, the thin, hooked nose, the tall, lean figure, and the dark, clever face were not Polish. Even in his father's factory the workers had been afraid of him, had suspected some Jewish trick, when he came to encourage them to revolt against the factory-owner. The village priest had been outspoken about it.

"Very nice of you, young man," he said, "to take an interest in the welfare of workers. But I don't think you ought to mix in."

"But why not?" asked Feldblum.

"Well, if you want me to be frank with you, I'll tell you. You're a stranger, a foreigner; you're a Semite, who doesn't understand the soul of a Christian people. . . . Leave all that sort of thing to us."

In discussions between revolutionaries and patriots Feldblum was pulled up sharply more than once. The patriots told him bluntly that he could not be expected to have the right point of view; he was a Jew. In the party, among the revolutionaries, that sort of talk was not heard. There the distinctions Jew, gentile, Christian, were unknown; but it often occurred to Feldblum as a queer circumstance that in the party work he was invariably assigned to the inside, technical jobs, the writing of articles, the printing of circulars, translations, and so on. It was queer. They would not send him out and let him do field work, in direct contact with the masses. And why? Because he was a poor speaker or because his Polish was deficient? Not at all. He was a good speaker, and he loved speaking. His Polish was excellent. But the party, while not itself recognizing the distinction between Jew and gentile, submitted to the existence of that prejudice among the workers and acknowledged that the workers would listen to attacks on Christianity from one of their own which they would not tolerate from the lips of a Jew.

Felix Feldblum suffered. He knew that this irrational attitude on the part of the workers was a survival which had to be uprooted; and the fact that the party, in its strategy, confirmed the attitude hurt him doubly. He suffered most, probably, from the repression of his natural talent for speaking. He longed to face masses of workers, to be in human contact with them, to talk, argue, persuade, win over, and inspire.

He was in the same position, in fact, as thousands of other assimilated Polish Jews. He was for ever on the watch for mention of his Jewishness, ready both to repudiate and to defend at the first signal of what he thought was prejudice. So now he was wounded by Kuchinsky's remark that the proclamation which the Tseka had prepared and which they were printing would not appeal to the workers because it was alien to the spirit of the Polish working-class and sounded more like a sermon delivered in a synagogue.

Certainly he disagreed with Kuchinsky's essentially terroristic philosophy, with its perpetual appeal to steel and fire, to swords and guns and bombs. He believed rather in the ultimate power of the ethical concept, backed by the inevitable laws of historic evolution. Only he would not have admitted that this divergence in view was characteristic as between Polish and Jewish groups, and that his inclination toward milder and more spiritual methods had something to do with the remnants of Jewish influence in his family. He saw the difference in philosophies; he attributed it to individual diversity. He was convinced that the right appeal to reason and morality would win the masses, and he proceeded enthusiastically with the printing of the Tseka proclamation. He felt that the time was peculiarly opportune now for a mighty appeal. The workers were embittered and disillusioned; most of the factories were closed or employing only a small fraction of their staffs. And here May 1st was approaching, the day which had, only a few years back, been declared by the international congress in Paris to be the day of the workers throughout the world. It was the first festival that Feldblum had ever acknowledged. He had never been told about the Jewish holidays, and therefore he knew neither New Year nor Day of Atonement nor Passover; he had never been inducted into the Christian Church; therefore he knew nothing about Christmas or Easter. May Day was his first experience of a day of celebration set apart from all other days. He wanted this festival to be magnificent and unforgettable. Not a worker should go to the factories. By thousands, by tens of thousands, the weavers of Lodz should parade through the streets, demonstrating the power of their organized will, which was about to liberate Poland from the tyranny of the Tsar, and themselves from the oppression of the bosses.

"This proclamation will do it!" he said contradicting Kuchinsky. "They'll answer it to a man."

Late in the night, when all the proclamations had been printed, Felix Feldblum and his friend Maria Licht left Kuchinsky's house and made their way home. They left separately and, like the experienced conspirators they were, walked a long time through quiet, out-of-the-way streets, making sure that they were not being followed. Near the house where they lived together as man and wife—Feldblum passing as a commission merchant—they rejoined each other.

"Nobody saw you?" asked Feldblum.

"No," answered the girl. "And you?"

"No one."

Their relationship was the exact inverse of that which obtained between Kuchinsky and Wanda Chmiel. The latter were man and wife in effect, without having married; Feldblum and Maria Licht were married for purposes of convenience, but did not live together as man and wife. They slept in separate beds and never touched each other. The arrangement was not uncommon among the revolutionary conspirators of Russia and Poland in those days.

"I'd like to be a few weeks older and see what happens on the 1st of May, see how the workers respond to the proclamation," said Feldblum as he undressed.

"They'll respond," said Maria Licht confidently. "They'll demonstrate."

They lay down to sleep in their separate beds. Dawn began

to glimmer in at the windows. In thousands of homes little naphtha lamps were being lit as the sirens began to scream across the city, calling the workers to the factories.

The workers of Lodz did strike and demonstrate, but it was neither on May 1st, the day of the international revolutionary movement, nor on May 3rd, the forbidden day of the Polish patriots, but on May 5th, an ordinary working-day.

After nearly a year of partial paralysis, the mills and factories of Lodz had begun to pick up speed, but there was a general movement among the manufacturers to indemnify themselves for their losses during the depression, and, as if by common agreement, they announced a general pay-cut of ten per cent. The workers, embittered by the long period of privation, in debt up to the ears, restless, moreover, as the result of the continuous propaganda issuing from the revolutionaries on the one hand and the secret Polish patriotic societies on the other, refused to accept the cut and struck.

The strike was far from complete. Those that decided to leave the looms stationed themselves near those who wanted to go on working, and argued with them. Arguments failing, violence followed, and the strikers dragged non-strikers away from their stools. From the looms the strikers proceeded in groups to the engine- and boiler-rooms and were prevented from making an attack only by the warning that they were liable to blow themselves up together with the factory and the non-striking workers.

In the streets masses of weavers, spinners, drivers, seamstresses with kerchiefs on their heads, marched in demonstration, pulling along with them sympathizing passers-by, and singing revolutionary and patriotic songs. They went from factory to factory, calling on their fellow-workers to put down their tools.

The owners and foremen of the factories in which the workmen had not struck ordered the gates closed. The strikers smashed the gates and poured into the factories. Many of the loyal workers joined them at once; those who refused were assaulted and thrown out of the factories.

"Up with the workers! Long live the brotherhood of labour!" rang through the city.

"Down with the employers! Down with the blood-suckers!"

The smaller Jewish employers, terrified by the demonstration, yielded at once and restored the pay-cuts. The larger employers stood firm. The workers in the Huntze factory struck in a body and sent a delegation to negotiate with the owners. They addressed themselves first to the nominal director of the factory, Albrecht.

Hat in hand, scraping their shoes on the rough wooden floor outside, lest they should dirty the shining parquetry, they sidled timidly into Albrecht's office.

"What do you want?" asked the fat director, reclining sleepily in his chair.

"We want to present a petition to the high-born director, if he pleases, not to take ten per cent off our pay. We can't go on working at the new rates."

"I'll talk it over with the noble owners," said Albrecht. "Meanwhile go back to your looms."

"We want an assurance from the high-born director that we'll get the old pay. Otherwise we can't return to the looms."

"I can't give you an assurance; we don't give assurances," answered Albrecht. "It's up to the owners. If they feel like it they'll restore the old pay. And if you want them to do you this favour, you'd better go back to work at once."

"We hope the high-born director won't be angry with us," said one of the older workers, "but may we ask that at least those who have wives and children to support shouldn't have their pay reduced. We can't feed our little ones at the new rates."

"Then why in hell did you marry and have children?"

[314]

exploded Albrecht, the bachelor. "The factory isn't respon
sible, is it?"

The timidity of the workers disappeared as if by magic.

"You filthy swine!" howled a German worker in corduroy
trousers.

"Son of a bitch!" came in Polish from another worker.
"Swabian hog!"

"Give it to him!" shouted others. "For our daughters, for
the girls he bought for a few dirty kopecks!"

"Take a couple of inches of fat off him, for the wives he
forced to lie down for him!"

Albrecht, astounded and alarmed by the change of tone,
rose ponderously from his large, heavy chair and took a few
steps toward the door. He got to it, but not unassisted. A
dozen hands were laid on his huge, clumsy body, and he was
propelled and pulled down the corridor. Melchior, in the
green hunting costume, tried to interfere, but went down, his
nose and mouth bleeding.

Albrecht fell, but there were enough workers to drag him,
screaming at the top of his voice, into the factory yard. They
pulled at his limbs and hair, they ripped the clothes off his
back, they battered him in blind rage.

"Hang him! Hang him! Cut the bastard's throat!" shouted
dozens of voices.

"Take his pants down and let him have it with a whip!"
screamed a woman's voice.

A few of the older workers shoved Albrecht's head into a
sack and tied the mouth with string. Then they bound his
hands to a broom, forced the almost fainting director into a
filthy wheelbarrow, and paraded him round the factory yard.

They spat on him, shouted unspeakable insults, and
screamed with laughter as they pushed the wobbling wheelbarrow, with its grotesque, groaning burden, through the
crowd. Seamstresses, hysterical with rage, lifted up their
dresses and showed the director their naked buttocks, forgetful of the fact that he could see nothing.

From the yard of the Huntze factory the workers, wearied
of their sport with Albrecht, rushed in a body toward the
Flederbaum factory.

"Bring the dirty Jew out!" they shouted as they ran through the streets. "Hang him on a lamp-post."

"Thirty per cent more pay or we'll break every window in his damned mansion and throw the furniture into the street!"

But by the time they reached the Flederbaum factory they found the gates shut, and in front of it a detachment of armed soldiers in command of a stern, bearded officer. Flederbaum himself was seated in his office, a revolver on his desk, the police commissioner of Lodz and several officers opposite him. One after another workers were brought in by policemen. The police commissioner put the same question to all of them, but did not wait for an answer.

"Why aren't you at work?"

"Your Highness! I can't buy enough food for my family on the pay—" began the worker.

"Shut your mouth, you scum!" shouted the police commissioner.

If the worker tried to say something more, he was stopped by a blow on the jaw.

Some of the workers were not even questioned. The police commissioner looked at them ferociously. "That's the face of a criminal," he snarled. "Keep him under arrest."

When the corridor was filled with workers who had been hauled in and arrested, the police commissioner posted several armed policemen at each end of the column and issued the order: "Take every damned one of them to the station. Don't let a single one escape." But when the column of arrested workers reached the street, they found it blocked by strikers. The army officer stationed at the gate drew his sword, waved it in the air, and shouted: "Get out of the way, you dogs!"

The mass of workers remained wedged across the street.

"Out of the way," yelled the officer, "or I'll shoot you down, you swine!"

Still the workers did not retreat. On the contrary, the mass moved slowly and ominously nearer the gate. The women in the crowd took off their coloured kerchiefs and waved them with friendly gestures at the soldiers, calling to them with pleading voices.

[316]

"Boys, you wouldn't shoot us down, would you? You wouldn't shoot your own flesh and blood, Christians like yourselves?"

The officer glanced swiftly from the crowd to the detachment of soldiers and back. He was alarmed. There was something appealing in the voices and gestures of the women, and he suspected that if he did not act at once, it would be too late to act at all.

"Aim!" he barked.

There was a clatter as the guns were brought up to the shoulder. The muzzles pointed straight into the crowd. For a moment the officer waited, hoping that the gesture would be enough. But the crowd did not budge. There was not anywhere a sign of fear.

"Fire!"

An irregular salvo broke the silence and was followed by a wild screaming and wailing, in which the voices of women predominated. The crowd broke, turned, and tried to retreat, but the rear ranks moved slowly, and the howling, panicky mass remained jammed before the factory gates. The detachment of soldiers, with bayonets fixed, kept thrusting at the terrified, squirming mass, which trampled blindly on the wounded. Slowly the square before the factory gates was cleared. The police arrested as many as they could gather in. When the square was empty the police commissioner came down and congratulated the officer on his firm handling of the situation.

"They'll all be back at work tomorrow," he said significantly.

But they were not back at work the next day. On the contrary, the incident before the gates of the Flederbaum factory had sent a wave of fury through all the workers of Lodz, and not a single factory opened the next morning. Dressed in their Sunday clothes, the workers assembled, by tens of thousands, in front of the police station, yelling for the release of the arrested workers. They also yelled for the police commissioner to come out and speak with them.

During the night an incident unparalleled in the annals of Lodz had taken place. A worker whose father had been shot

[317]

down at the factory gates had stolen into the police station and had stabbed to death the favourite dog of the police commissioner, a wolf-hound of the purest breed. The man was caught. The police commissioner was awakened and told what had happened. He dressed and came down to the station. He looked at the dead dog and at the arrested worker and said: "A hundred lashes with the nagaika."

At the seventieth stroke the worker no longer screamed, and at the seventy-fifth he no longer threw his limbs about in agony. The lashing did not stop. When the hundred was counted out, the police commissioner told the worker to get up and go home. The worker did not get up because he was dead, as a doctor who was called certified.

The police commissioner shook his head. "That was a mistake," he said. "We should have given him a rest every twenty-five strokes."

The commissioner instructed four men to cart the body out of the town and bury it somewhere in the woods. The police obeyed, and the commissioner hoped that nothing more would be heard about the incident. But that very night the story got out, and the workers assembled before the police station howled that they wanted to speak with the police commissioner. They wanted to ask him for the body of their dead comrade.

The police commissioner called out the fire-brigade and ordered them to turn the hoses on the crowd. The cold water neither budged the crowd nor cooled its fury. On the contrary, some of the workers began to pull up the paving stones and to throw them through the windows of the station.

In other parts of the city roaming bands of workers broke open the whisky shops of the Government monopoly. Word was brought to the police commissioner. He realized suddenly that he was faced, not with a crowd of workers, but with a city in revolt. Frightened, he telegraphed an account to the Governor at Piotrkov, with the question: "What orders?"

The Governor at Piotrkov telegraphed to the Governor General at Warsaw:

"What orders?"

[318]

The Governor General at Warsaw telegraphed to St. Petersburg:

"What orders?"

Petersburg answered Warsaw:

"Crush without mercy! Use bullets freely!"

Warsaw answered Piotrkov:

"Crush without mercy! Use bullets freely!"

Piotrkov answered Lodz:

"Crush without mercy! Use bullets freely!"

The police commissioner sent a messenger to the commander of the garrison to send out the troops. The commander sent back a message that there were not enough troops on hand for such an emergency. The Cossacks were needed.

The police commissioner telegraphed to Piotrkov: "Not enough troops on hand. Cossacks needed." Piotrkov relayed the message to Warsaw, and Warsaw sent out at once a regiment of the hated and dreaded Cossacks.

But before the Cossacks arrived, the mobs had everything their own way. They smashed every whisky store in town and drank as much as they could; what they could not drink they poured into the gutters. The party leaders, revolutionaries and patriots alike, pleaded passionately with the workers to leave the whisky alone; the workers refused to listen. They wanted to get blind drunk, and did. When they could hold no more, they armed themselves with lighted torches and ran through the shuttered streets.

The first person the mob found was a terrified little tailor, almost a hump-back, with big black whiskers. They seized him, lifted him in the air, and proclaimed him King of Poland.

"Long live the King of Poland!" they howled, and carried the babbling, stammering tailor at the head of the procession.

"Hurray!" yelled others, and pressed forward to kiss the tailor's dangling feet.

But suddenly the mood of the mob changed.

"Down with the Jews!" single voices began, and increased in number and power. "Down with the Jews!" the chorus was

[319]

taken up. The leaders of the mob turned in the direction of Balut. "Break open the Jewish shops! Teach the Jews a lesson!"

In Balut the Jews put up a stiff resistance. Butchers, draymen, porters, apprentices, armed themselves with axes, iron bats, and sticks and attacked the rioters fiercely. In Feifer Street, which was the street of the beggars, thieves, and pimps, the women poured boiling tar down out of upper-storey windows on the demonstrators. One young butcher swung his ax so fiercely at a rioter that he split his head from the crown of his skull to his chin. The crowd retreated, carrying the ghastly corpse with them to exhibit it in other parts of the town.

"Catholics! Christians! Look! This is the work of the Jews!"

"Down with the unbelieving dogs! Down with the murderers of the Christians!"

Rumours were born on the spot and spread with the rapidity of lightning.

"The Jews have set fire to a church!" women screamed.

"The Jews have torn down holy images and spit on them!"

"Down with the Jews!"

"Cut the throats of the blasphemers!"

The mounted Cossacks, riding hard from the nearest camp, arrived on the outskirts of Lodz in the afternoon of the next day. With them was the Governor. The police commissioner went out to meet them.

"What's the news, commissioner?" asked the Governor.

"A pogrom against the Jews, Your Excellency," answered the police commissioner, standing stiffly at attention.

The Governor pulled at his moustaches and said, reflectively: "Not bad." He smiled. "That will quiet the mob. Excellent, in fact."

He turned to the colonel in command of the Cossack regiment. "I think we'll spend a day or two out here," he said. "You'd better send word down the line."

The colonel issued orders to pitch camp, and within a few minutes the regiment was dismounted.

For two days the Cossacks remained quietly outside the city, while in the streets drunken mobs, armed with daggers

[320]

and iron staves, rioted against the Jews. On the third day, when the fury of the populace had worn itself out, the command to advance on the city was given, and the Cossacks cleared the streets without difficulty. The rioters were exhausted; their blood-lust was satisfied.

Some hundreds among the stragglers were arrested. The wretched little tailor who had been "crowned" King of Poland was hunted out and brought before the Governor. Wide-eyed, white as a sheet, trembling with terror, he stood before the Russian official, trying to understand the accusation which was brought against him.

"I understand you proclaimed yourself King of Poland," said the Governor, doing his best to suppress a smile.

"Your honour, God bless you and keep you," babbled the tailor. "I don't know what happened. I was just walking along the street when they got hold of me and lifted me up and began to shout: 'Hurray for the King of Poland!' I swear by God, and by God's son and his sacred wounds, I didn't ask to be made King of Poland."

"What shall we do with him, Excellency?" asked the police commissioner, grinning.

"Take him out, give him a taste of the lash, and send him home," answered His Excellency.

From police headquarters the Governor proceeded to pay a call on the Huntzes and Flederbaum. He found the latter with a bandaged head. With all his un-Jewish clothes and bearing, his trimmed beard and turned-up mustachios, Maximilian Flederbaum had been treated like some miserable little Jew of Balut in skull-cap and gaberdine. Rioters had seen him in his carriage and had pelted him with stones.

"Herr Flederbaum, I can't tell you how sorry I am," said the Governor. "I would have given anything not to have this happen." He made no mention of the fact that he had detained the Cossacks for two days outside the city while the pogrom went on. "If you can point to the hooligans who did that, I shall see that they are treated with the utmost severity of the law."

Flederbaum could not tell him who the hooligans were,

[321]

but he felt that it was almost worth while to have his head in bandages to get such an expression of sympathy from the Governor.

With the arrival of the Cossacks, the town went back to normal. The Jewish shops opened again. Jewish burial societies made the rounds, picking up the corpses. Doctors were everywhere, bandaging the wounded. The Rabbi of the city proclaimed a fast, and in the synagogues the white-faced Jews said special prayers to the Almighty. The workers, cowed and dispirited, stood in long rows at the factory gates, begging to be taken in on any conditions. They were taken in, but every employer made his own cuts now, and it was usually more than the ten per cent originally suggested. The chimneys of the factories sent out their heavy clouds of smoke, the sirens screamed in the morning, the machinery thundered.

The beggars swarmed out from Feifer Street, singing a new song:

Have you heard, good people, the dreadful news,
Of the crimes committed against the Jews?
On the very first day of the month of Iyar
The mobs assembled from near and far.

They came with torches and clubs and knives
To burn our houses and take our lives.
They burned and killed to their hearts' content,
And left ruin behind them wherever they went.

O God, our father, who lives in the skies,
Look down upon us and hear our cries.
Stretch over our heads Thy mighty hand,
And lead us back to our Holy Land.

Shamefaced and utterly discredited, unable to look their
fellow-Jews in the eyes, the leaders of the workers' movement
crawled through the streets. They who had so enthusiastically
called the oppressed proletariat to action and unity had not
a word to say for themselves. The smashed windows of the
weavers' homes looked at them mockingly, and Jews with
bandaged and bloody heads turned away from them with
loathing or stopped to spit back at them the words they had
once listened to so trustingly.

"Brother workers!" they jeered. "Fellow-members of the
oppressed working-class! Look at us! This is what we got for
believing you!"

"And serves you right, every one of you!" the women said,
spitefully. "Who asked you to listen to them? Who asked you
to run around like lunatics with your revolutionary books and
revolutionary leaflets and proclamations? Didn't you know
that the Jew always gets the dirty end of the stick?"

Most wretched of all was Nissan, the son of Reb Noske the
Teacher, whom they called Nissan the Wicked.

During the first days of the riots, when the workers in
whom he had seen the liberators of humanity and the heralds
of a new and glorious order had so loathsomely betrayed
themselves and their ideals, Nissan had fallen into a blank,
wordless despair. Impotent and disgraced, he had gone back
to his room, had flung himself on his bed, and had refused to
get up from it, either to wash or to eat.

He wanted to die. He wanted to shut out for ever from his memory the revolting scene of the Polish workers carrying in procession their "King of Poland" and rushing with lighted torches toward the Jewish quarter of Lodz. Oh, he had tried, for a few hours, to bring the workers to their senses. He, together with some of his comrades, had yelled, protested, tried to explain to the drunken workers the unspeakable ugliness of their behaviour. All he had to show now was a swollen face and a mass of scars.

He lay on his bed, feeding on the unspeakable bitterness of his heart. When his landlord, a Lithuanian Jew who had come to the city in the days of the expulsion from Moscow, offered to send for a doctor, Nissan turned his face to the wall.

"Don't take it to heart so," said the landlord. "It's all new to you, but I've seen it happen before, more than once, in Russia. And it'll happen again and again, as long as we Jews live among gentiles."

Nissan was stung into life.

"It's a lie. It'll happen only as long as the workers are oppressed." And forgetting that his landlord was not supposed to know that his lodger was a secret revolutionary, he burst into a tirade against the bosses and against the Government. The landlord looked at him and shook his head pityingly.

"You're still very young. There was a time when I felt like you and believed as you believe. But time has taught me. When they brought machinery into Lodz and displaced the hand-looms, there were anti-Jewish riots. When Russian students assassinated the Russian Tsar, there were anti-Jewish riots. Now when there's a strike, the workers make riots against the Jews. The time will come when the revolutionaries themselves will beat the Jews. . . . It'll always be like that—as long as we are Jews and they are gentiles. . . ."

"It's rubbish," shouted Nissan, clenching his fists. "Hold your tongue."

"Take my advice," said the other calmly, "and clean out whatever dangerous stuff you've got in the room. They're searching every house in the city."

[324]

Nissan started and came to. The Lithuanian looked at him keenly.

"Don't worry about me. I've known all along and I could have sold you out before. I know how to listen and keep quiet. Take my advice. There was a time when I, too, was all hot about this business of workers and revolutions and the rest of it. I, too, wanted to make a new and better world for the gentiles. . . . The first pogrom opened my eyes. . . . Forget it. There'll always be pogroms."

Nissan wanted to answer, but the other turned and left the room. Nissan remained alone with his anguish and despair. He heard in the yard the hoarse voice of a beggar singing the new song. The words sickened him. He felt as if a heavy stone rested on his heart.

But he refused to believe that there would always be pogroms. The road of liberty was a thorny and tortuous one; there would be set-backs and disgraces; but the goal would be reached in the end. He knew the history of other revolutions; they, too, had been marked by these treacheries. There were hooligans, stool-pigeons, agents provocateurs, who stirred up the lowest instincts among the masses, working always among those who had not yet become class-conscious and did not understand who their enemies were. They had been the ones to switch the attention of the strikers from the bosses to the Jews. He knew all this. He could not believe that this enmity toward the Jews lay in the nature of things.

He knew and believed, but that was only with his mind. His emotions lagged behind. He could not abjure the horrible pictures of the infuriated, drunken workers rushing through the streets with lighted torches in their hands, howling: "Down with the Jews! Kill the unbelieving dogs!" Workers they were, members of the proletariat, children of that oppressed and exploited class against which the power of the wealthy was being concentrated more and more brutally from year to year, from day to day. They it was who, together with the underworld elements who had joined them, had descended like wolves on their fellow-workers of Balut, the equally oppressed, equally miserable weavers and tailors and shoemak-

[325]

ers of Balut.

"Death now, only death," he muttered. "There's nothing left to live for."

He was so sick at heart, so listless, that he forgot his landlord's advice to gather up and burn the incriminating books and pamphlets which lay under his couch and in the cupboard.

He asked himself darkly whether he had not made a mistake. Perhaps human beings were just loathsome animals. Perhaps they were by nature mean, low, selfish, beastly, not as the result of economic conditions, as he had learned to believe, but simply because they were what they were. Perhaps nothing would ever wash out of their hearts the original heritage of vileness. Perhaps Schopenhauer was right, that philosopher whom he had first read in the old days when he first visited Feivel the rag-dealer, that philosopher whom he had later rejected for the optimistic Hegel and the practical Karl Marx.

He fell at last into a wretched slumber, disturbed by evil dreams. He was haunted by the sight of infuriated drunken mobs and the white, terrified faces of fleeing Jews. He heard voices raised in wild laughter, and through them the cool, mocking words of the Lithuanian Jew: "It will always be like that. There will always be pogroms." Between this wretched sleep and a torpor even more wretched, he lay there, without eating or drinking, without a change of clothes, for twenty-four hours.

Then, suddenly, he came to. The brilliant sunlight of a May morning was streaming into his room. Something had happened to him. The apathy and wretchedness which had oppressed him for the last few days had vanished completely. He was himself again. He felt the desire to live, to get up, wash, eat something, go out like a man and face disaster with the old faith and strength.

Nissan would not have thought of it in this way, but the resurgence of his indomitable faith made him more than ever like his father. The stern old moralist and pietist had learned to look beyond all sufferings, all set-backs and moral lapses, to the grand denouement of the Messianic deliverance.

Though it might be delayed through thousands of years, it was bound to come; and remembering this, old Noske the Teacher had shaken off the black thoughts that clustered about him in moments of despair. So now his son remembered that, whatever might be the delay, the revolution was bound to come, and he, too, threw off the doubt and wretchedness which had prostrated him. He would go out now, find his comrades, and bring them encouragement.

He cleaned the room and burned the pamphlets and books which might betray him to the police. Then he washed and went out in search of his comrades.

He had great difficulty in finding them. They had mostly crept away into hiding. Those that he did find turned their backs on him.

"Get out!" they said. "The weavers will mob you if you come to them again with talk of revolution and equality and liberty."

He went quietly to Tevyeh's house, but Tevyeh was not at home.

"Father is in Flederbaum's hospital," said Bashke, her face tear-stained. "A Polish worker cracked his head open with a brick. And don't let Mother see you. She says she'll kill you."

He went back to his room, feeling alone in the world. Alone he sat down and drew up a proclamation in Yiddish, explaining to the masses of Balut what had happened. He pointed out that it was one of the old tricks of the capitalist masters to provoke mutual hatreds among the workers; he described clearly how the police of Lodz had given the hooligans and the misled workers, who had been egged on by agents provocateurs, a free hand to loot the Jews, so that the rage which had been properly directed at first against the exploiters had been diverted foully against the true comrades of the Polish workers. He appealed to the Jewish workers of Balut not to give way to despair or to let themselves be drawn into hatred of the Polish workers, which was just what the capitalists and their servants the police wanted. He wrote carefully, putting all his reawakened passion and hope into the document. Alone in his room, he copied out the proclamation, in large letters, on several sheets, and alone after

[327]

midnight he went out to paste up the copies on the synagogue walls and corners of Balut.

Single-handed he was prepared to take up the fight again, to face the task of restoring the old enthusiasm to the workers, of clearing the atmosphere of the poisonous mists which had gathered in the last few days. He had almost finished pasting up his proclamations and was just leaving one of the synagogues when two policemen suddenly appeared, one on each side of him, and grabbed him by the arms.

"Don't struggle," growled one of them, "or we'll shoot."

Before he knew what had happened, he was handcuffed and was marching with the men to the police station.

Though it was long after midnight, the police station was alight and busy. When the outer gate was thrown open, Nissan saw two rows of Cossacks, with nagaikas in their hands, forming a lane that led up to the door of the station. "*Pashol, sheeny!*" shouted the policeman, and released Nissan.

He had to stay where he was and take the lashes of the Cossacks, or run forward as swiftly as he could toward the door at the other end of the lane. He ran, trying to shield his face from the lashing whips. The cutting blows descended on his head, his shoulders, his legs. Bleeding, quivering with pain, he reached the door and dashed in. The two policemen, who had followed behind, led him into the presence of the officer in charge.

"We found him posting up proclamations in Balut. Here are a couple of samples."

"Search him," the officer commanded.

The policemen ran their hands over his body and through his pockets.

"You, what's your damned name?" asked the officer.

"Speak properly to me," said Nissan, curtly.

The officer grinned suddenly. "Ah! One of the intelligentsia."

Nissan said nothing. With his handkerchief he wiped the blood and sweat off his face.

"We'll find out all about you later," said the officer. "Take him into the cells."

The main cell, into which they flung Nissan, was crowded

[328]

with prisoners. They were of all sorts: workers, rioters, thieves, drunkards, and even a couple of lunatics. The place stank atrociously. Every few minutes the door was unlocked and another prisoner thrust in. A babel of voices, protests, laughter, obscene joking, cries of pain, filled the bleak, white-washed room, which, illumined by a single small lamp attached to the ceiling, seemed to be darker than if there had been no light at all. A number of men stood at the door hammering wildly, asking the warders to be led out so that they could answer the call of nature. The warders, who had been fooled several times by such requests, paid no attention.

There were a few wooden benches along the walls, all occupied. Nissan found his way into a corner and squatted on his haunches to rest his aching limbs. A group of drunken prisoners surrounded him and clamoured for money. "The warder gets whisky for us," they hiccuped.

"Beat it!" said Nissan sharply. "I'm tired."

"He's an old jailbird," said one of the drunkards. "Leave him alone. You'll get nothing out of him."

The group left him and waited for other, less experienced prisoners.

Three days of pain and filth passed for Nissan before he was led out again. This time he was taken into a bright, cheerfully furnished office. Behind a green-covered desk sat a colonel of the gendarmerie, a smooth-shaven, carefully groomed young man with gold-rimmed eye-glasses glittering on his nose.

"Take a seat," he said courteously to Nissan. "I see you for the first time, I think. Are you an out-of-towner or do you belong in Lodz?"

"I belong in Lodz," answered Nissan.

"I don't know your name," said the colonel, smiling. "You wouldn't give it to the police."

"They beat me up," said Nissan angrily. "Look at my face."

"I'm awfully sorry," answered the colonel sympathetically. "I really am. But the times are so restless it's impossible to check up on everything. You fellows created such a confounded disturbance in the city that we had to call out the Cossacks, and they're a hot-tempered lot, you know; they knock you down first and make inquiries afterwards. . . . It wouldn't have happened if the gendarmerie had been able to handle the situation."

The colonel seemed to be anxious to establish the distinction between his own well-trained men and the irrepressible Cossacks.

"Will you have a cigarette?" he asked, and pushed a boxful toward Nissan.

Nissan took one. "Thank you," he said.

"You speak excellent Russian for a Lodz Jew," said the colonel, politely.

"I lived for some years in Russia, under police surveillance," said Nissan. "My name is Nissan Eibeschutz."

The colonel nodded his acknowledgments. "Thanks. It's the best way. We'd have found your name out in time, Mr. Eibeschutz, and you've saved us a lot of unnecessary trouble."

The colonel conducted the conversation very graciously, as if he were chatting with a social equal in a drawing-room. He tried to extract from the prisoner something about the structure of the secret political parties, and in the first place to which he belonged, the Proletariat or the Zvionzek or perhaps some other, newly founded.

"The trouble with you is," he said, as if in friendly criticism, "that you lack unity. That's bad for us too. It makes our work so much harder, since there are so many parties. There's a rumour of a new split in the Proletariat. What's your personal opinion?"

To this question Nissan answered nothing. The colonel picked up one of the proclamations which Nissan had been caught posting and compared it with the Russian translation prepared for him by the secretary of the Jewish community. He changed the subject of the conversation to the pogrom which had taken place.

"A very regrettable incident," he said, sighing. "I'm sorry it took place."

"It was your work," said Nissan briefly.

"Not at all," replied the colonel. "*Your* work. Jews oughtn't to interfere in our affairs. Your line is business; you ought to buy and sell, as you've always done. It's your specialty, and if

[330]

you stuck to it, it would be better for you as well as for us. . . . Think it over; you'll see I'm right."

"I have my own views in these matters," said Nissan.

"Well," answered the colonel, good-humouredly, "you're going to have plenty of time in prison to reconsider your views. I think you'll come round to my way of thinking. Just now you're tired and you need sleep. I don't want to overstrain you. We shall meet again. Meanwhile, if there's anything I can do for you, anything in my power, I would be glad to be of service."

"There's only one thing, colonel. Please don't send me back to the police cell. I want to be sent to the prison."

"I've already arranged for that," answered the colonel, and rang for the orderly.

Two gendarmes conducted Nissan in a droshky to the prison on Dluga Street. The gate-keeper looked angrily at the new-comer. "How many more?" he asked. "The place is full up."

Nissan was taken into an empty room, stripped naked, and searched. His clothes were examined inch by inch, and he himself was given a thorough searching. They took everything away, matches, purse, penknife, cigarettes, even his suspenders and tie. Then he was given a small kerosene lamp and led down a long corridor to a tiny cell. After the foul, crowded, stinking police quarters the cell, the narrow iron bed, the stiff grey coverlet, the small wooden stool were infinite luxury to Nissan. The door was locked behind him and he flung himself down to sleep.

But he had barely closed his eyes when he heard a tapping on the wall, in the code which had become familiar to him in other prisons.

"Good evening," said the taps. "Who are you?"

Nissan tapped out his name.

Nissan's neighbour gave his name in turn and asked: "What's the news in town?"

Nissan gave what little information he had; in return he learned that the prisoners did not expect to stay long in this place. They had it from reliable sources that the trials would take place soon, and that heavy sentences would be handed

[331]

out, eight and ten years. Nissan then asked in the code about the prison régime, the food, the hours of sleep, the periods of exercise. Above all he wanted to know whether there was anything to read. His neighbour answered him that there was a good secret library, accumulated by previous prisoners, and among them political books. Nissan was greatly relieved. As long as he could get books he would find prison tolerable, and if he was to be put away for years, he would at least have time to learn something.

One day he was astonished by the information, brought to him by the warder, that his bride was downstairs, waiting to see him. Without saying a word he followed the warder to the office and found Bashke, Tevyeh's little daughter. She carried a package, which the warder took away from her.

"What's in this?" asked the warder.

"Food."

"We'll look it over first," said the warder. "You can talk with the prisoner now."

Nissan stretched out his hand to the girl, who blushed a fiery red.

"Don't be angry with me, Mr. Nissan," she stammered in a low voice. "I couldn't have got to see you otherwise. They admit only members of the family and brides, so I said I was your bride."

"Thank you, Bashke," said Nissan, and stroked her head. Then he asked after her father and other friends.

"Father's home again," she said. "He's working. So am I. He sends you his regards." She paused, and, sinking her voice still lower, added: "He'll keep on doing what he's been doing till now. So will I."

"You're a good girl, Bashke," said Nissan, moved. "But be careful. And don't bring me any more packages. I've got everything I need."

Bashke looked at him with big, grateful eyes, then suddenly began to cry.

"But what is it, Bashke?" asked Nissan disturbed.

"They're so horrid, they're so beastly," she sobbed. "When they searched me— Oh, God, I was so ashamed!"

Nissan bit his lip. He understood. He knew something of

the humiliations to which women visitors were submitted.

"But you mustn't come any more, Bashke," he said softly. "You're only a child."

"No, please, I want to come," she gasped.

The warder broke in at this point.

"Time," he said, jangling his keys.

Nissan took Bashke's head between his hands and kissed her on the forehead.

$\mathcal{A}$ noisy, motley crowd filled the new railroad station of Lodz.

It was thickest and noisiest along the third-class cars of the long train which was about to set out northward, breaking later into one section which turned eastward toward the interior of Russia and another which turned westward to connect with the international lines. By far the greater part of the third-class passengers were destined for America, and among these Jews predominated. Lodz was sending out a huge contingent this year across the Atlantic. There were entire families, husbands, wives, and children; there were wives and children without the husband, who had preceded them by months or years, to prepare a home for them on the new continent; there were husbands just setting out on the journey; there were youngsters who were playing the pioneer for the rest of the family. They travelled with crates, bundles, packages, taking along bed-clothes, odd bits of furniture, tea-kettles, baskets of food, samovars, phylacteries, and prayer shawls. Screaming, panting, and perspiring, they jammed themselves and their innumerable belongings into the cars, squeezed their way back and forth along the corridors, listened to last, frantic instructions, kept losing bundles and finding them again, kept opening them to make sure they had not forgotten something, kept re-examining their purses and passports, all in one wild, panicky tumult which turned the station into a vast madhouse. Mothers clung to their little ones, arguing despairingly with the Russian conductors, whose language they did not understand. Pickpockets, purse-snatchers, and station thieves circulated in the crowd, lightening the burdens of the travellers. Fathers who were sending forth their sons into the unknown world, or were leaving them behind while they ventured out themselves, repeated, for the thousandth time: "Remember! Hold on to the Jewish law, whatever happens. Keep holy the Sabbath, put on phylacteries every morning, don't let a razor touch your beards"; and the sons replied automatically, for the thousandth time: "Yes, Father."

Polish peasant women were trying to smuggle into the train baskets of ducks and chickens and quarrelling with the conductors. Pious Jews in long gaberdines, having left their homes too early for morning prayers, were now making good the deficiency, and with phylacteries on arm and forehead, with prayer shawls draped over their heads, were standing in groups, swaying back and forth and chanting loudly. Lithuanian Jews objected to these public exhibitions, pushed their way through the worshippers, slung their bundles on to the upper benches, unwrapped their kettles, which were full of hot tea, and sat drinking enthusiastically. Women unbared their breasts and suckled their babies. Peasants took out packages of food, chewed on pork sausages, ate noisily, spat on the floor, and mocked the praying Jews. Children cried, hens clucked, somewhere in a sack a pig squealed, and a dog answered furiously. A yellow-bearded Jew, the conductor's "bouncer," pushed his way among the passengers. His function was to collect bribes from travellers without railroad tickets, dividing the proceeds with the conductor. Those without tickets or money he threw off the train. He disliked a man with a ticket as much as a man without money. "You'd rather let the Russian Government take it, eh, than let a fellow-Jew earn a few honest kopecks?" he sneered. The Russian conductor followed closely behind while his "bouncer" did the negotiating. Sometimes they found a passenger who had crawled under the seat among the bundles. They pulled him out and made him pay up or get off. Those that paid the bribes asked timidly in Yiddish: "Won't the Angel of Death

[335]

come this way?" They meant the Russian controller. "Angel of Death no come," answered the conductor, also in Yiddish.

Some ticketless passengers tried to bring down the size of the bribe below the set tariff. "What do you think this is?" asked the bouncer angrily. "A fish-market? This is a train with regular prices."

Farther along the track, opposite the second- and first-class cars, it was quieter. The well-dressed passengers sat at ease inside or stood chatting and smiling under the windows. A few Russian officers came, their orderlies carrying their shiny valises and brief-cases. Merchants strolled back and forth contentedly, looked at their gold watches, and blew cigarette smoke into the air. A couple of Polish aristocrats in hunting dress, leading their thoroughbred dogs on leashes, talked and laughed loudly. But there were more women than men in the first and second class; elegant ladies they were, setting out for their favourite watering-places abroad. They arrived with great quantities of baggage—dresses, shoes, and hats in all sizes and shapes of boxes. Some of them paraded up and down the platform, their long dresses sweeping the ground, their enormous hats a-flutter with feathers. The wives of Jewish merchants and manufacturers of Lodz already imagined themselves out of the country and conversed in German among themselves.

In bright-coloured, wide English clothes Max Ashkenazi, general agent of the Huntze factory, walked back and forth on the platform, puffing restlessly at a cigar and stopping every now and then to scribble figures on pieces of paper which he drew from his pockets or on the margin of the German newspaper which he carried or on the cover of his cigarette box. Voices greeted him, and he looked up and answered absently. Someone stopped and asked: "Where are you travelling, Herr Ashkenazi?" and Max Ashkenazi answered promptly and untruthfully: "I'm taking a little holiday."

"Have a good time, Herr Ashkenazi."

"Thanks." Max Ashkenazi turned away hastily. He did not like curious people. He did not want anyone to know that in this hot autumn weather he was leaving the stifling city not in order to rest himself somewhere in a luxurious holiday resort, but to plunge into the interior of Russia in order to drop in on customers and to anticipate the winter season. For now Lodz was returning to normal, and Max Ashkenazi was eager to make up the losses of the depression. It would be easier going now, he thought. The crisis had wiped out the little manufacturers, the hole-in-the-corner subcontractors who had always dragged the prices down and been a nuisance to the big producers. On the one side there was the renewed demand for goods; on the other side the workers had been so cowed by the depression and the brutal crushing of the riots that they would work for any kind of pay. Max Ashkenazi felt that the air was cleared now, the city was healthy, within a year or so the Huntze factory would be in a stronger position than ever.

The Huntze factory had suffered, though less, perhaps, than any of its rivals. Max Ashkenazi had kept his head during the crisis. He had held on to the supply of raw material, borrowing in order to meet current expenses rather than sell; for he had known that when things were stabilized again and orders began to come in, the factory with the largest reserve of raw material on hand would be first in the field. In another respect, too, the Huntze factory had come off well; it had hardly been touched during the riots. The offices and stock-rooms, too, had got off lightly. Anyhow, that was all past. The Governor General had left a garrison of Cossacks in the city. From now on, Lodz would be an ideal city for the manufacturer. Max Ashkenazi was confident.

He went into his second-class carriage and made himself comfortable. Then he took out his passport and examined it, frowning. It declared that Simcha Meyer Ashkenazi, of the Jewish faith, being a merchant of the First Guild, had the right to travel without let or hindrance in any part of Russia. He did not like the reminder "of the Jewish faith," or the record of his old, outlandish name, Simcha Meyer. He was Max now, as his visiting and business cards declared. But passports always insisted on the original name, and Max Ashkenazi was annoyed and humiliated whenever he had to

[337]

show the Government document.

He leaned out of the window and addressed one of the conductors.

"What's holding us up?" he asked. "We should have left some time ago."

"We're waiting for a batch of prisoners," answered the conductor. "Here they come, sir."

Max Ashkenazi nodded and leaned back. He was not interested in prisoners. He heard the sound of marching feet and of military orders, but he was busy again, calculating, jotting down figures, wetting the pencil in his mouth every now and then.

A company of soldiers in black uniforms, swords drawn, came marching in two files down the platform. Between them marched the prisoners. The soldiers halted, the two files turned to face each other, the officers walked back and forth glaring at the crowds which accompanied the convoy, the relatives and friends who were trying to exchange a few last words with the prisoners.

"Hold the crowds back!" they ordered the soldiers. "No conversations!"

Hundreds of prisoners were being sent out of Lodz in this batch. The police station and the local prison were being emptied and refilled steadily as the business of crushing the last remnants of revolt went forward. Most of the prisoners were, in fact, taken during the strike and the riots that followed, but they were a mixed lot. There were old, hardened criminals, whose lives were passed mostly in prisons; there were revolutionaries and strikers who had never been in contact with criminals before; there were peasants, pickpockets, street-women, and travellers who had no passports. Some—the old hands—were in chains and in prison clothes. Most of them were in ordinary dress. There were husbands and wives arrested together, young people, almost children, and greybeards. There was a company of swarthy gypsies in bright-coloured rags. There were mothers with children in their arms.

Their destinations differed. Some were being sent back to their home towns, others to local prisons, still others to Si-

[338]

beria. Among these last was Nissan Eibeschutz. Like Max Ashkenazi he was leaving for the interior of Russia, and not on a holiday. They would travel together part of the way. As Nissan passed under Max Ashkenazi's window, the latter chanced to glance out, and the two men saw and recognized each other. For an instant Nissan stood stock still, his face set sternly. Then he was thrust forward by a soldier. Max Ashkenazi dropped back into his seat and lit a fresh cigar. Nissan clambered into one of the bleak, filthy, crowded carriages reserved for the prisoners.

Taking his place at the heavily grated window, he looked back into the station and caught a glimpse of Bashke, Tevyeh's daughter, waving her handkerchief to him out of the crowd.

Day after day the bright sun poured its light down on the broad, grain-laden fields of Poland and Russia. The prisoners' train wound its way slowly from station to station, and prisoners who could fight their way to the windows stared out hungrily at the peasants bending down as they swung their sickles, at the women and children who bound the sheaves and sang at their work.

Within the train it was hot and filthy; from day to day the prisoners became less human, more brutish and hateful. Whatever was base and revolting in the individual came up to the surface as hunger, thirst, exhaustion, and dirt wore down resistance.

A young peasant girl with swollen face, torn dress, ripped clothes, and unkempt hair sat on the floor of the car, weeping despairingly. She had come to Lodz from a distant village, in search of work. On the way to Lodz she had lost her little bundle with the few coins she had taken along, the railroad ticket, and her passport. Arriving in Lodz without a ticket, she had been turned over to the station police, who detained her one night before they sent her back, on the prisoners' train, to her native village. But in that one night she had been abused by all the men in the station. Her village was twenty-four hours away from Lodz by ordinary train, but on this prisoners' train, with its frequent overnight stops, the journey might last weeks. She sat on the floor of the car now, insane with grief and shame.

[340]

"Jesus, Son of Mary," she moaned, rocking herself to and fro, "Holy Mother in heaven, what shall I do?"

Some prostitutes, who had been expelled from Lodz because they were without pass books, stood round her and laughed.

"You won't die from it," they jeered. "Nobody ever did. Anyway, you got broken in good and proper, you don't have to worry any more. We'll take you into the union."

The convoy soldiers in the car, who looked forward to making use of the peasant girl, also laughed, and added: "*Pravilna!* Right!"

On a wicker basket sat a young Jewish woman, wringing her hands. Her father had married her to an old man whom she hated, so she had run away to Lodz and taken service in a rich home. But her husband had discovered her whereabouts and had set the police on her and made them send her back to him as the law demanded. Every now and again the young woman turned frantically to her neighbours and cried in Yiddish and Polish: "Help me! Help me! Tell me what to do!"

"Poison him, you damn fool," said a woman in prisoner's garb. "That's what I did with my husband. And that's why I'm here."

An ancient beggar woman lay groaning on a heap of rags. In the city of a thousand beggars it was her bad luck to have been picked up by the police, who were now trying to return her to her native village. But she was so old that she did not remember where she was born. For years now she had travelled on these prisoners' trains, from one town to another, from one prison to another, escaping, being caught again, shipped interminably from point to point. When they tried to find out where she had been born she answered: "I come from God's earth. There was a beautiful church there, with holy pictures. . . ."

No one knew her, no village would receive her, no officer would issue a passport to her. Sick, decaying with old age, she lay on her rags, even easing herself where she lay. Now and again she drew out from under her dress dried husks of bread and gnawed on them.

[341]

"Take her out!" the prisoners cried to the convoy soldiers. "She's sick. She's stinking up the place."

"The old bitch won't die!" the soldiers growled, spitting on the heap of rags. "We've got to keep on dragging her from one end of Russia to the other."

There were in the cars desperate criminals in chains, who boasted of their murders; there were horse-thieves; there was a blue-eyed peasant with the face of a saint who, in a quarrel over field boundaries, had split his neighbour's head open with an ax; there was a little peasant who had stolen a trap from a nobleman's forest to make a felly for his wagon and had been given a nine-month stretch in prison; there was a broad-faced Tatar who had been a porter in Lodz and had failed to deliver two sacks of wool; there was a group of young fellows who had got into a fight at a wedding and had set on each other with knives; there were incendiaries and lunatics and thugs; the dregs of Russia were jammed into these cars, along with the political prisoners.

Nissan sat in a corner, on his little bundle of clothes. He breathed in heavily the thick, pestilential air and tried to close his eyes to the revolting scene around him. The neighbour in the prison who had tapped out the information that the trials would be swift and the sentences heavy had been right. The investigators had drawn up the indictments wholesale. The only witnesses called had been policemen and Government agents. The crown prosecutors on the bench, fat men with the thick chains of office about their necks, had listened to the revolutionary declarations of the strike-leaders as indifferently as to the pleas of the criminals.

For robbery and assault on Jews the sentence was six months; for helping to spread the strike, three years; for revolutionary activity, five to eight years in prison, with sub-sequent exile to Siberia.

Like the other revolutionaries, Nissan at his trial had delivered an impassioned harangue against the existing order, against the oppressors of the people, and against the officials of the Government. He had warned the judges that the day was not far off when they would be standing in the dock to receive sentence from those whom they were now sending to prison. The judges had not interrupted the speech; neither had they listened to it; they had sat there dozing and yawning. They had dozed and yawned through the speeches of the defence attorneys, with their voluminous citations of the law. It was familiar stuff to them. The sentences which they would deliver were already prepared, drawn up in accordance with instructions from the Governor General. During his speech Nissan had looked round the court for those to whom his fiery oration was really intended—workers and citizens of Lodz. But he saw only policemen, agents, and a few rich ladies who had come out of curiosity. The public had been excluded from the trial.

Now he was on his way to Moscow, where his first prison term would be served, but the journey, he knew, would take months. In the meantime he would be herded with the scum of the criminal world in all sorts of local prisons; and in between he would be travelling, as he was now, in a filthy car unfit for human habitation. These few months, he also knew, would be harder to bear than the years in the regular prison; but it was part of the system of punishment. He was without a kopeck. The little money which he had had with him at the time of his arrest had been taken away from him at the police station and not returned to him when he was transferred to the prison. The guard had told him that the money would be forwarded to him in Moscow, but Nissan knew he would never see it again. There stretched before him now a time of misery, privation, and humiliation. But it was not his personal destiny that preoccupied him now and lay heavy on his heart.

Like his father, he made few demands on life. As bread and water by measure had sufficed for the old man as long as he was permitted to give himself up to the law of God and the wisdom of the holy sages, so they sufficed for his son Nissan as long as he was able to study and spread the doctrines of his teacher, Karl Marx. More than that, both of them had known that only in poverty and want is the pursuit of truth and perfection possible; and both of them had known that the road which they had chosen was a long and painful one. And by now Nissan had already become hardened to his fate

[343]

and familiar with its cruelties. His first experience with prison and exile had taught him all he needed to know, and he was no longer appalled by the prospect of the years of confinement.

He was no longer the naïve, timid boy whom criminal prisoners could abuse and command. There was a sharp, authoritative air about him which warned them to leave him alone. He knew all the tricks of the prison world, the rights and privileges of political prisoners. Denied these rights, he protested and carried on until he either got his due or was thrown into solitary confinement. He knew also that, whatever prison he was sent to, he would be sure to find his own kind there, revolutionaries and idealists, ready to help him and one another. And then, not all prisons and prison officials were alike, and not all convoy soldiers and officers were alike. True, many of them were low, despicable characters; but one sometimes found decent, kindly men, who treated their prisoners—above all, the political prisoners—with no more strictness than the law required. But one consideration more than all others lightened for Nissan the burden of the future. He was desperately eager to deepen his knowledge of Marxism; he was as absorbed by it now as in the old days he had been absorbed by the philosophic and anti-religious books given him by Feivel the rag-dealer. And, queerly enough, nowhere in Russia could the study of Marxism be pursued more easily than in the great prisons. For Nissan, as for most revolutionaries, the prison had been an academy. When he left Lodz he had been a raw boy, stuffed with the crude educational material of the Jewish Enlightenment movement, the Haskallah; he came back from prison with a good grounding in modern knowledge. Now he wanted to complete his education. He was beginning to think for himself, and now had the habit of making annotations of his own in the margins of his Marxian books—the kind that his father had made in the margins of his religious tomes.

Not the prospect of prison, not even the immediate prospect of the unsettled months on the road, tormented him. He was preoccupied by something else.

In the car with him there were, besides criminals, beggars,

and prostitutes, a number of weavers, real proletarians. They had been arrested not only for participating in the strike, but also for attacking Jews and robbing Jewish shops. Now, on their way to prison, they cursed those who had dragged them into the strike. Had they been content to do nothing more than rob the Jews, they would have received only light sentences; now they were faced with years of exile.

They shook their fists in the faces of the strike-leaders. "Wait!" they said. "We'll pay you out for this."

It had all ended in miserable failure. Propaganda was at an end in Lodz. The word "socialism" was heard no more. Beaten and cowed, the workers had crawled back to their masters to accept any conditions. In Balut the phrase "May 1st," which should have been a fiery and exalting phrase, filled with implications of revolt, liberty, and human brotherhood, had become, for the Jews, synonymous with robbery and murder. From Lodz the song of the pogrom and of the revolt had spread over the whole country. It was sung even here, in the prison train, by the Jewish thieves.

He had not given up hope. He knew that in the long war between liberty and tyranny there had to be set-backs; battles would be lost as well as won before the day of ultimate victory. He still believed in the inevitability of the revolution, for he still could see the grim process of the concentration of wealth proceeding under ineluctable laws—proceeding to the breaking-point, which meant the collapse of the immemorial despotism, and the dawn of the day which would know no more distinction between classes, nations, and religions. Then would come the great age of freedom, and mankind would be cleansed of oppression, hatred, and envy, of all the meannesses and foulnesses which disfigured the human species. He saw all this as clearly as his father had seen the coming of the Messiah, and believed in it as fervently.

But meantime there was spread before him all that was ugliest and most loathsome in the world as it was. The prisoners fought among themselves, despised each other, were devoid of elementary decency and morals. Even their good-humour, so-called, was abominable in its lowness. They played disgusting tricks on each other, and the word "sheeny" was heard every other second.

Typical of their idea of a good time, of a harmless joke, was their treatment of a young peasant lad with blue eyes and a mop of flaxen hair. He was travelling for the first time in a prison train. The old hands decided that he had to be "sworn in" as a regular.

"What's your name?" they asked him.

"Antek," the boy answered.

"What did they put you in for?"

"For buying a stolen horse."

"Then you're one of us, and you'll have to be sworn in."

"Sworn in?" asked the boy, astonished. "Sworn into what?"

"Sworn into our company, you damn fool. You've got to swear to be one of us and never to squeal on a comrade. Are you a true believer?"

"Sure I am."

"Then you've got to swear on the Holy Bible that you'll be a good comrade. We'll tie up your eyes, then you'll kneel down and take the oath."

They bound the boy's head with a filthy rag. Then one of the older thieves quietly undid his pants, let them drop, and stationed himself near the lad. Another thief chanted in loud and solemn tones, like a priest at his office, the terms of the oath, and the kneeling lad repeated them after him word by word.

"Now, my son, kiss the book," said the officiating thief.

The oldest thief brought his behind close to the lad's face, and the latter put his lips forward and kissed it. A wild scream of laughter burst out in the car. The crowd of criminals became hysterical with joy.

"Boy!" shouted the officiating thief, "did you smell the sanctity of it?"

The peasant boy, realizing what had happened, had torn off the bandage and in an agony of shame and humiliation flung himself on the floor of the car.

Horrible they all were in Nissan's eyes, with their foul tricks, their thefts, their revolting "love-affairs" in the nights. The old doubts concerning the innate baseness and irredeem-

[346]

ability of man began to beat again in his mind, darkening the bright visions of the future which were his sustaining hope. Again like his father, he tried to strengthen himself by concentrating on his mission and by repeating to himself the articles of his faith. It would all pass; these abominations, these foulnesses, did not matter in the long run. From far off, the light of the final deliverance shone over the world, and for the sake of it one endured all manner of agonies, physical and mental.

He shut his eyes against the immediate world. He refused to listen to the indecent jokes, the horseplay, and the quarrels. Everything was unreal except the far-off vision.

XXXV

Round the spring in Carlsbad, the joyous Austrian summer resort, were assembled the élite of the merchant and manufacturing families of the city of Lodz. A tremendously elegant crowd they were, penetrated by the sense of their own graciousness, importance, and high social standing. They were very polite, very ceremonious, keenly aware of the dignity with which they should treat themselves and each other. *"Guten Tag!"* they said in lofty German as they passed each other at the spring.

Carlsbad was not as crowded this year as in previous years. Many of the families which had developed the Carlsbad habit, whether they needed the waters and the treatment or not, had been wiped out by the crisis. There were left only the strong families, the higher-ups in commerce and industry, and they felt more among themselves, as it were, and drank the Sprudelwasser at the spring with enhanced feelings of exclusiveness. The women trailed after them long dresses which swept the mosaic floors of the halls and walks—something which one could not do in the dirty streets of Lodz. The feathers nodded on their gigantic hats, the diamonds flashed on their fingers. The men in their short coats and tight trousers, or else in light-coloured jackets, high collars, and narrow, shiny patent-leather shoes, were perpetually lifting their silk top hats and waving their handkerchiefs in greeting.

"For the first time you can breathe during the season in

[348]

Carlsbad," said the men, with satisfaction. "We've managed to get rid of the riff-raff."

"It's certainly a pleasure to be able to take a walk without having to rub shoulders with the usual mob," answered the ladies. "Why, every cook and servant girl used to come to Carlsbad. The place was becoming impossible."

There was special cause for pride among the visitors in the fact that this year, after a long interval, Maximilian Flederbaum and his family were once again in Carlsbad. Even his daughters were welcome. They, like their father, had long avoided Carlsbad because it had become altogether too Jewish.

Among the visitors there was also Dinah, the wife of Max Ashkenazi, and her mother, Priveh. But Reb Chaim Alter was not there. Things were not going at all well with him, and, what with the crisis, he had been compelled to let his wife, his still blooming and still attractive wife, go alone. It had been a great blow to him to forgo the season, and a still greater blow to expose his wife to the dangers of the elegant summer resort. But there was no help for it. The fact was that only by selling some more of her jewels and getting an extra subvention from her daughter had Priveh been able to come to Carlsbad this year. For her the idea of staying in Lodz when everyone was in Carlsbad was quite unthinkable. She would never have survived the disgrace of it; she would have been unable to look anyone in the face. So she left her husband alone, and for the first time Reb Chaim's big hat-box passed the season in the cupboard in his house in Lodz.

Dinah came alone too, not because her husband had not the money to accompany her, but because he had not the time for such foolishness as holidays and health resorts. He could not understand how grown-up men could be so irresponsible as to let business go for weeks and months while, like children, they played around in the silly rooms and gardens of a summer resort. Nor was this because his affairs were in bad shape. On the contrary, it was known far and wide that he had come out of the crisis stronger than ever.

"He's away ahead of his so-called employers," they said

of him in Lodz. "He's got them in his hands, not they him in theirs."

But Max Ashkenazi knew that this was an exaggeration, though he was determined that before long it would be simple truth. He had, indeed, increased his holdings in the factory; he was, in effect, the director and manager and agent, all in one. Still, the Huntzes were stronger than he, and for the time being he was their employee. He was a long way from his ultimate objective, which was not simply the possession of the Huntze factory, but the dictatorship of the textile industry of Lodz. Nothing else would satisfy him. Therefore the idea of a holiday never occurred to him.

He worked harder than ever these days. The displacement of Albrecht, the old factory director, had become a virtual if not an official fact. Ever since that dreadful morning when the striking workers had pitched him into a wheelbarrow, stuck a broom in his hands, and paraded him round the factory yard, Albrecht had declined rapidly. His heart, oppressed by the heavy mass of flesh through which it had to pump his blood, had grown very weak. Nor did he mend his ways as his health failed. He still ate and drank heavily; he still paid Melchior to send him fresh country girls to his bachelor apartment. He had become unfit for work. He sat dozing in his enormous chair, the papers in disorder before him, his thoughts confused. He did not even dress properly; sometimes he let a sock trail over a shoe; sometimes he forgot to button himself, so that the office girls who came in answer to his call could hardly contain their laughter. He knew that he was sinking, and that the last remnants of power were gone from him; but he had given up the struggle. The Huntzes still let him sit in his director's chair, and he accepted it as an act of kindness. Nothing of the slightest importance was submitted to him now; Max Ashkenazi reigned as completely in the factory as in his own sales department.

Even if he had felt inclined to take a holiday, Max Ashkenazi would have considered this the least appropriate time. Never before had he advanced with such firm and rapid steps as in this period since the crisis. He had easily outstripped his brother Jacob Bunim again, and Lodz no longer mentioned them in the same breath. Package by package the Huntze stocks were accumulating in his private safe. They were like rungs on a growing ladder which led to the top of the factory chimneys, from which he would survey the territory remaining to be conquered. The threads of the business were already in his hands; the actual ownership was bound to follow. But the dissatisfaction in his heart rose not simply from his impatient and unsleeping ambition, and when he left on one of his journeys for the interior of Russia, to maintain his personal contacts with the customers of the firm, it was not simply the inadequacy of his achievements which harassed him. There was something else: the thought that Dinah never came to see him off, never came to meet him at the train, as other wives did when their husbands left and returned. The old empty life continued between them. She did her wifely duties silently; the years had not brought friendliness, much less affection. He still had no formal complaint against her, but he was still restless and dissatisfied. He could not spare the time to go with her to Carlsbad—not that she would have derived any pleasure from his company —and yet he was troubled by the thought of her alone there, in the pleasure city which attracted all sorts of shady characters, loose livers, women-hunters, adventurers. If old Reb Chaim trembled for his elderly wife, Priveh, what was he, Max Ashkenazi, to say? But taking time out to accompany Dinah was out of the question. His place was with his business.

Jacob Bunim, however, who for opposite reasons had less business to take a holiday, did go to Carlsbad and arranged it so that he travelled on the same train as Dinah and her mother.

Jacob Bunim, or Yakob, as he now called himself, had come badly out of the crisis. He had never taken his agency of the Flederbaum factory seriously. He had tried to substitute good-fellowship for hard work and sound business methods. He had extended credits without investigation, doing more business at the wine-table than in his office. The crisis had therefore thrown a good crop of bankruptcies into his lap, and he had almost lost his agency, together with the

[351]

heavy deposit lying in Flederbaum's vaults. It was his wife, Pearl, who at the last moment had come to his rescue.

As long as things had gone well with him and he had lived his high, gay life, Pearl had kept away from him, staying with her family in Warsaw. She could not stand him when he was his real, boisterous, jovial self. She could not stand his exuberant spirits, his rich, loud laughter, his riotous animal health. Surrounded by her pills and medicine bottles, she stayed at home, brooding bitterly on his happiness, hating him for the good time he was having. As soon as she heard that he was in difficulties, that he was threatened with bankruptcy and disgrace, she took train for Lodz and joined him.

She found him tolerable then, when she saw him worried and perplexed. She was ready to help. She sold one of the Warsaw houses which she had inherited from her mother, and put the money into his agency. She took a hand in the business, advised him, held off creditors, and helped choose new customers. To do all this, she settled in Lodz with her husband and they took an apartment together. During this period she became very friendly, too, with Dinah and Priveh, and the women met often, sometimes in Max Ashkenazi's home, sometimes in Yakob's, sometimes in Priveh's. But the two brothers never met.

Then, when Yakob's affairs had been straightened out, he reverted to his natural self, and therewith the brief period of comradeship between him and his wife came to an end. His appetite returned; he laughed loudly again; and, worst of all, he slept soundly through the nights. That seemed to irritate Pearl even more than his friendships with other women. Once again she took to tormenting him, and waking him out of his sleep.

"Don't sleep like that," she cried, shaking him. "Don't breathe so heavily, I can't stand it. I can't close my eyes for a minute."

Yakob stared at her in sleepy amazement. "But what good does it do you if I stay awake nights, too?" he grumbled.

She had no answer to that and therefore became angrier.

"How can you expect me to sleep," she wept, "when you do everything to torture me?"

[352]

She fled from Lodz and her husband, back to her home in Warsaw, her doctors, her bottles, and her pills, and Yakob took up his former life, forgetful of the crisis through which he had passed. Once more he sat joyfully in his big, flashing carriage, which rolled through the streets of Lodz; once more he haunted the most expensive restaurants and cabarets in Lodz. He left business to his subordinates even when he was in town. When the summer came and Lodz sweltered in its heat, dust, and smoke, he could not resist the call of the summer resorts. And this year he made it a point to find out exactly when Dinah and her mother were leaving for Carlsbad and reserved a first-class place for himself on the same train.

With all his old verve and gaiety he strolled from car to car. He had cigars for the men, boxes of chocolate for the women, jokes and compliments for both. Wherever he went, he left a high charge of good spirits and optimism; and when he came into the car where Dinah sat with her mother, with innumerable boxes and valises above and below, he pretended to be as surprised as they.

It was rather a long time since they had met. As long as Pearl had been with Yakob in Lodz and the three women had been intimate, Dinah had seen her brother-in-law fairly often. With Pearl's retirement to Warsaw, and Yakob's resumption of his bachelor life, the contact had been broken. Priveh had seemed to mourn the loss even more than her daughter. Now, when she suddenly saw him standing at the door of the car, she uttered a cry of joy.

"Yakob! You! If I weren't an old woman I'd throw my arms round you and kiss you to death!"

It was not only her liking for Yakob: it was the unexpected restitution of her status. She hated travelling like a widow or an old maid, without a man companion. Apart from the inconvenience of it there was the feeling of social deficiency. But here was a cavalier infinitely preferable to her husband, so much younger and handsomer, and more skilled in chivalry.

"Of all the luck!" exclaimed Yakob, beaming.

But he knew that they knew that it was not just luck. And

[353]

when Dinah chimed in: "It certainly is a piece of good luck! Mamma was worried about travelling alone with me." She felt the blush deepening on her cheeks. She was happy and distressed at the same time. Part of her distress arose from her mother's eagerness to bring her together with Yakob, for she suspected that her mother sought not her happiness so much as revenge on Simcha Meyer, the son-in-law who had treated her husband and herself so brutally. And yet the temptation was there, and she was afraid of it.

In the long, glowing summer days in Carlsbad, the peaceful, pleasant city, and still more in the quiet moonlit evenings, Yakob pursued her ardently. She tried, in self-protection, to cling to her mother, but the latter evaded her. It was always: "Diana, dear, why don't you go for a ride with Yakob? I feel like sitting alone in the park and listening to the music," and: "Darling, I feel too tired to go along. You take a walk with Yakob and I'll lie down and rest awhile."

Under the shadow of heavy, overarching branches they sat alone at night on a park bench, holding hands silently. As often as Yakob tried to bring his lips close to hers, she turned away, frightened, whispering: "No, no, no."

Yakob lifted her arm and passed it round his shoulder.

"Then let's sit like this," he murmured, "as we did when we were children. Do you remember, Diana?"

"Yes, I remember." She was trembling in a confusion of happiness and terror. What was she afraid of? She did not know. God, perhaps, or her children, or perhaps herself, her own passions, which for so many years she had schooled into quiescence and which now, deep down, were beginning to stir hotly.

"Take me home, Yakob, please," she begged, regretting the words as she spoke them. "Oh, please. I'm your brother's wife . . . I have children. . . . God is watching."

And when he tried to hold her closer, she tore herself from him and fled, terrified, toward her hotel.

XXXVI

From her German borders by the Vistula to her borders by the Amur in the Far East, Russia was in tumultuous motion. On the walls of ten thousand churches, public buildings, offices, and factories appeared the Imperial proclamation calling every true son of Russia between the ages of twenty and forty to the defence of the fatherland against the attack of the Asiatic hordes of Japan. By tens and hundreds of thousands they assembled, leaving the field, the factory, and the workshop, preferring the chance of war to the certainty of court martial and the firing squad if they failed to respond.

Side by side with the great dignified posters of His Imperial Majesty, Autocrat of All the Russias, King of Poland, Archduke of Finland, etc., etc., etc., appeared others, small, badly printed, and unsigned, pasted up, not by daylight in the presence of a respectful throng, but in the dead of night. The little posters contradicted the big ones. They appealed to the peasants and workers not to defend the fatherland against the Asiatic hordes and not to let themselves be drawn into the struggle between Russian and Japanese capitalists.

Day after day the police tore down the small, badly printed posters; night after night they were put up again in unexpected places. Crowds gathered round them and read avidly. Recruits who had never borne arms before, and even old-time reservists, were affected by them. There were mutinies; detachments on their way to the barracks broke loose from their convoys, smashed open Government liquor stores, and then fled. In Poland, Lithuania, White Russia, and the Baltic Provinces the revolutionaries were more active and more successful than elsewhere. Unable to lay hands on the agitators in sufficient numbers, unable to stem the flood of propaganda, the Russian Government resorted to a familiar stratagem— the deflection of the discontent of the masses into less dangerous channels: to wit, against the Jews. A systematic campaign of slander and hatred was instigated by the Government, and the angry masses were encouraged to revenge themselves on the true enemies of Russia, the traitors within, the unbelievers and Christ-killers. The tumult of the riots, the drums of the soldiers, the bells and benedictions of the churches, drowned out the complaints of the peasant and city women whose men had been taken away and the cries of the Jews. The workers' quarters in the cities seethed with anger, hatred, and revolution, but the trains continued to roll eastward toward the Amur, laden with men, cattle, and guns.

Two men were speeding in the opposite direction, from the Far East toward Lodz, in those fateful days. Both of them were feverish with impatience to get back; for both of them the outbreak of the war meant the beginning of a new epoch.

Max Ashkenazi sat in a first-class car and stared out at the snow-covered fields through which the train was speeding. Wrapped in a huge coat of Kamchatka furs, a big caracul hat on his head, he leaned back on the plush seat and in his impatience pulled at his sparse beard. Every hour was precious to him; and here the train was falling steadily behind schedule, as the snow piled up on the tracks, and the roads became impassable.

The war had caught him in the Far East, when he should have been on the spot in Lodz. There was nothing to do in the East now, though it was Lodz's biggest buyer; nothing to do, for the communications were cut off, the eastward-travelling trains were pre-empted by the army, and salesmen and merchants were scurrying homeward to see what they could save in the catastrophe that threatened. Several telegrams had reached Max Ashkenazi, asking for instructions. The railroads would not accept freight for the East; what was the good of filling orders which could not be delivered now? Max Ashkenazi looked at the telegrams and ground his teeth with impatience. How helpless they all were! How frightened! And the barons were, of course, abroad. Had he, Max Ashkenazi, only been on the spot! He would have shown them that in a time of war one does not need private customers! One does not worry about bankruptcies and orders and credits when a government needs supplies. True, the Huntze factory was not fitted out to produce military clothes; but what of that? How long would it take a good organizer to change all that? All you needed was the orders. Get those! Get them at once! The rest will follow.

He was sole director of the Huntze factory now. Old Albrecht had collapsed at last and had been buried with full honours. Max Ashkenazi had laid a big wreath of white roses on his grave and had taken over the director's desk, to the infinite disgust of the German foremen and higher officials. Not that there was much change in the management, for Max Ashkenazi had long left Albrecht with almost nothing to do. But the sight of that little, excitable Jew, who spoke a Yiddish German in a Polish singsong, who had the habit of grabbing people by the lapel when he wanted their attention, who wore expensive clothes and always looked like a caricature of a well-dressed man, the sight of this person in the seat of the vast, lordly, Teutonic Albrecht infuriated them. But he knew his business, this little interloper; and he seemed to be everywhere simultaneously, in the factory, in the salesrooms, in the interior of Russia, and in the Far East. He was irresistible. They despised him and obeyed him; they mocked his mannerisms and sought his advice.

They felt his crushing superiority at this moment when, helpless and bewildered, they awaited his return. And he, sitting in the train, felt his immeasurable superiority no less. Where they saw only disaster, from which they wanted to escape with a minimum of loss, he saw his great chance, and a double plan of action kept him in a continuous fever of excitement. Huntze stocks were low. All stocks were low in Lodz at this moment. Now was the time to buy. And then when those Government orders were landed, Huntze stocks would go up swiftly again. The factory would be saved—but whose factory would it be?

He had to act swiftly. There was only one man he was afraid of in Lodz—Maximilian Flederbaum, the man who had cleaned up millions on the new railroad station, through the friendship of the Governor. Now, however, the Governor at Piotrkov was probably no better than any other governor. The decisions lay with the Quartermaster General in St. Petersburg and his subalterns; but still, Flederbaum's money could buy them as easily as anyone else's. It all depended who made the connections first. How useful the Huntzes could have been now! They had immediate entrée to those circles, to the officers and sons of the aristocracy who controlled the fate of the army and of Russia. But it was like them to be abroad at this crucial moment. He would do it himself, then, and reap the double benefit.

When he arrived in Lodz after days of travelling, he did not stop at his home for longer than a few minutes. He did not take a bath or change his clothes. He was off to the factory, to give the first instructions for the impending change in the production. He returned from the factory late at night, and early the next morning left for Warsaw.

The way to the Western commander, whose headquarters were in Warsaw, lay through a trail of bribery which began with a certain popular actress who was the mistress of one of the commander's aides-de-camp. To her Max Ashkenazi came quite simply as an admirer of her art, though he had never seen her perform; but he brought with him a costly diamond ring and a huge bouquet of flowers. The flowers, preceding him, proclaimed at once a person of means. The ring, offered as a humble expression of admiration, indicated business. Max Ashkenazi sat a long time with the blonde actress, sickened by the atmosphere of luxury, weary with the tasteless and fulsome compliments which made up his side of the conversation, but determined to let the lady understand that if she could get him the introductions he needed, there would be still larger bouquets for her boudoir and flashier gems for her fingers.

[358]

He wanted swift action. Through the blonde actress he became acquainted with her lover and with a host of officers and adjutants who made up the entourage of the commander. It was a world of high living, innumerable parties, champagne, cards, and bribes. Sober amid drunkards, his heart filled with contempt for the empty, noisy, animal lives of these aristocrats, Max Ashkenazi pursued his aim steadily. Niggardly by instinct, he knew when to gamble big, and he knew also that this was one occasion when it was stupid to think of a thousand more or less. He was buying his future, and if he bought right, no price was too high.

He returned to Lodz with a foul taste in his mouth, and his head ringing with the shouting and laughter of the wild nights he had passed with the officers. In his pocket was the contract he had set out to get. It was of a size he had not dared to dream of. And it meant that no one else in Lodz would obtain the same kind of work.

Thus, while the other factories of Lodz stood idle, that of the Huntze brothers worked double shifts. The sirens hooted triumphantly across the city, the thick smoke covered the skies, as if to blot out all of Huntze's competitors.

"He's done it again!" was the cry in the restaurants and on the streets of Lodz. "This is Max Ashkenazi's private little war."

Max Ashkenazi did not encourage the barons to return from abroad. He wrote them that everything was going well; they had nothing to worry about; and he sent them all the money they needed. Meanwhile the stocks in his safe accumulated faster and faster.

The other man who returned from the Far East to Lodz was just as impatient as Max Ashkenazi, but he was compelled to travel much more slowly, and not always by train.

Nissan Eibeschutz escaped from his Siberian village on a sleigh. When this had taken him beyond the reach of his pursuers, he continued for a while on foot. Then he permitted himself to board a train, like a vagrant, hiding himself under straw on the cattle-cars. Sometimes he had to slip off the train and travel by whatever conveyance he could find.

Like Max Ashkenazi, Nissan was being recalled to Lodz by those who needed his guidance and leadership in a crisis. Lodz was again one of the centres of the revolutionary movement. The factory workers, most of them thrown out of employment by the shift of industry resulting from the war, were bitter and ready for action. The seeds of revolt which Nissan and Tevyeh had sown years before, and which everyone believed lost for ever, began to produce a substantial if belated harvest. Of their own accord the workers organized demonstrations and fomented strikes among those who could find employment. Revolutionary songs were heard again in the streets and workshops of Lodz, and Tevyeh and his friends sent secret letters to Nissan, telling him that the hour had struck and that he must make every effort to escape and return to Lodz.

Not much more remained of Nissan's sentence, and in a short while he would have been able to leave prison freely: he chose to escape rather than wait.

He had grown weary of his exile in that forlorn corner of the world. There was no employment of any kind, and the prisoners had nothing to do but sit around arguing and quarrelling. There was much diversity of opinion, for there were representatives of all the revolutionary parties, the old-fashioned Polish Narodniks, members of the Polish Socialist Party, Social Democrats, Anarchists, Nihilists, members of the Jewish Socialist Bund, and then later additions—new parties, groups, and subgroups which sprang up like mushrooms throughout the length and breadth of Russia. They made fun of each other's views, derided each other's programs, and got on each other's nerves. Nissan had argued and quarrelled too at first; he had defended pure Marxism against all the adulterations which Poles and Jews and others introduced by way of romantic nationalism and factionalization. He had been passionate and convincing, arguing with the feverish energy of a Talmud student and gesticulating like one. But he had wearied of it at last. Likewise he had not been at all popular among the non-Jewish prisoners. Despite his complete severance from Jewish tradition or even Jewish interests, they found him excessively Jewish. They did not like,

[360]

either, his relentless logic and his habit of perpetual study. He never took a drink. He never joined them on the hunt or in their wanderings in the forests.

The only one among the non-Jews who was drawn to Nissan was the Social Democrat Shchinsky. Himself a Pole, and a former student in a theological seminary, Shchinsky hated the Polish Socialists who brought confusion into Marxist thought by trying to identify it with national aspirations. Like Nissan, again, he was perpetually studying Marxist literature and found no time or had no inclination for hunting- and drinking-parties. He had brought with him, from his Jesuit seminary, the deep-rooted belief that the end justifies the means, and this he applied to the proletarian struggle for liberation. When he talked of the capitalist classes a spasm of bitterness contorted his face. He believed, of course, in the iron laws of economic development and of the natural collapse of capitalism, but he was impatient and would not wait till the process fulfilled itself. He wanted to hasten it. Without the knowledge of the party he had adopted and practised a policy of terrorism. He was arrested, sentenced to a long prison term, and after it exiled to Siberia.

"You've got to clean them up," he said to Nissan always. "Get them out of the way."

It was in the company of this Shchinsky that Nissan fled toward the revolutionary centre of Lodz.

When he stepped out of the railroad station, after an absence of so many years, Nissan thought he could smell revolution in the air. It rose out of the stones under his feet, out of the walls of the houses and factories. The deeper he walked into the town, the more numerous became the placards of the revolutionaries or the slogans painted on the walls. At most of the corners the policemen stood in pairs, often accompanied by an armed soldier.

Following a circuitous path and doubling often on his footsteps, Nissan made his way alone to the hide-out of which he had been advised in the secret letters to Siberia. He asked no one the way. When he reached the house, he saw the plant-pot placed in the window as a sign that the coast was clear and he could enter.

He mounted the steps and knocked. A red-cheeked, black-haired young woman whom he had never seen before opened the door.

"How is Uncle?" he said to her.

"He's much better," answered the young woman promptly, "and he sends you his regards."

Nissan slipped past the door. The red-cheeked young woman kissed him in greeting. "At last!" she said. "We've wondered whether anything happened to you. Are you hungry, comrade?"

"Some soap and water first, please," begged Nissan. "It's weeks since I've had a wash."

That same evening there was celebrated in the house of the red-cheeked young woman the betrothal of two of her friends. The tables were set, and on them were bottles of beer and whisky, cakes, sausages, and other evidences of festivity. The young man and the young woman, in holiday clothes, sat next to each other on the sofa. A stranger would have been astonished, however, by the apparent indifference of the chief participants to each other and to the ostensible purpose of the gathering. In actual fact, this was not a betrothal ceremony, but a reception to Nissan on his return from Siberia. The "betrothal" served to cover the meeting, so that the janitor would not report it to the police; and the game was carried so far that the terms of the "marriage" were actually printed on special forms, and the names of the "bride" and "bridegroom" filled in.

Among the "celebrators" there were only two with whom Nissan was acquainted: Tevyeh and his daughter Bashke.

"Lodz is ours," declared Tevyeh. "After you've had a few days' rest we'll put you to work. You're needed, Nissan."

"I'll start tomorrow," answered Nissan. "I've rested long enough; I'm sick of resting."

Within a few days he became active on the local committee. His public appearance, or reappearance, took place in the synagogue late in an afternoon, when afternoon and evening prayers were being said together.

The synagogue officials were astonished to see assembling, that afternoon, crowds of persons who had never or seldom been known to pray before. The beadle, suspecting what was afoot, waited for the end of the prayers, and when the last word of the last prayer had been intoned, strode forward, banged his fist down on the pulpit, and announced hastily that the preacher would now address the congregation. Before the preacher was able to put on his praying-shawl, some-one else, a worker, had mounted the pulpit, and at the same instant the door of the synagogue was violently closed from within.

The man at the door, a muscular, broad-shouldered labourer, called out: "No one is going to leave this synagogue until I open the door." The worker on the pulpit followed this with the crisp business-like statement: "The preacher will not address you today. I give the floor to the representa-tive of the workers. Comrade, the audience is waiting."

Nissan mounted the pulpit and glanced round at the crowd which packed the synagogue. He found it hard to begin. Years had passed since he had carried on a conversation in Yiddish, let alone addressed a meeting in that language. For a few minutes he stumbled along slowly, seeking the words he needed; but as he felt the high intensity of the emotion which filled the workers, as he sensed their confidence in him, in themselves, and in their mastery of the situation, his tongue was loosened and the language returned to him with a rush. He realized suddenly that his work of many years before had not been wasted; its results were apparent before his eyes. His address gathered momentum, grew fiercer from second to second, and ended in a fierce torrent of invective against the enemies of the working-class and of passionate encour-agement to his comrades.

The candles before the pulpit guttered and bent with the heat, the audience sat breathless under the spell of Nissan's words. The middle-class worshippers, employers, and shop-keepers, who had been trapped into the meeting, did not dare to utter a protest. They listened with the rest.

A tremendous change had come over Balut since Nissan had last walked its streets. He realized it now in the syna-gogue, and realized it even more strongly later, when he went out and took up his work with the committee. Crowds gath-

[363]

ered everywhere fearlessly, ignoring the police and their armed attendants. The workmen's circles were well organized, and worked day and night. Their membership had grown beyond all expectation and included every class of worker: weavers, shoemakers, leather-workers, stocking-knitters, cobblers, irreligious Jews in modern clothes, religious Jews in long garberdines, women in wigs and women who had refused to shear off their hair after marriage, but wore a red kerchief about their heads. Meetings were in progress everywhere, councils sat, strikes were called, literature was distributed openly, speakers addressed the crowds in the streets.

The workers' circles or exchanges had become the centres of the life of Balut. Apprentices came before them to complain of ill-treatment at the hands of their employers, or denounce their employers' wives for feeding them mouldy bread and sugarless coffee; housewives reported that they had been thrown out of their homes for non-payment of rent; servant girls asked for redress when their meagre wages were not paid them on time. The Unionists, as the workers' leaders were called everywhere, because of their ceaseless appeals for united action, became general advisers to the working-class population. Wives of truck-drivers came to lodge complaint against drunken husbands who did not bring home their pay, but spent it in drink; there were even couples who came with their marital difficulties and turned the workers' circles into domestic-relations courts.

On the pavements, under snow and rain, in the midst of the noise, tumult, and commerce of the streets, the committees carried on day after day. Here quick decisions were rendered, strikes called, delegates elected, ultimatums drawn up to be delivered to recalcitrant bosses. Committees were even sent with threats of direct action against profiteering grocery stores. Other committees were sent out to make the rounds of all the shops and to see to it that none of the clerks were kept after hours. Here, too, levies were assessed, and collectors sent round to shops and employers with a demand for the sum decided on.

No one dared to fight back. The workers' circles were all-

[364]

powerful at this time in Balut. There was no appeal from their decision, and there was no way of bribing them; they listened to no arguments, and they could not be cited before the courts, for any attempt to call in the authorities would have meant exposing oneself to the concerted vengeance of the entire workers' movement.

The ruler of the workers' circles was Tevyeh. He was everywhere. No important conference, no decision, no new piece of propaganda, no mass meeting, but what he had a hand in it. Always by his side, assisting, advising, and encouraging, was his daughter Bashke, now a grown woman. She could have married long ago; attractive as she was, she could have chosen as a husband a master worker, a small capitalist, and with him have started a little factory of her own. But it had never occurred to her to do this. She still clung to her father as she had done in childhood days, when she had defended him against his wife's curses. And, as in those days, she still looked up to Nissan, the returned exile, in the manner of some forlorn working-girl who has lifted her eyes to a brilliant son of a rich family, someone for ever beyond her reach. She hardly ever spoke to him, and when he addressed her, her face flooded with colour and she could not find words with which to answer.

Tevyeh had not the time or the freedom of mind to notice how his daughter looked at Nissan. He strode through the streets of Balut inducting Nissan into the work, and as he took him from one workers' circle to another, he said triumphantly: "See this! And this! They're all with us. We're the masters now in Balut."

His Excellency von Miller, Governor at Piotrkov, commanded the Chief Rabbi of Lodz and the leaders of the community to appear before him.

The leaders put on black silk gaberdines and shiny silk hats; the Rabbi put on the medal which had been sent him from the court in St. Petersburg; and all of them appeared before the Governor. But he was impressed neither by the black silk gaberdines nor by the gold medal. He banged on the desk and spoke harshly to the Jews of Lodz.

"I don't like the way your crowd is behaving," he said coarsely. "There's no respect for the law or His Imperial Majesty. I want you to understand that if you can't persuade your Jews to behave themselves, I shan't consider myself responsible. Responsible citizens, loyal subjects of His Majesty the Tsar, will take matters in their own hands, and you'll have no one to blame but yourselves."

The committee of leading Jews stood crestfallen before the Governor.

"Your Excellency," they murmured, "there are all sorts of elements among us, just as there are among the Poles and the Germans. We don't know what to do with these enemies of law and order."

"It's your business to know what to do with them," said the Governor sternly.

The Rabbi, who stood high in the opinion of the Governor and who had been mentioned even at court, answered, as always, very cleverly.

"We humbly ask His Excellency to inquire from his subordinates whether among strikers and rioters and inciters to disorder there has ever been found one Jew who wears the ritual fringes."

The Governor looked uncomprehendingly at the Rabbi. "Wears the what?" he asked sternly.

"The ritual fringes," replied the Rabbi. And he proceeded to explain, in high-flown and pedantic Russian, that every pious and God-fearing Jew wore next to his skin a special garment, a sort of sleeveless shirt, with fringes at the bottom, according to the Law of Moses. Such Jews were respectable and obeyed the laws of the land. No rebels were ever to be found among them.

The Governor made a note of this extraordinary fact. As soon as the Jewish delegation had withdrawn he called his secretary and issued strict orders to the police commissioner of Lodz to examine the underwear of every Jew arrested for seditious activity. Those that wore ritual fringes were to be liberated at once; all others were to be detained. The ingenious answer of the Rabbi to the Governor was repeated everywhere in Lodz, and everyone, including the Chasidic opponents of the Russian-Jewish Rabbi, admired his brilliant diplomacy.

The leaders of the community, the ones who had stood abashed before the enraged Governor, decided that the time had come for action. They called a meeting and decided to appoint preachers and teachers to make the rounds of all the synagogues and to impress upon the Jews of Lodz the virtues of humility and obedience. These preachers and teachers were sent even into the synagogues of the workers, among whom the pestilence of discontent raged fiercest.

But there was no observable improvement in the behaviour of the lower classes. The workers' circles remained as impudent and revolutionary as ever. Thereupon the community leaders called upon the Jewish toughs of Lodz to take action against the Unionists.

[367]

The toughs had always hated the Unionists. Before the latter rose to power, it was the toughs who had been the bosses of Balut. They had exacted graft from everyone, from servant girls who went strolling in the woods on Saturday afternoons, from their escorts, workers and apprentices who had no other period of leisure. When a young man went out walking for the first time with a girl, he was sure to be stopped by one of the toughs on the pretext that this was his girl, and that the new suitor had better indemnify the rejected "suitor" with at least a rouble if he did not wish to be laid up for a couple of weeks. It was useless for the girl to protest that she had never seen the tough before: it was well known that toughs never listened to arguments. Whenever a worker appeared with a new suit—which was mostly before Passover—he had to pay an excise tax to the toughs. If he refused he was sure to have his new suit ruined.

The Unionists had put an end to all that. There had been a few clashes between the toughs and the organized workers, and the victory had remained with the workers.

Apart from this, the Unionists had carried on a campaign of propaganda among the servant girls, persuading them to come to workers' meetings instead of going for walks in the woods. Likewise the workers' committees had pleaded with the young men to stop frequenting the red-light district, with the result that business fell off among the female friends of the toughs. Some prostitutes had actually given up their profession, leaving the red-light district and getting regular jobs. Moreover, before the rise of the workers' circles disgruntled workers had made use of the toughs in their battles against oppressive bosses, profiteering grocers, and heartless landlords; now they appealed to the committee and obtained justice free of charge. It had come to such a pass that several toughs had actually repented and joined the workmen's circles.

The Jewish merchants, manufacturers, and well-to-do householders of Lodz, who were compelled to pay tribute to the organized workers, would have been glad to pay twice the amount to the toughs to get rid of the others; but until the Governor put pressure on the leaders of the community, they had not dared to take the necessary steps. Now, goaded from below and threatened from above, they sent emissaries with big bribes to the leaders of the Jewish toughs. The temptation restored the courage of the latter. They began to organize an uprising against the Unionists, and their first allies were the truck-drivers. These last hated the organized workers because they had taught the young apprentice truck-drivers to demand better treatment and higher pay. Likewise the truck-drivers were a pious lot and could not stand the contempt with which the workers' leaders spoke of rabbis, saints, religious schools, and Jewish things generally.

But what infuriated the toughs and their allies, the truck-drivers, most, was the incident with "electria." A young worker of Balut happened to die of tuberculosis. The Burial Brotherhood of Balut at once sent its emissaries to the house where the corpse lay, in order to do the proper thing by the dead man. These emissaries even brought a praying-shawl with them with which to cover the corpse, for though it was known that the dead worker had not worn ritual fringes in life, it was considered proper that he should at least appear before his Maker in the garment of a pious Jew. Unfortunately for the Burial Brotherhood, its emissaries appeared too late on the scene. The representatives of the Unionists had anticipated them and carted off the corpse. But instead of swathing it in a praying-shawl, they had thrown over it the red flag of revolution; and instead of conducting the regular burial services, they had sung revolutionary songs all the way from the house to the cemetery. One of the women workers, a Lithuanian girl in a red dress, had stated openly that when a man dies no soul flies out of him, as superstitious people believed, but that his "electria" merely stopped working.

For some reason or other the Burial Brotherhood pounced on the words about the "electria" running out as the centre and symbol of the whole scandalous and godless procedure. The phrase captured the Jewish community of Lodz, and from Piotrkov Street to the other side of Balut one heard nothing but this word "electria."

"What's the world coming to?" Jews asked, horrified. "They don't even believe in a soul."

[369]

"Do you know what?" said others. "As sure as the sun shines, they'll bring a great pestilence on the city."

"Destroy them, wipe them out, without pity!" cried some.

"Turn them over to the police," advised others. "Let them be thrown into prison to rot in chains."

The pietists became so excited about the "electria" business that they were ready to assault the workers. The Rabbi himself said, in a sermon which was widely applauded, that Jews who expressed such heathenish opinions had excommunicated themselves from their people, were outside the pale of the Law, and deserved whatever happened to them. They had, said the Rabbi, brought death upon themselves, and, according to the Law, any man who tries to commit suicide by drowning should not be rescued; he should, on the contrary, be thrust deeper into the water.

But the truck-drivers and the toughs of Pepper Street were not content with curses and denunciations. They contemplated action; and now that the heads of the community were definitely on their side, they only awaited the opportunity to join battle. That opportunity came soon.

On Prevet Street, off Pepper Street, lived "Uncle" Zachariah, the owner of several whorehouses. Uncle Zachariah had no children of his own, and he therefore decided to win grace in the eyes of Heaven by bringing up an orphan girl and marrying her off to some decent working-man, which he accordingly did. The bridegroom was a cobbler of Balut, and the wedding was celebrated in grand style. On the bridegroom's side came cobblers, leather-workers, and saddlemakers; on the bride's side—she having no family of her own —came pimps, madames, and toughs, all the *haut monde* of the red-light district. The bridegroom and his friends were Unionists, without exception.

Right under the canopy, while the marriage ceremony was in progress, the first skirmishes took place. The officiating clergyman was the Rabbi of the red-light district, an undersized specimen who chanted the prayers through his nose. Among the Unionists there were some who openly made fun of the ceremony, and the blood mounted to Uncle Zachariah's bull-neck.

[370]

"Hey, you there, Unionist," he roared, "don't make fun of a holy man. I won't permit it!"

"Electria, keep your lousy jaws shut!" his guests seconded him.

The shoemakers, even more than the leather-workers and saddle-makers, were husky young fellows who did not take insults from anyone. They threw out their chests and answered: "If you want to shut our jaws, come and shut them!"

Fists were clenched, and battle seemed imminent. The little Rabbi suspended his prayers and held off the opposing sides. "Now, no fighting here, no scandals!"

The hotheads on both sides glared at each other, but said nothing more. Later in the evening, however, war broke out in earnest. The bridegroom had just finished making the customary little speech in which he showed off whatever learning he had picked up in his boyhood or could hire from the teacher who prepared him for the ceremony. When he sat down, the guests, still following custom, began showering him with gifts. The pimps and toughs threw two- and three- and even a few five-rouble bills; the shoemakers and saddle-makers could afford only coins, and now it was the turn of the toughs to mock.

"Come on, Unionists, let's see a decent present for the bridegroom."

"Hey, Electria, don't throw pieces of lead on the table. I didn't like the ring of that last coin."

"We have to work for every kopeck!" shouted back a young shoemaker. "We don't pick up easy money from women."

The toughs did not like that remark.

"Who's that meant for?" one of them growled.

"For anyone that wants it!" shot back from the other side.

The next instant a glass flew across the table, and a saddle-maker's face suddenly spouted blood and beer. The response was prompt, and a volley of half a dozen glasses flew the other way. Then followed plates, knives, forks, anything the infuriated guests could lay hands on. When these ran out, the men took off their coats, picked up chairs, and waded in. Knives were drawn. Women screamed. In less than half an hour the workers were beaten back out of the hall. The

[371]

toughs had outnumbered and outfought them.

The next day the cobblers, shoemakers, saddlers, and leather-workers of Balut downed tools and called to their aid the butchers and the young truck-drivers' assistants. Armed with knives, they descended on Prevet and Pepper streets and began to smash up the whorehouses. They threw the beds and the furniture into the streets and ripped open the cushions and the clothes of the prostitutes; they broke the pianos and tore up the indecent lithographs which hung on the walls.

"Go out and work for a living!" they shouted. "No more whorehouses and easy money!"

The half-naked women tore their hair and screamed for help. Uncle Zachariah's wife became hysterical and screamed: "Zachariah, Zachariah, save the girls! We'll be left without a business."

But Zachariah did not dare to interfere. The workers were well organized. Zachariah ran to gather his men, but before the toughs arrived, the red-light district was in ruins. A snow of feathers, mingled with broken glassware and crockery, lay underfoot. Finally the toughs came, accompanied by the truck-drivers, all armed with knives. They were no match for the workers; the shoemakers and butchers and leather-workers were adept in the use of knives. The toughs and their allies withdrew, bloody and defeated.

The victory of the Unionists made a tremendous impression among the Jews of Lodz. The toughs were afraid to show themselves on the streets, and if they ventured out they made wide circles round the workers' groups. The merchants and wealthy householders who had encouraged the toughs were terrified. Even the police were intimidated by the front which the workers had put up. The workers' committees became all-powerful. Employers did not dare to hold their employees one minute after seven in the evening; shopkeepers paid their assessments without a murmur; restaurant-owners submitted meekly when one of the workers' leaders came in with a crowd of the unemployed and issued the command: "Feed these men." The streets of Lodz became unsafe for the rich, and the private carriages which had rolled so

[372]

insolently through the city were now kept locked in the stables.

Meanwhile bad news filtered through from the remote front in the Far East. The Asiatic hordes refused to be intimidated by the true believers, and the forces of the Tsar suffered defeat by sea and land. The blind beggars of Lodz sang bitter songs about the Tsar and his generals, disguising the true names under transparent parodies. Cossacks began to appear in the streets of Lodz.

$\mathcal{T}\!he$ workers of the Huntze factory were on strike. Max Ashkenazi, general director, closed himself up within the factory, taking over the bachelor apartment of the deceased Albrecht. He was afraid to show himself in the streets. All night long the door of the apartment was watched by an armed guard.

Max Ashkenazi could not sleep nights, though the bed of the late Herr Albrecht was wide and comfortable. The Huntze factory was in a dreadful dilemma. Government orders were plentiful; but failure to deliver on the specified date meant heavy penalties, which more than swallowed up the profits. Max Ashkenazi had reorganized the factory; he had got everything set for the production of military goods; he had arranged for two shifts, so that the machines were to be kept going twenty-four hours a day. He had calculated everything perfectly. He had omitted only one factor: the workers. He had not thought it necessary to include them in his plans. The workers were always there; they did what they were told and adapted themselves to all conditions. But this one omission was his undoing. For a time the factory went on turning out military goods according to plan—and then suddenly a delegation of workers asked Melchior for an interview with the director.

Max Ashkenazi heard the request with astonishment.

"A delegation?" he asked Melchior. "I have no time for

delegations iust now. Tell them to come back when I'm not so busy."

Melchior delivered the message and waited for the delegation to withdraw. The workers did not budge. "Tell the director," they said to Melchior, "that we're just as busy as he is. If he can't receive us we will give orders to stop the machines."

Melchior took back the message. Max Ashkenazi listened, and he suddenly felt the seat grow hard and uncomfortable under him. He scratched his chin furiously, straightened out his tie, which, as usual, had crept to one side of his neck, and lit a fresh cigar.

"Show them in," he said.

When the workers entered he let them stand for a minute or two while he pretended to be deeply absorbed in some papers. He felt rather than saw that though they came in with their caps in their hands, they were not particularly respectful in their bearing. Neither the magnificence of his office nor his deep absorption had impressed them. He looked up, let out a cloud of smoke, and across the smoke asked sharply: "What's the matter?"

"We're a delegation of all the workers of this factory," answered one man, and he held out a paper. Max Ashkenazi itched to grab the piece of paper, crumple it up, and throw it down, as he had done many years before when a committee had waited on him in his father-in-law's house. But he restrained himself. These were other times. He remembered fat old Albrecht sitting in the wheelbarrow, a broomstick in his hands. Workers were not what they had once been. These men who faced him now were capable of pulling a knife on him. He therefore summoned all the patience he was master of and listened while the workers' demands were read off.

And extraordinary demands they were, too. The first was that instead of two shifts of twelve hours each, there should be three, of eight hours each. Max Ashkenazi jumped in his seat, as if hardly believing his ears.

"What's that? What's that?" he exclaimed. "Why, it isn't so long since workers were glad to work sixteen hours a day,

[375]

and now they're kicking at twelve."

"We can work twelve hours a day if you insist," said the leader of the delegation, "but in that case we want extra pay for the additional four hours."

"Impossible!" answered Max Ashkenazi curtly.

"For overtime above eight hours," the leader read forth, "pay at the rate of time and a half."

"Ridiculous!" exclaimed Max Ashkenazi.

"Pay for regular work to be increased twenty-five per cent," the leader read out.

"Is that all?" asked Max Ashkenazi, with a contemptuous smile.

"That's all for the time being," said the leader coolly.

Max Ashkenazi felt the blood rising to his head, but he held himself in. This was not the time for anger. He moved deeper into his armchair and said: "Sit down."

"We can stand," answered the workers.

Max Ashkenazi pulled at the little point of his beard and began reasonably: "It seems to me that though you are only workers in this factory, you can do a little sum in arithmetic."

The workers did not answer.

Max Ashkenazi leaned forward, took a sheet of paper, and began to dot figures on it. "If I were to yield on half of your demands," he said, pointing with his pencil at the figures, "the factory would have to lose money, and that the factory can't do."

"We've made our calculations, too," answered the leader. "The calculations of the factory aren't our business. They're the business of the director."

Max Ashkenazi shook the ash off his cigar with a hand that was so unsteady that he covered the lapels of his English coat with ashes.

"No," he answered. "It isn't just my business; it's your business as well. You're just as interested as I am that the factory shall not lose money; because if it does, it has to shut down."

"That's up to you," answered the leader.

Still restraining his fury, Max Ashkenazi began to talk in fatherly tones.

"It's easy enough to shut down a factory," he said. "It's not so easy to open it again. These are hard times. There are thousands of factory workers who would be glad to get work under any conditions. I've kept this factory going, so that all of you have had employment. Is this the thanks I get?"

"The director wasn't thinking of us, but of himself," said the leader calmly. "These are our demands. Either you meet them or we walk out."

Max Ashkenazi took another tack. He pretended to be helpless.

"I'm an employee here, the same as you," he said. "The factory belongs, as you know, to the barons. They're abroad just now, and I can't decide on such matters without them. As soon as they return I'll submit your demands to them."

"We know nothing about the barons," answered the workers. "We deal with the director. You can wire the barons. We'll wait three days for the answer. We won't wait till they come back from abroad."

During those three days of grace Max Ashkenazi tried to apply his old tactics. This time he did not send for Lippe Chalfan, but invited the chief of police to lunch in an expensive restaurant. He explained that this was no ordinary situation. The Huntze factory was producing goods for the army; it was therefore engaged in patriotic work. A strike was definitely a blow at the Government and its armed forces. It was up to the police commissioner, therefore, to call in troops and teach the strikers a lesson.

The chief of police wiped his long moustaches, wet with wine, and shook his head.

No, he was not at all inclined to interfere in the internal affairs of the factory. There was trouble enough without that. The police was intimidated. Every day another policeman was shot. The Governor, too, would refuse to send soldiers. These were not the old times. It would be best to reach an agreement with the workers.

Max Ashkenazi tried another tack. He sent for the workers' delegates separately and secretly, and to each one hinted broadly that if he would forget about the movement and all that sort of nonsense, the director of the factory would know

[377]

how to show his gratitude. But the delegates refused to take the hint. Some of them were insulted; others were afraid.

Max Ashkenazi played his last card. He sent out agents into the streets to pick up unemployed workers wherever they could. But not a single worker responded. Those that were not already infected with the revolutionary ideas of the strikers answered that it was more than their lives were worth to play the scab.

There was nothing for it, then, but to close the factory. The gates were locked, and Max Ashkenazi lived inside, in the late Albrecht's apartment. He hoped against hope that the workers would hold out for only a few days and begin dribbling back, but he knew that there was a spirit of determination abroad among the weavers of Lodz. Day after day he sat alone in his rooms. Food was brought to him from the outside. In sheer boredom he tried to read the cheap novels with which Albrecht had been wont to amuse himself on sleepless nights. They sickened him. He threw them down and walked back and forth through the rooms. He missed the noise of the revolving wheels, of the sirens screaming in the morning, of the walls shuddering under the impact of the machines. He could not sleep at night. He did not know what to do with his days. He did not dare to leave the factory.

In the city the revolutionary leaders were the masters; and the workers, Polish, German, and Jewish—but particularly the last—followed them blindly. At countless mass meetings there was open revolutionary talk, and Max Ashkenazi, director of the Huntze factory, was the symbol of the tyranny of the bosses.

These were great days for Nissan. He felt at last that the real battle was joined, and he was in the thick of it. This time he was not leading a frightened little crowd of hand-loom weavers—themselves tainted with bourgeois psychology —against an obscure little boss. No, this was the world of steam; this was the true proletariat embattled against the big bourgeoisie, the representatives of centralized capital. It had taken a long time to set these masses in motion. They were not like Jews, these Poles and Germans, eager to learn, quick to pick up, in their study circles, the theory of the inevitable

[378]

revolution. They had preferred to pass their free evenings in the inns and beer-parlours or in their *Gesangvereine*. And now, at last, the slow, ponderous mass had been set in motion. The revolutionary spark had been lit in the very heart of this citadel of indifference and reaction. True, these Polish and German workers still did not understand the larger significance of their action. They struck for higher pay. That was enough for them. But it was not enough for Nissan. All his efforts were concentrated now on the workers of the Huntze factory. Day and night he circulated among them, met them in their homes, in stuffy committee rooms, at meetings, in the streets. Content to sleep three or four hours out of the twenty-four, he foresaw the time when these Poles and Germans, these slow, unenthusiastic sons of the true proletariat, would become the leaders in the great fight.

To Max Ashkenazi, eating out his heart behind the locked and bolted gates of the factory, confidential agents brought reports of Nissan's and Tevyeh's activities. Max Ashkenazi bit his lips with rage. He could not understand what these men and their Jewish followers wanted of him. They did not work in his factory. They had nothing to do with the Huntzes. Why didn't they leave the Polish and German workers alone? These had never had any high-flown ideas before they had been stirred up by Nissan and Tevyeh and their like. Their only aim in life had been to get their wages at the end of the week and betake themselves to a beer-parlour. What difference did an hour more or less in the day's work make to them? Those Jews of Balut! Weaklings themselves, unable to put in a decent day's work, they could not bear to see the non-Jews working, either. If only the old times were here again, he would teach them such a lesson as would keep their noses out of other people's business for good.

But the old times weren't here! Neither he, Max Ashkenazi, nor the factory-owners generally, nor even the police. were bosses of the city. The workers were in the saddle, and their leaders were the Jews. Who, if not they, drew up those proclamations in which Max Ashkenazi was called all sorts of names, among which "Blood-sucker" and "Exploiter" were the least? Who. if not they, had poisoned the minds of

[379]

the thick-witted gentile workers, who had asked nothing better than to be left alone?

Tossing about at night in Albrecht's bed, Max Ashkenazi bethought himself that perhaps it would not be a bad idea to send for those Jewish leaders and talk the situation over with them. They were not fools, by a long way. They would listen to sense; and Max Ashkenazi had great faith in his own powers of persuasion. By far the most intelligent among that crew was Nissan. True, there had been something between him and Nissan, but that was years before; and besides, no one knew who had put the police on Nissan's trail. Since that time Nissan had doubtless been in prison often enough for his revolutionary activities, and the old incident had probably faded from his mind.

Max Ashkenazi got out of bed and composed a letter to his former schoolmate. He wrote to him in the old style of the Jewish scholars, with all the complimentary flourishes which they were wont to use when addressing each other. He asked the learned Nissan to do him the honour of paying him a visit in order that they might discuss matters of the highest importance to themselves and to the world at large. With many citations from the Bible and the Talmud ingeniously woven into the text of the letter, he explained that if he, Max Ashkenazi, made so bold as to trouble the distinguished Reb Nissan to come to him, it was not out of pride. Were it only possible, he would gladly betake his own unworthy self to the residence of Reb Nissan; but, as the latter knew, it was impossible, for various reasons, to leave the factory at this time. A wink to a wise man was sufficient. The pressure of circumstances compelled him to put Reb Nissan to the trouble of coming to the factory; he hoped that his humble request would not be refused.

The letter was sent by messenger to the committee, and several hours were consumed in debate as to whether this missive from the hostile camp should be given serious consideration. Should the letter be ignored? Should it be met with a curt refusal? Or should the invitation be accepted? Tevyeh was against sending anyone; he was afraid of some provocative act which would put the workers in the wrong.

Or perhaps hidden agents would be there to arrest the leaders on a trumped-up charge. Nissan disagreed. He knew that Max Ashkenazi was no fool. He was an extremely practical person, and if he had something to say to the revolutionary leaders, it was probably worth listening to. However, Nissan announced that he certainly would not go alone; not because he was afraid of Max Ashkenazi, but because his action might be misinterpreted by the workers. That same afternoon, accompanied by two Jewish comrades, Nissan knocked at the gates of the factory. They opened slowly and cautiously, like the gates of a besieged city, and the three delegates were admitted to Max Ashkenazi's office.

Max Ashkenazi rose courteously and shook hands with the three workers.

"Gentlemen," he said, beaming, "I am delighted to see you. Will you be good enough to take seats?" To Nissan he said genially: "Ah, it's always easy to recognize the scholar, even after twenty years." He did not know how to address him, whether in the singular or the plural, and waited for a lead from the other. But Nissan was cold and formal and did not acknowledge the compliment. Max Ashkenazi went on in the second person plural.

"Yes, and it's a good deal more than that since we both studied under your late father, Reb Noske. Do you know, I still remember the last lesson we did together; I can repeat it by heart. . . ."

And he began to chant the Talmudic text, word for word, glancing at the other two delegates.

"Do you remember it, Nissan?" he asked.

"I don't spend any time on the Talmud these days," answered Nissan coldly.

"That's a great pity," said Max Ashkenazi. "A great pity. I'm a busy man myself, but I manage to find the time to look into a Jewish book. And I'm not ashamed to tell you that I've even written one or two little things myself. One can be a business-man, you know, and still keep up one's studies."

He smiled at Nissan's companions. "This is a field which is probably strange to you gentlemen," he said. "I hope you don't mind my mentioning the fact—"

[381]

"It doesn't embarrass us at all," answered the two delegates briefly.

Max Ashkenazi glanced from them to Nissan. Decidedly he was not getting far with this sudden burst of scholarship. He reverted to his other self, Max Ashkenazi the factory director, dropping his ingratiating Yiddish and speaking German.

"Gentlemen, we'll get down to business. You know, of course, that the workers of this factory are on strike."

"We know."

"You know, of course, their conditions. It's impossible to consider them seriously. This eight-hour day, for instance—"

"Eight hours' work a day is enough for any man," answered Nissan.

Ashkenazi was silent for several seconds, while he watched Nissan closely. "For my own part, I am quite ready to sign up for a sixteen-hour day, as minimum. I work a great deal longer, as a matter of fact."

"You work for yourself, Herr Ashkenazi."

"Not a bit of it. I work for the factory and for the thousands of people it employs. If I had worked in that spirit, counting every minute, this factory would have closed down long ago, like the other factories. It was only through my efforts that the factory was kept going, not with one shift, but with two. We are all of us cogs in the big machine."

"But you get, for your day's work, more than an ordinary worker earns in a year, Herr Ashkenazi."

"Every man according to his merit," answered Max Ashkenazi, "and according to what he's worth to the factory. You may believe me, gentlemen, it wasn't for my looks that the barons appointed me the director. No, and not for my Jewishness, either."

He bent over toward the three men and assumed an intimate tone, lapsing again into Lodz Yiddish.

"You may be certain that I had to be worth a good deal to the owners if they made me, a Jew, the director of the biggest factory in the city. I hope you are under no illusions as to that. I'm not liked here, gentlemen. But I'm needed. And I'm paid accordingly. The man who can produce one yard of goods, gets paid for his yard. The man who brings in millions gets paid in proportion."

"That's the very thing we're fighting," answered Nissan.

"But, gentlemen," said Ashkenazi, as if in astonishment, "you don't talk at all like Jews. When a non-Jew, a thickhead, doesn't understand me, I'm not surprised. I showed my workers, black on white, that if I were to concede one half of their demands, I should have to close the factory. Everything has its limit. Even a machine can stand just so much pressure and no more. It cracks up. Now, you are Jews, and you can understand figures. Many of you, I hear, are students of economics. Here are my figures. Look at them. How can I possibly meet those demands?"

"We have a totally different way of reckoning," said Nissan. "We cut out the dividends of the owners and the huge salaries of the directors."

Max Ashkenazi rose from his chair. "Listen to me, gentlemen. We're not working just for the fun of it. We look at these things like business-men. If we don't get what we're entitled to, or think we're entitled to, we quit. That means we close the factory for good and leave thousands of men without a chance of re-employment."

"Is that what you called us here for, Herr Ashkenazi?" asked Nissan. "It really wasn't worth the trouble."

Max Ashkenazi walked back and forth twice, then stopped in front of the delegates.

"No, it isn't all," he said angrily. "It wasn't my purpose to talk with you about the factory. Let's not fool ourselves, gentlemen. You have nothing to do with this factory. Your place is in Balut, among the hand-loom workers. We of the steam factories employ only gentiles. But anyone can be a spoil-sport, anyone can interfere. You're interfering with my gentile workers; you're putting all sorts of ideas into their heads."

"We know nothing about Jews and gentiles," answered Nissan. "We know only of workers and exploiters, Herr Ashkenazi."

"*You* don't know," said Max Ashkenazi scornfully. "But ask the gentiles *their* opinion. *They* know the difference be-

[383]

tween Jews and gentiles. Unity! Unity! Just try to get one Jewish worker into a steam factory, and he'll come out in a hurry, and not walking on his own legs, either."

A distinct blush mantled Nissan's face. This was his weak point, and he knew it.

"The fault is yours," he answered. "You and others like you have kept the Jewish workers imprisoned in Balut."

Max Ashkenazi interrupted him. "We're not talking here as directors and working-men," he said. "We're talking as Jews. There is danger in the air, gentlemen. The streets of Lodz will flow with Jewish blood."

"We have our organized self-defence," answered Nissan, "and the workers are with us. If you're trying to scare us, Herr Ashkenazi, you might as well save your breath."

"It's a lie!" cried Max Ashkenazi, bringing his fist down on the table. "At the mass meetings which you address, the workers curse me, Max Ashkenazi, not as the director of the factory, but as the Jew. Don't you think I know how the gentile orators make fun of my Jewish name, my Jewish appearance, my Jewish pronunciation? And I know how the gentile workers guffaw every time I'm mocked from the platform. The Jewish shopkeepers in Balut tremble for their skins. You know as well as I do how often gentiles, Poles and Germans, have told them that if the times become too hard, the Jewish shops will be stormed and robbed. It's always been the Jew who pays. Remember the revolt and the pogrom, gentlemen. You are playing with fire."

The three delegates got up from their chairs simultaneously, as if at a signal.

"Herr Ashkenazi, we haven't come here to listen to nationalist orations," said Nissan. "You had no business to call us here for that purpose."

"Damned bourgeois impudence," growled one of the delegates. "I told you I didn't feel like coming. Let's go, Comrade Nissan."

The three men went out through the slow, heavy gates of the factory and hailed a droshky. The weather was ugly; the sky was overcast and a dirty rain drizzled down from the skies. The city lay soaking in mud; the few scraggy trees left in the streets of Lodz looked like old brooms stuck upside-down in the earth. The driver kept whipping his hungry nag, which slipped continually on the black, greasy pavement.

"Giddy-up, you filthy brute. Giddy-up!"

In Nissan's heart the same darkness and ugliness reigned. Max Ashkenazi's stinging words had left their bitter impress in his mind. He could not forget them.

"We must make certain of the condition of the defence," he said in a low voice to his two comrades. "We'll put it on the agenda for tomorrow's meeting."

"Right," answered the others, and pulled their coats tighter about them against the piercing cold.

A change had come into Max Ashkenazi's life. Ever since, for the period of the strike, he had taken up his quarters in the former apartment of the dead director, Albrecht, he seemed to have developed a liking for the place. He stayed away from home more and more frequently. And, in addition, he began to cut down on his allowance to his wife.

Dinah was wounded by his neglect in a manner she had never foreseen.

She could not hide from herself the fact that she was definitely a middle-aged woman. Like her mother she had retained an outward appearance of youthfulness, but even this would not bear too close scrutiny. Her chestnut hair was now thickly shot through with silver. The skin round her eyes had begun to loosen and to form into countless tiny wrinkles. Like a great many women in the early forties, she had begun to suffer from various illnesses. True, men would still look after her in the street, for she knew how to build up her figure and to hide the grey patches in her hair: but when she came home, when she undressed and removed the corsets and the combs and saw reflected in the mirror all the signs of her advancing years, her heart became heavy. It was heaviest when, lying in bed alone, she looked at the other bed, and noted once more that her husband had preferred to sleep at his apartment in the factory.

The children were not at home, either. The oldest, the boy

Ignatz, lived abroad. But even when he had been at home, he had not been a great joy to her. As a child he had shown himself a curious blend of the Ashkenazi and Alter characters; he had all the will to command and to shine of the former, all the laziness and self-indulgence of the latter. His school record was bad. His friendships were brief, violent, and quarrelsome. He hated his father, knowing how he had disappointed him; he loved his mother, but with a sick, cruel, and tyrannical love. He would torment her until she burst into tears; then he would throw himself at her feet and, weeping with her, would promise to be good. But the moment she stopped crying, he began to torment her again.

The contacts between Max Ashkenazi and his son were few and hostile. Always Max Ashkenazi would say, in astonishment: "It's incredible how the boy has inherited nothing from me," and always, when his back was turned, the boy would repeat the words, caricaturing his father's Yiddish intonation and gesticulating like a little Jew of Balut. He grinned with delight when he watched his father at table or when the latter left the house with cigar ashes clinging to the lapel of his coat. Sullen, ill-tempered, and solitary, he felt that he was not being permitted to play the high role to which he was entitled.

He managed, with much coaching, to get through the high school, albeit at a later age than any other boy; then he was sent to Paris, to continue his studies there. But he seldom put in an appearance at the university. He spent his time with cheap actresses and their male hangers-on, and wrote home regularly to his mother for more money. She, on her stricter allowance, had to sell pieces of jewellery, or borrow from friends, in order to send the boy part of what he asked for. If she delayed too long, she received letters in which he threatened to commit suicide.

Max Ashkenazi did not write to his son. He only told his wife to put in a few words for him.

"Tell him to study hard, Diana," he said.

"Why don't you write to him yourself?" she asked angrily.

"I'm dreadfully busy. You know that," he answered.

[387]

The daughter, Gertrude, was supposed to live at home, but her parents saw almost as little of her as they did of their son.

In appearance she took after her mother. She was slender and blue-eyed, with thick masses of brown hair. Like her mother, again, she lived in a world of her own, a world of fantasy and legend. But she differed from her mother in not being content with fantasy alone. She was stronger-willed, determined to take her share of happiness wherever she could find it. She hated Lodz, with its smoke, filth, and perpetual clamour, with its noise of wheels and of chaffering merchants. She hated her home, with its old, stuffy furniture, its darkness, and its atmosphere of unfriendliness. She dreamed of the time when she would turn her back on all this, and live her own life.

As a child she had been a great favourite with her grand-father, Reb Chaim Alter. In his house, at least, there was some gaiety. Here the Jewish holidays were observed, candles burned brightly, guests assembled at the table, there was singing and laughter. She even stayed with her grandfather for the Passover evening ceremonies. At home her father gabbled hastily through the prayers and retired to his own room, to take up his interminable accounts. At her grand-father's everyone sat up late, singing the joyous melodies of the Feast of the Liberation, drinking wine, and telling stories. Under her grandfather's influence she had even shown an inclination toward piety, much to the distress of her father, who could not understand what his daughter wanted with that queer, old-fashioned Jew. But it was a passing phase. She grew older and her visits to her grandparents grew more and more infrequent. But still she did not stay at home. She went to parties and dances, she visited the homes of her friends, she went out walking—anything was better than this mournful home of hers. In her own way she loved her mother, but she could not understand why she had lived with her husband all these years, or, for that matter, why she had married him in the first place.

"Mamma, did you love Father when you married him?" she asked, more than once.

[388]

Her mother avoided a straightforward answer. She told the child to return to her lessons, or not to ask foolish questions; so that it became clear to Gertrude that it had been a loveless marriage even in the beginning.

"What queer people you must have been!" she once said to her mother. "I wouldn't marry a man I didn't love, if you were to cut me to pieces."

When Gertrude was graduated from her high school, her mother began to consider the girl's future. She thought of bringing a change into the house, of getting new furniture, freshening up the place, and making it attractive to young people. Dinah Ashkenazi saw now that her own life was over. Her youth was gone. Yes, men still turned round to look after her in the street, but her confidence in her own attractiveness was gone, and in her heart there was the sinking feeling of rapid downward motion. There was left to her only the possibility of living herself out partially in her daughter. She wanted to see her Gertrude settled happily.

The passing of the years had also brought a change in her attitude toward her husband. She had not learned to love him, but the steady pressure of his achievements had had their effect on her; she could not help realizing that he was an exceptional person. There was a bigness and energy and largeness of vision about him which did set him apart. This little man had his mannerisms, but she realized slowly that it was he who understood the world, and not she; it was he who had the knowledge and experience; all she had was her books, silly books, the effect of which had begun to fade. And with all his mannerisms and peculiarities, Max Ashkenazi did have even a certain personal impressiveness. Like most women in the forties, she began to turn back to her husband, seeking, not a life of love, but of duty and devotion.

She began to talk to her husband about Gertrude. "Max," she said, "Gertrude is no longer a child. We ought to make our home a place to which she can bring friends, a home like all homes." She had, for some time, begun to call him by his German name.

But it was at about this period that Max Ashkenazi was alienating himself from the house, passing his nights more

[389]

and more frequently in his bachelor apartment in the factory.
Even on Sundays, when the factory was empty, he would stay
away. Only now and then he would telephone home. "I'm
frightfully busy," was the brief formula.

At first Dinah Ashkenazi thought nothing of it; then a
strange uneasiness crept into her mind.

Was it possible, she asked herself, that her husband had
someone? That he was not staying alone in the bachelor
apartment?

The idea was so comical—Simcha Meyer Ashkenazi having
a love-affair—that she laughed outright. But then, as she
brooded on her own empty life, the absurdity of the idea dissolved. Why wasn't it possible? And why hadn't it been possible in the past? He was sly and secretive, this husband of
hers. Perhaps it was one of the office girls who stayed behind
with him after hours and week-ends. Perhaps it was an actress
who came to visit him secretly, when everyone was gone from
the factory. There were actresses enough in Lodz ready to sell
themselves. And then, perhaps—most painful thought—it was
not a bought love at all; it might be the genuine thing; some
loose woman—she didn't have to be an actress either—who
had fallen in love with her husband.

Dinah sat long hours before the mirror, looking at the
loose skin round her eyes, at the patches of grey in her hair,
taking in the bitter thought that she was no longer the woman
to attract men. How stupid she had been not to have remembered that one does not stay young for ever! And she had
aged more rapidly than her husband. He had acquired even
a certain attractiveness with the years, an assurance which
came from his succession of triumphs, his widening control
of power. He was as energetic as ever. His eyes were as bright
and restless as of old; there was not one gray hair in his head;
his skin was unwrinkled. If he could only learn to carry himself properly, to wear his clothes right, he would even be
handsome in a way. She had often heard other women, friends
of hers, say that and she had always smiled. But they were
right. And here was the proof of it! Some woman had fallen
in love with him.

The more she thought about it, the more she was convinced

that this was what had happened. And now this husband of hers, who had never had a place in her thoughts, became her sole preoccupation. She felt herself growing smaller and smaller, while at the same time he loomed larger and larger, a man who had achieved wealth and fame, a man that women desired.

How different was the feeling of jealousy when, instead of being read about in a romantic story, it was one's own experience! It was not beautiful and sad and tearful; it was harsh and ugly and painful. It was like a sore place, a constant, hateful irritation from which there was no escape.

Sometimes she tried to deceive herself into the belief that it was really his devotion to his work that kept her husband away from his home; and sometimes, in the attempt to escape from the gnawing at her heart, she took to fearing that something had happened to him. Then, in the face of her own good sense, she would get up in the middle of the night and call up the factory. But there was never an answer. She only heard the muffled ringing at the other end, and after a time she put down the receiver and went to the window, afraid that at any moment people would come running to the house to tell her that something had happened to her husband. Sometimes she dressed, left her room, and went to look for her daughter. But Gertrude was seldom at home. She was at a dance, or at a party in the house of a friend. She was taking her happiness where she could find it. Dinah sat at the window in a dull stupor until the first factory sirens sounded through the dawn.

It was a woman, right enough, who had torn the last threads which held Max Ashkenazi to his wife and home, but not a young and beautiful woman, as Dinah Ashkenazi believed. It was an elderly, homely, and quite unattractive woman.

A very bad time had set in for Max Ashkenazi with the ugly defeat which he had suffered at the hands of the Unionists. His plans had been magnificent; he had worked them out with a perfection of detail of which only he was capable. On a conservative calculation he had seen himself majority owner of the Huntze stocks before the war ended. And it had all come to nothing! The vast profits out of which he had hoped to buy up the remaining stocks had been swallowed up by the strike. There had been penalties to pay the Government for non-delivery of orders; there had been bribes, costly trials, and cancellations. In the end Max Ashkenazi remained what he had been before, director of the Huntze factory, with a solid block of stock in his possession; but he was not master. He was still the employee of the barons. True, they had gone on selling stocks, for even the gigantic dividends of the factory did not suffice to cover the cost of actresses, stables, gambling, and the support of penniless aristocratic friends; but those stocks did not fall into the hands of Max Ashkenazi. They were in the open market.

He was sick of working for the barons. The pride of being director had long since evaporated; he was standing still, not advancing. His position was secure enough, in spite of the constant intrigues of his inferiors, in spite of their secret reports to the barons. But how long was he to go on devoting his best energies to others? Here he was, a middle-aged man—he had to admit that—still the servant of his bosses. Years would pass before he could hope to complete his purchase of the stocks; for it was useless to expect again such a golden opportunity as the war had offered him and the Unionists had turned to nothing. That came once in a lifetime.

There was the shame of it, too. In the eyes of Lodz he had already been as good as master of Huntze's factory. Voices had become more respectful in his presence, and he had felt the new increase of authority which streamed from him in the mere expectation of his triumph. Overnight the triumph had been snatched from him. Lodz laughed at him. And to crown the disgrace, his brother Yakob had one of his periodic visitations of blind good luck, so that the city, vicious, light-minded, malicious, took a special pleasure in witnessing the discomfiture of Max Ashkenazi.

Yakob Ashkenazi's new success began with a divorce which made things look exceedingly black for him. For years he and his wife had been on the point of breaking permanently with each other. It was Pearl's family that, ashamed of the disgrace of it, persuaded her over and over again to try to make it up with her husband. So there would be brief intervals of outward peace. Pearl Ashkenazi would come down to Lodz and set up house with her husband again. A few months would pass—sometimes only a few weeks—and the sick, embittered woman would find her husband unbearable again and return to her home in Warsaw.

They had no children, and the trouble lay with her, not with her husband. For this they had the assurance of every doctor they consulted. Yakob did not reproach his wife, but the pleasure which he always found in playing with children galled her more than spoken words could have done. If she did not like to see him hearty and boisterous with his friends, if she could not stand his radiant, shameless health, she suffered most when she saw him romping with the children of one of their friends.

"Yakob!" she would cry, restlessly. "Can't you behave like

a grown-up person? Have you no sense of dignity?"

She found it especially painful when Yakob played with his little niece, Gertrude. The two brothers, Max and Yakob, never saw each other; but during those intermittent periods when Pearl was in Lodz with her husband, the women were together a great deal. The meetings took place always in Yakob Ashkenazi's home, and Gertrude conceived a violent liking for her uncle. When she was a child it was her uncle Yakob who bought her the most expensive dolls; and when she grew older it was always to him that she ran when she was in trouble or when she wanted to be amused. He took her riding in his big, brilliant carriage through the streets of Lodz and in the surrounding fields, and often he would hand over the reins to her and let her drive for herself.

In her childhood Gertrude was the perfect image of the little girl her mother had been in the days when she came to Reb Abraham Hirsh Ashkenazi's home to play with Jacob Bunim, and as she grew older, Yakob still saw in Gertrude the young woman he had once loved and lost. A stranger might have seen no harm in this friendship between uncle and niece, but both Pearl and Dinah, to whom the past was known, were tormented—each in her own way—by the sight of the young, beautiful girl and the elderly, handsome man playing their childish games. They were alarmed and horrified when Gertrude, already thirteen years old, still behaved toward her uncle like a baby, still climbed on his back and, shouting with laughter, took hold of his beard and pretended she was driving a horse. Her laughter had a dangerous note in it; her flushed cheeks were not those of a child; and when she hugged her uncle and exclaimed: "Uncle, darling, best Uncle, I love you," her voice betrayed to Pearl and Dinah something which they dared not acknowledge even to themselves.

For Dinah, mingled with fear and bitterness, there was a strange, obscure happiness in the love which, she sensed, Yakob still felt for herself rather than for her daughter. But she was afraid. She took her daughter to task.

"Aren't you ashamed of yourself," she said, when Yakob was gone, "to act the baby like that? At your age I was already

[394]

engaged to be married. Don't you know what it means to be grown up?"

Pearl was more direct. When the play was at its height she would interrupt with an impatient cry. "Stop it! I can't stand the noise!" And when she was alone with her husband, she said bitterly: "I don't care what you do behind my back, but I expect you to behave like a gentleman in my presence."

Yakob did not understand her. "Can't I even play with a child?" he asked. "My own niece?"

"Ah, we know those nieces," she said furiously, and flung out of the room.

The relationship between Yakob and little Gertrude helped a great deal to shorten the visits of Pearl to Lodz. Then, after years of this unnatural, divided life, the open, definitive break came, and they were divorced. There was one person who heard the news with a pang of pleasure; that was Max Ashkenazi. This, he believed, was the end of his brother. "No more connections," he thought, savagely; "no more help from his wife. The seven fat years are finished, and there's nothing to live on during the seven lean years." It was a peculiar joy to Max Ashkenazi to think of Yakob left with nothing but the whip of that magnificent carriage in which he had rolled triumphantly, for so many years, through the streets of Lodz.

Max Ashkenazi's happiness was shortlived. Hardly had the divorce between Yakob and Pearl taken place when the devil's own luck, which had attended Yakob Ashkenazi all his life, turned up again.

This time it was none other than Maximilian Flederbaum's daughter Yanka, the thrice-divorced young woman whose affairs had always been the diversion and scandal of Lodz.

How long they had been carrying on secretly before the divorce no one knew; but the day after Yakob was given his freedom he was driving Yanka about openly in his carriage.

Lodz gasped. Yanka was known to be crazy and shameless when it came to her love-affairs. In a few years she had run through three husbands and several lovers. But she had never paraded her love as brazenly as she did now. At all hours of the day the two of them were seen together in his carriage, he

[395]

holding the reins, she snuggling close to him, even kissing him in the presence of the mob.

"It'll last from Passover eve to Passover morning," said the Jews of Lodz.

"Maybe," answered some. "But while it lasts, Yakob Ashkenazi will have both hands in the pot."

Malicious friends brought the news to Max Ashkenazi.

"Your brother's done it again, Herr Director," they said.

"I'm not interested in his affairs," answered Max Ashkenazi.

"He'll get the control of the Flederbaum factory," they suggested. "There's talk of a marriage."

"Gentlemen, I think we were talking about something else," said Max Ashkenazi.

The bluff was too transparent, for the hostility and rivalry of the two brothers was now part of the history of the city. Yet no one guessed, probably, the wretchedness in Max Ashkenazi's heart. It might or it might not come to a marriage, but meanwhile Yakob Ashkenazi had moved into the Flederbaum factory as director, leaving his general agency in the hands of subordinates. More than that, he had moved into the director's apartments, next door to the Flederbaum mansion. There was no one to restrain the fantastic Yanka. Old Flederbaum was out of the running. He lay in bed or was pushed about in a wheel-chair, a paralysed and dying man. He had been stabbed in the head by a dismissed workman, and though his life had been saved, he was nothing more than a bundle of flesh. Of his children, only Yanka took an active interest in the factory. The other daughters were in Warsaw with their husbands; they would have nothing to do with Lodz, the city of Jews and commerce. The sons were queer. They were interested only in religion, spiritualism, and the occult. They spent their time with priests and monks. They had not openly accepted Christianity as yet, but they attended church services frequently. Yanka, with all her crazy love-affairs, was not without ability, but it would have been impossible for a woman to conduct a factory; and even if it had been possible, Yanka was too absorbed in her men to attend to the million details of the business. But she had authority enough to displace the old director and to put Yakob Ashkenazi in his place. She did this partly because she wanted to have her Yakob near her; in part, too, because it pleased her to do the outrageous and unexpected thing.

How could one stand up against a conspiracy of fate, Max Ashkenazi asked himself. Over and over again that miserable brother of his, the thickhead who had been a dunce at school and was a fool in business, whose life had been one long riot of animal self-indulgence, over and over again this Yakob had triumphed over him. It was incredible. It contradicted all common sense. Here was one man who, from boyhood onward, had laboured, calculated, planned, given himself up to his career without thought of comfort, surmounting one obstacle after another; here was another who, brainless to begin with, had wasted his years in riotous living, had denied himself no comfort or indulgence or vice. And where did the two of them stand? The wastrel had carried off triumph after triumph, carelessly, indifferently almost, so that he stood on at least an equal footing with the other; yes, in a sense on a higher footing, simply as the favourite of fate. And who knew what was yet reserved for him? Marriage with Yanka, complete control of the Flederbaum factory, and what else?

With all his modernism and essentially irreligious make-up, Max Ashkenazi began to feel that there was a dark destiny at work against him, and a feeling of helplessness welled up in him. Somewhere an invisible hand had written it all out, long, long ago, and all his efforts and agonies were wasted.

How bitter, how bitter and unjust it all was! Great God! If he had had one half of the luck of his brother! If this one gift of the Flederbaum factory had fallen into *his* lap from the skies! What could he not have done with it? What worlds would he not have conquered? And it hurt doubly to see this incomparable opportunity wasted on a fool and a glutton while he, Max Ashkenazi, still had to play the subordinate to the thick-witted barons.

Then out of his despair was born a deep and passionate resentment. This couldn't go on. A man could bear just so much and no more. He had to do something, at once; he had to lay his hands, somehow, on a vast sum of money and buy up the control of the Huntze factory overnight. He would show them yet! He would make Lodz gasp at his resourcefulness and daring! He would stand up against destiny and smash his way through it as he had smashed his way through a thousand obstacles.

It needed this passion of resentment, this fury of rebellion, to crystallize in Max Ashkenazi a resolution which even he would not have dared to consider in the normal course of events.

During his travels in Russia he had become quite friendly, though solely in the way of business, with a certain elderly woman, the widow Margulies, owner of an immense sugar-factory in Kharkov. The liking was mutual, though perhaps with greater emphasis on her part, and it was based on their respect for each other's abilities. This childless widow, who lived alone in a vast, palatial home, had more of the man than the woman in her. She was ruthlessly practical and hard-headed, as her employees knew only too well. She directed her affairs with the coolness and solidity of an experienced industrialist and merchant. Even in appearance she was masculine; she was large and broad-shouldered, without a trace of feminine softness about her. The extent of her fortune Max Ashkenazi could only estimate from the transactions which had passed between them; it was certainly enormous.

More than once this woman had hinted to him that if ever she were to marry again, it would be just such a man as Max Ashkenazi—a man of affairs who handled people and enterprises like a master. To such a man, she said, if she could find him, she would be willing to turn over her entire fortune.

At first Max Ashkenazi had simply smiled at the compliment. Later it had seemed to him that there was something more in the words than respect or courtesy. If such a woman could be said to soften toward anyone, she softened toward him, and it was gradually borne home to Max Ashkenazi that the widow Margulies was not just being polite; she was making definite hints.

Still he could never have brought himself to consider her words seriously if this last, infuriating triumph of his brother's had not, as it were, torn him loose from his foundations and placed the issue of his life violently in front of him. It was in the paroxysm of his revolt that he first said to himself: "This is the solution!" and stopped dead, half-frightened, half-amused at the suggestion.

"Mad!" he said to himself. But when the first fright had passed he looked around him, as though afraid of having his thoughts overheard, and said to himself: "Why is it mad?"

Why was it mad? What happy home life was he threatening? What thing of value was he about to destroy?

And, reviewing the course of his life with Dinah, the long record of coldness, wretchedness, and humiliation, he perceived that what at first blush had seemed mad was, on the contrary, extraordinarily sensible.

"I have no wife," he said to himself. He had neither wife nor children. This woman he had lived with, whose very body he had had to beg for or take by violence, had estranged even his offspring from him. His son was a fool who hated his own father; his daughter was an empty scatterbrain. He was actually alone in the world.

To help him out in the solidifying of the resolution, he summoned a mood of self-pity. What a mess he had let this woman make of his life! What had she had besides her good looks? The dowry he had received with her had been contemptible. All his abilities and gifts he had been ready to dedicate to her; he had fawned on her, he had raised her to wealth and prominence; and never a word of encouragement, no, not even of acknowledgment. Why had he put up with it? For what insane reason was he to put up with it any longer?

Oh yes, she had of late relented a little toward him. She had shown him a little attention and had actually deigned to suggest that they begin to conduct a home like other, more normal homes, at least for the sake of their daughter. How gracious of her! Now that she was a middle-aged woman, now that her skin was wrinkling and her form sagging, she was ready to be kinder to him. Well, suppose he were to show her that it was too late? In the forties a woman is on the decline, a man is in the full tide of his strength. If she had

[399]

been a true wife to him, it would be different. There would be gratitude and friendship to hold him to her. This she had not earned.

He would leave her; not to take up the kind of life his brother had always led, a life of lewdness and self-indulgence, but in order to rescue whatever happiness the coming years might still offer him. He would marry a sensible, intelligent woman who would know how to appreciate his virtues, a woman rooted in life, not misled and corrupted by silly, romantic books.

True, people would disapprove. It would look bad. Well, what of that? When had he cared about the strictures of his fellow-citizens? And what did their disapproval mean? Let him but get the Huntze factory in his hands, let him but become the foremost manufacturer in Lodz, and they would grovel at his feet, whatever his private life was like; they would fawn on him as little dogs fawn on a mastiff.

When the resolution had taken definite and final form in his mind, Max Ashkenazi set about the execution of it with characteristic thoroughness.

After the strike—and while the Russo-Japanese war still dragged along—he began to absent himself systematically from his home. It was best, he thought, to create first a distinct and formal estrangement, so that the announcement of his intention would fall on prepared soil. Often when he came back from a journey he did not go to the house the same day, but passed the night in his apartment in the factory. When his wife telephoned, he answered briefly: "I'm frightfully busy."

He experienced an extraordinary delight in picking up the telephone, hearing her solicitous inquiry, and rebuffing her with this commonplace formula. He was reimbursing himself for all the humiliations she had inflicted on him in the years past.

Then began a series of journeys to Kharkov, and the tending of the friendship with the widow Margulies, who was to become his new life-partner.

She was easy to talk to, this widow. She understood at once and she called things by their names, without beating about

[400]

the bush. But she was careful and business-like, too. She said, simply, that she had always felt that he was the man for her, and she would consider it an honour as well as a piece of great good fortune to become his wife. It was true that she managed by herself, controlling her employees with an iron hand, conducting her own negotiations with gentile merchants and farmers; but she had to admit that she felt lonely. She wanted a home life, too. More than one match had been proposed to her; there was no lack of men ready to marry a woman in her position. But until Max Ashkenazi had appeared on the scene, she had found no one she could really respect, not one she could entrust her life and fortune to. She had great faith in Max Ashkenazi, she said. She was convinced that the two of them, in partnership, would go very far. She was ready to liquidate her business and to throw as much money as was needed into the buying up of Huntze stocks. But it was clear to him—was it not?—that she could not take a step until he had divorced his wife. The moment he was free, she would be ready to marry him and to take up her home with him in Lodz.

"You understand that, I hope, my dear Ashkenazi," she said to him at one of their interviews. "I will not put one rouble into the Huntze stocks until you are as free as I am."

Max Ashkenazi did understand, but he was astonished by her firmness.

"But, my dear Mrs. Margulies, don't you trust me?"

He drank up hastily the last drops of tea and put the glass down.

The big, solidly built woman, with the hard, mannish voice, poured out another glass of tea, moved the plate of jelly closer to Max Ashkenazi, and answered without a trace of emotion:

"I have all the respect in the world for you. But what would you think of me if I acted hastily and without foresight in such an important matter? Friendship and business are two separate things. We aren't children any longer, Herr Ashkenazi. We can wait a little. First the divorce."

Max Ashkenazi rose to his feet and, balancing himself on his toes, as he always did when he had something impressive

[401]

to say, answered: "I shall get the divorce."

On his return to Lodz, he went from the station direct to the factory. That evening, when he had attended to the most pressing business in hand, he sent for his lawyer and consulted him on the divorce.

"The first question I must ask," answered the lawyer, "is whether at the time of your marriage you signed a half-and-half settlement, according to which your wife is entitled to fifty per cent of all your property in the event of a divorce."

"No, thank God," answered Max Ashkenazi.

"That's lucky," said the lawyer. "It simplifies matters."

He gave Max Ashkenazi instructions as to the first steps, and that same night the latter sat down at his desk and composed a careful letter to his wife. It was a dry business letter, written in involved German. It began by acknowledging the fact, which she would hardly contradict, that their life together had not been successful for either of them. It went on to point out that under these circumstances it was obviously sensible for the two of them to part, though in all friendship. He was ready, of course, to make adequate provision for her and for the children. He would be grateful, therefore, if she would let him know, immediately, what she had in mind as a suitable arrangement. He wound up with the hope that, given the right spirit of goodwill and common sense on both sides, the most painful features of the divorce could be passed over with a minimum of discomfort, and signed himself most respectfully hers, Max Ashkenazi.

He copied out the letter a second time, read it through with great satisfaction, and lay down to sleep more content than he had been in many months.

$\mathfrak{X}li$

$\mathcal{D}$inah's first reaction to her husband's business-like letter was a bitter outburst of rage and wounded feminine vanity.

It was late morning when she received and opened the communication. For a moment after she had read it she stared in stony silence at the cool, offensive lines. Then she cried suddenly: "Gertrude, Gertrude, my daughter!" She ran through the rooms, crying: "Come here, quick, come here!"

She went into her daughter's bedroom and found her still sleeping. Panting, she shook the girl into wakefulness, and when Gertrude opened her eyes and asked sleepily: "What is it, Mamma?" she thrust the letter at her.

"Look at this! Read it!" she cried, and pressed both her hands to her temples.

Startled, the girl looked hastily through the letter and broke into a long peal of laughter.

"Oh, Mamma, how funny! How utterly funny!"

Dinah looked at her in a daze. "What are you laughing at?" she asked in a frightened voice.

"But, Mamma, what do you expect me to do? Cry?" the girl answered. "Why, this should have happened years ago." And, getting up, she threw her arms round her mother.

"Leave me alone," gasped Dinah. "Let me go!"

She snatched up the incredible letter and fled to her own room. There she read it through again, and every sentence sent the blood pounding harder into her temples. Had *he* written this, Simcha Meyer Ashkenazi, the little Chasidic gutter-snipe, the loathsome, ill-bred money-grubber, whose very touch had been repulsive to her, and who for years had crawled at her feet, begging in vain for a kind word? Was it he now who thought himself too good for her, for Reb Chaim Alter's only daughter?

At first the sense of outrage was so violent that she had only one wish: to meet the disgusting creature, spit in his face, and grant him the divorce on the spot, so that she might not bear his name for a moment longer than was necessary. She would accept nothing from him; she would throw back at him his filthy offers of "provisions" and "arrangements." She would ask only for the money which her father had given him, the money which had been the beginning of his fortunes. Then she would turn her back on him and never see him again. The children would remain with her. Let him not dare to come near her or them! Nor would she ever let the children visit him. She would leave this house and wipe out from her memory everything that was in any way connected with the man who had broken her life. She would go back to her parents and live with them as in the days of her girlhood.

But before long this feeling of overweening pride gave way to one of the utmost humiliation and outrage. She sank into ignominious depths.

"It serves me right! It serves me right!" she panted over and over again. If she had been able to live with this unclean lout so many years, if she had put up with him of her own free will and had not broken with him betimes, but had waited instead until he cast her off, like an old shoe, then she deserved everything he did to her. Ah, how happy he would be now to get that divorce! No doubt there was a string of women waiting for him, young, pretty, seductive women, ready to sell themselves for cash. He would marry again, he would blossom out, have a rich, gay home, begin life anew, while she sat, alone, despised, and an object of laughter, in her parents' home. He had taken her in the full blossom of her youth, he had used her up, and he was through with her. All those wretched years of emptiness and unfulfilment came crowding on her. They had sapped her life, taken the brightness out of her eyes, and wrinkled her skin. Now this husband had come to the realization that it was better for them to part, so that he could start all over again.

Why, of course it was better—for him! For him, not for her! She should have done it long ago, as her daughter said; immediately after the marriage, or after the first child; yes, even after the second child. But she had always been a slave—first to her parents, and then to her children. For their sakes she had submitted, till she had become middle-aged, and sickly, as women become at that time of life, and there was no sense at all, for her, in leaving her husband. And apart from the loneliness and helplessness which now faced her, there was the unutterable shame of it. To be rejected so brutally, while the world looked on! She would not let him! She would not submit this time! She hated and despised him, but she would not give him up. She would not make it easy for him.

Then on this mood followed another of utter dejection and remorse.

It was all her own fault. She had been altogether too haughty. She had driven her own husband away from her by her contempt and unfriendliness. She had never offered him a kind word or given him a smile. Granted that she had not been in love with him, and that she had been married to him against her own will; but there the situation was, and she should have come to terms with it. So many other women had done it; why not she? She had chosen instead to live herself out in silly books. Into these her girlhood and young womanhood had been poured, and these she had taken instead of the realities of life. She had not built a house for herself; she had not even troubled to create friendships. Instead, she had alienated her husband and had failed to draw her children close to her. Now her punishment had come upon her.

What were her children to her? Her son used her as a source of money. Her daughter thought of her as a foolish, weak-willed prude. Neither son nor daughter had any pride in themselves or their family. The first was sunk in low, vicious pursuits; the second, refusing to be intimidated by life, was snatching at happiness wherever she could find it.

The thought of her daughter sent a sharper pang through Dinah. It was not merely for the sake of the high life and the gaiety to be found in the Flederbaum mansion that Gertrude went there so often. It was much more for the sake of her uncle. Others might still think this an innocent friendship between niece and uncle, but Dinah was convinced that, whatever it had been in the beginning, the relationship was now definitely tinged with danger. Who knew how far it might go? Again the fault was hers, and that for many reasons. If she had not bungled her life so clumsily, if she had taken the man she wanted, years ago, this same Yakob whom her daughter desired, it would never have come to this pass. But Yakob had never fulfilled his love toward her, and now it passed over to the daughter. She, the mother, was only of the same age as Yakob, but she was a withered woman, while he was in the bloom of life. Who knew if she would not have remained much younger, too, if she had had the strength and courage and sense to do what she should have done instead of finding refuge in her story-books.

Dinah sent the maid for her mother, bidding her come without delay.

Priveh came, a big, bony old woman, with a certain majesty in her bearing, accompanied by Reb Chaim, white-haired and bent, but still bright of eye. When Priveh had read through the letter, she turned loose the torrents of her fury not only on Max Ashkenazi, but on men in general, with a special place for her husband.

"If I had that toad here," she cried, flourishing her umbrella, "I'd break this across his neck. He thinks he's too good for my daughter. I'm going to the factory this minute. I'll slap his face in front of everybody!"

"Privishe darling," her husband begged her, "don't excite yourself. Your heart! Leave this to me. It's a man's business."

"A man?" his wife flung back scornfully. "You're an old rag, not a man. And you've always been an old rag when it came to dealing with that beast."

She already knew that Reb Chaim Alter had failed to protect his daughter at the time of the marriage, as other fathers did, by the half-and-half property clause. If only this clause had been included in the marriage contract, Max Ashkenazi would have let the eyes drop out of his head before suggesting divorce. On those terms, indeed, it would not have been worth while. But then, Reb Chaim Alter had never been a man of foresight.

"Bungler!" she railed at him. "Duffer! You want to play the man now, do you? First you let yourself be stripped by that dirty little rogue; now you've delivered up your own daughter to him unprotected."

Reb Chaim shrank from his wife. "But for God's sake, Priveh!" he stammered. "We're not living in the wilderness, are we? There's still some justice in the world. I won't take this lying down. I'll run to all the rabbis in this town."

"All right, run, you old fool, run fast. A fat lot of good the rabbis did you in the past. A fat lot of good they'll do you now. Let me handle this."

She sat down at the telephone, called up the Flederbaum factory, and asked for Herr Yakob Ashkenazi. When he answered, she summoned the best Polish at her command—she would not dream of speaking Yiddish to him on the telephone—and implored him to leave everything, no matter how important, and come at once. "Yakob darling," she clamoured into the telephone, "it's a matter of life and death. Come right to the house. Simcha Meyer isn't here. Hurry, dear Yakob."

Yakob came dashing in only a few minutes after he had received the call.

"What is it?" he asked, alarmed.

"Here! Read!" Priveh handed him his brother's letter.

A look of mingled incredulity, contempt, and fury spread over Yakob's face as his eyes ran over the letter. "The filthy low-life!" he exclaimed. "The cheap blackguard." When he had finished the letter, he flung it down and dropped into an armchair.

"Dinah, dear," he exclaimed, "I'll stand by you. I don't care if it costs me a fortune—I won't let him do it. Don't worry about money. I'll see to that. I'll turn the whole thing over to my lawyer."

Priveh ran over to Yakob and imprinted two loud kisses on his cheeks. "I knew it!" she exclaimed. "I know my Yakob!" She shook her head and added: "I deserve to be

[407]

whipped for not having understood you better, Dinah. You remember how you pleaded with me and with your father to give you Yakob instead of Simcha Meyer?"

Dinah blushed furiously. Reb Chaim would not let his wife's remark pass uncontradicted. "Priveh, I tell you it was destiny. It wasn't in our hands."

That afternoon open war was declared in the Ashkenazi family. On the one side stood Max Ashkenazi, a man accustomed to getting his own way through sheer obstinacy and endurance, embittered that there should be new obstacles in the way of the realization of his great plan, goaded to a frenzy by the impudent and gratuitous intrusion of his brother on the scene; on the other side stood Yakob Ashkenazi, generous, impulsive, a gambler, ready to throw his last kopeck into the fight where a friend was concerned, a man dangerous because he was lucky and now doubly dangerous because he was filled with the energy of a high indignation. Between the two men stood Dinah, her children, and her parents. As soon as the fight broke out, Reb Chaim Alter and his wife moved over to Dinah's; they would not let her live alone at a time like this, and they would not have her leave the house, either. When Solly Knaster, Max Ashkenazi's agent who collected the rent from the tenants in the courtyard of the house, brought this piece of information to his employer, the latter jumped up in a fury.

"Idiot!" he exclaimed. "Why did you let them in?"

"But, Herr Ashkenazi," whimpered Solly, shrinking before Max Ashkenazi's anger so that he looked like a very old, very small, and very defeated rooster, "how was I to stop them?"

So they were organizing against him! Reports were brought to him of his brother's frequent visits to the house. Max Ashkenazi stopped his allowance to his wife. He stopped remittances to his son abroad, his wife's darling. He waited to see what would happen, and he asked little Solly Knaster for reports.

"There's everything you want in the house," reported the agent. "Mrs. Ashkenazi is living like a queen."

No, clearly as long as Yakob Ashkenazi stood by Dinah, his favourite strategy of starving his opponent out would not

[408]

serve the purpose. And Yakob Ashkenazi would stand by as long as he had a kopeck in his pocket. The divorce came no nearer. Max Ashkenazi had no grounds for divorce. The tricks which his lawyers tried on Dinah were met by counter-trickery from Yakob's lawyers. The civic courts failing him, Max Ashkenazi turned to the Rabbinic courts. But Yakob warned Dinah against accepting a summons from them, and to the beadle who brought the summons he said: "If you don't want your neck broken, get out, and don't ever dare come near the house again."

Max Ashkenazi then cited his father-in-law before a Rabbinic court, and Reb Chaim came; but he could not compel his daughter to come.

Green with rage, Max Ashkenazi decided on a policy of petty persecutions such as would make Dinah's life miserable and compel her to appear in court and grant him a divorce. He began by suing her for the house she was living in, and obtained an eviction order against her. Yakob Ashkenazi sent his lawyer to the court and promptly had the eviction order voided. Max Ashkenazi then began to issue arbitrary orders to Solly Knaster, now to cut off the water-supply, now to turn off the gas—all in the name of efficient administration.

Yakob Ashkenazi waylaid the agent in the courtyard of Dinah's house.

"Listen, you," he said sternly, grabbing the frightened little man by the lapels, "stop playing tricks with the house. If you don't, I'll whip the dirty hide off you."

"But what can I do, Herr Ashkenazi?" cried Solly Knaster. "I have to obey orders. I have a wife and children." Tears began to roll down his cheeks.

He reported this incident, along with much more, to Max Ashkenazi when he brought him the rent-roll at the end of the week. Max Ashkenazi was glad to note that he was getting under his brother's skin. He scratched his scraggy little beard rapidly.

"Tell me, Solly," he asked, "how are the beams on the second floor, above my rooms?"

"They're very good beams, Herr Ashkenazi," answered Solly.

"You fool," said Max Ashkenazi, "they're very bad beams and they may give way any day."

"They're very bad beams," repeated Solly, weakly; "they may give way any day."

"The floors will have to be torn up and new beams put in or there'll be an accident."

"Yes, certainly, I can understand that," stammered Solly.

"In that case I think you'd better call the plasterers and carpenters tomorrow and start work."

"Of course, Herr Ashkenazi."

"And see that the job is done properly. Let's have no haste about it. You may find out, when the floors are torn up, that all sorts of little improvements are necessary in the structure."

"Certainly, Herr Ashkenazi. I'll find lots of improvements necessary."

"Very good. And keep your mouth shut. Our conversations are nobody's business but ours."

"Certainly, Herr Ashkenazi."

The next morning the plasterers and carpenters appeared at the house. They tore up the beams above Max Ashkenazi's former rooms; they turned the house into a bedlam. Dust and noise filled every corner.

Priveh sent for the agent and slapped his face. "That's for your tricks," she said.

Little Solly put his hand up to his face and began to weep. "What shall I do?" he wailed. "I have to take orders. I have a wife and children."

A few days later new carpenters came, with chisels and crowbars, and announced that they had been instructed to remove the ovens, as the walls had begun to crumble behind them. Priveh bundled them out of the house, but they returned and insisted that these were their orders. Soon after, Solly Knaster leased the house adjoining Dinah's apartments to an embroiderer. All the day long, and late into the night, the machines rattled and hummed, so that sleep and rest became impossible. Priveh screamed that she would run to the factory and scratch out Simcha Meyer's eyes, but she stayed in the house and with her daughter suffered whatever Max

Ashkenazi could think up in the way of persecution.

Dinah went about in a daze. She could not read during the day; at night she lay awake and wept over her miserable and humiliating fate.

On the walls of the city of Lodz, among the bright-coloured signs and shingles of shops, with their paintings of shoes, hats, and pieces of meat, their rampant lions looking like mangy tom-cats, their elegant young men with red and yellow faces and slender canes in their hands, their massive white brides with bouquets of flowers in their swollen red arms, among all sorts of Yiddish, Russian, Polish, and German announcements, appeared immense proclamations declaring the city to be in a state of siege. At the bottom was the signature of Brigadier-General Kanitzin, who informed the inhabitants of Lodz that for the duration of the state of siege they were forbidden to assemble in the streets or in private houses, to spread rumours calculated to lead to a breach of the peace, or to refuse to obey the orders of the police and the military in the streets. Anyone ignoring these orders was liable to arrest and trial by courts martial invested with full power to inflict any penalty up to and including the death-sentence.

Side by side with these magnificent proclamations, and sometimes even pasted on top of them, were others, the proclamations of the revolutionaries, which called upon the inhabitants of Lodz to assemble publicly and privately and to demonstrate against the powers that were, to arrange strikes, to discredit the Government, and to ignore the police and the soldiery, all of which was more easily said than done. For armed soldiers, in charge of local police commissioners and their assistants, roamed the streets of Lodz and arrested any-

[412]

one who looked as though he might possibly incite the population, or himself be susceptible to such incitement. In short, they arrested anybody whose face was not to their liking. In the police yards there stood double lines of Cossacks with nagaikas in their hands, and every arrested man had to run the gauntlet between the outer gates and the police office. The nagaikas whistled, the arrested men ran, screaming.

The meanest and most savage of the police officers was the assistant commissioner Jurgoff, a lean, bony man who always wore his hat tilted on one side and who never appeared in the streets without an escort of soldiers and spies. His nose stuck out from under the tilted peak of his hat, smelling the air for revolution and revolutionaries. The arrested men were no longer sent to the prison on Dluga Street, which was filled to the doors. They were housed in the local barracks, which were transformed into prisons in these trying times. However, few of the men arrested by Jurgoff ever arrived walking straight. They generally had to be carried or led and were lucky if they escaped the preliminary handling with nothing worse than the loss of a few teeth. When Jurgoff and his Cossacks appeared on the street, there was a general scattering of the population.

Samson the plasterer, a Unionist, who was called Samson the Prince because he dressed like a dandy and curled the points of his moustaches upwards, informed the chairman of his local that he was ready to do for Jurgoff, the assistant police commissioner; and he therefore requested the committee to supply him with a bomb. The committee took the matter under advisement, but its deliberations wore out the patience of Samson the Prince, who decided to act on his own, without the ratification or assistance of the committee. He went to a student friend of his, a chemist, and had a bomb made for him. He donned his best suit of clothes, so that he looked like a rich young man about town; he gave an extra curl to his moustaches; he put the bomb into a small, pretty box, which he tied with a ribbon; and he bought himself a bouquet of roses. Thus equipped, he went out into the street, for all the world like a young lover about to call on his

[413]

sweetheart. Women smiled as he passed them, as though with envy of the lady who was about to receive the present. Policemen and soldiers grinned.

Samson the Prince finally reached the corner where the police commissioner Jurgoff stood surrounded by soldiers. He backed away carefully, putting a good distance between himself and the group, and then suddenly flung the package.

Assistant Police Commissioner Jurgoff was torn to pieces. One of his legs, still encased in a brightly polished boot, spur and all, was found on an adjacent roof. Soldiers came running from all directions and began to fire blindly along the street; when the street was cleared, they lifted their rifles and fired into the windows of the houses. The hospitals were filled that night with dead and wounded. They had to be laid out on the floors of the wards and corridors. Many bodies were carted away to police headquarters, and the police refused to admit those who came in search of missing friends and relatives. It was arranged that the dead should be buried secretly, in the night. Meanwhile, in the various barracks, the soldiers polished their guns and boots so as to look their best at the grand funeral of Assistant Police Commissioner Jurgoff. The military band cleaned its instruments and rehearsed the dead march. When evening fell, the streets of Lodz were forcibly cleared, and the inhabitants were told to go home and sleep.

But Lodz did not sleep.

In the poor streets surrounding the factories, and in Balut, the workers were awake. It was a hot summer night, and the women and children had fled from the vermin-infested houses into the courtyards and put down their straw mattresses wherever they could. The men did not lie down to sleep. The revolutionary committee had issued an appeal, which travelled by hand from courtyard to courtyard, calling upon the workers to march on police headquarters and rescue the bodies of the workers, so that they might be buried with full honours. Orators stole through the darkness from yard to yard and proclaimed a strike for the next day. In the morning, when the factory sirens screamed their message across the city, no one responded. By thousands and tens of thousands the workers, men and women, accompanied sometimes by

[414]

children, streamed in procession through the streets, converging toward the administrative centre. Like spring freshets heading for the main river they overflowed on to the pavements and dashed themselves against the walls. Like spring freshets, again, they seemed to pour upward from an inexhaustible source, issuing from cellars, from holes, from wretched huts, till it seemed that they would flood the entire city and carry everything before them.

They marched slowly and firmly, their heads lifted high, their footsteps deliberate. The women, carrying red flags, broke into revolutionary song:

> Red flows the blood of freedoms martyrs,
> The headsman's at his work again.

The deep voices of the men responded:

> But swift the judgment day draws nearer,
> And we shall be the judges then.

Jewish, Polish, and German flags, all of them a bright red, fluttered above uncovered heads, above the black curls of Jews and the flaxen hair of Poles and Germans. The rhythm of feet and voices intoxicated the marchers. From alleys and from courtyards contingents kept pouring into the main streams, which all finally poured into Piotrkov Street, the symbol of wealth and authority in Lodz.

"Close the shops!" roared the workers. "Hats off!"

The shopkeepers and passers-by obeyed.

At one of the main crossings sat an officer on horseback. Behind him was a solid wall of soldiers, their rifles, with bayonets fixed, glinting in the sunlight.

The demonstration came to a halt.

"Back!" shouted the officer.

No one stirred.

"Back, or I'll give the order to fire!"

Still no one stirred.

The officer drew his sword and waved it in the air.

"Fire!" he shouted.

[415]

A salvo of rifle-shots broke through the tense, dusty air.

The crowd swayed and bent like a field of grain under the sickle of the reaper; then came a counter-wave from behind, which thrust the foremost ranks forward on the bayonets of the soldiers. Lowering his sword, the officer made a motion toward the demonstrators, but at that instant a stone flew out of the crowd and struck him in the head. He rolled off his horse. The soldiers drew backward as the crowd advanced.

"Barricades!" a hundred voices roared. "Throw up barricades!"

"Barricades!" the crowd thundered.

The demonstrators broke ranks. The street-lamps were torn out of their sockets, paving stones were pried loose, doors were lifted off their hinges, signs were pulled down; carriages and carts were commandeered and the horses unharnessed. Drivers and draymen, left with their horses and whips, wept, but no one listened to them. The carts were thrown over and the barricades built around them. From near-by houses and courtyards the workers brought tables, chairs, planks, and iron bars. A passing wagon-load of flour was seized, and the sacks used to fill up the cracks in the barricade. Seen from a distance the revolutionaries looked like a nestful of ants scurrying about with their burdens. Street-cars were added to the building material, pulled off their rails and overturned as if they were playthings. The shouting of the rioters, the crash of falling cars and uprooted street-lamps, the hammering at the barricades, drowned out the groaning of the wounded, who were carried into near-by courtyards, and the wailing of their women.

Lodz was paralysed. Houses and places of business were locked, and those inhabitants who were not in revolt kept off the streets. Only the poor and the working-classes were abroad, and they were masters of the city. They stayed behind their barricades all day and into the night. Youngsters brought them food from their homes, and in between dragged more stones and planks to add to the barricades. But the city was quiet. Only now and then a shot was heard. No fire or light was lit anywhere.

Behind a buttress of planks, barrels, and sacks sat Nissan,

Tevyeh, and Bashke, waiting, along with thousands of others. The clear moon swung up through the June night, shining through an atmosphere that had suddenly been cleared of all its dust and factory smoke. There were no fires and no glittering lamps to dim the lustre of moon and stars; lucid and tranquil they shone down, as if upon some sleeping village. A light wind brought into Lodz the smell of fir and acacias from the forests outside the city; it stirred the uncovered hair of the men and played with the folds of the women's dresses.

Bashke lifted her eyes to the night heavens, which she had never seen in such purity and brightness before from the streets of Lodz. She breathed in deeply the scent-laden air, and her breast rose with happiness and exaltation.

"To die like this!" she whispered to Nissan, and closed her eyes.

"No," he whispered back, taking her hand. "We have to live."

She clasped his warm hand tight and felt something strong pouring into her from him, flooding her veins and reaching back to her fingertips and the roots of her hair.

"Comrade Nissan," she murmured, "why do we run away from happiness? Aren't we, the fighters, entitled to happiness too?"

"Yes, Bashke, we are. But we shan't be able to taste that happiness until we've ended the fight, until we've won liberty."

"Shall we live to see that day?"

"We have to believe that, Bashke," he answered firmly.

At the first break of day regiments of Cossacks closed in on the barricades. The order to attack was given, and the soldiers, with bayonets fixed on their rifles, dashed forward. They were met by a fusillade of stones, faltered, and then turned back.

The officer in command changed his tactics.

"Fire!" he ordered.

A stream of bullets poured into the barricade, but did not penetrate. All day long there were these alternations of fruitless attacks and fruitless shooting. Late in the afternoon a number of soldiers managed to break through into houses

[417]

which looked down on the interior of the barricades, and began to shoot into the mass. A panic broke out among the workers. Some began to run.

"Comrades! Stand firm!" shouted the leaders.

The workers stopped running, but the shots from the windows continued, and as one man after another was picked off, the panic returned. This time it seemed as if the commands of the leaders could not arrest the panic.

Bashke sprang out of her shelter, mounted a barrel, and, waving a flag, began to sing one of the favourite revolutionary songs.

> Sing loud the song of war and freedom!
> Lift high the flag above the throne.

The loud, ringing woman's voice succeeded where the orders of the leaders had failed. Ashamed, the men turned back to the barricade. The chorus of Bashke's song was taken up.

On a roof a long way down the street squatted two soldiers and saw in the distance the girl wrapped in the red flag.

"Think you could pick her off?" asked the taller one.

"I'm damn certain I can," answered the shorter one.

"You can like hell. I'll bet you a cigarette you miss."

"It's a bet."

The small soldier took careful aim, screwing up his left eye as he laid his cheek along the rifle. He fired. They saw the little red figure sway and fall off the barrel.

"Got her!" exclaimed the marksman.

"Right!" answered the other, took off his hat, and extracted a cigarette from under the lining.

The workers scattered from behind the barricades. Among the others Nissan and Tevyeh fled, carrying Bashke. The blood ran over her dress and through the red flag.

With feverish eyes and lips that twitched spasmodically, Tevyeh the weaver walked back and forth in front of the iron gates of the Flederbaum hospital. Now and again he paused, lifted his head, and stared dumbly at the curtained windows behind one of which lay his Bashke.

They would not admit him to her. Two orderlies in white dresses had lifted her from his and Nissan's arms and had closed the gates in his face.

"Come on Saturday," they said; "no visitors allowed on week-days."

Tevyeh had stood a long time holding on to the bars of the gates like a dog thrust out of the house on a cold winter's night.

"Let me in," he kept crying, in a child's voice. "I want to see my Bashke."

They paid no attention to him.

He began to run back and forth in front of the gate, looking up now and again at the curtained windows. He tired of this and instead ran round and round the hospital, as if looking for an open door through which he could steal in. But he found none. Every time the gate opened, Tevyeh ran up panting, asking to be let in. The big, red-faced doorkeeper grew tired of him and thrust him forcibly away, growling: "Get the devil out of here."

Tevyeh finally bethought himself, dug up a coin, and handed it to the doorkeeper. "Let me in," he begged.

The Pole took the coin, but did not admit Tevyeh.

"There are too many of you," he said gruffly. "The director won't have any visitors. It's no use."

From time to time the gates opened to admit the emergency ambulance bringing in wounded from the city. From time to time they opened to let a black hearse out. The drivers forced their way brutally through the crowds of women. These were mostly poor funerals, and the survivors gave small tips. The drivers were in a hurry.

"Come on, there!" they growled. "Let's get through."

The women ran after the hearses, beating their breasts and screaming. Against this stream of mourners came another, the ambulances and droshkies which were bringing in the wounded. Or sometimes the wounded came on foot, assisted by comrades. Occasionally policemen brought in a heavily wounded soldier, over whom they stood guard in the hospital, till the last moment. Outside the hospital the relatives of the wounded wandered back and forth, Tevyeh among them, pleading to be admitted.

He was the most obstinate of all. He did not go home either to eat or to sleep. In the night he was still there, wandering round the walls of the hospital. His wife came and tried to drive him home with curses. He did not hear her.

From friends in the crowd he begged pieces of dry bread to eat and coins with which to bribe the attendants that they might bring him the latest reports. He ran after the doctors as they came out, and, weeping like a woman, begged them to save his Bashke. Tevyeh, the proud, angry revolutionary, had forgotten all his pride and his class consciousness. He humbled himself before the doctors, those well-fed, well-clad members of the upper class, and implored them for news.

"It's bad," they said, shaking their heads. "The bullet went through the lung."

Every time he heard this, Tevyeh felt his heart stop beating. He would then run from the doctor back to the gate and begin to wail again. He redoubled his efforts and, repulsed a hundred times, crawled again to the attendants and doctors and nurses, begging to be admitted. He was so insistent that,

[420]

against the regulations, he was admitted to the hospital in the night.

He was conducted up the huge, dimly lit ward, in which the beds stood thickly near one another. From every bed came a voice of pain and despair. The night nurses in the white dresses were continually disappearing from the ward. The patients kept calling to them, groaning and begging for help.

"Quiet, there!" the nurses said crossly. "You aren't the only ones here."

Older women complained audibly: "What do they care about the sick? They're always running out to the doctors and their assistants. That's what the poor must always expect in a hospital."

Among a dozen others stood Bashke's bed, with a chart at the head, bearing her name, the nature of her sickness, and the temperature. She was breathing with difficulty, like a steam engine about to break down.

"Air!" she gasped from time to time. "I can't breathe!"

Tevyeh fell on his knees at her bedside. "Bashke, my child, my daughter," he sobbed, taking her hand, "what shall I do for you?"

"Air!" she repeated. "I can't breathe any more."

Distracted, Tevyeh got up and ran to the nurses and the night assistants.

"Do something for her," he implored them, "dear, good friends, help her." He wrung his hands.

"We can't do anything. Wait till the doctor comes."

Tevyeh ran to the doctor's office, but he was not admitted. When at last they let him see the doctor and he forced the latter to come to Bashke's bed, he did nothing. He approached the bed angrily, felt Bashke's pulse, and turned away.

"Open the window a little," he said to an attendant. Then, turning to Tevyeh: "You've no business in here. This is a hospital. We know our duty without having to be reminded by you."

Tevyeh threw himself on the floor by the bedside. How gladly he would have given away the last bit of air in his lungs to help her.

"Daughter," he moaned, "but what can I do for you?"

Bashke's hand sought his. "Father, darling," she whispered. The next instant she was choking again. She opened her mouth like a fish gasping on dry land and threw herself about on the bed.

"I'm choking!" she managed to get out. "Save me."

Suddenly she began to tear the bed-clothes from her and to claw at her nightgown, her body, her hair.

Tevyeh began to scream, so that the patients shouted at him and the ward was thrown into a turmoil. The night attendants seized him and carried him out of the ward.

He continued to run round the hospital walls, pursued by Bashke's ghastly voice: "I'm choking! Save me!"

In the early morning a watchman came out and beckoned to him. Tevyeh understood then that it was the end. He staggered up into the ward. Bashke lay motionless in her bed, drenched with perspiration. He touched her hand. It was cold and unresponsive. The assistant felt her pulse and made a brief gesture. Bashke did not call out any more. She only breathed heavily. Soon her teeth began to chatter. Her eyes opened wide, the eyeballs rolled upward. Then, for an instant, they came down and rested on Tevyeh before they closed again. Tevyeh began to cry out:

"Quick, help, someone!"

The assistant came back to the bed and took Tevyeh by the hand.

"It's over," he said.

Tevyeh fell across the bed and would not let them touch his daughter's body. They pulled him away from the bed, and when he looked at it again he saw only the outline, in the bed-clothes, of the body that had rested there. Bent double, almost crawling like an animal, Tevyeh made his way down into the yard, looking in the twilight for the morgue. Two watchmen tried to pull him out of the hospital yard, but he fought them off. He sat alone among the corpses, watching over his daughter's body.

Later in the morning came his friends and comrades, Nissan among them. Tevyeh did not hear what they said to him. They were quite strange to him.

[422]

There was a great funeral, attended by thousands of work-ers. The dead woman was wrapped in a red flag. Wreaths of flowers were carried in the procession. Wherever the funeral passed, shops put up the shutters and passers-by uncovered their heads. Spectators crowded the streets and the windows. Tevyeh walked alone at the head of the cortège. All this seemed remote from him, remote and hateful. He could feel nothing and see nothing but his own horrible loss. Wherever he turned, the wide-open rolling eyes of Bashke stared at him, making his blood run cold.

At the cemetery there were revolutionary speeches and revolutionary songs. Tevyeh could not stand it. He could not bear to see the choir arranging itself carefully in rows, as if this were a festival. The singing began. He heard the clear, soaring voices of the women, the deep response of the men. What did all this have to do with his daughter, his Bashke? The loud, optimistic speeches of the orators, calling to further battles, to life and freedom, stung him. What good was life and freedom now if she was dead, his Bashke? Worst of all was the fiery speech delivered above the new-covered grave by a member of the revolutionary committee.

He was a famous orator, this revolutionary leader—a splendid specimen of a man, tall, dark-eyed, his head crowned by black locks. His gestures were noble, his voice, rising and falling rhythmically, under perfect control. Now it rose to passionate indignation, now it sank to a whisper of pity, now it sang of the coming victory. The crowd was in his hands; it was lifted to heights of enthusiasm, it was plunged into an abyss of sorrow, it followed every mood and intention of the orator; and he, more and more aware of his success, became more and more enamoured of his role. Tevyeh felt every word like a separate knife-thrust. It was on his Bashke's grave, on the fresh earth which covered the dead body of his daughter, that this performance was taking place.

Finally the orator took out the bloodstained blouse which Bashke had worn when she was shot down. He waved it aloft and thundered:

"By the blood of our fallen comrade, we swear to carry on the fight to victory."

[423]

Tevyeh could stand it no more. He dashed forward, snatched the blouse from the orator's hand, and, thrusting it under his coat, pressed it convulsively to his heart.

"Leave me alone!" he gasped, tearing himself free from the hands which tried to detain him.

His behaviour was a great disappointment to the assembled workers. There was a general feeling that the fine mood created by the orator had suddenly been dissipated.

Tevyeh sat down on the grave of Bashke and looked around him with wild, wide-open eyes. Near him stood Nissan, his face black, his lips closed tight. He made no gesture and uttered no word of reproach.

There was silence in the crowd. The twittering of the birds, drowned till then by the melodious voice of the orator, was heard again. In the distance was heard the hooting of one of the factory sirens.

Martin Kuchinsky, former member of the Proletariat Party, now member of the Polish Socialist Party, was surrounded by police and Government agents. Streets, roads, and railroad stations were covered. It was impossible for him to get out of the city.

Eight days had passed since he and his group held up the mail at the railroad station of Rogoff, near Lodz. In full daylight they shot down the soldiers, broke into the mail-car, seized several bags, and escaped into Lodz.

Kuchinsky was highly satisfied with his work. From the newspapers which he bought the next morning, he learned that the haul was worth two hundred thousand roubles, contained in three mail-sacks. With such a sum the party could begin a decent program of activities. But when his men reassembled at the arranged rendezvous, on the third day after the hold-up, the booty they brought did not tally with the newspaper reports. Instead of three mail-sacks, they brought only two; instead of two hundred thousand roubles, there were only one hundred thousand.

Martin Kuchinsky was wild with rage.

"Where's the rest of the money?" he asked his men.

"This is what we took. There wasn't any more."

"The newspapers say there was twice as much."

"This is what we took. We've brought it all," the men repeated.

"I'm not going to stand for banditry in the terrorist organi-

[425]

ation," cried Kuchinsky, banging the table. "If any man has taken a rouble for himself, he'll pay for it with his life."

"Is this what we get for risking our lives?" asked one of the conspirators hotly. "We're ready to stand trial before a party committee. And if you can't prove your accusation, we shall want justice, *our* justice, for the insult."

The conspirators left the house hastily.

Kuchinsky appealed to the Tseka. But the Tseka refused to interfere.

"We have nothing to do with this," was the answer. "Comrade Kuchinsky, we shall never know where political terrorism ends and banditry begins."

Kuchinsky threw down the sack of money disgustedly and left the meeting. "From now on I'll manage alone," he said, angrily.

A difficult time followed for the former veterinary student. He had broken with his comrades and with the party. The police were hot on his trail, and there was not a corner in the great city where he felt safe. He was reluctant to jeopardize the lives of his personal friends by appealing to them for help, for he knew what it meant to be caught giving him refuge. Nor was there any way of escaping from the city.

He knew that his days were numbered, and he had made up his mind to sell his life dearly. In his flight from hiding-place to hiding-place he carried with him several loaded revolvers and a large supply of bullets. The police would not try to take him alive; they would wait till they had him in a corner and shoot him down. But he was determined that he would empty every revolver at the police before they got him; and he would keep the last bullet for himself. The thought of this clean, fighting end gave him courage and even a certain lightness of spirit.

He knew that the search which was closing about him centred particularly on the stations and on certain districts of the city. He therefore walked the streets openly; he went into churches and knelt with the worshippers till the last moments of the service; he haunted the libraries and sat for hours brooding over books which did not hold any interest for him. He wandered into the public markets, into squares, wherever crowds assembled, and like a wild animal he was perpetually alert as to what was going on around him. He derived much pleasure from the newspaper accounts of the hunt.

The days were not so bad, but the nights were dreadful. He could not go to a hotel, even with false documents. Every hotel employee in the city had his picture. He did not dare to pass the night in a house of prostitution either; most of the prostitutes were in the pay of the police. There were no parks or gardens in the city. The evenings were tolerable. He could sit in a restaurant, and when he had outsat his meal, go to a second restaurant. Once he even went into a synagogue and sat in a corner, swaying back and forth as he saw the others do. He even muttered to himself, as if he were repeating prayers, and no one paid any attention to him in the crowd. Once or twice he stole down into a baker's cellar and played cards with the workers; bakers were notorious gamblers, and they did not care whom they played with. Then, when all doors were closed, began the difficult hours. He crept around from shadow to shadow like a homeless dog. He envied the cats who leapt over walls so easily or squeezed their way into cellars through the gratings.

After the third night he felt he was through and he let himself be picked up by the first streetwalker that offered herself. She took him into a little garret.

He sat there, dumbly.

"Why don't you get undressed?" she asked him.

"I'd rather sleep through the night like this," he said, "with my clothes on."

"What's the matter?" she asked, offended. "Don't you like me?"

"It's not that," answered Kuchinsky. "You're really very pretty. But I'm all tired out. Let me sleep here, will you?"

He took out his guns and placed them at his head.

"Don't you dare to go out of the room even for an instant," he warned the girl. "If anyone knocks at the door, wake me up. I'll pay you in advance for the night. That'll be best."

"I'll wake you," said the girl, casting a frightened look at the revolvers. "Are they loaded?"

"Certainly."

"You can sleep," the girl went on. "You don't have to be afraid. Even if they come after you, you can get out through that upper garret and then out on the roof."

Early in the morning the girl woke him.

"Hey, mister, they're ringing the bell downstairs."

In an instant Kuchinsky was on his feet. He picked up his guns and crept out through the window into the upper garret. Peering down through the dirty window, he saw below, in the street, a posse of police in charge of an officer. The men were all armed with rifles. The officer hid himself behind the police.

"Hey, Kuchinsky, give yourself up!" shouted the officer.

Instead of answering, Kuchinsky sent a shot through the window into the mass of men below. The officer sat down on the earth at once and ordered his men to fire into the house. The ensuing battle between Kuchinsky and the police lasted several hours. Every salvo from below, Kuchinsky answered with a shot through the window. When only three bullets were left, he sat down to wait. He was keeping these bullets for himself, and he would use them only at the last moment, when the police were about to seize him.

He kept peering down. The police were still afraid to advance. They kept lifting their guns and firing, until they noticed that no more replies came. They called to Kuchinsky. He did not answer.

"He must be dead," said the officer. "Which of you men will climb up there and make sure?"

"I will, your honour," answered one of the men, and without waiting for further orders he entered the house and ran up the stairs. Kuchinsky drew back and hid himself behind a mass of linen hanging in the garret. He held his revolver ready. He heard the policeman fumbling at the door. He heard his name being called. He remained silent. The policeman opened the door cautiously and thrust his head in, and at the same moment Kuchinsky brought the butt of his revolver down on it heavily. The policeman pitched forward without a groan. With feverish haste Kuchinsky drew off the man's uniform and his boots; he picked up the hat

[428]

and the gun and then crept forward to the window, just showing his form.

"Hey, what's the matter up there, Romanka?" shouted the officer.

"Send up some men," growled Kuchinsky in a strangled voice.

There was a dash for the door. Several dozen men, with the officer at their head, came galloping up the stairs.

"Look in every corner," panted the officer. "Take him alive."

In the darkness and confusion Kuchinsky slipped down the back stairs and out into the street. No one had noticed him.

When the police finally discovered the bloody body of their comrade, Kuchinsky was far away. The officer set up a howl of rage and alternately tore his hair and that of his men.

"Fools!" he yelled. "Sons of bitches, and grandsons of bitches! I'll have every one of you shot."

ᏨᎧᏫᎧᏁᎬᏫ Konitzky of the gendarmerie, a Pole who had gone
over to the Orthodox Russian Church and was now at the
head of the political police of the revolutionary city of Lodz,
rubbed his soft white hands with joy and twirled his blond
moustaches higher and higher.

"Bravo!" he exclaimed to his agents. "Excellent work! I'll
see that you get a decent reward."

Colonel Konitzky had reason to rejoice. After months of
planning, after countless disappointments, after infinite ex-
penditure of labour and cunning, he had managed to land,
in a single big haul, the entire committee of the Unionists of
Lodz. With them he had managed to capture their secret
printing-press, together with a great quantity of printed
propaganda. Now the committee was under arrest, guarded
by a special squad of secret service men.

The colonel was much happier with this triumph than
with the success of the soldiers against the barricades of the
workers. Himself a military man, the colonel did not believe
in military repression of revolution. He had more faith in
ideas than in guns. It had always been so, ever since he had
been a student of philosophy and psychology in the University
of St. Petersburg. He had even been a revolutionary in his
younger years and had carried on dangerous discussions at
secret meetings. Later he gave up this childish folly, betrayed
his comrades to the police, and entered the service, working
his way up to the rank of colonel. For all that, he had never

lost faith in the power of the word and the idea, and the pen was still, in his opinion, mightier than the sword. He believed firmly that revolutionaries ought to be fought with their own weapons, word for word, idea for idea, propaganda for propaganda. And therefore Colonel Konitzky paid special attention to the writings of the revolutionaries and was much better informed on Marxist and Socialist theory than he had been in his student days. In his office desk, next to his revolver, always lay the newest political publication and the most modern work on psychology. He was for ever preaching that the only way to uproot a disease was by finding the specific; the only way to capture a fortress was by mining it from within. The higher-ups in St. Petersburg were not much taken with his theories; the iron hand was their way, and had always been. But Konitzky was obstinate. He had already practised his methods with some success in certain districts in Lithuania and Poland. When Lodz became a centre of revolution, he was entrusted with the pacification of the city.

Konitzky was an excellent man for Lodz. Himself a Pole, he had grown up, in his native town of Bailystok, on a Jewish street, and he spoke Yiddish almost as well as Polish. He had studied German later. He was thoroughly acquainted with the population of the city, and immediately on his arrival he threw himself with tremendous zeal into the task of bringing a spirit of law and order into Russia's greatest manufacturing centre of textiles and revolutions.

A parvenu, with a genuine hatred of the lower classes from which he had sprung, Konitzky nevertheless placed himself on the side of the ordinary people as against the intelligentsia. He considered the masses mere mud and manure; the intelligentsia was the dangerous element which was trying to give the masses a role for which they were totally unfit. His fight was therefore with the intelligentsia. He wanted to see it wiped out completely. But here again he was opposed to brutal methods. Simply killing off the intelligentsia would not do. The individual could be destroyed; his words were taken up and repeated and spread by others. Colonel Konitzky had other, more subtle ideas. The way to do it was to

[431]

introduce a spirit of mistrust, hatred, and war between the masses and the intelligentsia; make the masses resentful of these superior creatures; turn them against those who would get them into trouble. Above all, Konitzky liked to win over to himself, and turn into secret spies and agents provocateurs, the best spirits among the revolutionary leaders. He was sure that everywhere one could find malcontents, men who had not attained to the leadership which they thought they merited, men who had been insulted and denied promotion, who would lend themselves to his work.

Besides, as a student of psychology Colonel Konitzky knew that every man has some special weakness, some peculiarly exposed point, in his physical and nervous make-up; and he had a natural instinct, like that of the animal which makes with its teeth for the most vulnerable part of its victim, for finding out how resistance could most easily be broken down. He knew that among men arrested for the first time there were many types of reaction. Some men could not stand being struck; others took a blow easily, but could not, *per contra*, stand having a light always in their cells and went out of their minds if they were not permitted to fall asleep in darkness. Some were indifferent to a death on the gallows, but were seized with a sick trembling when they were locked up with criminals and the scum of the underworld; others fell to pieces when the word "gallows" was mentioned; there were some who could be broken down by shouting and threats; there were others who could be won over by kindly words and gentleness.

Whenever political prisoners were brought into the gendarmerie station, Colonel Konitzky made it a habit to observe the prisoners secretly through a little hole in the panel. His light, thoughtful eyes took in every gesture and every grimace. Before a prisoner was brought to him for his personal examination, he would have his men treat him roughly, strike him, kick him, and subject him to every humiliation. Konitzky observed the prisoner's reactions closely and noted down carefully whether, on being kicked by a soldier, he jumped in terror, or set his teeth grimly, or collapsed, or went into a blind hysteria of helpless rage. He noted also whether the prisoner turned pale when the officer stared in stony fury into his eyes, and whether his legs began to tremble when he was separated from his comrades and led away, and whether, on being stripped, he betrayed a feeling of disgust. All these observations were of great value to Colonel Konitzky. They formed the basis of his plan of campaign with every man.

Most of all, Colonel Konitzky liked to play the decent sort to the revolutionaries who were brought before him. The reason was twofold. First, he was afraid for his skin. More than one official had been removed, by bomb or bullet or knife, in these troublous times. The revolutionaries could not wipe out the entire officialdom, so they concentrated on the men with a reputation for cruelty, and Colonel Konitzky had no ambition to lay down his life for his Tsar; that he left to the stupider sort. Second, he had certain accounts to settle with General Kunitzin, officer in command of the troops which invested the city. Here, as everywhere else in Russia, there was bad blood between the gendarmerie and the regular army. The more the soldiers got themselves hated for their coarseness and brutality, the more ambitious was Konitzky to shine as the gentleman. Let the army officers draw down upon themselves the concentrated revenge of the revolutionaries.

So, during the first few days of their arrest, the prisoners did not see the colonel. He was ensconced in the little spying-room from which he observed the behaviour of the revolutionaries under the rough treatment which he instructed his officers to mete out. When he was finally brought into the picture, he presented such a contrast, with his quiet speech, his gentleness, and his sympathy, that most prisoners—especially those who had never tasted arrest before—were completely taken in.

During the brief period of his stay in Lodz, Colonel Konitzky had produced excellent results. His agents had wormed their way into every revolutionary group, the Polish Social Democratic Party, the terrorists, the German Social Democrats. He had succeeded in stirring up the workers against their leaders, in founding new splinter parties, so that the movement threatened to disintegrate with the number of secessions and subdivisions. He experienced the greatest difficulty with the Jewish Unionists and their movement. They were better conspirators than the others, and it was harder to break into their circles. Likewise the rank and file were more intelligent; it was not so easy to win the goodwill of a Jewish worker—who was often quite well trained in the theory of the movement—with a couple of drinks and a few roubles. A few of them Colonel Konitzky had managed to bribe; but they were obscure little fellows, without ability or influence. Likewise he did not trust them; indeed, he never trusted a man who let himself be bribed cheaply. What he needed was a first-class man, a member of the central committee.

That was why he rubbed his hands joyfully when he learned that the entire group had been taken. Apart from the excellent impression which this would make in St. Petersburg, there was the prospect of testing every individual separately and of finding—as he surely would—the man he had been looking for.

In civilian clothes, with dark glasses covering his eyes, Colonel Konitzky sat in his secret room and watched the prisoners being led in. He scrutinized them individually, his sharp eye noting every expression and movement. Yes, it was a magnificent haul, and St. Petersburg would appreciate his worth now. But as far as he himself was concerned, his interest was concentrated chiefly on one pair—the printers of the committee, so-called husband and wife. He did not believe that they were actually married or even lived together. On general grounds he distrusted these revolutionary pairs; "marriage" was simply a practical arrangement. On more specific grounds he was even more convinced that they were not what they were pretended to be. The woman was young, fresh, and extremely attractive. She was certainly, he decided, of very good family. Her eyes were bright and frank; her bearing was proud and fearless. Colonel Konitzky felt a slight moistness coming into his mouth as he watched her withdraw haughtily from the insolent gaze of the examining officer. The man who passed for her husband was a small, lean fellow, prematurely aged, hirsute, red-eyed from long night work, and pale from continuous confinement. He trembled before the gendarmes, and in his eyes alternated fear for himself and miserable uncertainty lest he betray himself in the presence of the woman.

"He's her slave above everything else," Colonel Konitzky noted. "A first-rate coward. His hands tremble."

This was the man, he decided almost at once. The others were undoubtedly more important; they were leaders of the type which interested St. Petersburg. But this terrified fellow was what Konitzky was looking for. It was not difficult to size up the man. He was obviously a half-baked intellectual, a worker drawn into the committee for two reasons: his practical usefulness and his status; the committee always liked to have in its ranks one or two "pure" proletarians. It made a good impression on the masses. Konitzky had met the type before. It was not genuine. It belonged neither to the intelligentsia nor to the workers and was at home nowhere. It suffered from repressed ambition and was always feeling insulted and ignored. It made the best material for Konitzky's special methods.

He sent for the officer in charge of the preliminary investigation.

"Get that printer away alone," he ordered.

"Yes, sir."

"Put him through a third degree. But don't touch him. Just threats."

"Yes, sir."

Konitzky's "third-degree" technique was familiar to his men. The prisoner was taken into a small, dark room, which was separated by a thin wall from another room in which a little comedy was staged. An agent played the role of a political prisoner who was being put to the torture by a crowd of gendarmes. The real prisoner could hear everything but see nothing.

"Come clean!" roared the investigator. "Every damned name on your list. Either that or—" and a lash whistled through the air.

"Never!" the agent replied firmly. "Not one name!"

[435]

"Strip him! And let him have it!"

The prisoner in the dark room heard the lash falling, as he thought, on naked flesh. He heard the screaming of the "revolutionary."

Konitzky, watching the prisoner through the hole in the wall, saw him jump convulsively every time the lash struck. He smiled delightedly. When the comedy had lasted several minutes, he gave instructions to suspend the "investigation."

"Give him a bit of time to think," he said, indicating the trembling man in the dark room. "Then go through the business again after an hour and keep it up once an hour all night."

"Yes, sir."

"Begin again tomorrow. Then bring the prisoner to me on the third day."

"Yes, sir."

All through that night and through the next day and through the second night the game was kept up in the room adjoining the prisoner's cell. There was no sleep for him. As soon as he had fallen into a doze, the lashing and the screaming were resumed. Sometimes the torture was varied. The "revolutionary" was doused with ice-cold water. Glowing cigarette tips were applied to his naked flesh. With every new torment the screams became wilder. Finally, the "revolutionary" broke down and sobbed: "Let me go. I can't stand it any more. I'll tell you everything."

The agents then burst into the prisoner's cell to tell him that it was his turn next. They found the man lying on the floor, his face and clothes drenched with sweat.

But suddenly they pretended to change their minds and went out. Another "revolutionary" was taken into the adjoining cell and put to the torture. Meanwhile the prisoner lay shuddering in an agony of expectation. When they finally came for him, to lead him before the colonel, he could not stand without assistance.

"Please, shoot me," he babbled, "only don't torture me."

They dragged him laughingly out of the room and into the colonel's office. When they tried to leave him there, he fastened himself on the door-handle, and they had to tear him away by brute force before they could get out. The prisoner stood there pulling madly at the handle. Behind him, through another door, Colonel Konitzky entered, clean-shaven, in neat uniform, with half a dozen medals glittering on his breast. His face wore a kindly, good-humoured smile.

"Good evening," he said softly, going up to the prisoner. "Why do you stand at the door? Won't you take a seat?"

The prisoner whipped round and stared at the colonel, unable to utter a word.

"Aren't you feeling well?" Konitzky asked gently. "Shall I help you to a chair?"

He led the wordless prisoner to a soft armchair and sat down opposite him.

"Tea!" he called out. "And some cakes."

An elderly gendarme came in quietly, carrying a tray with two glasses of tea and a plate of cakes.

"Have some," said the colonel in a friendly, natural voice. "It'll warm you up. And the cakes are very good."

The prisoner looked dumbly around him.

"What is it?" asked the colonel. "What makes you so nervous?"

"I want to be shot," muttered the prisoner. "Don't torture me."

A smile of astonishment came over the colonel's face.

"But what are you talking about?" he exclaimed. "I'm a soldier, not a butcher. I don't know what kind of stories you've been listening to. You'd better drink that tea."

The prisoner stared at the colonel.

"Are you serious?" he asked, weakly.

The colonel rose, went over to the prisoner, and felt his pulse.

"Have they done anything to you?" he asked paternally.

"No," answered the other, still trembling. "It was somebody else, in the cell next to mine."

"What was it?"

"They were torturing somebody. They lashed him and burned him. It was horrible."

The colonel made a grimace of disgust.

"Those regular-army brutes!" he exclaimed furiously.

[437]

"They're not decent. They're not human. I shall report them. You may be absolutely certain."

The prisoner stretched out two lean, shivering hands. "Three days it lasted," he cried. "It was abominable."

"Drink some of that tea," said the colonel soothingly. "You are frightened. And with reason. But you're under my protection now, and no one will dare to lay a hand on you."

Slowly and carefully he nursed the prisoner into a state of tranquillity. He held the glass to his lips and wiped his mouth for him. When the man had regained his self-control he offered him a cigarette and drew him into conversation.

Colonel Konitzky's conversations with political prisoners were not of the cut and dried sort. He left commonplace cross-examinations to others. What he liked was a friendly chat on a higher plane. Most of all he liked to show a prisoner —especially if it was one of the semi-intellectuals—that he, Colonel Konitzky, was not a boorish official of the old school. He was himself an intellectual, with a thorough knowledge of Marxist and Socialist theory, something of a liberal, if you please.

"Well, I hope you're feeling a little better, Mr. Trilling," he said cheerfully.

The prisoner started to hear himself called by his real name.

"My name is Boruch Rosenblum," he stammered

The colonel smiled indulgently. "It's as you like," he said. "I can call you by the name on your papers. I'd rather call you by your real name, though. During the investigations of these last few days we've managed to get all your names, among other things. I know, for instance, that among the committee you've always been called Comrade Butsche."

The prisoner turned pale. Had his comrades betrayed everything? The colonel noted the deepening pallor.

"If you'd like to write a letter to your family," he said, "you can do it now. They're deeply worried about you at home. Your father was here to ask about you. A fine man of the old school; I felt sorry for him. He isn't young any more, and he's terribly unhappy about you. You know how the older generation looks on these things."

[438]

Comrade Butsche felt himself weakening under this soft, human treatment. He was like the soldier who, trained for years in peace-time manœuvres, forgets everything when he is under fire for the first time.

"My father!" he exclaimed, and suddenly interrupted himself. He set his lips.

"As you like, young man," said the colonel, sighing. "I was only thinking of the old man. He made a very fine impression." He changed the subject abruptly.

"I must say that your position rather astonishes me," he said, his voice full of respect. "You are, it appears, a weaver by trade. I took you for an intellectual."

"Can't a weaver be an intellectual?" asked the prisoner, blushing slightly.

"Oh, yes, there's no reason why not. But it's unfortunately very rare in Russia. We're still a backward people, I'm sorry to say."

The prisoner opened his red eyes wide on hearing these words. The colonel smiled, as if a trifle embarrassed.

"I can see a little sarcasm in your look," he said. "Yes, I know. One doesn't often hear such words from a servant of the Tsar, a blood-sucker, an enemy of the working-class."

"I didn't say that," answered the prisoner hastily.

"But it's what you're thinking. You're bound to think like that, because that's the picture you've been taught to accept as true. And not without reason, I'll grant you that, because God knows there are among us not a few proud aristocrats, feudal lords of the old type, who do their best to justify the opinion which has been spread concerning all of us among the workers. But it's a mistake to think we're all tarred with the same brush. Thank God, we have in our ranks men of modern ideas—and you'll find them in the Government, too —who want to see the Russian worker brought up to the standard of the west European countries. I'm one of them myself. I come from the plain people. My father was a working-man, and the life of the workers is not an alien world to me. I'm happy when I see one of us climbing up the ladder of success. It's something like class consciousness, as you would say; my own belief is that it's something in our blood."

[439]

Two red spots appeared on the cheeks of the prisoner.

"I don't understand," he muttered. "I can't make it out."

Colonel Konitzky interrupted.

"You're looking at my uniform and my epaulettes, and you're astonished. But surely you, as an intelligent man, won't deny that under a military hat, not less than under the round hat of a worker, you can sometimes find a mind capable of thinking for itself, and under a military uniform, too, there's a human heart sometimes. The greatest Russian thinkers, fighters, and writers have worn military uniforms, as you doubtless know from your reading."

The colonel caressed his uniform and became very earnest.

"Don't think, my friend, that I was born in a uniform. There was a time when I wore the clothes of the poorest workers. And I haven't forgotten my youth, either, with its dreams and ideals, yes, and even its revolutionary plans. We all pass through that stage. Then one becomes older. Life becomes sterner, heavy duties press on us, and the old, easy enthusiasms subside. Don't believe it if they tell you that we of the service think only of wine, women, and song. And don't believe, either, that I've lost every interest in higher things. I'd much rather pass an hour in intelligent conversation with a man like you than sit down to a game of cards. I'm not the only one. There are many of us who still find time to look into a volume of philosophy. And though our dreams are gone, there are still sleepless nights, when strange thoughts haunt us, about human beings and about class divisions, and about this Russia of ours, this great, unhappy country which suffers and bleeds, and about one's own flesh and blood, the poor, the workers, those that gave birth to us. . . . Blood is thicker than water. . . ."

The prisoner could not help warming to these words. He forgot his first fears. He became natural, even courageous.

"I still don't understand," he exclaimed. "How could you go over to the enemy and fight your own kind?"

He caught himself—too late! "I'm sorry," he stammered, "I didn't mean—"

The colonel leaned over and put a warm, fatherly hand on the prisoner's narrow shoulder.

[440]

"Young man, I like your frankness. It's the one quality I prize most in our own kind, in one of the people. None of the evasions and mental gymnastics of the intelligentsia, the superior creatures. . . . You don't have to apologize for what you've just said, and you don't have to weigh every word you utter in my presence. I have enough of that all day long from my subordinates here. You've asked me a man-to-man question, and I'm going to answer it man to man.

He went quickly to his desk, opened it, and drew out a photograph.

"Look at this picture," he said. "Do you recognize this man?"

The prisoner examined the photograph. He saw a typical young revolutionary student, with long hair and dreamy eyes. Near him sat a girl, holding a book in her hand.

"No," said the prisoner. "I don't recognize him."

"You'll find it hard to believe that this is a photograph of myself," said the colonel, smiling. "But look closely. I had this picture taken in St. Petersburg at the time of my first arrest."

"Arrest?" asked the prisoner, blankly.

"Yes, my friend, arrest. And not for theft, as you may well understand, but for revolutionary activity. Born of poor parents, I wanted, like you, to liberate my class. I was easily won over by the intellectuals, as so many others have been. But I was lucky enough to see through them in time and to drop them."

"I don't understand you," said the prisoner, uneasily.

"Listen to me, my friend," said the other warmly. "If you were one of those intellectuals, one of those lofty spirits who condescend to the people in order, as they say, to rescue them and make them happy, I wouldn't speak with you as frankly as I do. I would simply do my duty. Because I know that crowd. Those men are not interested in the workers; the workers are strange and alien to them. They look down on the proletariat and have an inner contempt for it. Wait, don't interrupt me. These intellectuals come from rich homes; they aren't acquainted with the working-man, they don't feel his emotions. Their so-called revolutionary passion

[441]

is something born in the imagination, out of boredom and idleness and out of the fashionableness of being a radical. You yourself are a working-man, born and brought up in poverty, oppressed by the rich possessing classes. Your fight is honest and serious; it's in your blood. You'll understand me; we both come from the same class, we've both tasted the same poverty. I tell you that we, the workers, shall never, never be able to go hand in hand with the intellectuals, with those scions of the rich. I've seen it in my own case; I've felt the bitter effects of the dishonest in my own life. It had turned me against them; against them, the intellectuals, not against the people."

The prisoner was so eager to speak that his Adam's apple bobbed up and down in his throat. But the colonel gave him no chance.

"Take a close look at the Russian situation and you'll see that the struggle isn't one between the poor and the rich, as would be natural enough; no, it's a struggle between two divisions of the rich for the control of power—between the intellectuals and the others, both members of the ruling classes. Who were the first Octobrists? Aristocrats, princes, dukes, and counts who wanted to get hold of the Government. To them the masses, the people, were an instrument for the furtherance of their own ambitions. Who were all the later revolutionaries? They were all members of the upper classes, for which the people poured out its blood. Examine the present struggle. Who are its leaders? Again the same type, dragging the workers after themselves. Because it's characteristic of the intellectual to use someone else's hands to get the chestnuts out of the fire."

The colonel unbuttoned his uniform, so that every vestige of formality disappeared, and he sat with his prisoner like one friend in homely converse with another. He fixed his eyes gravely on the other, who dropped his.

"And now, my young friend," he said, "can you tell me, briefly and simply, what it is you're fighting for?"

"What I'm fighting for?" repeated the prisoner. "You know it without my telling you. For the working-class. For freedom."

[442]

"Do you mind if I take those two ideas separately?" interrupted the colonel. "Let's talk first about that which interests you, as a member of the working-class, more than anything else: the fight for the working-class. We'll talk of liberty later."

"Yes, but without liberty there can't be a fight for the working-class."

"That's a very naïve point of view," retorted the colonel. "And when you speak like that, it isn't with the voice of the son of the working-class; it isn't the blood of the proletariat speaking through you. It's only the phraseology of the intelligentsia, the propagandist lesson."

"I don't understand you," answered the prisoner.

"Let me explain," said the colonel, touching the prisoner's knee. "The word 'liberty' has a great deal of charm about it, and the intelligentsia use it freely, to captivate the masses with. But as a concept it is extremely obscure. Have you ever been abroad? No? Well, I have. I've travelled a great deal. Let me tell you that the constitutional forms of government which are so common in the west, which give the working-man the so-called right to vote and assure him a secret ballot, have done very little for him. The only guaranteed right he has is to starve—just as his elected representative has the constitutional right to deliver revolutionary orations against the oppressors of the working-class, while he himself receives a salary from the Government. Liberty is something for intellectuals only, the ones who get themselves elected by the working-class."

"But under a Socialist régime," said the prisoner, "we shall be the workers."

The colonel looked at him with a pitying smile.

"Absurd," he said. "The worker will for ever remain the producer, the builder, while the intellectual will always be his leader. I'm not talking of individuals. You personally may succeed in working yourself up and becoming an intellectual. I'm talking of the class as such."

"But under socialism there will be no classes."

"Those are empty fantasies, young man. There will always be two hostile classes: the workers and the idle intellectuals.

The workers are only privates in the armies of the intellectuals, who carry on a war for power among themselves. This was the case in the French Revolution. Danton and Robespierre fought each other for the power, and the blood of the workers was poured out to decide the issue. We have the same situation in Russia today. And I tell you, therefore, that the true duty of the intelligent worker is to refuse to be drawn into an alien struggle; he must concentrate on his own struggle, the fight for the interests of the working-class. It was the realization of this duty that drove me, the child of poor parents, from the camp of the intellectuals and made me their enemy. This is what every intelligent worker should do. And then I assure you that you will easily reach your goal, for no one would dare to oppose your just demands."

The prisoner sat trembling with impatience; his face was crimson, he had a hundred things to say, but the colonel would not let him get a word in. And now the latter suddenly changed the topic and passed over from the political to the personal.

"Listen to me," he said very softly, very intimately. "I know your life. I can read it off as if it were an open book before me. For I myself have passed through this life. The intellectuals have drawn you into their struggle. They have spoken of equality and brotherhood. But how much brotherliness was there actually in your ranks? The leaders have lived mostly abroad, passing resolutions, while you, the worker, were directed to work a secret printing-press, where you lived for months without getting a glimpse of the sky or drawing a breath of fresh air. You were entombed; you saw no friends, you saw neither your parents nor your brothers and sisters. It was a life more dreadful than the severest punishment in prison, worse than solitary confinement; a living death."

"Intellectuals have done the same thing," said the prisoner.

"I know. You mean your companion, whom you gave out as your wife. But I'd rather not talk about that. I don't want to hurt your feelings."

The prisoner sprang to his feet.

"What do you mean?" he cried. "What is it?"

[444]

"Nothing," said the colonel, repressing a smile. "It's better not to talk about it."

"But you must talk about it," insisted the prisoner, whose face had gone white.

The colonel drummed on the desk. "No, I'd rather not," he said. "But it's amazing how naïve and trusting people of your sort can remain and how easily the intellectuals get you into their trap. . . . As far as *you're* concerned, the talk has always been highly moral; it's always had to do with comradely relations between man and woman, independent of sex. It's been extremely idealistic, hasn't it?" The colonel permitted himself to smile openly.

The prisoner wriggled in his seat.

"We were husband and wife," he said.

"Do you think you'll get me to believe that rubbish?" answered the colonel contemptuously. "Do you take me for such a fool? I know those marriage arrangements among comrades. You were husband and wife as far as the janitor was concerned. Within the house, however, she kept you at a distance; she avoided you, as intellectuals always avoid more intimate contact with a member of the lower classes. With comrades of her own class she didn't talk of Platonic morality, of comradely relations. There the relationships were different—oh, very different."

The prisoner leapt up. "It's a lie!" he yelled.

The colonel laughed out loud this time.

"Why should you force me to say what I don't want to say?" he asked the prisoner. "They treat you much worse than you treat them. You workers are their admirers, their blind followers, ready to suffer all sorts of torment without letting a word escape you. They're not capable of such heroism. They can't stand the idea of torture. They give us your names even before the screws are put on. I know how much a young man like you has suffered. Always to be in the house with the girl one loves, to be her husband in the eyes of the world, but to have to keep one's distance, bearing as best one can those contemptuous looks. . . . To see, in the other person, revulsion trying to mask itself as high morality. . . . And at the same time this holier-than-thou

[445]

wife who is not a wife carries on love-affairs with all the leaders. They were laughing at you all the time, they were mocking you. . . ."

"You have no right—" yelled the prisoner, utterly forgetful of his first terror.

"Perhaps I haven't. But I have certain little love-letters which were found among your 'wife's' papers in the search. Very interesting they are, too. . . ."

The colonel went to his desk, opened the drawer, poked around among some papers, and then seemed to change his mind. "No," he said, "I don't think I can let you have this very interesting information about the lady, or about the others whom you deified so passionately, at this time. It's a little too early. Some other time, when the occasion presents itself. Perhaps I'll find it easier then to convince you. However, our talk today was more personal than official. We shall meet again. Meanwhile let me ask you to think over seriously the things I've told you."

The prisoner sat stunned. Konitzky dropped his voice till it became almost caressing in its friendliness.

"Remember, if the door is open for you, there's no need for you to bash your head through the wall. Learn to differentiate between those two problems: the struggle of the worker for his daily bread, and the struggles of the intellectuals with each other, into which workers are foolishly drawn. If you learn this, we—I mean you and I—will be spared much unpleasantness. We shan't have to face each other as enemies. We shan't have to fight each other."

"But we don't fight you, it's you who fight us. You shoot at us when we march out to demonstrate peacefully."

The prisoner had much more to say, but the colonel put an authoritative hand on his shoulder.

"It's been a genuine pleasure," he said courteously. "I trust we shall see each other again before long. Meanwhile I wish you a very restful night."

The gendarmes led the prisoner out. This time he was not taken to the room next to the torture-chamber, but to a clean, comfortable cell. The first meal they brought him had been prepared, not in prison, but in a near-by restaurant, and the smell of it was delicious. But the prisoner did not make a move toward it. He was hungry, but he could not eat. Nor, in spite of the clean, comfortable bed and the sleepless nights he had passed listening to the screaming in the adjacent chamber, could he close his eyes for an instant.

He lay turning over feverishly everything the colonel had said during the long interview; his mind jumped from the political to the personal, from the personal to the political. Always it was the personal that hurt most. It was as though, somewhere in his brain, a nest of worms had bred, and the loathsome, biting little reptiles were crawling back and forth through the grey matter.

Was it true? he asked himself a thousand times. Had the comrades betrayed him? Had they given out everything? It could not be otherwise. The colonel knew too much. He could not have got the information elsewhere. And it was so accurate, so exact, too. . . .

Lodz came to life again.

The war in the Far East was ended, and vast, remote Russian territories opened again for business. Orders poured in on the manufacturing city, and factories worked double shifts.

Strikes were a thing of the past. The returned soldiers who had failed to conquer the Japs turned on the Jews and revolutionaries, the enemies of the Tsar. The job of repressing discontent was taken away from the police and given to high military officers, and if the police played any role in the work, it was indirect. They contributed the organization of the underworld. Thieves, pimps, drunkards, and criminals at large were taken out of prison and installed in tea-houses where priests and Government officials preached war against all Jews, liberals, and strikers. Long-bearded and long-robed monks with crosses in their hands, nuns in black carrying candles, market-women, policemen in civilian clothes, drunkards, streetwalkers, cripples, lunatics, and blackguards gathered in these places, or marched through the streets of the cities, singing patriotic songs and attacking Jewish passers-by or robbing Jewish shops and homes.

In Lithuania and in White Russia armed soldiers joined the mobs of Jew-baiters and helped to crush the Jewish self-defence. Bearded Russians were brought into Poland for heavy railroad work and—incidentally—pogrom activities. Prisons and barracks were filled with arrested workers and strikers, and the courts martial, which now had charge of the

[448]

"criminals," worked swiftly and smoothly. There was hardly a train leaving for the interior of Russia which did not have several cars with bars on the windows for prisoners being transported to Siberia.

In Jewish towns and villages fasts were proclaimed by the rabbis because of the pogroms, special prayers were said, collections were made for the widows and orphans. But now, instead of the Unionists of aforetime, wandering preachers and rabbis occupied the pulpits and carried on the public activity. They exhorted the people to godliness, submissiveness, and obedience to the rulers of the land. The revolt of the younger generation collapsed and parents were once more able to assert their authority. There were sporadic outbursts of the old rebellious spirit; here and there the Unionists called a meeting or arranged a demonstration or even exhibited a red flag. But there was no response. Many of the revolutionaries, sons and daughters of well-to-do parents, began to look on their former convictions as a youthful folly. They returned to the universities and prepared for a career, or they made successful marriages and went into business. Or else, instead of relapsing into respectability, they gave themselves up to licentious lives. Many fled across the Atlantic, to America or the Argentine. The leaders took refuge in Switzerland, and there continued their furious discussions among themselves. Others were in prison or in Siberia.

Lodz was at work once more. Russia needed goods to make up for the period of quiescence. The manufacturers of Lodz were once more in the saddle. They gave great receptions to the military and the high city and state officials. They lost money regularly to the officers and provided a large weekly salary for General Kunitzin, the virtual dictator of the city. They also bought him a magnificent carriage and a pair of horses in appreciation of the severity with which he ruled Lodz. Not a whisper of protest was heard from the workers. Lodz made money, ate and drank, sang in the cafés, gambled at cards, and made merry generally.

A great time, too, had come for Max Ashkenazi. He had triumphed over all obstacles and realized his great plan.

[449]

Yakob had put up a good fight for his sister-in-law, had spent money freely and given her all the legal protection she had needed. In fact, Dinah had not been defeated in frontal attack; she had simply been worn down. She had not the inhuman endurance of Max Ashkenazi; and Yakob, enthusiastic at first, was not a natural born fighter and could not sustain her spirits for her. Her parents, too, after the first flutter of indignation, collapsed under the systematic and relentless persecutions of their son-in-law. Besides, they, like their daughter, at last became ashamed to take money from Yakob. Ignatz, Dinah's son, kept writing from abroad, demanding more money and threatening suicide; and Max Ashkenazi held out the tempting bait of a solid settlement—nothing less than one hundred thousand roubles. He got his way at last.

It was not easy for him to part with an amount which represented a thick bundle of factory stocks, but he was playing for big game. The widow of Kharkov, who had told him that he could not touch a rouble of her fortune until he came with his divorce, would now have one more proof of his determination and ability. Indeed, it was on her advice that he consented to raise the bribe—such he considered it—to this figure, more than ten times the sum he had received as dowry with his wife.

However, he obtained a double divorce, one from the civil authorities and one from a Rabbinic court, and a complete and unconditional release from all future obligations toward the woman who had been his wife. The civil divorce was cold and formal; but the Rabbinic divorce, with its traditional effort to reunite the couple, was painful. They stood, Max and Dinah, in the little Rabbinic room, their heads lowered, their voices uncertain, listening to the innumerable questions which the Rabbi put to them concerning their absolute insistence on the divorce, and answering, over and over again: "Yes."

"My God, how long will this last?" whispered Dinah to her mother. "I can't stand it."

"A divorce is not a light thing," said the Rabbi, overhearing her. "The holy Law does not grant one easily."

[450]

Dinah left the room at last without even casting a glance at the man with whom she had passed the best part of her life. In the droshky she fell on her mother's neck and burst into tears.

"Why am I being punished like this?" she sobbed. "What have I done to deserve it?"

Priveh held her close and comforted her.

"My daughter, you'll marry again, and you'll find happiness with someone. You've got a good fortune to offer, and you're still young and attractive. There'll be many a good man wooing you."

"No, Mamma, don't speak of such things," wept Dinah. "It's all ended for me."

If Dinah kept her eyes obstinately turned away from her husband, Max Ashkenazi, on the other hand, found himself every now and then looking intently at the wife he was divorcing. With her pale skin, her sad, blue eyes, her slender form, she looked strangely attractive and accessible. He could not help thinking, by contrast, of the widow Margulies, the elderly, broad-shouldered, big-boned, stony woman with the manly voice and manly gestures, and when Dinah went from the room without casting a glance in his direction, something in his heart protested; there was a realization of a certain emptiness of which he would never rid himself, and he felt as though he were standing above an abyss into which something precious had slipped out of his hands, and his hands felt forlorn and superfluous.

He came to abruptly. He saw in front of him, instead of the widow Margulies, a vast heap of Huntze stocks, the mastery of the factory, the foremost position in Lodz. His regrets disappeared, and he left the Rabbinic court with firm, decisive steps. The same night he took train for Kharkov, his divorce packed in among his other papers.

Lodz had predicted that the love-affair of Yanka Flederbaum and Yakob Ashkenazi would last from Passover eve to Passover morning, and Lodz was almost right. Mad Yanka's infatuation with Yakob ran its course, reached its climax, and declined; within six months she was as passionately in love with an Italian tenor of the Warsaw opera as she had ever been with Yakob or anyone else. It was not her fashion to linger over outlived loves. She left Yakob as frankly as she had taken him. But they remained good friends, still calling each other by their first names and using the familiar second person singular; and Yakob's position as director of the Flederbaum factory was confirmed.

But instead of one affair, Lodz now had two to talk about; for while mad Yanka was flaunting her new love in the eyes of Lodz, as was her wont, Gertrude, Dinah's young daughter, was paying open court now to her uncle.

She was done with the equivocal niece-uncle game; she had dropped all pretences and excuses, and whenever Yakob tried to put that façade up again, she grew furious with him.

Clinging to him, her hands thrust into his thick black hair, her body pressed close to him, her lips seeking his, she knew only that she was a woman desiring this man, whoever he might be. When Yakob tried feebly to thrust her from him, she clung closer.

"Stop it, Gertrude," he said. "You're too old for that now. You're not a baby any more."

"I know I'm not a baby," she cried, "and I want you to stop treating me like one. I'm a woman, and I want you to kiss me. No, no, no, not like that. A real kiss, a hard one!"

Yakob tried again to turn the relationship into a joke. He laughed, but the laughter sounded false and foolish.

"I know that you love me just as I love you," Gertrude whispered. "Yakob darling! Yakob! Do what you like with me! Only kiss me and love me!"

He was afraid of her, and afraid too of the stirring in his own blood. All that he had felt for Dinah, the girl's mother, was awake in him, with something more—the something that was expressed by Gertrude's lips, the one feature in which she did not resemble her mother. For, unlike Dinah's, they were not tender, small, and quiet. They were heavy and stormy. They attracted men's eyes first. Slightly open, so that the white teeth showed, they betrayed Gertrude's furious hunger for life, her impatience and self-will. This was not a woman whom parents and relatives could manage and mould; nor was it a woman who would accept, as a substitute for her own experiences, the silly, romantic descriptions to be found in books.

When her mother and her grandparents talked to her of a match, she laughed in their faces. Reb Chaim and Priveh were more concerned than Dinah, for they still had hopes that their daughter would marry again, while she herself was utterly indifferent. But it was out of the question for the mother to marry again before her daughter had been disposed of; and so the grandparents were busy finding a match for Gertrude. Reb Chaim Alter had a sober, reliable business-man in view; Priveh was angling for a doctor.

"Our little Gertrude doesn't belong to the old school any more, Chaim," she said to her husband. "She wants something modern. My doctor's the man for her."

They could not even get Gertrude to listen.

"Grandmamma," she said, "I don't want anyone, and I don't need anyone."

"But you do need someone, child," said her grandmother. "Tell me, have you picked someone yourself? Are you in love with anyone?"

"I'm very much in love with someone," answered Gertrude, bursting into shrill laughter, so that Priveh could not make out whether the girl was serious or not.

She was not going to let herself be trapped or compromised. Her father's obstinacy and purposefulness was in her blood, but it was turned to ends of self-indulgence. She was not to be deterred by the babbling of those dotards, her grandparents, or by the sentimental hesitancy of her mother, or by the timidity of her uncle. The first she would ignore, the second she would win over, the third she would take by storm. She knew that the last was the easiest task, for the resistance was unwilling and unreal, the arguments were foolish, put forward only to be overthrown.

"Yakob," she whispered, clinging close to him, "I know you love me. Marry me."

"You're a foolish girl," he answered, struggling with himself, ashamed of what Dinah would think, ashamed of the world at large. "You mustn't dare to say such things. Someone might hear—"

"Let them hear! What do I care?"

"Child, I'm old enough to be your father."

"But what does that matter, as long as I love you?"

"Gertrude, you're young. Girls at your age often fall in love with elderly men. But it passes. Marry someone of your years."

"I'm a grown woman, and I know what I'm doing," she said firmly.

Beaten back, Yakob took another tack and revealed his inmost fears.

"Gertrude, we can never be husband and wife because of your mother. There was a time—you understand—when we were in love with each other. This would be a terrible blow to her—especially at this time."

"Whose fault is it," asked Gertrude swiftly, "if she didn't know how to manage her life?"

Yakob stared at her open-eyed. "Gertrude," he answered, shocked, "you're speaking of your own mother. You're every inch your father: another Simcha Meyer."

Gertrude burst into tears.

"Why do you torture me, Yakob? Is it a sin to love and want to be loved? Haven't I the right of every woman?"

She fell on her knees before her uncle; she seized his hands and kissed them imploringly.

"Don't thrust me away from you. I want you. Take me and do whatever you like with me. Forget who I am and think of me only as of a woman who loves you and whom you love. . . . My beloved, my king. . . ."

Yes, she was a replica of her father in her obstinacy, in her inability to take no for an answer from life. The world's censure, her mother's pain, her uncle's moral reluctance, meant nothing to her except as she saw in them her natural enemies, the barriers between herself and her desire. She would not let Yakob rest until she had overcome him, or, rather, forced him to overcome himself. Shamelessly and deliberately she played up to him, awakening in him agonies of desire, pouring the heat of her body into his until his scruples were lost in the torment of his hunger. And when

[454]

she had wrung his consent from him, she ran to her mother.

Dinah listened in stony and horrified silence to the girl's pleading, and felt about her the arms which had been thrown so passionately round the man she had herself loved, her Yakob. She could not pretend to herself that she was taken by surprise. How many nights had she not passed in bitter-sweet meditation, recalling the light in Yakob's eyes, the warmth in his cheeks, when Gertrude had clung to him in their niece-and-uncle games, telling herself that it was all meant for her, the woman he had lost? But even if meant for her, that emotion of his was equivocal and horrible. For it was the child, the daughter, after all, who was the immediate object of his excitement; and it was with an agony of shame that Dinah discovered in herself the signs of a true jealousy, directed against her daughter. She might well have expected this denouement, only she had not dared to face it; and when it came, openly and brutally, she did not know what to say. She heard in her daughter's frantic, resistless pleading the voice of her own forfeited happiness, for which she herself had been unable to speak. The dreadful pain of her mis-spent life welled up in her, making it impossible for her to say no to the girl, and equally impossible to say yes. Gertrude had thrown herself at her mother's feet, she clung to her knees.

"Mamma, Mamma, sweetness, I know I'm being bad to you, and I've never been good to you; and I know I shouldn't do it, I oughtn't to. But I can't help it. Mamma, do it for your little daughter, for your Gertrude's happiness. I can't live without him, I can't."

"Get up," whispered Dinah at last. "Get up. Do whatever you like. Only don't ask me."

Gertrude rose from the floor, a wild radiance shining in her face; and then, exactly like her father when he had carried an important point, she raised herself on the tips of her toes, spreading out her arms and throwing back her head.

A shudder passed through Dinah. "Please go!" she begged her daughter. "Let me be alone."

Gertrude sped from the room to carry the good news to her uncle.

[455]

In the head offices of the Huntze factory the armchairs were drawn up about the neatly ranged baize-covered tables ready for the annual meeting of the directors and the principal stockholders. Melchior the doorman, his sideburns a shade greyer now, but his cheeks as rosy as ever and his green huntsman's uniform with its brilliant stripes down the sides still as gay as of old, stood proudly and stiffly at the door, deriving dignity from the solemnity of the occasion and the importance of the assembly.

Among the assembled there were some of the foremost and wealthiest citizens of Lodz: blond, rotund Germans, with smooth-combed hair, in light-coloured clothes; Jewish bankers in sober black; a Polish nobleman with huge moustaches, out of his element; an elderly woman, lean and hungry-looking; and, finally, the Barons Huntze themselves, haughty, blasé, their monocles fastened in their eyes, their weak, weary faces still betraying, with every grimace, the plebeian origin they had done so much to disguise.

The directors and stockholders greeted the barons obsequiously and were snubbed for their pains. The barons were in evil humour. The only man who seemed to behave naturally at the meeting was the chief director, Max Ashkenazi. He wore an English check suit. His face was clean-shaven except for the tiny pointed beard, which on this one occasion was neatly combed. The white dots on his coloured satin vest positively shone—each dot asserting itself separately.

[456]

And Max Ashkenazi's face was filled with gaiety and good humour.

The meeting did not open yet. In accordance with the custom established since the change of the form of ownership, the chief director, Max Ashkenazi, gave an informal report and conducted the guests personally on a tour of inspection. First he asked them to approach the charts which hung in the office. They were a condensed history of the progress of the Huntze concern since it had become a corporation.

"When I joined the concern, gentlemen," said Max Ashkenazi, "the factory had three thousand workers. Today it has eight thousand. The number of looms has increased proportionately, of course. This diagram will show you the steady increase in the volume of business. The line comes down a little here—the only serious interruption. That, as you know, was the year during which there was more striking than working. But, as you see, it didn't take us long to catch up and to continue the upward march."

The visitors blew thick clouds of smoke from their cigars. They were highly satisfied with the tone of the report.

"This map, gentlemen," continued Max Ashkenazi, "shows you the growth of our territory. The green flags are—if I may so put it—the points we have captured since I assumed office here. You perceive that many of them go right outside the boundaries of our country. Since I came here, our export trade has greatly increased."

"Very fine," murmured the visitors, feeling themselves expanding with the territory.

"This chart, gentlemen, shows you the history of our stocks on the market. If you'll compare all these diagrams and maps you'll see how every fluctuation in the stocks is connected with the increase or decrease in production and the expansion of territory. It is not difficult to understand why Huntze stock has risen almost continuously."

This came nearest home to the visitors. The murmurs of approval swelled into a chorus.

When Max Ashkenazi set out with the visitors on a tour of inspection of the factory—ignoring the offers of engineers and chemists to act as cicerones—the Huntze brothers went

[457]

home. They had always loathed the factory; but they had special reasons now for hating it. They had had to leave their winter sports abroad in order to attend the meeting of the board; also, they were in an extremely uncomfortable position. They had been selling too many of the Huntze stocks; and of late quite recklessly. Luck had been against them at the card and roulette tables. They did not look forward with pleasure to the forthcoming meeting, and they could not understand the enthusiasm of Max Ashkenazi and the other stockholders in the workings of the factory. They sat at home, drinking one schnapps after another, waiting to be called when the ceremony of inspection was over.

Meanwhile Max Ashkenazi proudly conducted the visitors through the enormous works. He took them first through the great yard, surrounded by warehouses and stockrooms. No workers were seen in the yard; the communications between the departments were mostly underground.

"Gentlemen," said Max Ashkenazi, "we will make this round systematic, so that you may inspect the entire organization, from the arrival of the raw material to the shipping of the finished product."

They went through underground streets, lit by red electric lights, to the receiving warehouses, connected by a private line with the national railroad. The cars came up to the door of the warehouses, and the cranes lifted out the bales of wool and cotton, the barrels of dies, and machines. A line of workers moved the unloaded goods forward swiftly.

From the receiving warehouses Max Ashkenazi led the visitors to the boiler-rooms. The doors of the ovens stood open, and an incandescent glow lit up the faces of the half-naked stokers who fed the coal into the flames. From time to time inspectors checked the thermometers and pressure-gauges. The workers looked with astonishment at the procession of well-clad outsiders.

"Damned hot!" said one visitor, spitting, and moving away from the oven.

"Hey!" roared a foreman, "load her up!"

Max Ashkenazi smiled. This was not a bit like the little hand-loom factory in which he had made his start.

The visitors were glad to get out of the boiler-rooms to the weaving-rooms. Vast lengths of machines, lost in a blue haze, stretched before their eyes, floor after floor. The workers, mostly women, were stationed in front of the machines. Their chief occupation seemed to be knotting up threads which had snapped during the running of the loom. With swift, well-timed gestures they slipped off the empty spools and slipped on full ones. The gigantic hall shook with the rhythmic beat of the machines. The visitors watched in a dreamy fascination.

Max Ashkenazi put some questions to a worker. A visitor, watching the conversation and unable to hear a word of it, put his lips close to Ashkenazi's ear and shouted: "How can you carry on a conversation? I can't hear a word."

Max Ashkenazi put his lips to the visitor's ear. "You get used to it," he shouted, laughing.

From the weaving-rooms the group went through the washing, bleaching, and dyeing departments. Clouds of steam, laden with evil-smelling gases, assailed the visitors. The half-naked workers, in wooden clogs, clattered over the stone floors. "Let's get out of here, Mr. Director," gasped one of the visitors. Max Ashkenazi led them out into the clear, cold winter air, and they returned to the office.

All were now ready for the meeting. A messenger was sent to the adjoining Huntze palace for the three brothers, who arrived at last, sour-faced and ill-tempered. The eldest of them went to the head of the long, green-covered table to take his place there as was his habit. But at that instant Max Ashkenazi, already at the place of honour, pressed on the little bell, and announced:

"Gentlemen, I have the honour to inform you I am today the possessor of sixty per cent of the shares of the Huntze Manufacturing Company. According to the regulations, it is therefore my duty to take over the chairmanship of this meeting of the stockholders."

A deathly silence followed and all eyes were fixed on the Huntze brothers, from whom they were switched to Max Ashkenazi and then back again. Some sort of statement was expected from the Huntze brothers, but not a word came.

[459]

The silence continued, growing increasingly painful. The oldest brother, the one who had approached the chair at the head of the table, stepped back slowly. The silence was broken by Max Ashkenazi, who took his place before the chair, said crisply: "I hereby declare this meeting open," and sat down.

A German secretary, a sheaf of papers in his hand, approached Max Ashkenazi respectfully, with the words: "The agenda, Mr. President." Within half an hour the name "Mr. Director" as applied to Max Ashkenazi seemed to have been forgotten by everyone in the room.

The Huntze brothers did not sit out the meeting. They left early, in a body. By the same evening they had left the town, loathing it more than ever. And that same evening the presses of the Lodz newspapers were preparing the great news for the morning readers. But they might have spared themselves the trouble. There was hardly a restaurant, a café, a theatre, a synagogue, a workshop, or a home where the story of the new king of Lodz was not being repeated a hundred times.

$\mathfrak{I}n$ a luxurious, plush-upholstered car of the international Petersburg-Warsaw-Paris express sat Yakob Ashkenazi, director of the Flederbaum factory, and his young niece and wife, Gertrude. They had just left Lodz for their honeymoon, which they were to spend on the Riviera.

On the Polish side of the frontier the fields were covered with snow. The locomotive puffed joyously as it cut its way along the path cleared by the gangs of peasants in heavy fur coats. Through the clean, broad windows of the train the newlyweds looked at the broad fields, the telegraph poles, white on one side, the wires sagging under the weight of snow, the peasant huts almost snowed in, and the wayside crosses with their sacred images. Black crows were outlined against the faintly red glimmer of the heavens, harbingers of greater frosts.

"Gertrude," asked Yakob Ashkenazi suddenly, playing with the ringlets of her hair, "did you remember to pack your bathing-suit?"

"Bathing-suit?" exclaimed Gertrude, fixing astonished eyes on her husband.

"Why, yes. In two days we shall be bathing in the Mediterranean."

The look of astonishment changed to one of radiant joy. "Oh, Yakob, what a marvellous world this is! A month of winter among palm-trees in sunlight. . . . And it's the first time I've gone out of Poland. Yakob, are you happy?"

"Of course I am."

"Ah, you're not as happy as I," said the young woman, snuggling up to him. "A man can't be as happy as a woman. He hasn't the same feelings." She covered his lips, his hands, his eyes with kisses. "You bear!" she whispered. "You great, big, hairy bear. Crush me to death! Eat me up."

She loved him oppressively, tyrannically. She could not bear to let him out of her sight. She could not sit patiently by when he left the carriage to smoke a cigar or to exchange a few words with another passenger. Even in the dining-car she insisted on sitting next to him, rather than opposite him, so that she might press against him, throw her arms round him, and whisper into his ear.

"Gertrude, behave yourself," murmured Yakob. "People are looking."

"I won't behave," she answered. "What do I care, as long as I've got you?"

In the train, speeding across frontiers, rushing through the night, they drained the cup of their happiness. In an ecstasy of submission Gertrude fell at the feet of her husband and clung to them with a gesture of slavishness. "My prince, my king, my ruler!" she cried to him.

In the darkness of night, across a snow-covered field on the edge of a frozen lake, Nissan Eibeschutz, in the company of two frontier smugglers, dragged his heavy valise. He was stealing out of Russian into German territory.

This Nissan Eibeschutz was no longer the little local agitator that he had been years before. He was a man high in the councils of the Tseka. He was leaving Russia secretly in order to attend an international conference of the revolutionaries, and throughout the dangers he was courting, the bitter physical discomforts he was enduring, no thought of his own fate and condition occurred to him. It was for the sake of the movement that he entrusted himself into the keeping of the two ruffians who were conducting him hastily through the frozen fields and for the sake of humanity that he flung himself into the snow every time he thought he heard a suspicious sound behind him.

[462]

"Make it faster," muttered his guides. "We've got to get to the other side of that lake."

In the cold city of Lodz the snow was trampled into mud as fast as it fell; only around the enormous palace which had once belonged to the Huntze brothers and was now the residence of Max Ashkenazi, king of Lodz industrialists, and his wife, the former widow Margulies, it lay in dirty, frozen patches.

They were gone, the Huntzes, and this time for good. They had hated Lodz all their lives; they had hated it while their father was living, and they had continued to hate it after they had inherited the immense factory. They had lived abroad always, tearing themselves away reluctantly from their pleasures only once a year, when they had to attend the meeting of the stockholders. They had severed long ago whatever social connections they had once had in the vicinity, and the palace they had inherited together with the factory had stood empty, except for its servants. With its immense complement of lackeys, gardeners, carriages, and maids, it had served them as a symbol of pride; they were able, during their brief visits, to inhabit as their own the most pretentious home in the province. Now, with control of the factory in the hands of the Jew Max Ashkenazi—that same fantastic little person who had once come crawling to them to offer his services—they saw no sense in ever seeing the filthy city again. They had nothing in common any longer, they agreed among themselves, with this disgusting Polish-Jewish pigsty. They wanted to sever the last connections with it—the stocks which they still possessed, and the palace. They offered both to Max Ashkenazi, and Max Ashkenazi bought them both.

He did not need the palace; he did not need the carriages, the lackeys, the footmen, and the servants. But he wanted them in order to round out his position as the king of industrialists. Factory and palace went together, and he could not tolerate the idea of another than himself living in the palace. He therefore took it over exactly as it stood, with its furniture, its statues, its bronzes, its pictures, its crockery and cut-

[463]

lery, its hunting trophies and carriages and servants. He even kept the baronial coat of arms.

In this vast, oppressive building they lived alone, he and his second wife.

Alone with her he sat at the enormous dining-table, built to accommodate dozens. The massive oaken walls, the solid side-pieces, the complicated candelabra, the pictures of slaughtered animals, stared at them. Max Ashkenazi looked smaller than ever in the midst of this grandeur. The butler, in short coat and velveteens, brought in the glittering dishes and the wines with ritual-like precision and placed them before the silent pair. Neither Max Ashkenazi nor his wife had any pleasure in these foreign foods, these fowls and vegetables and sauces. They had no liking for the aristocratic wines. The butler took away from the table almost as much as he brought to it. Wordless and majestic, he seemed to feel how alien was all this splendour to the elderly man and woman facing each other across the vast table; so did the huge wolf-hound, another reminder of old times, sprawling quietly on the hearth and looking with half-closed, bored eyes at his new masters.

It had not taken the wolf-hound long to find out that these strangers at the table were not interested in him. They did not pet him; they did not scratch him behind the ears. In fact, they seemed to be afraid of him and avoided him. He had tried several times to lick the woman's hand, to show her that he was ready to transfer all his fidelity and affection to her, but she had started away from him and wiped her hand. In the same way, when he laid himself at the feet of the man, the latter got up and went to another chair. He learned, therefore, to keep away from the dining-table, and he sprawled on the skin before the hearth, merely watching. Then when the woman, relenting, put on the floor a plateful of leavings and called to him, he refused to get up. He was well enough fed and it was not food that he needed.

"Unfriendly brute," she said to her husband. "I don't know what we want him around here for."

"Let him be," said Max Ashkenazi, quietly, though he would have been glad to be rid of the dog. Somehow the dog, too, was part of it all, one of the necessary details in the perfection of his, Max Ashkenazi's, acquisition and triumph.

The meals were long and dreary. The butler refused to be hurried, and Max Ashkenazi longed to be out of the place, back in the factory, where he belonged. He was more at home giving orders to subordinates than with these stately servants and their complicated, frosty ceremonial. He had not the courage to get up from the table before the butler brought in the box of Havana cigars. Then he rose, excused himself hastily, and fled to his office, where he breathed freely again.

Even longer and drearier were the nights.

Madame Ashkenazi's maid worked long every night to prepare her mistress for bed. She combed and plaited the thin, greying locks of the elderly woman. She washed with perfumed water the hard, heavy body and rubbed salves into the brown, tough skin. She massaged the mannish hands. She laid out soft, clinging, costly nightgowns and heaped the broad, comfortable Louis Quinze bed with cushions. Very inviting it looked by itself, but not all the perfumes and creams and laces used in the preparation of Madame Ashkenazi could disguise her years or make her attractive. A chill seemed to emanate from the formless body and from the greying, perfumed locks. Whenever she moved, the folds of her flesh and of her double chin trembled like jelly, and the bed creaked under her.

"Max," she called to her husband, "why don't you come to bed?"

She tried to put some softness into these few words, but they issued heavily from the thick throat. Max Ashkenazi felt as if a cold wind had swept through all his flesh. He glanced up at the picture hanging above the bed, a naked girl fleeing from a goat-footed satyr, and he suddenly remembered Dinah, his divorced wife. She had been slender, too, and her head had been covered with the same brown ringlets.

Heavy-footed, like a man mounting a scaffold rather than a bridegroom approaching a bride, Max Ashkenazi approached the bed with the silk coverlet half turned down.

He slept badly in the big, comfortable bed. All night long he heard the chiming of the innumerable clocks in the Huntze palace. Slowly, musically, and with stately insistence, as if participating in a religious ritual, they counted the hours. The cushions under Max Ashkenazi bulged, as if stuffed with stones. Whichever way he turned he was uncomfortable. Finally he rose and put on his dressing-gown.

He picked up a candlestick and stepped softly out of the room. Interminable the halls stretched in front of him. The horns of the countless hunting trophies glowered down at him in the half-darkness. Swords and spears and creeses, a deadly array, fantastically un-Jewish, threw back the light of the candle. Into Max Ashkenazi's mind came fables and stories learned in his boyhood and almost forgotten, stories of murders, of the torturing of Jews, stories of the bloody pogroms of the days of Chmielnicki, stories of autos-da-fé in Spain, stories of heroic Jews who had died for the sake of the Holy Name.

He hurried on among the ponderous and costly pieces of furniture, between rows of pictures always with the same themes: the hunt, wild animals, bloodshed, knights, hunting dogs, wild boars, bears, lances. In other rooms naked nymphs, satyrs, drunken Bacchuses. All were his! How strange that was! What had they to do with him, with this little Jew in the dressing-gown, holding up the candle and staring bewildered on all sides of him?

He went into the dining-room, with its brown oak walls and carved beams. Wine stood on the sideboard, but he did not go near it, though he had a bitter taste in his mouth. Instead he sank into an armchair. The wolf-hound, asleep on the skin before the fireplace, started slightly, opened its eyes for a moment, yawned, and fell back to sleep.

Ashkenazi could not rid himself of the thought of Dinah. Where was she now? What was she doing? He began to recall moments in their life together. He wondered whether she would marry again. Then, becoming his practical self again, he tried to thrust her from his mind. They were done with each other. They were divorced. He had paid her out a great deal more than the dowry which she had brought him. Everything was over. These were useless, pointless thoughts. But they returned, in spite of him. He continued to think of Dinah and of the children.

[466]

Ignatz was in Paris. He was a man now. What did he look like? He was not an Ashkenazi; nothing of the Ashkenazi mind—all Chaim Alter. Still, Max Ashkenazi could not help feeling that he would like to see this son of his. And then Gertrude. Ah, she had behaved badly toward him, more so even than his son. She had not consulted him even once about this life on which she had now entered. She had gone off! And with whom? With that worthless, witless, characterless rake, his brother, who was more than twice as old as she. Why had she done it? Because she was as bad as he. She could have married decently. She could have had a handsome dowry and got herself a worth-while husband of her own age. She had preferred the elderly roué Yakob Ashkenazi. And now she was on her way with him to their honeymoon in southern France. This much he had learned from little Solly Knaster.

A spasm of rage and hatred contracted his heart. How did this Jacob Bunim, this nobody, always manage to do so well by himself? How had he managed to ensnare this young and beautiful girl? Did he love her? Or was it done out of spite, out of hatred of his brother Max? And how characteristic of him to leave his business in the thick of the season in order to spend a month with his new wife on the Riviera! That was Jacob Bunim all over. He had always been stupid and irresponsible, and he always would be. And he was bound to end badly. For this streak of luck could not last forever. No, he would not always find women to push him. Women always! First Kalman Eisen's daughter had given him a big start in life and had helped him through crisis after crisis. She dropped out. Then came Flederbaum's daughter, who had made him director of the factory. She had left him too. This time it was Gertrude: the brother had become a son-in-law! How loathsome! How beastly! And probably Yakob was laughing at him. She too! It was ghastly. No honour anywhere, no decency, no kindness.

A small, shrunken figure, he cowered in the big armchair. The vast palace stretched on all sides of him. The clocks continued to chime out the hours with multiple melodies. The bronze Mephistopheles on a pedestal in a corner of the room grinned down at him.

[467]

Book Three

Over the shattered asphalt of the roads leading from Germany into Poland, through forests and townlets and villages laid waste by the World War, rolled a long procession of German cavalry, infantry trucks, wagons loaded with civilians, and heavy mounted guns. The Polish peasants came out of their straw-covered huts, shaded their eyes with their hands, and gazed dumbly at the strange vehicles and the strange riders. The peasant women with coloured kerchiefs on their heads cowered frightened against the latticed fences and crossed themselves piously. The flaxen-haired children and the village dogs received the invaders with a noisy shouting and barking.

In the little towns the Jews came out of their squat houses and gazed with astonishment in their black eyes at the newcomers. Boys in long, queer gaberdines and girls with shocks of black hair waved at the procession and called out greetings in Yiddish. Men came creeping out of the holes and cellars where they had hidden themselves from the Russian soldiers who, before their retreat, had wanted to take revenge on the Jews for the defeat they had suffered at the hands of the Germans. German colonists came down from the upper storeys of their windmills and ran to welcome their fellow-Teutons: "*Grüss Gott! Willkommen!*"

They came from Prussia and Saxony, from Bavaria and the Rhenish Provinces; they streamed into Poland from every part of Germany.

[471]

For in Germany there were many mouths to feed, and land was scarce, while in neighbouring Russia there was much land, fruitful fields, cattle, wood, and minerals. So the masters of Germany took men from the fields, factories, and workshops—putting women in their place—and shipped them into neighbouring Russia. They came, however, armed with steel and fire, as conquerors. Their first objective was Poland, which bordered on Germany.

Young and old they came, short-sighted city workers with spectacles, blond-bearded peasants, schoolboys with red cheeks and the first down of manhood on their lips, old men wrinkled and grey. The trucks and wagons of the invaders had painted on them the legend "To St. Petersburg." The soldiers wore hobnailed boots and helmets surmounted by glittering spikes; on the leather straps of their uniforms were printed the words: "God With Us." The bayonets on their rifles were double-edged. One edge was to cut the body of the enemy, the other to saw through barbed wire. Slowly and steadily the stream moved eastward, overwhelming village after village, town after town, city after city, by the Vistula and Varta rivers.

Behind the soldiers came chaplains in military uniforms and with crosses on their helmets. Their mission was to encourage the soldiers to slaughter and conquest in the name of God, and to help them plant the Protestant faith and the speech and folkways of the Germans on the conquered soil.

Soldiers in the prime of their manhood were few on the eastern front; those were needed in the west. Toward Russia the rulers of Germany sent mostly *Landstürmer*, elderly men whose fleshy bodies could hardly be contained by their uniforms. Before and behind, the massive bodies threatened to burst the leather straps; the spiked helmets sat crooked on the shaven heads with their thick neckfolds. Clumsy, stiff, and uncomfortable in their uniforms, these elderly men followed their officers like mediæval serfs following their baronial leader. Ragged, their boots worn to shreds by the impassable roads which the Russians had ripped up in their retreat, they sang, with cracked and hoarse voices, their songs of victory:

[472]

The Germans have a gun so wide
Twenty men can sleep inside,
And every time it fires a shell
It makes a noise as loud as hell.
>   With every ball
>   Ten Russians fall!
>   With every crack
>   Ten Frogs go smack!
And Papa Krupp will fix them all.

As the German army advanced, it reorganized the occupied
territory systematically. The ground was cleared of debris, the
roads were restored, the bridges rebuilt, the telegraph poles
reset, the fires extinguished, the rolling stock repaired. The
Germans cut down from the trees and the roadside gallows
the stiff corpses of the German colonists and the Jews whom
the Russians had hanged in the rage of their defeat. They
tore down the Russian proclamations from the walls and
fences, and in their place pasted German proclamations calling
on the population to submit to its new rulers, to surrender
all weapons, denounce all spies, and hand in immediately a
statement of all its possessions, in particular grain, cattle,
potatoes, cloth, copper, brass, and all raw materials. Disobedience would be dealt with summarily by courts martial.

The great city and centre, the warehouse of incalculable
quantities of material, on which the Germans had their eye,
was Lodz. Toward that point the armies thrust forward obstinately, step by step, mile by mile.

The military governors set over captured cities in this
territory were almost invariably East Prussian aristocrats, who
were more or less acquainted with the Poles and their ways.
When Lodz was occupied the military Governor appointed
by the high command was Baron von Heidel-Heidellau, the
penniless East Prussian landowner who had married one of
the daughters of Heinz Huntze. To Heidel-Heidellau the
war was a godsend. In peace times his aristocratic connections
and his intimate acquaintance with the highest officers in the
German army had been of little use to him; with his friends

[473]

in the saddle, however, he found a career open to him. From an obscure captain of reserve he rose rapidly to a colonelcy, and as the husband of a native of Lodz he was considered the right man for the governorship of that city. Besides, as the successive commandant of a number of smaller towns occupied during the advance of the German army, he had shown himself such a ruthless administrator, and had thrown the Polish population into such a state of terror, that his superiors had conceived a high opinion of him.

During the early days of the war the attitude of the Poles toward Germany and the Germans had been mostly hostile. Soon after the outbreak of hostilities, when the German armies had begun to pour over Poland, the Tsar had issued a proclamation promising the Polish people independence if it would help in driving out the invader. In every Polish town and village the Imperial decree of liberation was posted up and attracted eager crowds. The Polish masses took the promise at its face value. Polish nationalists felt that their hour had struck, and they therefore issued fiery appeals to the manhood of Poland to enlist in the Russian Polish legions organized by the Russian government. Side by side with this resurgence of Polish national passion there was a tremendous wave of hatred against the Jews, who were everywhere denounced as the friends of Germany, as spies and traitors in her pay.

All sorts of stories and rumours concerning the Jews were concocted and spread by word of mouth or printed in the patriotic Polish newspapers. It was asserted that the Jews hid diamonds in their beards and smuggled them out of Polish into occupied territory. Jewish funerals conducted, not corpses, but consignments of gold. Most active among those who spread these rumours were the Polish shopkeepers, who saw an opportunity of getting rid of their Jewish competitors. The Russian command listened eagerly to these stories. Jews were arrested by the thousand, hanged on improvised gallows, flung into prison, or exiled to Siberia. In the villages, where the Polish peasants had their own special quarrels with the more affluent German colonists, it was the latter who became the victims of the new conspiracy. Of them it was

[474]

reported that they had worked out a system of signals with the wings of their windmills and regularly relayed military information to the German army. The Russian command, which suffered one defeat after another, was only too ready to find a scapegoat, whether Jewish or German. So it was that Jews and Germans trembled in their houses as long as the Russians commanded the territory.

But when the Germans occupied the country, the condition of the Jews did not improve. It so happened that in one of the smaller towns captured by the German army there was more than the usual resistance, and shots were fired from one of the houses on the advance patrols. Baron von Heidel-Heidellau, in charge of the district, decided to teach the population a lesson which would be remembered for ever. He set fire not only to the offending town, but to several surrounding villages, so as to make sure that the flames would be visible over the entire province. In the city of Kalisz another untoward incident took place. The deaf and dumb water-carrier was challenged by a soldier at a street-corner and, naturally, hearing nothing, continued to walk on. The *Landstürmer* shot him down. Thereupon several passers-by raised an outcry that the man was deaf and dumb. The *Landstürmer*, understanding not a word of the outcry, promptly fired into the crowd. A young drayman picked up a stone, threw it at the soldier, and caught him in the head. With blood streaming from his wound, the soldier was led back to the headquarters outside the town, and broke in on Baron von Heidel-Heidellau while the latter was sitting at his noonday meal. The Baron drank down his beer, wiped his lips, and then ordered the alarm to be sounded. When the troops were assembled he ordered Major Frösker to bombard the town. Houses began to collapse, fire broke out at several points, people fled through the streets in a lunatic panic. The heads of the community came running to the Baron and threw themselves at his feet. It was of no avail. As the inhabitants fled from the burning streets they were shot down systematically by the Germans. All night long the houses blazed. Corpses of men, women, and children lay by the hundred in the streets. The flames proclaimed far and wide, to Jews and Poles, the "revenge" of

[475]

the Germans. The example was effective. Thereafter the Germans had no trouble.

Baron von Heidel-Heidellau's prompt action was highly praised by the Commander-in-Chief of the eastern armies. He was awarded the iron cross and, shortly thereafter, placed in charge of the city from which he had taken a wife.

When Lodz had been occupied by the army, he arrived, with his adjutants, his baggage, and his hunting dogs in the city which he had so loathed in years past. The police commissioner's headquarters had been cleared out and prepared for him. Von Heidel-Heidellau's adjutant, a young lieutenant with the red cheeks of a girl and the brutal manners and impulses of a Junker, met him at the door, and, drawing himself rigidly to attention, reported that the house had been searched from top to bottom for explosive material, and none had been found. But von Heidel-Heidellau cast a hasty and contemptuous glance around him through his monocle and slapped his glove against the door-post.

"I won't stay a moment in this pigsty," he snarled. His nose wrinkled, as though assailed by an intolerable stink. "Give me the map of the town!"

When the map was produced he put it under his adjutant's nose.

"Here, look at this, lieutenant," he said, curtly. "Do you see this street? There's a big factory there, and a palace near by. A Jew lives in that palace. I'm going to live there, you understand."

"*Ja wohl*, colonel," answered the lieutenant, clicking his heels and looking fearfully into his commanding officer's face.

The Baron lowered his voice suddenly and spoke out of the corner of his mouth. "The requisitioning of private homes isn't exactly in form during the first days of an occupation," he said, "unless there's a special reason. For instance, if someone fired a shot from the house, you understand."

"*Ja wohl*, colonel," answered the adjutant.

"Good. How do you reckon to manage it?" asked the Baron, shooting a glance sideways at the adjutant.

"I'll take a squad into the street, colonel, and institute an inquiry. And if it happens that any shots were fired from that house, then I'll—"

"Lieutenant," snapped the colonel, "you're a first-class idiot. It doesn't matter a damn to me whether shots were fired from that house or not. If there wasn't any shooting, there should have been. All that matters to me is to have the palace requisitioned. Is it beginning to penetrate?"

"*Ja wohl*, colonel," answered the lieutenant, blushing like a village girl.

"And I want the house cleaned out, so that there's no stink of Jewish garlic in the corners. I'd like to sleep there tonight. Is that clear?"

"Yes, colonel!" The adjutant saluted and clicked his heels.

When the adjutant, at the head of a squad of armed men, burst into the palace, they did not find the owner at home. Max Ashkenazi was in Russia. Day after day he had delayed his return, while the German armies drew nearer and nearer. To his wife's frantic telegrams he had invariably replied: "Frightfully busy! Coming soon!" And then suddenly it was too late. Lodz was occupied, a wall of steel separated the province from Russia, and the wife of Max Ashkenazi, the former widow Margulies, found herself utterly alone in the world. Friends she had none in Lodz. All her connections were in Russia. Here, in the city of her husband, she was surrounded by strangers, and there was no way of getting word to Max Ashkenazi. Lonely and frightened and filled with foreboding, she had watched the approach of the Germans. And now they were here! In her very home!

Pale and trembling, she faced the young adjutant. "What has happened?" she stammered.

"Are you the owner of this house?" asked the lieutenant harshly.

"Yes, sir."

"You are under arrest."

He said nothing further. A soldier was detailed to watch the old woman, while the lieutenant conducted the squad through the rooms. They found nothing except a few rusty swords and some old hunting guns which the Huntzes had

[477]

left behind. The lieutenant drew up a long report, in which he stated explicitly that someone had fired from this house on passing German troops. The report was then read forth sternly to Madame Ashkenazi, who was subjected to a severe cross-examination.

Her cheeks flaming, her voice choked with fright and resentment, the old woman protested that it was impossible. No one could have shot from the house. There was nothing to shoot with. There was no ammunition in the house.

The young lieutenant worked himself into a fury, as he had so often seen his commanding officer do.

"Do you dare to assert," he yelled, "that my soldiers are lying? Consider yourself lucky that you aren't put before a firing squad. You are free. You may leave the house."

The old woman wrung her hands.

"But you won't put me out on the street, in God's name!" she wept.

"The house is requisitioned," said the lieutenant, savagely.

A guard was stationed at the door. The German flag was draped over the Huntze coat of arms on the gates, and a placard was put up: "Requisitioned." In a daze Madame Ashkenazi powdered her face to cover the feverish red spots, seized an umbrella, and went out into the street, as if she intended to assault someone. She found a droshky and asked to be driven to the army headquarters. By sheer force of will she broke through as far as von Heidel-Heidellau's office, but that was as far as she got. She was ejected from headquarters and told to go wherever she liked.

That same evening a lustrous automobile brought von Heidel-Heidellau to the Huntze palace. A grin of satisfaction spread over his features as he mounted the marble steps, listening perfunctorily to the report of his adjutant. "Excellent!" he muttered. "Excellent!" The doors were flung open for him, and he strode in like a conqueror.

A feeling of triumph, a sense of regal power, swept through him. Standing before a full-length mirror, gazing on his long, military figure, on the resplendent uniform, on the dazzling spiked helmet, he could not help comparing himself with

[478]

a Roman proconsul of old taking possession of the palace of a barbarian. It was the helmet, with the leather strap fitting snugly round his chin, he decided, which put the finishing touch on the resemblance. But the deeper source lay in his own masterful self.

A magnificent dinner had been prepared for the Baron. The cook had outdone himself, happy to be practising his art once more for someone who would appreciate it. The German butler fussily wiped the cobwebs from a bottle of wine. The Baron drank thirstily.

"From Baron Huntze's old stock, Excellency," murmured the butler.

"Take this damned sword off," commanded von Heidel-Heidellau.

Freed from his sword, the Baron flung himself into a chair. "And my boots!"

The butler knelt and pulled, but the boots stuck fast. The Baron swore and kicked the kneeling butler. "Clumsy idiot!" he growled.

The butler, too, was happy. After all these years in the service of a Jew who had no demands and who did not know how to treat a servant, it felt good to submit again to a real master.

The Baron ate and drank with noisy gusto and kept staring about him with relish at every detail of the immense dining-room. The meat and wine acquired a peculiarly delicious taste as he reflected on his position; there was something indescribably pleasant to be eating and drinking, precisely in this place, at the expense of the conquered, and every morsel of food, every gulp of wine, tickled his pride and his sense of power. He ate ferociously, reverting to ancestral type, and retasting the ferocious happiness of the robber barons from whom he was descended.

After he had rested from the heavy meal, sprawling in a chair, he made ready for his bath, but when he had undressed, and was stripped of his uniform and his helmet, he looked singularly unmilitary and unimperial. The servant who helped him saw half the man he had seen before. The Baron was old; his skin was wrinkled; the blue veins stood out like

[479]

ridges on his shrivelled legs, his aged belly sagged, and he trembled as he stood under the shower. There was nothing Roman about him then. He looked rather like an ancient rooster plucked of most of his feathers.

The Baron felt the difference, and hated the manservant who could see him at that moment.

"Faster, you fool," he yelled, as the man rubbed his brown, flapping skin with a sponge.

Covered up in the Louis Quinze bed, a heap of silk-covered cushions under him, he felt better again. He sent for the young adjutant, the lieutenant with the rosy cheeks of a village girl, and asked for the day's report.

The adjutant stood close by the bed and read out the most important news of the day, together with a digest of events in the occupied town. Then he handed his commanding officer a list of the death-sentences pronounced by the court martial. There had been a few cases of resistance; a few men were suspected of being Russian spies. The Baron looked at the list, but he did not bother to read the individual names. He asked for a pen and affixed his signature. His mind was not on his business.

"Sit down here, lieutenant."

The adjutant sat down timidly on the edge of the bed. The Baron took his hand, drew the lieutenant closer to him, and began to stroke his cheek.

"What a sweet-looking boy you are!" he whispered, forming the words queerly in his old mouth, from which he had removed his teeth for the night.

The young officer blushed to the roots of his hair.

"Oh, no, please, colonel," he murmured.

The Baron smiled and drew him closer. He felt again like a Roman patrician. . . .

Max Ashkenazi had acted with more than his usual foresight.

Soon after the outbreak of the war, when the German armies had begun to pour into Poland, he had come to the important decision that Lodz had to be moved into St. Petersburg—now known as Petrograd.

There were many reasons for this decision, reasons immediate and remote. In the first place, the Russian Government had removed its banks from Poland into the interior of Russia. Gold was no longer in circulation, but even Russian notes were no longer issued by the Polish banks to their depositors. Max Ashkenazi had not only considerable cash deposits in the banks, but papers of all kinds, stocks and bonds and notes which would be of no use to him if he remained in Poland, cut off from Russia. In the second place, he knew that if Lodz was separated from the Russian hinterland, it was done for. Its markets lay to the east, not the west. Lodz could do nothing as part of German territory. The Germans had all the technical development they needed. It was primitive Russia that had used and could use Lodz. And then, on general grounds, it was hard to do business with Germans. They were not generous and careless, like the big-souled Russians. They clung to their money. If there was a mark or a rouble to be earned, they would do the earning. A man like himself, an industrialist and organizer, had a place in Russia; in Germany he would be competing with men as good or better.

It was no trifling enterprise. The railroads were being used in those days almost exclusively for soldiers and munitions, and when Ashkenazi made his first shipments of raw material from his warehouses into the interior of Russia he had to have them labelled as munitions—a device which was suggested by the Russian military commander of Lodz after Ashkenazi had stimulated his ingenuity by a fat bribe. Later part of the machinery was crated, and that too was shipped into Russia, but then he was interrupted by the first German occupation of Lodz. There were three such occupations, the last one being permanent, and in between the occupations Max Ashkenazi worked with demonic energy and persistence at the transference of his business into Russia. But the task became increasingly difficult as the backward and forward movement of armies and demoralized civilian population reduced the last remnants of organized transportation to a state of complete insanity. Whatever could be done Max Ashkenazi did. He argued with governors, generals, and railroad directors; he pointed out the patriotic character of his enterprise—he was moving beyond reach of the advancing enemy Russia's most necessary life-source, her industry. He backed arguments with bribes, and bribes with compliments. He worked day and night, multiplying himself by sheer persistence of effort. But in the end one half of his machinery and a good portion of his raw material were left behind in Lodz. Before the third German occupation of that city Max Ashkenazi was informed by high Russian officers that this time the Germans were coming to stay. Max Ashkenazi accepted the situation. He was not going to remain under German rule. He had no more faith in Lodz. He was casting in his lot with Russia.

On Russian railroad sidings, in stations, depots, and warehouses, huge crates of machinery lay rusting. Others than Max Ashkenazi had by now seized on the idea of transporting their industries into Russia. But having begun later than Ashkenazi, they were far behind him in their preparations. In the crazy disorganization of the railroads, and particularly during the last mad evacuation of Lodz, most of these men had lost track completely of their shipments. Mechanical looms, boilers, spare parts, odds and ends of their factories were scattered over a huge area between Lodz and Petrograd. Max

Ashkenazi was the only one who had retained a working picture of the situation, and he flew like one possessed between Petrograd and the depots, dragging together what was left of his factory, to reconstruct it in the heart of the Russian capital. Dressed in a huge sable coat, which gave him the aspect of a Russian, he fought and bought his way into chancelleries and ministerial offices, armed himself with all sorts of special permits and orders, flung money right and left, and advanced with patient fury toward his objective.

The chaos on the Russian railroads during that period was the result of a complete moral as well as physical collapse. As the Germans advanced deeper and deeper into Poland, the superficial Russian overlordship of one hundred years crumbled and disappeared. There was a wild, cowardly flight eastward. Thousands of officials, from governors to assistant clerks, thousands of churchmen, from archimandrites to bell-ringers, were in the panicky, fleeing mob. The crawling trains were jammed with Russian judges, police commissioners, Orthodox nuns, censers, merchants, executioners, teachers, monks, gendarmes, frontier officials, with their wives and children, their clothes and furniture, their bankbooks and ikons, their archives and Church treasures and Tsarist flags.

In hospital trains and trucks the wounded were moved by thousands and tens of thousands, and at every station the dead were carried out so that their filthy straw beds could be occupied by others. Prisoners of war, packed in like chickens, filled other trains: Austrians mostly, on their way to Siberia. From all the Polish prisons a stream of convicts and revolutionaries poured eastward too, and with them were mingled peasants who had been arrested for showing the road to German troops, shepherds accused of signalling to the enemy with whipcracks, and many other varieties of spies and traitors, real and fancied. Old and young travelled, women and children, simple-witted peasant boys and city labourers, German colonists, Ruthenian peasants, Galician Jews with pious earlocks, priests, rabbis, sextons, grave-diggers, apaches, deserters —all in one pullulating evil-smelling mass, every car under a convoy. Many of them had not the remotest idea why they had been arrested, nor was anyone able to tell them. There were

[483]

no records obtainable about them. All they knew was that they were under arrest.

Most miserable in this flood of refugees and prisoners were the expelled Jews. To cover his hopeless incompetence and distract attention from the smashing defeats which came upon him, one after the other, Grand Duke Nikolai Nikolaievitch had instituted a series of mass expulsions against the Jews of Poland. Entire districts were set in motion; bands of Cossacks appeared in Jewish towns and villages and drove the population out in herds, setting fire to the homes and the shops to make sure the refugees had nothing to return to. Sometimes these communities moved out on foot, carrying their scrolls of the Law, their Sabbath candlesticks, and the remnants of their household goods in bundles; sometimes they were loaded on to railroad cars on which appeared the famous legend: "Eight Horses or Forty Men." But as a rule the number of persons squeezed into these rolling prisons was nearer a hundred. Cut off from all help, starving, unwashed, these Jewish communities and fragments of communities were hunted from one part of Russia to another under armed military guard. The soldiers tortured their charges, spat on them, and treated them like spies. For days at a time the prisoners were not permitted to leave the cars; they could not get off at stations to obtain a little warm water to wash with, or call a doctor for the sick, or even to satisfy the demands of nature. In the midst of this hunger and filth, diphtheria, cholera, and scarlet fever broke out.

Here and there, when the convoys reached a town with a larger Jewish population, some sort of relief was organized for the refugees. Committees came to the railroad station with food for the living and shrouds for the dead.

At such stations and depots, in the midst of the indescribable confusion and misery, Max Ashkenazi and his agents were always to be found, inquiring, seeking, hunting out the lost and mislaid shipments of the goods and machinery of the Huntze factory. While the sick and the dying were being carried past him, while disease and hunger and chaos had descended on the world, he pursued with fantastic resolution his one obsession—the gathering together of his organiza-.

[484]

tion, and its reconstruction in Petrograd. And he was successful. While the rest of the world had lost its bearings, this man in the big Russian sables advanced steadily toward his objective, and with the war in full swing opened his factories in St. Petersburg and began to deliver fabrics to the Russian army.

His achievement became a legend. The Quartermaster General, who placed the orders with him, was astounded.

"Max Abramovitch," he asked, "how the devil did you manage to get the thing going? We military men have been quite unable to disentangle ourselves."

"Will and energy, Your Excellency," answered Max Ashkenazi.

"It mightn't be a bad idea to put you on the General Staff," said the Quartermaster, half jesting, and sighing deeply several times. "Ah, Russia, Russia, the devil take you! . . ."

Just as in the old days Max Ashkenazi, operating now in the Russian capital, gathered together the refugee manufacturers of Lodz and founded a corporation. He needed all these men and whatever they had been able to rescue from the ruins of their native city. On Viborg Island in St. Petersburg rose the new Lodz-in-Petrograd, with Max Ashkenazi as the uncrowned king. It was he who directed production, obtained orders, arranged deliveries, fixed prices, and gathered in most of the profits. His best customer was, of course, the army, which, unlike private buyers, did not worry about cost and was ready to let a man earn something in exchange for a little consideration.

The factories worked seven days in the week, in three shifts. Raw material was brought all the way from Turkestan. Foreseeing a shortage of machines and spare parts, Max Ashkenazi sent men through the Russian cities to buy up old machinery which could be converted to his purposes. Price was no object, for there seemed to be no limit to the profits. "Lodz" grew by leaps and bounds.

"Gentlemen," said Max Ashkenazi to a meeting of his partners, "I am going to make of this new 'Lodz' something that the old Lodz never dreamed of. When I told the ministers and generals that I would transfer the industrial centre of

[485]

Russia from Poland to the heart of Russia, I was laughed at. I've done it. But this is only a beginning. We are in Russia now, and not in Poland."

The Jewish refugees of Lodz who had managed to find a foothold in Petrograd discovered among themselves a community feeling which they had not been aware of in the old days. They formed a separate colony; they met in their own cafés and restaurants to exchange whatever news was obtainable about their home town and to read out the infrequent letters which, by way of the Red Cross and Switzerland, managed to get through to them after months of delay. A Lodz Association was formed, with its own headquarters, where, on a free Saturday, the members would gather for prayers, and where a carnival ball was held now and again. Collections were made, too, for stranded Lodz refugees, wherever they might be in Russia. Meetings were held, community affairs settled, officials elected with the usual oratory; and everywhere Max Ashkenazi was busy—the leader of Lodz-on-the-Neva.

But he did not neglect his Russian connections; indeed, he spent as much time with Russian officials and officers as with his fellow-refugees. As in the old days, he frequented cafés, cabarets, and flashy restaurants, not for the sake of the food, the entertainment, and the women, for none of which he had any use, but for the sake of the men who could be useful to him. He ate little, drank not at all, had no interest in the women. He loathed the beastliness of the high officers to whom he had to cater; he despised them when, in their fits of drunkenness, they took to smashing the furniture or fighting among themselves. He did his best to hide his contempt; he spent money freely, pretended to lose it at cards, praised the Russians for their great-heartedness, and waited for the opportunity to gather in his army contracts. There was no other way, in those days, of getting orders.

When he left this dissolute crowd and returned to his office, near the new factories, he breathed freely. His outward humiliations left no inner scar. He was himself. Whatever he did was subservient to one aim, the acquisition of power, the concentration of wealth in his own hands. It did not matter

[486]

whether he achieved his aim by toadying to corrupt officials and officers or by straightforward production and selling. Yes, he was definitely more at home in the factory, with the machines humming about him, with secretaries bringing reports, with customers who tried to outwit him. But in the last analysis, only results counted for him.

And these results he was achieving: in Petrograd, no less than once in Lodz, Max Ashkenazi was a power to be reckoned with.

Colonel von Heidel-Heidellau governed with a hand of iron the city of Lodz, "the Polish-Jewish pigsty" which he had learned to hate so thoroughly in the days when the daughter of Baron Huntze brought him home as her bridegroom. Day after day new orders and proclamations were posted up on the walls and shutters.

He turned his attention first to the streets, which he wanted to see as clean and orderly as those of a German city. The Polish militia, which was permitted to carry only clubs, occupied every corner and forbade the assembling of crowds, or even individual loitering. The Jews of Lodz found it hard to accustom themselves to this regulation. Ever since Lodz had become Lodz and Piotrkov Street had been Piotrkov Street, the Jews had loitered there in twos and threes, in knots and crowds, gesticulating with their little walking-sticks, buying, selling, and arguing. With chalk and pencil they had scribbled calculations on the walls and signs, on any empty and accessible space. The street was their market. To be driven from the streets was almost as bad as to be driven from home. At first the Jews refused to obey, or found it impossible. Moved on from one corner, they flowed together at another. The militia began to ply its clubs; on a few occasions a fire hose was trained on the illegal assembly. Willy-nilly the Jews of Lodz learned to obey.

Very hard, too, they found the regulation which made it an offence to let fall a scrap of paper or a cigarette butt in the

[488]

street. Spitting, too, was forbidden. Every day the inhabitants
of Lodz had to whitewash the deep gutters, tar the garbage
cans in the yards, and clean out the cesspools. Militiamen
prowled the poorest streets and alleys of Balut and seized old
Jews with beards and old Jewesses with wigs; these they led
off to the city baths, to give them a thorough cleaning. The old
men had their beards shaved; both they and the old women
had their heads cropped close. Their clothes were passed
through the disinfecting plant. But the more Baron von
Heidel-Heidellau washed and scrubbed the population, the
more fiercely raged the epidemics he sought to suppress:
typhoid, cholera, and scarlet fever.

For while Baron von Heidel-Heidellau cleaned the streets
of crowds and the back yards of cesspools, he also cleaned the
city of food and work and hope. The mills stood idle. The
chimneys lifted their blackened heads into the clear sky, emit-
ting not a wisp of smoke. The sirens were dumb. The workers
could now sleep late—they could sleep all day if they wanted
to and their empty bellies let them.

The first thing the Baron did was to send his *Landstürmer*
into the factories and remove all the transmission belts.

A delegation of the alarmed Lodz industrialists came in
stiff black clothes and white linen to the city commandant, to
point out to him—as if this elementary fact had escaped his
attention—that with the leather belts removed, the wheels
could not turn, the looms could not work, the factories could
not produce. The delegation was admitted to the Huntze-
Ashkenazi palace, where the Baron was installed. Yakob Ashkenazi was a member of the delegation, and in this wise got
his first glimpse of his brother's princely home. In the hum-
blest German he and his fellow-members of the delegation
pleaded with the Baron not to destroy the city and its industry, but to restore the transmission belts.

Baron von Heidel-Heidellau sprawled in the armchair and
stared through his monocle at the leaders of Lodz.

"I can't do a thing for you," he said curtly.

The delegation tried to touch a humane and social chord
in the heart of the Baron. They spoke of the workers, who
would have to starve if they could not be given work. The

[489]

Baron listened coldly. Then, when the delegation became more urgent, more insistent, he banged the table with his fist.

"Your workers are not my business," he shouted. "I have to think of my soldiers."

The transmission belts of the Lodz factories were made of thick leather of the best quality, and furnished thousands of German soldiers with excellent shoe-soles. Baron von Heidel-Heidellau's men stripped every factory in the city and suburbs, and carloads of leather were shipped into Germany. Next came the copper boilers, ovens, utensils, and parts. Copper was needed for the making of munitions. Nothing was too large or too small for the Baron's men. The tips of church spires, the seven-branched candelabra of synagogues, door-handles, the Sabbath pot of the Jewish housewives, the Friday night candlesticks. But the biggest yield came from the factories. The copper was followed by shipments of such machine parts as could be adapted to use in German factories. Day after day the Baron stripped from the city and its factories the essentials of its daily life.

Ashkenazi's factory led the way in contributions to the war needs of Germany. Whatever Ashkenazi had left behind, the Germans led out through the underground passages to the private railroad line: boilers, machines, bales of raw wool and cotton, crates of finished goods, corded wood from the near-by forest. Madame Ashkenazi protested in bad German mixed with Russia. Her folded umbrella grasped tightly in her hand, she tried again and again to reach the Baron. She never got past the door of her own palace.

For the machinery and goods removed from her factory, Madame Ashkenazi received German vouchers, payable after the war. Day after day she came to the factory, though there was nothing for her to do there except pick up the German vouchers and lock them in the iron safe. But there was nowhere else for her to go, in this city of strangers. She sat in her husband's office and passed the time by looking through old accounts. When night came she walked across the yard to the apartment which had once belonged to Albrecht and afterwards to Max Ashkenazi. She lay awake most of the night, waiting for the morning to come so that she could go back to

[490]

the office. Of all her servants there was left only one maid, who cleaned and cooked for her and at night prepared her for her bed, braiding her thin grey locks and tying them with silk ribbons, as on the nights when her husband had still been with her.

In Balut, among the hand-loom workers, it was almost as quiet as in the steam factories. Most of the looms stood idle and were covered with white sheets. Tailors, stocking-knitters, seamstresses, embroidery-workers, shoemakers, leather-workers—all covered their machines in a perpetual Sabbath. On the city which had once panted with feverish activity a dreadful calm descended, and the streets had the aspect of quiet lanes by country cemeteries. The Polish workers who had immigrated from the villages returned to their homes. The Jews, the city workers, wandered around pale-faced, their tongues dry in their mouths, their useless hands hanging down.

Lodz hungered. All the entrances to the city were guarded by soldiers in spiked helmets, who let nothing come in and nothing go out. They looked through the straw of the peasant carts for such contraband as a sack of grain, a chicken, a cheese, a handful of eggs, or a sack of butter. They passed their hands over every newcomer—man or woman—lest a piece of bread or meat or even a potato be moved from one place to another without their permission.

Everything—the grain in the fields, the potatoes stored in the cellars, the cattle in the sheds, the chickens in the coops, every new-laid egg, every pregnant sow—was marked and entered into the records. They requisitioned the fruit from the trees, the wool on the sheep, the grass on the meadows. They made holes in the non-fruit-bearing trees and drained them of their sap. They took the fowling-pieces from peasants and landlords, so that they might themselves hunt hares, rabbits, foxes, wild pigs, and wild geese. They requisitioned the nets of the fishermen, to do their own fishing. Even the homeless cats and dogs were hunted and skinned and the carcasses sent into Germany for the animals in the city zoos.

In addition to the *Landstürmer*, the officers, and the officials who day after day sent heavy packages of food to their

[491]

families in Germany, there came a host of civilians, thick, fleshy men in green mountaineering clothes, with feathers in their hats. With yellow protectors on their hobnailed shoes, to keep the soles from wearing out, they wandered through the villages, requisitioning, buying up wherever they had to buy, and paying next to nothing, cleaning out the land like a swarm of locusts. And while the wealth of Poland flowed out of the country into Germany, the population of Poland was fed meagrely, by the card. The bread which was distributed by measure was prepared according to formula. The bakers were closely controlled, and were compelled to mix ground chestnuts and potato-peelings into the dough, so that flour might be saved and sent into Germany. The bread was dry and heavy; it tasted like clay. It could not be digested, but lay like a load on the stomach. Children were made sick by it.

The rich were still able to get food from the army of smugglers who sprang up in the country, but for the poor there was no hope. They used up in the first week the bread-cards which were supposed to last them a month, and during the remaining weeks they wandered around feebly, with burning eyes and trembling limbs, living on offal and whatever they could beg. The cleanliness of the city could do nothing against the weakness induced by starvation, and while the Germans mowed the grain in the fields, death mowed the children in the city.

Never in all her life had Keile, the wife of Tevyeh the weaver, he who had always been known by the title of "Tevyeh the-world-isn't-coming-to-an-end," been as happy and as prosperous as during the time of the German occupation of Lodz.

She was making up in her old age for the misery and wretchedness and poverty of a long life. In the middle of the week she cooked great hunks of meat, and the smell of her pots was carried with the steam of them through the length and breadth of Pepper Street: grilled livers and broiled onions and fat soups were proclaimed far and wide. To Keile, wife of Tevyeh the weaver, came dozens of neighbours for a spoonful of flour, a potato, a piece of bread for a child; and Keile was generous; she gave freely.

No, it was not her husband, Tevyeh, who was filling her latter days with plenty and contentment. He was what he had always been. He still worried day and night about the state of public affairs; he still surrounded himself with young people, read revolutionary books, disappeared for days at a time, just as if he were a youngster himself, as if his close-cropped beard were not grey and his face wrinkled with age and suffering. In the palmy days of the growth of Lodz he had not been able to provide for Keile and his children; much less, then, could it be expected that in this time of want and evil he would blossom out as the great provider. For all that Tevyeh could do, Keile and her children might have lain down to die of hunger, or wandered through the streets with hands stretched out to passers-by. But Keile had a great God in heaven, keeping guard over her. It was true that her mad husband denied the existence of God and sneered at her pious practices—the separation of milk dishes from meat dishes, the lighting of the Sabbath candles, and all the hundred other laws of the Jewish housewife's ritual. But she had never paid any attention to him. Let him, she had said, go with that sort of talk to the young louts who were his companions. "They," she told Tevyeh, "may think you very clever. To me you're not worth the Rabbi's toe-nail. In my house the food will be kosher."

That much she had been able to insist on: no child of hers would swallow a spoonful of meat soup which had been defiled by contact with a milk dish. The Friday night benediction, which every pious Jew intones in the presence of the assembled family, was unknown in her poor house. She was herself incapable of substituting for her atheistical husband, for she could not read the prayers and did not know them by heart. Therefore on Friday nights she had been compelled to attend the benediction in the house of a neighbour, as if she had been a widow, God help her. But the laws of kosher food she had observed in all their severity; and she had taught her children to make the proper blessing before taking a mouthful of food; she had made them repeat the night prayer when they went to bed; she had taught them to kiss the mezuzah on the door when they came in and went out. One daughter of hers, it was true, had preferred to follow the evil ways of the father; Bashke had turned from God and God's commandments, and therefore she had been punished. She had been cut off in her youth. Her other children Keile had saved from Tevyeh's malevolent and godless influence. From their childhood on they had been taught to regard their father as a fool or a criminal, and when they grew up they refused to have anything to do with him. Some of them had left Lodz, had gone with their husbands to America. Others were still at home, and they were the source of their mother's prosperity.

Tevyeh's daughters were smugglers—among the most skilful and most successful in Lodz—and like the faithful children they were, they brought their earnings home to the mother

[494]

who had brought them up in decent ways. They no longer lived in a cellar, but had a whole apartment, with a kitchen, with gas and water, on the first floor of a house on Pepper Street. Keile, for the first time in her life, was able to dress decently; she had week-day clothes and Sabbath clothes. She wore on her head a handsome black wig, and carried herself with the dignity becoming the happy mother of a successful family. She had at last a house she could be proud of: new beds and new sideboards, photographs and pictures on the walls, blue crockery and plenty of cooking-utensils.

She knew that all this had come to her as a reward for her long and faithful service to the Lord. Was it not like Him, indeed, to defer payment till the moment when everything seemed utterly hopeless and all the world was in distress? The sinners reaped *their* reward, and Keile hers; they hungered and were naked, she feasted as never before, and lived in such a house as she could not have dreamed of in the days of Lodz's prosperity. Unable to read a holy book, Keile did not forget to deal kindly by her poor neighbours. She was able to drop fistfuls of copper coins into the collection-box of Rabbi Meir the Wonderworker, in whose saintly memory money was collected throughout the world to be sent to Palestine, where it was distributed among poor and pious Jews who studied the word of God night and day. Twenty times a day Keile paused before this box, and her thick lips murmured prayers to the great Rabbi of old, and to God in heaven, that the blessing which had come upon her house might continue for ever, and that her daughters might pass safely through the dangers of their daily work.

She had reason to pray. The Germans searched regularly even the poorest houses. Wherever they found a small store of food not explained by the rationing cards, they confiscated it; after two or three such confiscations the offender was thrown in prison. Keile's house was full of smuggled goods. Under the green covers of the high beds, inside the cushions, were sides of beef packed in straw; there were boxes of potatoes and heads of cabbage under the beds and behind the sideboards; sacks of flour hung between the clothes, and even behind the pictures on the walls there were packages of saccharine. All these stores were well enough hidden, and besides, Tevyeh's daughters and their bridegrooms had bribed a few minor officials among the Germans. But real safety lay only with the Lord, and therefore Keile's prayers never ceased, and every day the collection-box of Rabbi Meir the Wonderworker grew heavier with her offerings.

"For the sake of the kosher food which I have always served in this house," she murmured, "and for the sake of my gifts to the poor, I implore you to pray for me, Reb Meir, to protect me and my children and my house."

On week-days Keile's daughters were not at home. With peasant shawls drawn over their heads, with their boots on their feet, with sacks on their back, they wandered from village to village, buying up flour, meat, eggs, and vegetables. They did not travel by the open roads, which were guarded by the Germans, but by crooked and forlorn footpaths, and across muddy fields. At night, by secret paths, they stole back into the city, bent double under their loads, the sweat of weariness and fear pouring over their bodies.

Sometimes they had to spend the night in a farmer's barn; sometimes they were caught by a German, who threatened to take them before the local commandant. Then their only hope lay in bribery, or in a pitiful story, or in feminine appeal. Dreadful and dangerous work it was. But their reward was given them at the week-end, when they and their bridegrooms and their mother celebrated the Sabbath in happiness and plenty. Then the house was made clean, the floor was strewn with fresh yellow sand, the dishes were full, the pictures shone down from the wall, the tin candlesticks, which were left when the Germans took away all the copper, were scrubbed till they were brilliant. Pretty paper flowers were placed in the glass vases, and the blue crockery was ranged on the shelves. A velvet cloth, adorned with golden Hebrew letters and a Shield of David, covered the fresh-baked twisted loaves on the table. There was only one note of discord. Tevyeh, the father, still refused to make the Friday night benediction. But now, at least, Keile was not forced to go to a neighbour's house to hear the prayer said by a man. She had men of her own; or at least her daughters had, and they filled the house on Sabbaths and holy days; they even left their Sabbath clothes there, and their linen, so that they could come and change without having to go home.

Nor were these lean and starved weaver apprentices, but sturdy, broad-shouldered merry fellows, who wore short coats and high boots—smugglers, every one of them, good money-makers and free spenders. They were not embittered souls, like Tevyeh, and though they were not exactly pietists, but shaved their beards, carried money on the Sabbath, and even smoked secretly on that day, they did not refuse to say the Sabbath benediction when Keile handed them the beaker of wine, or to say the prayer over the white Sabbath bread. Give God His due, they said, and give people theirs. When they were all seated at table, the girls all washed and adorned, the young men in their Sabbath clothes, their faces bronzed with their work and shining with good humour, Keile felt her heart swell with happiness; her prayers redoubled, and her mind was filled with thoughts of serene years to come, of marriages and grandchildren and a ripe old age.

The house was gayest, however, on Sabbath afternoons, when Keile's daughters brought their girl friends in, and the bridegrooms their men friends. The furniture was pushed aside, and the couples danced. There was singing and laughter. Sometimes a German who helped in the smuggling was brought in; he would be shy at first in this strange company, but he soon felt himself at home, sang German songs, cursed his superior officers, and let the young men try on his military coat. Keile knew that at such times it was wiser for her to go out; young people liked to be alone. She sat then on the door-step with her neighbours, speaking about the potato famine or listening to the fortunate woman who was able to read out to the others from the Yiddish translation of the Pentateuch.

In his own house Tevyeh was a lost and lonely figure. His wife and daughters glanced away from him, looked at each other, and shook their heads. They did not ask him to go out and earn money; they did not need his help. Nor did they mind providing for him. What difference did one more mouth make? What they did expect, now that the house was well provided for, was that their father should adorn it as the figure-

[497]

head. Surely he could at least say the Sabbath benediction and be the first to cut into the Sabbath loaf with the proper prayer. He could make himself friendly to the young men who frequented the house, and sometimes drop a hint about the unseemliness of very long engagements. Keile herself said something now and again to the young fellows, but they paid no attention to a woman. A father is different; young men are more respectful to their brides when the father takes a hand.

But Tevyeh had nothing to say to these young men and refused to play the respectable, comfortable householder and father. As of old, he had his young revolutionaries, his books, his pamphlets, his newspapers, and his secret meetings. He did not ask his daughters how they made a living, he did not ask the young men what their intentions were. He even refused to attend the betrothals which were celebrated in his own home, in the presence of a Rabbi and a congregation of ten pious Jews, with all the traditional ceremonies, including the breaking of plates in memory of the destruction of the Temple. The daughters begged him to show himself at the ceremony, Keile wept before him, all in vain.

"I won't sit at the table with those sanctimonious servants of the Lord," he said, over and over again.

He was seldom at home except in the nights, when he came to sleep a few hours. He would drop in at any time for books or documents, and then Keile would try to detain him.

"I'm laying the table, Tevyeh," she cried. "Where are you running to, you lunatic?"

"I'll eat somewhere," he would reply darkly, while he stuffed his pockets with papers.

The young men offered him cigarettes and tried to get into political discussions with him, but Tevyeh had nothing in common with these smugglers in the high boots.

Rebuffed, the young men tried to make fun of him.

"Reb Tevyeh," they asked, "when are you going to drive the Germans out of Lodz? You're always fighting with them, aren't you?"

"They'll be out, they'll be out!" snapped Tevyeh. "They'll go faster than the Russians. If you only had eyes to see . . ."

"Reb Tevyeh, you'd do better to come out smuggling with

[498]

us," they answered. "We'll show you an easy way of making a few marks."

The house with its pictures and furniture was hateful to him; he could not bear the sight of Keile in her pious wig mumbling before the mezuzah on the door or the portrait of Rabbi Meir the Wonderworker. He could not stand these young men in the high boots, or even his own daughters. He was filled with resentment and loathing by the friends they brought home, by the bribed German soldiers, and by the sight of the smuggled goods. He refused to partake of the fat meals which were laid on the table. Only one thing in the house was dear to him, the yellowing photograph of Bashke, hanging up on the wall in the midst of the pictures. As for the rest, his soul was ashamed of it. He could not invite into this bourgeois nest any of his friends, and he could not stay in it himself. Early in the morning, before the others had risen, he would be dressed and would steal out to the workers' club or to the working-men's kitchen.

To him the house was at its most loathsome early on a Sunday morning after the jollification of the Sabbath night. The table had not been cleared, but was still littered with nutshells, apple-peelings, half-empty glasses, and cigarette butts. On the chairs lay, in wild disorder, women's stockings and underwear. Stretched out on chairs covered with cushions lay one of the young men, who had stayed too late to go home. His high boots stood up like sentinels in the middle of the room, his trousers hung from a nail by the suspenders. The little white collar stood out in the darkness. Everything bespoke an unbecoming masculine intimacy in this houseful of young women. His daughters lay asleep in the beds, their limbs flung out wildly from under the covers in the heat of the night. On the floor and on chairs lay brassieres, hairpins, and other feminine articles of attire. Tevyeh was ashamed of the picture and ashamed of these daughters, so utterly alien to him.

He dressed hastily and pulled out his papers from their hiding-place. Keile heard him and, in a voice in which was mingled contempt and pity, called to him:

"Fool! Where are you running at this hour? Wait! I'll give

[499]

you at least a mouthful of coffee before you go out."

"I'll get coffee in the working-men's kitchen," muttered Tevyeh, stuffing the papers into his pockets.

Keile looked at him dumbly and in the half-light saw his white, hungry face, his narrow shoulders, his bent figure. As Tevyeh went out she shook her head in its white night-cap with red ribbons, and lifted her eyes to heaven.

"Almighty God," she murmured, "can't You drive the madness out of him, so that he may be like other men? He enjoys nothing in this life, and he has forfeited the life beyond the grave too."

She crawled heavily out of bed and went in her bare feet into the kitchen. She drove out the bugs and cockroaches from the pots and began to prepare breakfast, her lips muttering the morning prayer, the words all twisted and mispronounced.

Outside, a cock crowed, sending its morning call over the city which the factory sirens no longer awakened.

One man in Lodz was determined not to yield to the commands of Colonel Baron von Heidel-Heidellau, and that was Tevyeh the weaver, the leader of the Unionists and chairman of the Workers' Executive Committee. Between these two, the one in the palace, the other in the working-men's kitchen, there was constant war. Every day von Heidel-Heidellau issued new edicts; every day Tevyeh issued new counter-edicts, calling for disobedience. The Baron's edicts were pasted up by soldiers in the daytime; Tevyeh's were pasted up secretly, at night, and, whenever possible, right on top of the Baron's.

When the Baron learned of a Workers' Executive Committee which had dared to issue proclamations defying his authority, the blood rushed up into his face. He sent for the lame Polish police commissioner, Schwanecke, and almost spat into his yellow-whiskered face.

"Clean them out!" he yelled. "Get those Jewish vermin out of the city! They're at the bottom of it."

The frightened Schwanecke mobilized the police in the blue cloaks and warned them that if they knew what was good for them they would catch the midnight prowlers who pasted up the revolutionary proclamations. Double guards were posted in the streets at night, hiding in doorways and at dark corners. A few of the revolutionaries were caught and brought before Schwanecke, who took out on them the insults he had suffered at the hands of von Heidel-Heidellau. With hands and feet tied, the prisoners were thrown on the floor, and the lame police commissioner kicked them in the stomach and spat on them. The white-faced, starved men kept their mouths shut, and not one leader was betrayed. Schwanecke had the prisoners put into solitary confinement and kept them for weeks on a diet of bread and water—four ounces of bread daily, just enough to prevent them from dying. Still they would not speak, and the posting up of the revolutionary proclamations went on. Cruelty getting him nowhere, Schwanecke resorted to softer methods. He promised some of the prisoners their freedom if they would only give him a few names; and if from time to time they would bring him a little interesting information about the workers, they would be amply rewarded. The bribes were as ineffective as the tortures. Schwanecke at last realized that he could do nothing with these prisoners. He had them sent into Germany, to do forced labour.

"There's one place where you'll have to obey, you damned lice," he said.

On the day when the prisoners were shipped into Germany, Schwanecke covered the city with posters, giving the names, the offences, and the sentences, as a warning to all others. The next morning half of his posters were covered over by proclamations of the Workers' Executive Committee.

The first clash between von Heidel-Heidellau and Tevyeh the weaver was precipitated by the food problem.

Comfortably ensconced in the Huntze palace, the Baron was preoccupied day and night with one task: how to ship more and more foodstuffs out of his region into the German fatherland. And it suddenly occurred to him that he had neglected the working-men's kitchens. A committee of prominent citizens, among them Yakob Ashkenazi, had founded these kitchens, where a worker could obtain, once a day, a plate of thin soup and a small piece of bread. They were to be found in every part of the city, but they were thickest in Balut.

Von Heidel-Heidellau considered these kitchens superfluous. They used up enormous quantities of flour, potatoes, and barley which ought to be shipped to Germany. He sent for the committee which administered these kitchens, and issued two orders: the portions were to be decreased, and the bread adulterated.

"Your Excellency," pleaded the committee timidly, "we can't mix more adulterants with the flour. It won't hold."

"Our dietitian," answered the Baron, "will give you a certain formula. The bread will hold. It's an invention of his."

When the committee tried to protest that if the nourishment in the bread was decreased, it would mean a rise in the mortality figures, the Baron flew into a rage.

"There's room enough in your damned cemeteries, isn't there?" he yelled.

The committee withdrew, reluctant but obedient. The next order given to the bakers contained the formula invented by the German dietitian. There was a saving in flour, much to the Baron's contentment. Having succeeded in his first efforts, he was emboldened to try again; and day after day he decreased the per-capita quantity of potatoes, barley, and fats. One day the Baron issued an order that no meat fat should be used for the soups, and that oil was to be substituted. The next day he again decreased the quantity of barley. Then it occurred to him that a great source of waste was the peeling of potatoes before they were put into the soup. He therefore ordered that in future the potatoes were to be boiled in their jackets. The dietitian who had invented the formula for almost flourless bread now discovered that the jacket was the most nourishing part of the potato. The Baron was delighted. He sent for the German, Jewish, and Polish newspapermen, and had the dietitian give them a lecture on the food value of that long-neglected article of diet—the jacket of the potato. "You see, gentlemen," said the Baron, "I am greatly concerned with the welfare of the population. I want you to make the people understand that it is for their good that the order has been issued to drop the potatoes whole into the soup made in the public kitchens."

The newspapermen wrote warm articles in praise of potato-peelings, and the cooks in the workers' kitchens did as they were told. Only Tevyeh and his men felt that the limit had been reached, and that this last swindle was not to be borne.

[503]

Tevyeh was the only leader left among the workers; Nissan was somewhere in Russia; the other leaders had been caught and either exiled to Siberia or sent to the front. On Tevyeh's shoulders rested the responsibility for the workers' movement in Lodz, and he chose to open his fight against the German oppressor on the issue of the kitchens.

The morning after the first meal with unpeeled potatoes had been served in the working-men's kitchens, there appeared on the walls of Lodz, in scores of copies, a fiery proclamation directed against the military masters of the city. In bitter language the Workers' Executive Committee denounced the Baron for having deprived the workers of Lodz of every possibility of employment, and, when they were reduced to the status of public charges, seeking to starve them to death. At scores of secret meetings Tevyeh and his committee urged the workers to revolt.

Von Heidel-Heidellau lost all confidence in the lame police commissioner with the yellow whiskers. He determined to take a hand himself and decided to kill two birds with one stone. That same day he sent several squads of soldiers to the working-men's kitchens and had the youngest and strongest-looking among the workers arrested on charges of sedition. Without even a semblance of a trial the prisoners were put on trains and sent into Germany to forced labour.

For a long time the Baron had been worried by the lack of responsiveness on the part of the civilian population to the appeals being sent from Germany for able-bodied workers. In the fatherland labourers were badly needed in field, factory, and mine to replace the mobilized soldiers. As the war continued year after year, the drain on the male population was such that the country was threatened with paralysis. The rulers of Germany began to look to Poland not only for food, but for civilian man-power. But the civilian population of Poland was not too eager to entrust itself to the Germans. From those that had responded to the appeal came back letters in which the condition of the workers was portrayed as being no better than that of prisoners of war. The country was starving, and one might as well remain at home, in Poland, where at least one was not forced to sweat ten and twelve and fifteen hours a day under guard, like a convict.

The workers' opposition opened up a new source of labourers to Baron von Heidel-Heidellau. There was also this particular advantage in the strategy: that as he removed the able-bodied young men from Lodz, the very young and the old would be less inclined to oppose him. Steadily, day after day, workers were arrested, on any pretext or on none, and shipped into Germany. Two workers standing on the street were liable to arrest for illegal assembly; a worker who looked unwashed could be arrested and taken to the delousing plant. If he was young and healthy he was not allowed to return home. Or else men were simply picked up, without any show of legality, and sent under convoy to Germany.

The proclamations against the Baron multiplied, their language grew fiercer. They contained, besides denunciations of the Baron, terrifying descriptions of the conditions under which forced labour was being performed in Germany. Protests were signed by the families which had lost their men. Appeals were made to international law.

And as the struggle between von Heidel-Heidellau and Tevyeh the weaver proceeded, the latter was reduced to fearful shifts of poverty and insecurity. He stopped frequenting his own home. He frequented no home regularly, but slept every night in a different place. In the fury of his campaign against the German conqueror he forgot about food and rest. Besides directing and sustaining the small band of conspirators, he wrote frequent and detailed denunciations of the Baron to various Social Democratic leaders in Germany. He gathered lists of the illegally arrested and forwarded them to Berlin. He carried the matter so far that there were inquiries about the actions of the Baron from the capital.

What hurt Tevyeh most was the gradual moral decay of his fellow-weavers. They who had once been proud to call themselves workers, producers, members of the proletariat, were forced in these bitter times to turn their hand to anything. They became pedlars and smugglers. They sold candy on the streets. He would meet them as they walked with their trays, or their buckets of pickles, and they would blush to meet his gaze.

[505]

"We've turned merchants, Comrade Tevyeh," they muttered. "We never believed it possible."

Some of them went round from yard to yard buying up junk, but this was the lowest one could sink, short of actual begging on the streets. And to this last shift many were reduced. The women, the spinners and seamstresses, gave themselves to the German soldiers for enough food to sustain their wretched bodies. There were men who had once been active in the party who now smuggled food and sold it to the rich, maintained suspicious little shops which were covers for houses of prostitution, and had a good deal to do with soldiers. They had forgotten the decent past. Many died in that time, either of undernourishment or disease or both. And Tevyeh watched the rot eating into the revolutionary movement and was heartsick.

He did not lose faith; he only found it hard, very hard, to carry on, without any assistance from the outside. He believed that the revolution was coming, but meanwhile things were happening which bewildered him. He did not know how to explain them. His reading was inadequate—he knew that—but he felt that some explanation existed. He missed Nissan. Nissan would surely have been able to put everything in its right perspective. For instance, this steady degeneration of the workers' movement in the west: this defection of the Socialists into the ranks of the war parties; this voting of war credits; this wearing of uniforms by men who had sworn never to support the bourgeoisie in its imperialist aims. Good heavens! There were Socialist leaders who stooped so low that they joined delegations to kings and emperors. It was incredible.

It was all too much for this old, exhausted, hungry, and hunted hand-loom worker. And yet upon him rested the burden of leadership. To him younger people looked for encouragement and new spirit. Nor did he fail them. It was only in the nights, on the hard bed which was his refuge from his pursuers, that he sometimes permitted himself to face the bewilderment in his soul. And then everything looked black. But during the day he continued obstinately, if only for the sake of the handful of young people who still believed and still followed him.

These were the ones who stood firm and who were prepared literally to die of hunger rather than sell their birthright to remain workers.

"No peddling," they swore, "and no smuggling. We'll see von Heidel-Heidellau strung up from a lamp-post before we'll let him do that to us. We're workers, and we'll remain workers, Comrade Tevyeh."

These were the ones who helped him in the copying and posting up of the proclamations. They helped in the organization of a special working-men's kitchen which was a club and a centre of propaganda in the evenings. They attended his meetings and persuaded others to attend. Without them Tevyeh would have been lost indeed.

There was in Balut a big unfinished building of red brick, begun before the war by a rich Jew of Lodz and abandoned with the outbreak of hostilities. When the Russians withdrew from Lodz, the workers of Balut occupied the building, and in its bleak rooms, which still lacked windows and doors, they began to organize a club. They whitewashed the walls and hung up pictures of Karl Marx, Engels, and Lassalle. The women adorned the walls and ceiling with paper streamers. Some carpenters nailed a few benches and tables together. And this became the workers' club of Balut. Later on, it was also the working-men's kitchen. Here hundreds of the unemployed weavers, and even such of them as had taken to street peddling, assembled in the evenings, and for them the lectures and discussions were as important as the soup and bread which held their bodies and souls together.

During the darkest days of the occupation these youngsters did not lose heart. They observed the workers' holidays; they had a choir and an orchestra; they formed a dramatic society. And in the big red kitchen, during meal-times, when all were assembled, Tevyeh addressed them and strengthened them in the fight against the German masters of the city. More than once the agents of von Heidel-Heidellau broke into the building. But there were guards posted at every corner and every window. When a suspicious-looking character was seen approaching, the signal was given, and when an agent of the Baron entered, he saw only workers sitting quietly at their evening meal. There were arrests in spite of this—but they were arrests without reason, such as took place everywhere else in the city; and the workers, feeling that they were no worse off here than anywhere else, continued to assemble.

Looking on this, the remnant of what had once been a powerful workers' movement, Tevyeh felt himself torn between pity and pride; pity for the fallen, for those who had not been able to endure, pride in those whom neither hunger nor privation nor humiliation could discourage.

Out of his long, thin neck, above which bobbed his greying head, the words came pouring passionately. "Your time will come!" he assured his young comrades. "That is the iron law which our great teachers have given us!" And he pointed with a trembling hand at the three pictures on the wall.

In Max Ashkenazi's factories on Viborg Island in Petrograd there was a complete stoppage of work. His workers, together with thousands of others in the Russian capital, were on strike. At the door of every factory soldiers were stationed.

Max Ashkenazi was in a fever of indignation and impatience.

Everything had been going along marvellously, especially at the very moment when the strike broke out. The plans of the Russian high command had called for a vast offensive against the German and Austrian armies, in which millions of Russian soldiers would be flung against the eastern front simultaneously with an attack on the western front by the British and the French. In preparation for the huge offensive enormous quantities of munitions and supplies of all kinds were being piled up. Clothes were needed for the newly mobilized soldiers, underwear, shoes, bandages, cottonwool. Max Ashkenazi had enlarged his factory and adapted his machinery to many uses. He was even turning out bandages and cottonwool. These were days when he could afford to buy machines on sight, build new factories, expand without thought of expense. For the army paid; and the army did not argue about prices or make terms or give notes. It put down cash, and often in advance.

His profits were immense. He could not have reinvested them in his own factories even if he had wanted to. But he had not wanted to. He was acting, once again, with his in-

[509]

stinct for the future. Bonds were no good. Stocks were no good. Papers of any kind were no good in these troubled and shaky times. Farms, houses, factories, good, solid, visible, and tangible possessions, were what Max Ashkenazi wanted. And so he was always surrounded by agents and commission men, and besides attending to his own business, he was for ever galloping around in his big carriage from end to end of the city, buying, estimating, adding to his possessions. He flew up and down the marble steps of banks, in and out of ministerial buildings and military offices. He was everywhere and had a share in everything.

Then suddenly, in the full swing of his good fortune, came the strike. Thousands of men and women downed tools and refused to enter the factory.

The strike began with something not related to the work and its conditions, but with the question of bread. The Russian capital was not receiving enough flour to feed its inhabitants. Transportation was tied up with military needs, and in the city the broad-bearded Russian shopkeepers with the white aprons speculated with the supplies on hand. To the workers' wives who came with their poor kopecks the shopkeepers pulled a long face and spread out their arms in a gesture of helplessness: "We have nothing, my dears. Our shelves are empty. God be my witness!"

They pointed up to the images of the Virgin above the shelves, illumined with green and red lights in their niches, and swore again by these that there was no food in Petrograd.

The housewives, exhausted with the day's labour, returned empty-handed to their homes and had nothing to set on the table for their menfolk and their children. Then they began to assemble before the city shops, and waited, stamping to keep their feet warm, and shouting. But the shops remained closed. The women were joined by elderly workers, and by Volhynians in fur coats and caps, who vented their bitter rage in open words.

"What kind of life is this we lead? A long day of labour, and at the end of it not a bite to eat. Blast them and curse them!"

"Burst the shops open! Break into them!"

[510]

"We've got to stop working! If they don't feed us we can't be expected to work."

Instead of bread the Minister of the Interior, Protopopov, sent out the Volhynian regiment which had distinguished itself in 1905 by its faithful service to the Tsar and its brutal repression of the striking workers in Poland. But the hungry crowds, refusing to be intimidated, still assembled in the streets, and particularly in the Nevsky Prospekt. Protopopov then ordered the bridges to be closed, so that the city workers might not be joined by the workers on Viborg Island. The workers crossed over the frozen Neva by thousands and tens of thousands. Red flags were lifted, and everywhere the cry resounded: "Bread and freedom!" Orators, raised on the shoulders of the crowd, exhorted it to action. A red flag was thrown over the statue of Alexander II, and the crowd roared: "Down with the monarchy! Long live the Republic!"

A company of soldiers, headed by several mounted officers, arrived at the square. The officer in command drew his sword and ordered the demonstrators to disperse. No one moved.

"I warn you!" he shouted. "If you don't go home I shall order my men to fire on you."

Still no one moved.

The officer rose in his stirrups, turned to his men, and shouted: "Ready! Aim!"

The women in the crowd ran out in front and cried out to the soldiers: "Shoot us! We are mothers who want bread for our children!"

Others advanced toward the soldiers, presenting themselves to the bayonets and crying: "Kill us! We are your mothers and sisters! They took away our men and sent them to the war. Now they won't even give us bread for our little ones!"

The officer became panicky, fearing the effect of these cries on his men. "Fire!" he yelled.

But no one fired a shot. Instead, the soldiers lowered their rifles sullenly. A great shout of joy rang out in the square, and men and women ran forward to embrace the soldiers.

The revolution had begun.

[511]

The pure joy of high expectation realized filled Nissan Eibeschutz, of Lodz, when he heard the tumult in the corridors of the Kresti prison of Petrograd, when he heard the turning of keys in the cell doors, and the approaching cries of the liberators: "Political comrades, come out! The revolution frees you!"

These were the words he had been waiting for every day and hour of his life. This was the inevitable which was foretold by the iron laws of Marxism. Whether he would live to hear the words or not was uncertain and did not matter. The event could not be calculated to the minute. But it might arrive any minute. And here it was. The day of socialism had dawned!

If his faith had needed strengthening, or his calculations confirmation, he had found it in the outbreak of the war. He had suffered in the midst of the riot of nationalist passions, of mass murder and human sacrifice; but he had seen beyond the misery of the moment. This, too, was inevitable, this final collapse of the rotten bourgeois world. So in the first year of the war he had, at the secret party meetings held in the Russian capital itself, given a most favourable diagnosis of the situation. The capitalist rulers of the world, at war with each other in their struggle for markets, were being compelled to the last dangerous step of arming the proletariat. The proletariat would inevitably turn the weapons against the capitalist imperialists. This was the end. . . .

The other delegates to the secret conference had derided him as a wild visionary. They did not believe that this war indicated the end of bourgeois rule. That had a long course to run yet. But Nissan stood fiercely by his opinion. This was capitalism's last sickness. Riddled by disease, inwardly corrupt and incapable of resistance, the system was ready to collapse. And therefore Nissan had submitted a series of resolutions dealing with immediate action, as if the power were about to pass into the hands of the workers. The delegates to the conference had rejected the resolutions; others were proposed, dealing with more immediate realities.

The conference, as it happens, did not get far in any sense,

[512]

for the sessions were interrupted. The police surrounded the house and arrested the conspirators.

"There's your revolution, Comrade Eibeschutz," sneered one of the men as they were being led away to the Kresti prison.

"It doesn't matter," answered Nissan, with an impatient gesture. "You will see that I'm right."

So, during the entire period of this last imprisonment, he had continued to foretell the collapse of the existing order. He had continued to argue with his fellow-prisoners, until he became a standing joke, so that every time a cell door was heard to open in the corridor, somebody would cry out: "Comrade Eibeschutz! Here comes the revolution and liberty!"

When the moment did come, and on a day late in February the cell doors were flung open, and voices called out: "The revolution frees you!" the prisoners remained seated for a moment in sheer astonishment. It was incredible to them. Only Nissan took it calmly. He went out to the office for his clothes and his few possessions. His comrades followed slowly.

"Comrade Eibeschutz, forgive us!" they said. "You were more far-sighted than we."

"Comrades, let us embrace," said Nissan, his face shining. There was an all-round embracing, in which the soldiers participated, too.

The joy that invaded Nissan was almost blinding in its intensity. He hardly saw the big truck into which he and his fellow-revolutionaries were packed, so that they might be led through the streets of Petrograd and hailed by the crowds of workers and soldiers. Everywhere their ears were assailed by the roaring of thousands of voices: "Hurrah for the political prisoners!" The liberated men in the automobile shouted back: "Long live the revolution!"

Like a country boy on his first visit to a big town, Nissan did not know where to look first. A great holiday light was shining on the city, on the walls with their proclamations and on the faces of the parading masses. Everything filled him with joy.

[513]

Finally the automobile was brought to the Tauride Palace, the steps of which were black with students, workers, and soldiers.

"Long live our revolutionary brothers!" they thundered, as the loaded automobiles drew up.

"Long live the free masses of a free country!" responded Nissan, waving his fur hat.

As he descended from the truck, a woman, a stranger, threw herself into his arms and, sobbing with joy, kissed him. With hot lips Nissan kissed the woman, whom he had never before seen. Everything was good in his eyes, everything shone in that happy hour, the people, the buildings, even the beggars on the street. Good, too, seemed that massive, broad-shouldered and broad-bearded deputy who came out of the Duma and in the bass voice of a singing priest greeted the arriving trucks. That official greeter had nothing of the revolutionary in his appearance. His carefully combed beard and his soothing bass voice were reminiscent, rather, of some metropolitan of the Church. But in Nissan's eyes, at that moment, he was a magnificent and glorious figure. The bliss that was in Nissan's heart, and flowed through his flesh and bones, filled him with love for the whole world. He wanted to embrace and kiss everyone. The happiness that was his now would last for ever.

In this joyous and transfigured spirit he threw himself into the work of the party in Petrograd.

The city which was responsible for the welfare of the one hundred and fifty million inhabitants of Russia was itself in a state of chaos. The factory workers were still striking, the trolley-cars remained in their barns, the police had disappeared, the Provisional Government had not yet taken hold. In the Tauride Palace the Duma, split into innumerable parties, argued and debated day and night. In their own committee-rooms sat groups of revolutionaries forming the Soviets of the Workers and Soldiers and preparing the new elections. Every now and again a few men and women would break into the deliberations of the Duma, screaming: "You talk and talk and talk, and meanwhile the workers are starving. Throw open the shops! We're hungry!"

[514]

Nissan was everywhere. He helped in the distribution of food, the reorganization of the factories, the making of theoretical decisions, the negotiations with generals and admirals. In a military truck he flew from factory to factory, to organize the elections. Toward the end of the day he would suddenly be aware of a dreadful weakness in his limbs, and he would remember with astonishment that he had had nothing in his mouth since morning. He would ask for a glass of tea and a piece of dry bread. He had very little money. On leaving prison he had received back from the office only a fraction of what had been taken from him. But all this did not matter, just as it did not matter where he was going to sleep at night. It sometimes happened that after a day spent in running from one great palace to another, he would creep late at night into some poverty-stricken worker's room, to sleep a few hours on a hard bench, or on a few chairs put together. But the joy that had blossomed in him when he had heard the footsteps of the liberators in the corridors was still with him, bright and unquenchable. He saw everywhere the soldiers with the red cockades on their bayonets. He saw the free crowds assembled in the squares of the capital, their dark floods surrounding the old Imperial statues; and the blood raced happily in his veins.

"It has come!" he murmured to himself. "It is here! I have lived to see it!"

New-Lodz in Petrograd was in full swing again. Instead of two shifts of twelve hours each, the factories worked three shifts of eight hours each. Instead of time and a quarter, night workers received double. The unions, too, had obtained increases for their members, women as well as men. However, work went forward slowly. There was more talking than weaving at the looms. In addition, there were countless new workers' holidays, parades, demonstrations, and what not. Workers absenting themselves for these "official" occasions were paid full time. And then workers' delegates appeared every now and again in the factories, representatives of the various parties, Mensheviks and Bolsheviks, and Socialist Revolutionaries. The workers left the looms and boilers to listen and to applaud. Every speaker, whatever his shade of opinion, was enthusiastically received.

Never in all his long career as manufacturer had Max Ashkenazi worked under such amazing conditions. But he kept quiet.

At first, when his workers, together with thousands of others throughout the city, abandoned the factories and poured into the streets, he merely smiled. He had no faith in the "revolution." He remembered the year 1905 in Lodz, with its strikes, its revolution, and its slogans of freedom and fraternity. Many of the Lodz manufacturers had taken fright, had spoken of moving their establishments into the interior of Russia. Max Ashkenazi had remained unshaken. He knew

[516]

that in the end the shoemaker must return to his last, the weaver to his stool, the servant to the kitchen, and the manufacturer to his profits. And so it had turned out. The eternal order reappeared, and the world remained what it had always been. The pauper was still a pauper, and the man with money continued to make money, as in the days before the strike. Max Ashkenazi had grown up with Lodz; he knew its workers; he knew that every so often they went off on a revolutionary spree, only to come crawling back to their jobs with their tails between their legs. The world had always been like that; it always would be; it would have its rich and its poor, its masters and its servants. It could not continue otherwise.

And therefore he shrugged his shoulders and smiled when his colleagues, all panicky, told him and one another that the end was near and that the Government was in a tight place. "Rubbish!" he said, decisively. At worst, a few bombs would be thrown, a few students would be arrested, a few soldiers would be called out, and then it would be all over.

He drove around the streets in his carriage and saw here and there the first skirmishes between the police and the crowds. "Wait," he said grimly to himself. In a few days the Cossacks would be called out. A few rounds would be fired. The strike and the revolution would disappear as suddenly as they had emerged.

When the Cossacks refused to fire on the crowds, Max Ashkenazi was astounded. He had never heard of soldiers refusing to obey the commands of their officers. Such things were not in the cards. But still he did not lose faith in the régime. This was a coincidence. Other regiments would be called out, and they would do the job. There were soldiers enough in Russia. Then, when regiment after regiment revolted, and the soldiers tore the epaulets from the shoulders of their officers, Max Ashkenazi began to waver, and he looked fearsomely at the crowds on the street.

"Incredible!" he muttered in German. "Absolutely incomprehensible!"

His disillusionment grew from day to day. Ministers of the crown were being arrested by common soldiers! As if they had been street toughs or pickpockets. Ministers of the crown!

[517]

Those mighty personages whom he had approached trembling. Then came the last blow. The Imperial train was arrested and the Emperor was forced to abdicate. Max Ashkenazi was thunderstruck. How could they do such a thing? Not that he had any sympathy with the Tsar. He had read more than once of the freeing of condemned pogrom leaders by Imperial orders. He had also read somewhere that the Tsar had insulted a Jewish delegation which had come to greet him, carrying the holy scrolls of the Law. The Tsar had turned from the delegation and had noticed only the priests. No, he had no affection for the Emperor of Russia. But the Emperor was the Emperor, the symbol of all ultimate force, stability, and authority, the sacred individual whose likeness was stamped on every gold coin in the Empire. In a few days he was overthrown, he and his ministers and his suite.

"I can't understand it!" said Max Ashkenazi to his colleagues. "It doesn't make sense."

For the first time he began to be afraid of those strange creatures the workers, whom he had always despised.

He began to perceive a tremendous force in those Russian yokels, those gross, unclean, lumpy slaves who filled the factories and who could not even sign their names—a force to be reckoned with, lest it break loose and destroy everything. If they were capable of overthrowing an Emperor who had been guarded by millions of soldiers and countless cannon, what chance had a manufacturer or a merchant?

It was a meek and wary Max Ashkenazi who reopened his factory shortly after the revolution. He did not quite know how to speak to his workers and how to give them orders. He sat on the edge of his big chair in the director's office, and before the delegation had quite finished stating its demands, he had already yielded everything. When the delegation was gone, he stood behind the door of the office, his hand at his ear, trying to catch the discussions that were going on among his employees. He wanted to know what all those arguments, those interminable debates, were driving at.

He even came down to listen to the orators who were sent to address the workers. He heard those that called for immediate peace and a division of property, and those who

[518]

wanted the war prosecuted to a successful conclusion before the institution of socialism; those that believed in temporary co-operation with the bourgeoisie, and those that would not sit at the same table with their class enemies. Every orator spoke with the most passionate conviction, and every one was vehemently applauded. Max Ashkenazi did not interfere, did not enter into arguments with his factory hands. He understood that it was best for him to look, to listen, and to keep his tongue between his teeth. Still, in his heart, he could not help siding with the moderates, with those who pleaded that the war be pushed to a victorious conclusion, while the workers co-operated with the bourgeoisie.

Max Ashkenazi was not a war patriot or a fire-eater. As a matter of fact, he had always considered war ridiculous, and he had never been able to look at a gun. Often he had stretched a point in giving a man a job if he could thereby rescue him from military service. But he had looked upon the war as upon a natural phenomenon which could be turned to advantage from the business point of view. He needed the war. He needed the big orders it brought him. He could hardly refrain from applauding, therefore, when he heard an orator demanding that the war be carried on until the enemy had been driven from the soil of Russia. He despised war, he shuddered at the sight of blood, but he was a business-man, a manufacturer. He wanted to see his factories working day and night. That was the sense of life to him. In the desire for the big orders which would keep every bit of machinery productively employed, he forgot the nature and meaning of war. He did not see and hear the shooting. The word "war" became an abstraction to him. Or, rather, it was a name for a certain type of goods. There were spring goods, summer goods, autumn goods, and winter goods. And there were also war goods. And war goods were the best of all, yielding the largest profits. It sickened him, therefore, to hear orators calling for the end of the war, and it seemed to him right and just and business-like and sensible when other orators pleaded for the continuation of the war.

A few weeks passed and a certain measure of peace was restored to the soul of Max Ashkenazi. He adapted himself to

[519]

the new situation, as he had always adapted himself to circumstances beyond his control. Besides, it was not by any means as dreadful as it had seemed in the beginning; and perhaps there would be an improvement. Perhaps all this excitement would subside, the talking and shouting would come to an end, the old order would return.

Meanwhile, things were certainly not as they had been. The working-hours were shorter, the pay was higher, there was always trouble with the trade unions, sickness and accident benefits, and what not; and the boss was only half a boss. He could no longer do and say what he liked in his own factory. Well then, thought Max Ashkenazi, so let it be. He did not even feel any hatred in his heart against his workers. If they had been capable of turning the tables on their masters, they deserved every advantage they had won. Only one thought pursued Max Ashkenazi, now as always, crowding out all emotions of resentment: how could he go on making money? The workers were in the saddle—good luck to them. Every man for himself, and they had won out. The point was, how was the factory to continue producing profits for *him*?

Revolution or no revolution, the world would remain more or less what it had been. Every man had his job, and his, Max Ashkenazi's, was to accumulate wealth. So, when the factory began to move again, when the workers were back at their stools, the engineers back at the boilers, he too was in his element again. True, production went on more slowly than before, but the war continued, the Quartermaster General placed new orders, and profits rolled in. There were even advantages in the new situation. Prices went up, and profits with them. The new men did not have to be bribed, either. So Max Ashkenazi began to make good the losses he had suffered during the period of revolution. It was only externally that he bowed to the new régime. He no longer drove through the streets of Petrograd in his private carriage. That was too ostentatious. He hired a public hack. Likewise he put away his huge sable coat. But, as before, he continued to buy up houses, offices, factories, feeling more definitely than ever that these were the only secure possessions.

Then one day there appeared in his factory an old, familiar

figure out of the remote past. It was a delegate who was sent to address and organize the workers, an elderly man in poor clothes, with a worker's cap on his head, with a grey little Jewish beard and with whiskers which suggested the ear-locks of a pietist. Max Ashkenazi at once recognized Nissan, the son of Reb Noske the Teacher. At the sight of his old schoolmate Max Ashkenazi felt his heart suddenly constrict with fear. Perhaps the man had come to pay him back for all that he had done to him in the past. He might have him arrested. Anything was possible. But he was greatly relieved when he heard the speech which Nissan Eibeschutz delivered. It was moderate. It contained no bitter threats against the bourgeoisie. Nissan only appealed for proletarian unity, for the sake of the safety of the revolution. He even spoke of a temporary alliance with the progressive elements, until order was restored and the real induction of the Socialist program could begin. Max Ashkenazi breathed more easily.

Like a clever politician, he did not even wait for the other to come to him, but sought him out among the workers and offered him his hand.

"How are you, Nissan?" he asked, in Yiddish. Then he quoted from the Talmud: " 'Mountain cannot meet with mountain, but man can meet with man.' Do you recognize me?"

"As easily as a bad rouble," answered Nissan, smiling.

Awhile the two men looked at each other in silence. Finally Max Ashkenazi spread out his hands in a gesture of helplessness and said: "It turns out you were right, and not I." Then he quoted again: " 'Who is the wise man? He who foresees the unborn.' You've conquered us."

"Not quite," said Nissan. "The fight isn't over yet, Mr. Ashkenazi." He spoke in Russian, so that the workers might understand him. "We'll let you go on working awhile, developing the factory, concentrating capital, so that we can take it over more easily. And that day isn't far off."

Max Ashkenazi's face fell. Fear returned to his heart, and he was uneasy in the presence of this workers' leader whom he had more than once defeated in the old Lodz days.

"If there were fights," he murmured uneasily, "they weren't

caused by ill will, but by circumstances. We too, the industrialists, weren't always free to do what we would have liked to do as men and as human beings. We had to act as businessmen. We were the slaves of our businesses, and of circumstance. . . . Now both of us have become wiser. We are more experienced, time has taught us. . . . I hope you no longer feel any enmity toward me."

"You acted as one of your class is bound to act," said Nissan. "The personal side doesn't interest me. . . . As your class enemy I shan't act worse than you did, Mr. Ashkenazi. Let's get into the saddle and win the people over to us, and we shall take what belongs to us. The factories will pass over to the workers, to those that built them." He indicated with a gesture the men grouped about them.

"But the workers, too, will need good business directors," said Max Ashkenazi, smiling. "Your affairs won't go of themselves. . . ."

Nissan drew his thin mantle close about him and hurried out to the car which was waiting to take him to workers' meetings in other factories.

Seven hundred and three deputies were elected to the new Constituent Assembly, and among them were two revolutionaries whose careers had begun in Lodz and crossed and recrossed in the course of the years—Nissan Eibeschutz and Paul Shchinsky. They had served together in Siberia; they had fled together from their exile at the outbreak of the Russo-Japanese war; they had worked again in Lodz. They had been separated after that, and then again they had met, in prison. The revolution had freed them both. Now they walked together, elected representatives of the Russian people, toward the Tauride Palace. But in their clothes, as in their bearing, they were worlds apart. Shchinsky was dressed in military coat and boots, a revolver strapped to his side. He was of the group which had seized the power, the Soviets whose soldiers and sailors, drawn from Kronstadt, held the city. In the old days Shchinsky had clung grimly to his Marxist books; now he clung as grimly to his revolver. Nissan was clad in a flimsy mantle, and his pockets were filled with pamphlets and newspapers. Still, as of old, he believed in the power of the word, justice, the voice of the people.

As the two men drew near the Tauride Palace they observed a strange spectacle. Armed soldiers and sailors lined the entrance to the hall where the first session was to be held. But they were not there to honour the elected representatives of the Russian people. The majority of the deputies were received with insults and denunciations.

"Hang the traitors!" the armed men roared. "Counter-revolutionaries! War patrioteers! Lackeys of the capitalists!"

Only the representatives of the Bolshevik Party were permitted to pass in peace.

Nissan seized Shchinsky by the sleeve of his military coat. "Listen!" he said grimly. "Your men! And they mean me! I'm the counter-revolutionary because I'm not of your group! I'm the war patrioteer and the lackey of the capitalists!"

The vast Tauride Palace looked more like a barracks than a parliament house. Soldiers with guns and hand-grenades were everywhere. The glitter of bayonets passed through the corridors. The galleries of the Assembly were filled with swarthy, tattooed sailors.

"Smash the place!" they bellowed. "Blow up the anti-revolutionary pigsty!" The guns were pointed downwards; fingers itched on the triggers.

The deputies were pale with excitement. The fury of the armed troops hung like a thunderous canopy over the Assembly, ready to fall at a moment's notice. The correspondents of the foreign newspapers looked on, frightened. They had never seen a parliamentary opening of this kind before.

The first to take the floor were the representatives of the Soviets. They proposed that, before anything else was done, the Constituent Assembly ratify as law all the decrees they had proclaimed since their seizure of power in the city of Petrograd. The deputies of the other parties were thrown into an uproar.

"Down with the dictators!" came shouts. "You are the servants of the Constituent Assembly, not its masters. The Constituent Assembly represents the will of the people."

At this point a representative of the Soviets took the floor and read out a prepared resolution.

"Inasmuch as the Constituent Assembly is an outlived form of representation of the will of the people," he yelled above the tumult, "a form not answering to the needs of the present moment, when the people is threatened with destruction by its enemy, the bourgeoisie, the Assembly is declared dissolved."

The deputies shouted themselves hoarse, banged on the tables, waved their arms. Then Paul Shchinsky gave the signal to the soldiers and sailors. At the point of the bayonet the deputies were driven from the hall, and out into the streets.

The city was lightless, for the lamps were smashed. The street-cars were all at a standstill. At that late hour no one was abroad except the soldiers and sailors who occupied Petrograd. They clustered at corners, their weapons glinting darkly. They stood around their field-kitchens, which sent out sparks into the night. In the squares, near the monuments, cannon were stationed, their iron muzzles pointed upward.

Broken, humiliated, astounded, Nissan wandered through the murky, deserted streets. For this hour he had waited all his life, for the hour when a free Russia would send to the capital the representatives of its will. For this he had struggled, for this borne imprisonment, exile, and loneliness. And the hour had come! He had even been privileged to be elected a member of the Constituent Assembly. Now he had been driven out of it! Cursed at, spat upon, he had been driven out at the point of the bayonet. And by whom? By his own kind, his comrades, soldiers and sailors, co-workers in the revolution. There came over him the abysmal despair, the dark, impenetrable wretchedness which had assailed him long ago, when the Polish workers had changed a May Day demonstration into a pogrom against the Jewish weavers of Balut.

He crawled wearily into his tiny room, threw himself on his narrow bed, buried his head in the pillow, and sobbed for the great triumph which he had lived to salute and which he was not permitted to share.

All night long, shots rang in the streets of Petrograd.

A spirit of depression and anxiety reigned in the house of Yakob Ashkenazi, director of the Flederbaum factory. Since the beginning of the last German occupation not a wheel had turned, not a bale of goods had gone out. Like the Huntze factory, Flederbaum's had been stripped of everything that could serve the conqueror, from the machine belts to the last parcel of raw material in the stockrooms. The only income, if such it could be called, consisted of the vouchers handed out by the Germans in exchange for requisitioned materials; and even these vouchers were post-dated, until after the war. The occupation had not only destroyed every means of making a livelihood; it had cut off most of the Flederbaum capital, too. The Russian banks had withdrawn before the advancing Germans. The debtors of the factory were on the other side of the war front. The great majority of bonds and stocks in the Flederbaum safes were without value. On the little that had remained, Yakob Ashkenazi had carried on. Now this was almost exhausted.

The Flederbaum sons, the mystics who spent their days and nights in prayer, or playing patience, or discussing ineffable mysteries with priests and monks, were not interested in the state of the factory, and were perhaps incapable of understanding it. They only knew that when they needed money they asked the director. They had no other relation to the institution. Yanka, the daughter, was too busy with her love-affairs. As middle age crept upon her, her passions became more violent, her indifference to the world's opinion more marked, her lovers successively younger. She, too, did not try to find out what was happening to the factory. She needed money—that was all she cared about.

A third drain was Gertrude, Yakob's wife. From the day of their marriage on, her love had been possessive and rapacious. She had inherited from her grandmother, Priveh, the wife of Reb Chaim, an extraordinary faculty for getting rid of money. She felt unbearably humiliated if her clothes were not the smartest, her furs the most opulent, her jewellery the most dazzling, among the young women of Lodz. Her receptions had to outshine all others. The extravagance she had from her grandmother was matched by the ambition she had from her father. No place but the first would satisfy her.

At first she had been too absorbed in Yakob to attend to her social conquest of the city. She had fastened herself on her uncle-husband, who was more than twice her age, like a leech. Her love was frantically possessive. She could not bear to see him look at another woman; she seized his hands whenever he applauded an actress enthusiastically; she was jealous even of his men friends and insisted that he abandon them for her. She wanted to absorb every atom of his energy, so that nothing might be left for anyone else to enjoy. Every laugh of his, every smile, belonged to her. Enslaved by her passion, she enslaved and exhausted him in turn. She did not care what his moods or his preoccupations were. When she wanted him, he had to be ready for her. And in those early days she wanted him always.

After the first wild months of love, she flung herself with the same demonic impatience and energy into her social career. Yakob, too, was by nature a spendthrift; but he was shocked by the frantic extravagance of his wife. She was quite unaware of the meaning of the word "cost." If the whim seized her to redecorate and refurnish her house, to change the tapestries and the pictures, she consulted no one—least of all her husband; she simply went to the most expensive dealers in town and placed her orders. Of course she refused to live in the comparatively modest director's house near the Flederbaum mansion. She said the place looked like the gardener's lodge at the gate of an estate. She wanted a mansion of her own. She was entitled to it. She could not live without it. It had to be the most striking in the city, too. She would have it rebuilt, from foundation to garret; she would choose the woodwork and the furnishings; she would make it an expression of herself.

She became so absorbed in her new pursuits that Yakob had time to recover and to begin longing for her again. But with this person of extremes there was no turning back. She had wanted nothing but her husband; now she wanted anything but her husband. Without a word of reproach or warning, Yakob handed her whatever sums she asked for. He only put in a word about himself: could she not spare a little time for him? No. Not just now. "I'm dreadfully busy, Yakob," she said, "just too dreadfully busy."

When the mansion was ready, there began a series of receptions and dances. That time of life had arrived for Yakob— he was then in his middle forties—which called for rest and quiet. He had had his fling. He was tired of noise and flashy gaiety, of crowds and empty laughter. He longed to settle down. But just at this time he was being pulled back into the maelstrom. When Gertrude was not entertaining or giving a ball at home, she dragged him along to the entertainments of her friends. He was not master in his own home; and he could not keep pace with his wife outside the home. In addition to the physical weariness which oppressed him, there was a constant worry which he dared not betray. His income was far behind his expenses. He began to borrow and to hand out promissory notes.

On rare evenings Gertrude would be overcome again by her first love for Yakob. The old, frenzied passion seized her suddenly. She would fall at his feet again, imploring him to take her, to do whatever he liked with her.

Then Yakob would let himself forget, and in the masculine pride and happiness of the moment, he would believe that he could straighten out his life with her. For a long time he had been pursued by the thought that if she would only have a child, she would perhaps change. But he loved children for their own sake, too. He had wanted them from his first wife, the sickly Pearl, who could not have them, and as he grew older, the hunger for offspring became sharper in him. He pictured his first child as a girl, a blonde, laughing, tender little creature. The three of them, Gertrude, the child, himself. It might mean peace and happiness at last. Perhaps that demon of restlessness in his wife would be exorcized; perhaps the mad light in her eyes, which filled him with fear, would soften into the tenderness and kindness of motherhood.

When he found the courage to broach the subject, Gertrude started from him furiously.

"Yakob! Don't dare to mention that again!" she cried. "I won't let myself be buried in baby-clothes and diapers."

She stood erect and looked at her slender, flowing figure in the mirror. A look of satisfaction, mingled with half-concealed lust, came into her hard blue eyes.

"Phoo!" she exclaimed. "Is this how you'd like me to look?" And she sketched a round, ugly gesture before her stomach.

Years passed before she satisfied him and gave birth to a child. But it was a girl, fulfilling all of Yakob's secret longings, and the man in the middle fifties, whose black beard was now streaked with grey, was happy again and almost became a child himself. For a time he let the little one fill out all the empty places of his life. Gertrude, whom the bearing of a child had made more beautiful than ever, was seldom at home. She did not nurse the child herself. She was still too busy with her receptions and dances; busier than before, in fact, as though she was afraid that this life of unrestrained and uncalculating gaiety was drawing to a close. But every free moment Yakob spent in the nursery. He dandled the child on his knee; he rolled about with her on the floor; he sang to her and taught her her first words. He began to think of additions to his family. He saw himself, a settled man, a patriarchal figure, surrounded by children as lovely and lovable as this first one.

He came slowly and bitterly out of these dreams when he realized that Gertrude could not be weaned from her madness. Though she had been the aggressor, though he had warned her against marriage with a man so much older than herself, it was she who now looked upon herself as the wronged one. She felt that it was too horrible to be, at her age, the wife of an elderly man, who had enjoyed himself in his time and now wanted to pull his wife into the domestic peacefulness which was all that he was fit for. Her extravagance took on a tinge of vengefulness. If her husband could not be her lover and her playmate, as she wanted him to be, he had to make it up in other ways. And thus, though the war years came and the Flederbaum factory was closed, her extravagant demands did not cease.

The balls and impromptu dances continued in their mansion; they became even livelier. But now, among the young guests, there appeared figures which had not been known before in Lodz—German lieutenants and captains with tall figures and scarred faces. They came condescendingly, somewhat ashamed that the privations of war reduced them to frequenting a Jewish house and mingling with unclean Polacks. But they danced gladly with the hostess, and between coarse military jests they whispered compliments on the quality of her wines and the rarity of her beauty.

Yakob Ashkenazi shook hands with the guests, with the young men about town, with the German lieutenants and captains, and bade them welcome to his home; but his blood ran cold with anger and jealousy. He looked at these young men and he remembered his own early manhood. He remembered the grin *he* had suppressed when an elderly husband had dissimulated his rage and jealousy, while he welcomed *him* in his house. He knew the comedy well, but now he was playing in it a part which he had never dreamed of. He knew the young men, with the cruel mockery in their hearts; he knew the young wives, with lust and treachery in theirs. He knew the dances, too, and the seemingly innocent gestures, the whispering, the holding of hands, the hints and invitations. What he had once read on the lips and in the eyes of other men's wives these blackguards now read—and perhaps with justice—in Gertrude's eyes. How it all came back! The politeness with which one of them approached the table, asking *his*, the husband's, permission to dance with his wife! How many times he had done it! How many times the young woman had thanked him, almost in as many words, for rescu-

[529]

ing her from the impossible boredom of her husband's company. He knew it all! He knew the excuses which wives bring home to their husbands when they stay out too late; he had helped to compose so many of them. He knew, too, the mood of tenderness in which a woman leaves her lover, a tenderness which she transfers to her husband, half naturally, half as strategy. Yes, even in those far-off days he had found disgusting the treachery of the women who gave themselves to him. He had loved those women; or, rather, he had been unable to do without them. But he had always understood their meanness, their cruelty, and their falseness. Now he saw it from the other angle, and it was infinitely more revolting and more painful.

He could not sit through these receptions, which lasted until the early hours of the morning. Better be mocked in his absence than in his presence. He had one source of consolation; he would go to see his little child.

He went to the other end of the house and in the darkened room sat down by the child's bed and listened to her even, innocent breath. The anger in his blood died down, and life acquired meaning for him again.

From one of the farther rooms Dinah, his mother-in-law, came in on tiptoe.

Since her parents had died, Dinah lived with her daughter. She was alone in the world and without means of her own. The fortune given her by Max Ashkenazi at the time of the divorce had been deposited with Russian banks and lost. From her son Ignatz she heard nothing. Only at the outbreak of the war he had written her that he had joined a French regiment. A quiet, lonely figure, she moved around ghostlike in her daughter's house, and sat at table with her and her husband, the man she had loved. She still sought consolation for her wasted life in her books, in the sufferings and triumphs of imaginary persons. For the rest, she had her grandchild, who was to her not her daughter's child so much as Yakob's. More than once, feeling the little arms around her neck, she imagined that the child was her own, her own and Yakob's.

She came in quietly now and saw Yakob, tired and broken, sitting by the child's bed. The sight of him sent a pang

[530]

through her. She approached him, unheard, and put her hand on his shoulder.

"Yakob," she murmured, "go to bed. I'll sit with the child."

Yakob looked at her out of wide, sad eyes.

"I'm not sleepy," he said. "I can't sleep."

"I don't sleep nights, either, Jacob," she answered, using the name by which she had called him in their far-off childhood.

𝕭𝖊𝖙𝖜𝖊𝖊𝖓 the Polish legionaries which Major Martin Kuchinsky, leader of the shock troops of the Polish Socialist Party,
had sent into Lodz to recruit the youth of that city, and the
German army of occupation, there were perpetual quarrels.
These Polish legions, independent units commanded by their
own officers, had been formed under the ægis of Austria, and
the Germans had always looked down with contempt on their
Austrian allies. In the first place, a German was never certain
of being answered in a civilized language when he addressed
a soldier wearing the Royal and Imperial uniform of Austria.
Those Austrians were such a miserable mixture of races—
Hungarians, Czechs, Poles, Ruthenians, Bosnians, Roumanians, and even gypsies. Except for a few simple words of command, they understood no German. One couldn't sit down
with them over a glass of beer. One couldn't even exchange
greetings with them. Accustomed to a unified land, with a
single language, with a single way of life, the Germans despised the Austrians for having been unable to impose on
this patchwork of peoples the German language and German
customs.

In the second place—and this was even worse—the Austrians
were poor fighters. They lost one battle after another, and
the Germans were for ever under the necessity of coming to
their help. The soldiers in the German ranks looked down
on the Austrian soldiers, the German officers looked down on
the Austrian officers. These latter were, in the eyes of the

[532]

proud Junkers, the motliest crew that gentlemen had ever been compelled to mix with, sons of peasants and of city shopkeepers, with a sprinkling of Galician Jews of Tarnopol and Kolomea. At the dances in the officers' Casino one occasionally had to rub shoulders, in the literal sense of the words, with dark-haired, darked-eyed riff-raff which in civilian life one saw only at a decent distance. It was the practice of the German officers to snatch up the best quarters in an occupied town, leaving the officers of their allies to shift for themselves. The highest posts, too, went to German officers. This contemptuous disregard of their rights bred in the Austrian officers a deep, ineradicable resentment.

German soldiers would often pass an Austrian officer and pretend not to have seen him. Or, if they did salute, the gesture was careless and disrespectful. If the Austrian reported them, they were severely reprimanded, of course, but somehow the reprimands did not discourage the German soldiers. They continued to ignore the Austrian officers.

After the series of defeats which the Austrians suffered in the Russian spring offensive, the hatred between the two armies rose to fever pitch. Then, when the independent Polish units appeared, the Germans felt that this was the last insult. The Germans had to rescue their allies, and all their allies thought of was how to increase the number of useless units they commanded. Besides, the Germans had a special and as it were private loathing for Polacks. To see them in uniforms of their own, to hear them singing their own national patriotic songs, put the Germans into an ecstasy of rage. Whenever a group of Polish legionaries began to sing, in their incomprehensible, drivelling Slav language, a patriotic song, the German *Landsturm* troops would break in with an offensive song of their own:

> Lousy Polack, dirty Russ,
> Both of them are bad for us.

The Polish legionaries of Galicia, who understood German, boiled with anger. But the *Landstürmer* went on singing their song at the top of their voices. The relations between

[533]

the armies grew so tense that German soldiers deliberately, openly, and without any pretence at absent-mindedness passed Austrian officers without giving the salute.

Baron von Heidel-Heidellau growled with disgust when he was informed that his allies the Polish legionaries had arrived in their Polish peasant carts to recruit the youth of Lodz. He had never had any use for Poles, except on his estate, where they had proved themselves willing and obedient workers. That was all they were good for. They were cheap, and they worked all hours, and they never gave any trouble. But as soldiers! And as officers! It was an insult to him to be commanded to treat with them. But orders were orders, and such was the will of the General Staff. What allies those Austrians were! Were there not Poles in Germany too? But Germany had made them learn the language of the country, had made them part of the Reich. Never would Germany have tolerated on her own soil an alien unit, with an alien language. Never would she have permitted a separate army, with separate uniforms and a separate command. That was the trouble with the Austrians. They could not fight and they could not govern. They were politicians; they were talkers. Now they had talked the German high command into opening Lodz to the Polish legionaries. What sort of a war was this?

Baron von Heidel-Heidellau carried out the orders of his superiors. He furnished quarters for the Polish troops, the worst he could find in Lodz, old sheds with leaky roofs and rotten foundations. He arranged for the delivery of provisions, insufficient and mouldy. He would see to it that the subservient spirit which he had managed to instil into the Polish civilian population would not be spoiled by the sight of these troops of the Polish fatherland.

When the revolutionary party called Proletariat fell to pieces, Felix Feldblum and his comrade Martin Kuchinsky both passed over to the Polish Socialist Party, which had accepted the double program of socialism and an independent Poland. As in the old days, the two men continued to work together. Feldblum operated the secret press, issued the party newspaper, translated Socialist books into Polish, and carried

[534]

on propaganda among Polish workers. As in the old days, he suffered imprisonment, was liberated, and returned obstinately to his task. At the time of the Russo-Japanese war Feldblum had worked more feverishly than ever in Lodz. His bitterest enemy had then been Paul Shchinsky, the Social Democrat, who had branded the Polish Socialist Party as reactionary and chauvinistic. Whenever the two men met, Shchinsky sneered at Feldblum the Polack, with his faith in the mission of the Polish people and his half-witted romanticism.

The outbreak of the World War found Feldblum in Galicia, in hiding from Colonel Konitzky. At first Feldblum was arrested, as a Russian, but he was soon liberated so that, together with his comrade Kuchinsky, he might organize Polish legions to help in driving the Russians out of Poland. Many of the Polish Socialists, fired by the idea of a free, Socialist Poland, put on the uniform of the legionaries. Feldblum, too, became a soldier. Together with the others, he believed that the greatest enemy of human freedom was Russia; together with them he believed, too, that a Poland freed from the Russian yoke would set an example of equality and fraternity to all the world.

In his soldier's uniform Felix Feldblum did not make a very warlike impression. He was already an elderly man. His huge shock of hair and his little beard were streaked with grey. His eye-glasses were still in the habit of slipping down to the tip of his nose, giving him a most unsoldierly appearance. Tall, thin, slightly bent, hasty, absent-minded, he looked more like a masquerader. But he was a faithful soldier. He went along with the youngest and strongest to the front, suffered in the trenches, and volunteered for the most dangerous work. He rose from the ranks. His friend Kuchinsky, a major, had him decorated and promoted.

Now he was in Lodz, working with his fellow-officers at recruiting the Polish youth of the city. In officer's uniform, with a sword dangling at his side, he strode through the streets of Lodz, in which he had once helped to build barricades, and showed himself openly after many, many years of the secret life of a conspirator. The German soldiers, contemptuous of all Polish officers, guffawed at the sight of this gaunt, comical figure with the shock of hair and the little beard, whose every step and gesture betrayed the Jewish intellectual. Even among his own men Feldblum caught glances of amusement. The peasant boys with turned-up noses and blond heads saw nothing authoritative in the elderly man with the eye-glasses on a cord; he looked more like a lost schoolteacher than an officer.

Nor did he feel much more at home among his fellow-officers. There had come into the original Polish legion new elements which were not interested in socialism and liberty and knew nothing of Feldblum's honourable record. They sank into a regular army life; they were interested in cards, drinking, promotion, women, and dirty jokes. In their eyes Feldblum was a ridiculous figure, as strange to them as they were to him. He did not drink or play cards; he did not laugh at their jokes or have any of his own to tell. He did not even notice when German soldiers passed him without saluting. He was democratic with his own men and befriended them in a manner unbecoming to an officer. He had no pride of rank; he did not, like his fellow-officers, enjoy swaggering around in his uniform.

His ways were queer. Instead of going to dances and drinking parties, he spent his free time in the library, studying or translating. He still lived the life of an intellectual. His eyes, instead of taking in and enjoying the life around him, were always held close to some book.

Feldblum suffered keenly as he watched his own comrades, one-time fighters for revolution and liberty, sinking to the level of the new crowd which had invaded the legion, acquiring the upper-class snobbishness of officers, learning to despise the masses and the men they commanded. He could not help noting that Kuchinsky himself was forgetting his high principles and becoming more and more the professional soldier. Instead of continuing the old work, Kuchinsky was surrounding himself with the newcomers and avoiding his one-time comrades. He even became intimate with the military chaplains. He encouraged his men to sing purely patriotic songs, in which there was no hint of revolution and socialism.

[536]

Feldblum tried to hide the truth from himself. He shut out reality by carrying on as in the old days. He arranged literary evenings; he spoke to his fellow-officers and to his men of the mission of the Polish people, which had been fitted by much suffering to lead the world toward justice. He read enthusiastically from the works of Mickievich, Norvid, and Vyspianski, and prophesied a liberated Poland which would be an example to all the nations of the earth. At times he managed to deceive himself; there were moments when he believed it all and told himself that he was working for a great cause worthy of every sacrifice. Then he would come to himself. He perceived that the men listened and did not understand. There was an invisible but impenetrable wall between him, the enthusiast and believer, and those strange, blond-headed men grouped around him. He understood then that his work was in vain, his beliefs were foolish, his enthusiasms silly. They were not his kind. They were—how strange that they should so suddenly and easily have fitted into this role—soldiers!

"He's a queer fellow, that Feldblum," said the officers among themselves. "There's something strange and uncomfortable about him."

"A Jew," said others, shrugging their shoulders.

Nissan Eibeschutz's prophecy was fulfilled with dreadful suddenness for Max Ashkenazi. The wealth he had concentrated passed out of his hands at a single stroke. True, Nissan himself did not appear in order to fulfil his own prophecy; there came others, however, and they were swifter than Nissan.

No, the world did not return to its old ways, as Max Ashkenazi had believed it would. The cobbler did not go back to his last, the manufacturer to his profits. The world was turned upside down.

In the palaces of Petrograd Red guards warmed their feet at the fires into which they had thrown the costly furniture of the rich. There was neither coal nor wood in Petrograd. The soldiers made firewood of the fine mahogany and rosewood pieces; chairs, tables, and picture-frames went into the fireplaces. They cut pieces from the leather armchairs to mend their boots and made handkerchiefs of the silk and sateen coverings. They even tore down precious hangings and cut them into wrappings for their feet, or handed out pieces as presents to their women. The rich, the one-time rulers of the city and Empire, did not know where to turn in their terror and helplessness. The banks had been seized, the safes sealed, the factories nationalized, the houses requisitioned. The walls of Petrograd were covered with proclamations, signed by Major Paul Shchinsky, concerning nationalization and requisitioning of property and the arrest of recalcitrant individuals. In the streets of the city huge streamers fluttered in the wind; in white letters on a red background they declared that the palaces now belonged to the hovels, that the might was in the hands of the Soviets, that the time had come to plunder the plunderers. Other banners carried pictures; a Red soldier with his bayonet thrust into the big belly of a bourgeois, who spouted blood; a peasant with his boot on the thick neck of a landlord; workers with muscular hands pitching out of a building an Orthodox priest, a Mussulman mufti, and a Rabbi, all three fat and greedy-looking, all three holding sacred vessels in their hands.

So they came one day to Max Ashkenazi, to plunder the plunderer.

With torn, open jackets, the shoulders of which still showed the remnants of epaulets which had been ripped off, with guns slung over their shoulders by pieces of string, with hand-made cigarettes between their lips, or chewing sunflower seeds, with red ribbons on their chests, with tattered boots on their feet, they came into the factory and occupied it.

"Comrade workers!" shouted the leader, a young man in a student's cap. "Remain in your places, all of you. The factory now belongs to the Soviet of Workers and Peasants. A meeting will be called shortly."

Swiftly and energetically the young man strode into Max Ashkenazi's office and approached the desk.

"What can I do for you?" asked Max Ashkenazi, with forced calmness, as if he had no idea of what was happening. "Take a seat." He pointed to the chair opposite his own.

"Get up from that place," said the young man curtly. "It belongs to me."

Max Ashkenazi rose quietly and took out the key to the safe. The young man in the student's hat lifted his hand.

"Put that key down," he commanded. "Nothing must be removed."

"I wasn't going to take any money out," answered Max Ashkenazi; "just some private things."

"There are no private things," said the young man. "Everything belongs to the workers and peasants. You will hand over the keys. Then you will be free to go."

[539]

Though he had been expecting this for several days, Max Ashkenazi was filled with a great astonishment when he found himself on the street, and the factory door closed behind him with a bang. He stood there for several minutes, completely paralysed.

Thrown out! He could not quite grasp it. Thrown out, plainly and simply thrown out, like an unwanted dog!

When he came to himself, he still did not move. He did not know which direction to take. The young man in the student's cap had told him he was free to go. But where? He had nowhere to go. For the first time in his life he found himself with nothing to do, with nothing to occupy him. He stood there feeling as superfluous as one of his own Lodz workers who had been shown the door and who had heard the factory door bang to behind him.

He was a superfluous being in this huge city. He was superfluous and naked. His houses had been seized, his money in the banks sealed up, his stocks and bonds completely devaluated. No, he said to himself, there are no eternal things. Even houses and factories are not eternal things. He had thought to prepare himself against the worst by putting his money into solid, tangible possessions. Now they were all gone. Everything that he had built up in Petrograd, all his earnings of the war years, machines and buildings, all gone, at one stroke.

During the weeks that followed, Max Ashkenazi was like a man who had been stunned by a hammer-blow and had never come to properly. It was incredible! All that labour, all that planning! How he had sweated! He had given up his nights, he had forgotten to eat during the days, he had broken down countless obstacles, he had moved a city from Poland into Russia, he had performed miracles! There, in Lodz, he had left behind him the hulk of the factory. He had brought with him everything that he could carry, and here, in this strange city, he had built anew, from the foundations, built marvellously, recouping in a few years of mad labour all that he had lost, and adding greatly to it, till his possessions were reckoned in millions. Now—gone! Simply taken from him! Weak anger seized him. This was robbery, open robbery. They took a man who with his own hands had built up a fortune, giving his life to the task, and they turned him into a pauper. Just so! How could such a thing happen?

He looked at the big placards which called the population to "plunder the plunderers." What drivel was that? He did not feel like a plunderer. He had robbed no one. He had merely done business. True, there had been certain painful transactions, with former partners, with rivals, and so on—but that was business. He who was smarter raked in the profits. But that wasn't robbery. It was calculation. It was superior management. The same thing with his workers. He had not compelled any man to work for him. He had paid, as other industrialists paid, with an eye to profits. Max Ashkenazi had nothing on his conscience. He felt himself to be as innocent as a new-born lamb. The name robber did not fit him. It fitted only those who came in the middle of the day with guns slung over their shoulders to take from a man everything that he had accumulated.

Those were wretched and lonely days for Max Ashkenazi; and the nights were worse.

Dressed in the poorest coat he could find among his clothes, a working-man's hat drawn down over his eyes, he wandered through the strange city, street by street, avenue by avenue. Petrograd, which had so recently been brilliant with light, alive with luxury, filled with carriages and officers and elegant ladies going to and from the restaurants, the theatres, the cafés and palaces, was dismal and forlorn now. A universal poverty had descended upon it. In front of the co-operatives stood long rows of men and women, waiting their turn to get a piece of bread or a salt herring. The prices increased crazily from day to day, even from hour to hour. The peasant who brought a jug of milk into the city was afraid to sell it, lest by the time he tried to buy something with his money, it be worthless. He was confused by the fantastic figures. And thousands like him looked uncomprehendingly at the queer banknotes with the incredible amounts printed on them.

Max Ashkenazi emptied his pockets of their last banknotes and bought himself food in the market-place. He retired

[541]

with it to his own room and prepared it himself. But his room was without water and without fire. The weather was bitter cold, and often the pipes froze in the night, so that even the well in the yard was useless, and water had to be brought from a distance.

He was occupying one of the poorest rooms in his own palace on the Kamienny Ostrovsky Prospekt. His tenants and servants had fled, the latter to their villages, the former he knew not whither. In their places had moved in working-men, and Red soldiers and sailors. Day after day they had arrived, thrusting Max Ashkenazi from one room to another.

"Hey, little father," they asked, looking suspiciously at the proletarian clothes which sat so ill on him, "what crowd do you belong to?"

Max Ashkenazi did not answer. He had nothing to say. He shrank into a corner or slipped out of the room, to be away from the soldiers and sailors, who reeked with a mixture of joy, drink, brutality, and righteousness.

When they insisted on an answer, he replied, in a pitiful voice: "I'm a war refugee from Poland."

"You'll have to move a little farther, old man," they said. "For a war refugee you take up too much room. And you've got too many things, a regular furniture store."

They shoved him from room to room, till he had one of the poorest in the house, where he now lived, doing everything for himself. Day and night he heard around him the tumult of his unbidden guests. They turned the place into a bedlam. They smashed the furniture, tore down the hangings, burned everything in their portable tin stoves. They drank and they rioted; they danced, sang, brought their women in, and filled the nights with their wild laughter. He shivered with cold, though he lay buried under the bed-clothes and the heavy sable fur, which he did not dare to put on during the day. Through his resentment and wretchedness he was aware of wonder and envy at the care-free gaiety of the men and women in the other rooms. After all, they too had nothing; besides, any day the men might be called away to battle. Yet they had the strength and the spirit to sing day and night. How different it was with him! His body was old. All the weakness

[542]

and decay to which he had paid no attention during the insane rush of his acquisitive years asserted itself with double insistence now. He could not sleep. His limbs ached; his skin burned; he was dry and hot inside. And there was no one to help him; no one to bring him a glass of tea or a pitcher of warm water. This man who had directed great factories and commanded thousands of men felt himself incapable of looking after his own weary old body.

The young men and women in the high boots laughed uproariously when they saw him crawl out of his room with the porcelain pitcher in his hand to bring himself water from the well in another street. In his weakness and uncertainty he would slip and fall down. His hands trembled comically when he fumbled with the rope at the well and tied it round the ear of the pitcher. He had been so quick and skilful in the manipulation of papers; he was slow and clumsy when he tried to split a log of wood. From day to day he became more helpless, more ragged, more dirty.

The interminable, sleepless nights were worse than the days. He heard, in the pauses of the insane merriment around him, the sound of shots. Through his little window he sometimes saw a redness in the sky. Houses were burning. The little tin stoves of the soldiers were dangerous things; they threw out sparks; or they were upset. It might happen some night in his house.

But more terrible than the shooting and the fires was the perpetual danger of a visit from the Red guards. They were for ever seeking out the former rich, questioning them, searching their rooms for gold and precious stones, for secret documents and arms. He had neither secret documents nor arms; but before the Bolsheviks had taken possession of his factory he had hidden away, in the cellars of friends and acquaintances, small stocks of goods. With prices as they were today, these small stocks were worth a fortune. Max Ashkenazi would have liked to get rid of them, at any price, before it was too late, before they were found and traced to him. Between fits of terror which came upon him when he thought he heard the palace bell ring out in the middle of the night, announcing the Red guards, he thought feverishly of schemes to sell the goods. It was difficult and dangerous. One could not move goods openly. One could not even consort openly with other former merchants. There were spies everywhere.

He had also hidden away, in corners of the palace, where nobody would think of looking, small quantities of gold and a few precious stones. He had also sewn some jewels into his clothes, into his sable coat, and under the collars of his other winter coats, where they could not easily be felt. He would have been glad to escape from the city without selling his merchandise, but there was no way of leaving it without the necessary papers, and Max Ashkenazi had no inclination to visit the Government offices, which were filled with Red soldiers, and women with peasant kerchiefs on their heads. He wanted to keep out of their way. The less frequently his name was mentioned in the city which was controlled by Paul Shchinsky, the better for him. He remembered that man too well, out of the far-off past in Lodz. And Shchinsky no doubt remembered him.

Yes, perhaps he could get through if he stripped himself of all his diamonds and his gold and went out literally naked. But how could he do that? How could he arrive in Lodz utterly penniless, a beggar, a pauper? And yet to try to smuggle out the diamonds might cost him his life. More than one man was now lying flat six feet under for making the attempt. If one could only find the right men to bribe! That was it! A frightfully dangerous business, of course. He did not know whom to trust. There were spies everywhere.

Shivering in his bed at night, he was seized with a great self-pity. What had he come to this accursed city for? Ah yes, for money, of course. He had seen his great opportunity in the midst of the chaos of the war. Russia! He would found a new fortune there. And it had all turned out wrong. This time he had been too far-sighted, too clever. He had wanted too much. He had tried to force the hand of destiny, which is a mistake, always. A man, he reflected, should be content to let things go their normal course.

He thought of his brother, Jacob, who had always taken things simply. That was the right way. He thought of him with envy, but without hatred. He had remained in Lodz,

[544]

and no doubt everything was going well with him, as it had always done. He was probably at home, with wife and children, leading a quiet, sensible life, as he himself might have done if he had not been possessed of the crazy idea that nothing was good enough for him.

He thought of his daughter Gertrude, and for the first time in his life it occurred to him that, after all, she had been an exceptionally intelligent and capable person. What confounded luck that Jacob Bunim had had, to get her as his wife! He, the father, had of course not come to the marriage; he had never seen his daughter again after that day. From Gertrude his thoughts passed to Ignatz, his son, no longer a boy, but a grown man, somewhere. He tried to remember what Ignatz looked like, and the picture refused to present itself to his memory. Yes, a stupid fellow, who had hated his father; yet Max Ashkenazi would have liked to see him again. Perhaps he was married now, very likely to a gentile woman. Perhaps he was a father. He had been told that Ignatz had joined a French regiment. He had always been a fool, with a liking for stupid, un-Jewish things. It might be that he had been wounded in the war; or that something worse had happened. Max Ashkenazi shuddered at the thought.

Then Dinah flashed into his mind, and her image was vivid enough, as he had seen her for the last time, on the day of their divorce. Painfully he recalled his life with her. She had never loved him; but that might not have been wholly her fault. He had never sought to understand her or to play a part in her life. He had always been too absorbed in his affairs. She had been so beautiful. That divorce had been an utterly insane business. She had not wanted it. He had insulted her with it, before the whole world. In those days she had even begun to like and respect him. And considering that she did not love him, and he had done so little to win her love, she had behaved very decently toward him. She had not been like other women who, in a like position, betrayed their husbands and turned them into objects of ridicule. All those years he had lived with her, knowing that she did not love him; and just when she had begun to change, that mad idea had come to him of divorcing her.

[545]

She had seemed beautiful to him on the day of the divorce, when he had thrown her over for his second wife. A clever, able woman, this second wife of his, the former widow Margulies; a woman who had respected him and helped him. She had remained behind in Lodz to keep an eye on his possessions, and no doubt she had fulfilled that duty well. A man, really, not a woman. Hard, able, and older than himself. There had been no happiness with her. She was not the woman to come to for solace and warmth and happiness after the day's torments. He remembered the empty, senseless nights with her. And Dinah had still been beautiful when he left her. Why had he done all this? For the sake of money, possessions, power—and now none of these were his. How stupid! How utterly stupid! It could have been so different. He could have been in his own home this day, happy with his own wife and with his children.

In the midst of the self-pity which blinded him with tears, he thought consolingly of the something that was left to him in Lodz, the factory and the mansion over which his second wife was keeping guard. It had been his good luck that he had been unable to burn all his bridges behind him. Now he would be able to return, and from now on he would know how to live. He would make peace with his children, and with his brother. He would be done with stupid rivalries and quarrels. Life had taught him. He would even make friends with Dinah and help her in whatever she needed.

He would be softer toward the world at large; he would not sell himself again to this idol of gold. It was not worth it. A man's duty was to be content with moderate success; no one had a right to conquer the whole world. Yes, he would interest himself in others; he would take up philanthropic work and perform many kind acts. If only he could get out of this hell of Petrograd, back to his native city, to his own friends and his own flesh and blood. He would make a place for himself again. He was not through yet. No, not he, Max Ashkenazi. It was only here, in Petrograd, that he could do nothing; but then, the city and country had gone quite mad! Quite mad! How else explain the fact that he, Max Ashkenazi, had to fetch his own water from the well, chop his own wood, cook his own meals, like the soldiers and peasants and city louts around him? There, in Poland, in a land which had retained its sanity, he would get on his feet again.

Thinking these sweet thoughts, he even reconciled himself to his dreadful losses in Russia. "Let them choke with the factory," he thought, "they'll get no good out of it; they'll ruin the country and themselves with it." As long as he could get away, back to his own. Thank God he had been foresighted enough to hide away the little stock of goods and gold, and the small quantity of jewels! With God's help he would find a buyer for the goods, and he would escape from the land which had gone mad.

Thoughts like these recurred more frequently as the weeks passed, and his courage slowly returned to him. He was ready to give away a large part of the wealth that still remained to him if he could only escape with the rest, and he believed that if he looked carefully he would find his man. Certainly it was not easy. In the turmoil of the revolution he had lost sight of many of his friends. When he went to their homes, he found only soldiers, who either did not know what had happened to the former proprietors or would not tell. He had to make new connections; but he was not the man to shrink from difficulties. Money would do everything for him. He knew of course that there were some people whom money could not buy; there were fanatics and lunatics and visionaries who neither lived nor let live; but they were in the minority. The greater part of the world still had its senses. The question was how he could get to one of the men on the inside.

In the old days he had had his lists of officials, with the price opposite each name. Now he knew no one. But of one thing he was certain: there were no governments without venal officials, and this Government was no exception. Why, there was already talk in the streets about officials who sold in the public markets the goods they had requisitioned from the bourgeoisie. This was, in Max Ashkenazi's eyes, quite normal; the world was that way. The only danger was that he might fall into the hands of one of those idiotic fanatics who really meant what they said. It was unsafe to approach even a fellow-Jew, for among the Bolsheviks those Jews were the worst, the most intractable. One had to be fearfully careful. It was a matter of life and death.

Max Ashkenazi now spent the nights considering how he could reach one of the higher-ups—none of your snivelling little officials—and make a decent deal with him. It was much more sensible to give away a good slice of his possessions and escape with the rest than to be penny-wise, to play with some minor official, and to run the risk of losing all. The man was waiting somewhere; he had only to be found. Patience and energy! And, above all, courage! With these he would get out of this difficulty as he had got of many a difficulty in the past.

During this time Max Ashkenazi underwent a religious conversion, and remembered the God whom he had forgotten in the rush of his business activities. He even went to synagogue every day, and at night, when he lay down to sleep, he said the night prayers which his father, and his father's father, had said before him from time immemorial. It was only God who could help him now, for in His hand was the fate of every living thing.

In the nights he calculated and planned and prayed. The shooting went on, fires were lit, truckfuls of soldiers passed, making the windows tremble, and with every sound Max Ashkenazi started, afraid they were coming for him. "Let them not come for me!" he prayed. He felt that if they found his stock of goods, if they discovered his diamonds, if they took away from him the last remnants of his possessions, he might as well lie down and die, there and then. For who would succour him? Who would feed him, who would care for him if he fell sick? He would die like a dog, and no one would even look round at his carcass.

When the danger was past and he knew that he was safe, he buried his head in the pillow and resumed his calculations and his prayers.

six

The person for whom Max Ashkenazi prayed appeared suddenly; like a delivering angel he descended unannounced from the sky.

One day, as Max Ashkenazi came out of the synagogue, where Jews forgathered to pray, discuss exchange and the price of potatoes, and bewail the dreadful decline of Judaism, he was stopped by a round little man with a smiling face, big, bushy moustaches, and wide-open black eyes which were at once cunning and childlike. The stranger did not say anything at first. He only looked long and earnestly at Max Ashkenazi, then, with a sweeping and respectful gesture, took off his hat, a hard derby of a type rarely seen during that period in the Red city.

"Gospodin Ashkenazi! I am delighted to see you, sir!" exclaimed the queer little man in Russian. He was at once familiar and obsequious, and his words and the manner of his approach recalled the times before the revolution, when a rich man was a somebody, and everyone knew it.

Max Ashkenazi looked at the man and tried hard to remember where he had seen him. His mind remained blank. During his long scrutiny the little man continued to smile, showing the milk-white teeth under the lip covered by the black moustache. At the same time he seemed to be concentrating, helping Ashkenazi to remember, like a mother trying to prompt her child at a public recitation.

"Well now, well now, Gospodin Ashkenazi! Look at me

[549]

more closely, my dear sir. It's impossible that you should have forgotten me. . . ."

In the old days Max Ashkenazi would not have spent two seconds with such an odd person; he would have told him straightway to go to the devil. All sorts of pests used to run after him, trying to ingratiate themselves with him: merchants, travelling salesmen, commission men, and agents of all kinds. He would hurry past them, and, if forced to stop, just hold out a fishy finger and look at them coldly. No doubt this odd person was one of them. But which one? Since he had never paid any attention to the small fry, they had all looked alike to him. In these dangerous times, however, it would not do to snub anyone. Ashkenazi did his best to remember, but in vain. The cheerful little stranger with the round eyes which were both cunning and childlike had to introduce himself.

"Miron Markovitch Gorodetzky, agent, an old customer of yours, Gospodin Ashkenazi!" he announced proudly.

Max Ashkenazi plucked at his beard nervously. The stranger heaved a deep sigh, but in the sigh there was more contentment than distress.

"If I only had half the money I've spent with you, Gospodin Ashkenazi, I would have no more worries. No, no, I would be a happy man. But it doesn't matter."

The quick, tumbling words, the lively delivery, the cheerfulness of the man, produced a startling effect on Max Ashkenazi. There was, decidedly, something pleasant and reassuring about this stranger with the hard derby in a city of working-men's caps. There was a world of confidence and gaiety in the round eyes; they reminded one of the good old times.

"Are you a St. Petersburger?" asked Max Ashkenazi, to begin the conversation.

"Why, no. Personally I'm from Odessa," answered Gorodetzky. "That is to say, I was born in Odessa. But I've lived in practically every town in Russia; we're even fellow-townsmen from Lodz, if you like. I was quite a youngster when I came to Lodz. I've worked for some of the best firms there. Fine town, Lodz. I had lots of good times there. Such women! Beauties, every one of them."

The little man passed the tip of his red tongue over his lips, as if retasting something. "Beauties!" he repeated, and forthwith began to tell Max Ashkenazi of his happy experiences with some of them. Max Ashkenazi listened impatiently for a minute and then interrupted. He had never been able to stand this kind of talk. Besides, he wanted to find out if there was any point in continuing the conversation.

"Now that the seven fat years are gone," he said, "I suppose there's no more room for agents."

The little man stopped chattering, looked gaily at Max Ashkenazi, took him by the arm, and stepped a little closer, so that he could talk into his ear.

"There's always room for a good man, Gospodin Ashkenazi. May that Polack of yours, Shchinsky, have as many boils on his neck as the number of deals I swing every week in this very town!" His mouth was so close to Ashkenazi's ear that he tickled it with his moustaches.

"And what does our friend Shchinsky say?" asked Max Ashkenazi, indicating, on the wall near by, one of the posters which warned the population against speculation, private business, the hiding of merchandise, and similar crimes.

The little man looked at Ashkenazi with profound pity in his merry eyes.

"Shchinsky puts posters on the walls, and Gorodetzky does business as usual," he answered, rolling his eyes in every direction. "Only yesterday I got rid of a carload of merchandise and made a good fat profit on it."

Ashkenazi's heart gave a sudden leap, and he felt the blood running faster through his veins. This was the finger of Providence! God had not abandoned him! He could hardly believe his own ears. But Gorodetzky did not give him time to think.

"I'm very, very happy to have met you again, Gospodin Ashkenazi," he chattered on. "The fact is, I'm not exactly what you would call a pious person. But I do remember every year to say the Kaddish in memory of my dead father, no matter how busy I am. After all, a man has to remember the Kaddish, if he remembers nothing else."

"Why, certainly, certainly," murmured Max Ashkenazi.

[551]

He was pleased to hear that this little man remembered the Kaddish every year for his dead father. It agreed with his own reawakened faith in God. Indeed, there seemed to be something specially significant in this fellow's concession to the call of religion. Max Ashkenazi was touched. He took hold of Gorodetzky's arm, as, in the old days, he would have taken the arm of some important Russian merchant.

"I can see you're nobody's fool," he said.

Gorodetzky acknowledged the compliment with a happy smile.

"I've never let myself be fooled by laws and decrees and that sort of rubbish," he said softly. "For years I couldn't get a permit to live where I wanted to in Russia. I couldn't travel where I wanted to. I mean, they told me not to. And I told them to go to hell. I've been in every corner of Russia. There isn't a town that doesn't know Miron Markovitch Gorodetzky. Most of the time I used to live in the police commissioner's house. That's always the safest way. Nowadays they tell me I can live wherever I like, but I mustn't do business. So I tell them again to go to hell, and I do all the business I want to. And, of course, again under the noses of those commissars. . . . The safest game, I tell you."

The man retreated a step and once more looked earnestly at Max Ashkenazi, as if seeing him for the first time. He made a circular motion with his right hand.

"All of them!" he said, closing his fist. "I've got them right here. Live and let live."

Ashkenazi liked this man more and more every minute. He thought hard, looking for an approach to his subject. He knew this type, with its liveliness, energy, ingenuity, and infinite adaptability. These were the men who had built Lodz, carried its goods into every corner of the Russian Empire and beyond, and brought the wealth of half the world into the city. They were liked everywhere, for their gaiety and infectious laughter, their jokes, their tricks, and their slyness. The Russians, in particular, loved men like these. They had a marvellous prehensile faculty for finding the official who would let his palm be greased, and a marvellous way of getting to the point. Max Ashkenazi made up his mind to

[552]

hold fast to this man. He would dispose of the stock of goods, now hidden away in cellars; he would also arrange for him to get out of the country. And he would do it in the safest way conceivable: to wit, via the commissars themselves. But Max Ashkenazi was still cautious: life and death in the power of a word, he remembered, and he let the man talk on.

"How did you come out of the catastrophe?" asked Gorodetzky.

"So-so," he answered, non-committally.

That was enough for the other.

"Listen, Gospodin Ashkenazi," he said, his tone become earnest suddenly. "I have an idea that we two can do business. You're not the kind of man to let those thieves strip you clean. Every merchant with a grain of sense hid away some of his stocks in good time. Now they fetch fancy prices. I can put you next to all the buyers you want. As for getting the goods out, don't you worry about that. Leave it to Miron Markovitch Gorodetzky. And as far as my share is concerned, we won't come to blows about that, either."

Max Ashkenazi was silent. This was too important a matter to be done in a rush. The other, however, pressed him.

"If you don't feel safe about the money, I'll show you all the cash you want, and in any kind of money. Tsarist money, Kerensky money, anything you like. Even foreign money. It's all one to me. Besides, if a man is thinking of getting out of the country, he usually wants to have some foreign exchange in his pockets."

Max Ashkenazi stepped back from the chattering Gorodetzky and looked him over from head to foot.

"Who told you I want to get out of the country?" he asked, suspiciously.

Gorodetzky laughed and then again became earnest very suddenly.

"Now listen to me, Gospodin Ashkenazi," he said slowly and quietly, not at all in his usual babbling style. "I know who you are and what you are. I've always been a poor man, and I always shall be. I've got no place to go to. Anyway, I can look after myself here, in Petrograd. And if I can't, well, there'll be one Gorodetzky fewer on earth, and one more in heaven. But you, Gospodin Ashkenazi, will go home, because you've a home to go to. You won't be the only one I've managed to get out of this town. I've got more than one letter from the other side to prove it."

And before Ashkenazi could protest his faith, the other had snatched a package of papers from his inside breast-pocket and was going through it rapidly with his plump fingers.

"My dear Miron Markovitch," he began to read out. Max Ashkenazi interrupted hastily.

"For heaven's sake, man, not here on the street," he muttered. "And you don't have to read me those letters."

"Gospodin Ashkenazi," said Gorodetzky, putting the package back hastily in his breast-pocket and hurrying along with Max Ashkenazi, who had walked off hastily, "God Himself has brought us together. I tell you we'll do things, the two of us. And if you should happen to need a little cash just now, why, just say the word. Good Kerensky money, none of this Bolshevik rubbish—"

Max Ashkenazi did not want to take any money. "Good day," he said, holding out his hand. "We'll talk this over again soon."

"Good. Here in the synagogue," said Gorodetzky. "Good morning, sir."

He took off his derby with a great flourish and added another farewell in Lodz German: "Your servant, sir."

Ashkenazi walked away, his heart in a turmoil of hope and uneasiness. More than ever the streets and walls of this city were alien to him. He wanted to get out. The stones burned under his feet.

Gorodetzky turned up again, sooner than Max Ashkenazi had expected, and carried out his promise with a speed that left the latter rather breathless.

He had incredible connections, this plump little man with the laughing, foxy eyes: obscure merchants in side streets, mysterious buyers who received consignments and shifted them as if by sleight of hand. They seemed to trust Gorodetzky implicitly, for when Ashkenazi had sold them the unseen goods and had admitted that he had no way of delivering them, the buyers were not taken aback at all.

"Miron Markovitch will look after that," they said confidently. "We rely on him."

Miron Markovitch did look after it. The goods were taken away in trucks, by men in military leather coats. Gorodetzky stood by his principle, which was to break the law always with the assistance of the guardians of the law. "It's the best way," he kept repeating, contentedly.

"Good work!" said Max Ashkenazi when the last of the consignments had been removed from their hiding-place. He was happy to have completed the first half of his task. He slapped Gorodetzky on the back and handed him a fat bundle of notes, representing his commission. Gorodetzky took the bundle carelessly and dropped it into his pocket, without even bothering to count.

"Come along, Gospodin Ashkenazi!" he exclaimed. "We'll

wash that transaction down with a little drink. Like in the good old days."

Despite his dislike of drinks and celebrations of this sort, Max Ashkenazi went along. He wanted to remain on good terms with this heaven-sent deliverer. Holding his arm tightly, Gorodetzky led him down the street.

"Hey! Driver!" He hailed a black-bearded cabman in a flat, cylindrical hat. The two horses harnessed to the carriage did not seem to belong to the new era; they were plump and well fed.

"What's the matter with you, man?" exclaimed Max Ashkenazi. "How can you go driving through the streets nowadays?"

"Gospodin Ashkenazi, leave all that to me," Gorodetzky reassured him, showing the white little teeth behind his black moustaches in a joyous smile.

Ashkenazi got into the carriage reluctantly. He did not feel at all happy; but Gorodetzky sprawled back comfortably on the cushioned seat and gazed down negligently on the passers-by. When they alighted, Ashkenazi put his hand to his pocket uncertainly. He had no idea what one paid for a ride these days. Gorodetzky stopped him, drew out several notes, and threw them to the driver.

"Thank you, sir," the driver exclaimed, and, bowing low in his seat, took off his flat, shining cylinder of a hat.

In the restaurant, which looked very poor on the surface, Miron Markovitch ordered a royal meal, with hors-d'œuvres, entrée, roast, and dessert. He also ordered a little bottle of excellent cognac. Max Ashkenazi had not seen or tasted such food since the day when the Red soldiers and sailors had occupied his palace. Whatever he had eaten since then he had prepared with his own hands.

"Try this horse-radish, Gospodin Ashkenazi," said Miron Markovitch, serving his guest. "The sauce is excellent. So is the cognac." He poured out a glass for each of them. "Good luck! May this be only the beginning of a very successful association!"

The good, solid food and the cognac warmed the two men into a kindly humour. Miron Markovitch's eyes sparkled

[556]

more brightly than ever. He kept leaning over to put his hand benevolently on Max Ashkenazi's shoulder or to tap him significantly on the knee.

"Well, you'll have to admit that Miron Markovitch knows where to get a decent meal in this god-forsaken town, eh?"

As he went on eating and drinking, he became more and more sentimental and confidential, just like a Russian. He wanted to bare his soul to Ashkenazi. He told him the story of his life, from the days of his boyhood in Odessa, when he used to help his widowed mother deliver chickens and geese to the houses of the rich, through his experiences as a young man in Lodz, his promotion to a salesman's position, his travels throughout Russia, down to the present moment.

"It's been a hard life," he said, becoming sad. "It was no joke for a Jew, who had no right to travel in Russia, to have that sort of job. But Miron Markovitch knew how to manage. He went everywhere just the same. There were some who counselled me to be baptized, to become a Lutheran, for instance. That would make things easier for me. But Miron Markovitch isn't a renegade. No, my little brothers, I said to them; I don't do that sort of thing, or my name isn't Miron Markovitch Gorodetzky. No coat-turning for me!"

Max Ashkenazi was greatly pleased by the discovery that Miron Markovitch was no turncoat. That and the saying of the Kaddish in memory of his dead father proved something. The man was reliable. Miron Markovitch felt the impression he had made, and his soul was bathed in contentment.

"No, no," he went on, passionately. "I know I'm no saint. You know how it is when a man travels. You can't get kosher food; you eat anything. You can't observe the Sabbath. You commit—you'll pardon me for mentioning it—other sins; there are women, you understand. . . . But Kaddish, and the Day of Atonement, and the Jewish God, that's a different story. I've never betrayed them."

Miron Markovitch filled the glasses again and again. After the first drink Max Ashkenazi, as was his wont, poured the cognac into his plate or at his feet, in order to keep his head. Miron Markovitch did not notice. He swallowed glass after glass. His merriment disappeared altogether. He began to weep. He described to Max Ashkenazi all the sadness of his life. He told him of his young wife at home, who deceived him over and over again when he was on the road. It was dreadful. Max Ashkenazi tried to console him, but Miron Markovitch would not be consoled. He came over to Max Ashkenazi and kissed him affectionately.

"You're just like a father to me," he blubbered, and he began to thank Ashkenazi for all the kindness he had shown him, though Ashkenazi could not remember a single thing he had ever done for him.

Then, suddenly, he rose from the table, ran to the sink, and began to pour cold water over his head. He returned as cool and as sober as if he had not touched a drop. He was once again the cheerful, energetic, and resourceful agent and salesman.

As rapidly as he had set about the selling of Ashkenazi's secret stock of goods, he now set about the arranging of the journey. First he introduced Ashkenazi to two men who were dressed half in military uniform, half in civilian clothes, half Russian and half Finnish. Big, sturdy fellows they were, tanned by sun and wind. They were as taciturn as Gorodetzky was garrulous; they listened without taking the pipes out of their mouths, but every now and again they nodded, to show that they were in agreement with him. They would take along on their next journey Miron Markovitch's passenger.

Max Ashkenazi did not feel comfortable in the presence of these two taciturn giants in the piebald clothes, but when he was alone again with Gorodetzky, the latter assured him that they were the best fellows in the world. They had looked after a great many "shipments" for him, as some of those letters he had shown Ashkenazi the other day testified. Their main activity was smuggling. They brought food and other merchandise from Finland in a small fishing-boat. They were expert sailors and oarsmen. They always returned to Finland empty, except for the occasional illegal passengers they took on. They had never had an accident; they had never been picked up. And anyway they were working hand in glove with one of the commissars.

The arrangements were completed. Miron Markovitch did

more than obtain the passage for Ashkenazi. He provided him with foreign exchange; he helped him pack; he sewed the precious stones into little canvas bags which Ashkenazi could wear next to his body. All in all, he made himself indispensable.

On the day of the journey the two men attended synagogue. Max Ashkenazi prayed with unusual fervour, repeating carefully every word in the prayer of the Eighteen Benedictions. In particular he paused over the passage which invokes the wrath of God on men of evil intentions and bad heart, and he raised his eyes to heaven, seeking protection.

In the evening Max Ashkenazi stole out of the house with his few parcels. A droshky was waiting for him, to take him to the Baltic station, whence he would go by train to the seashore, and there he would be met by the smugglers. It took a long time to put the train together. Ashkenazi was restless and impatient; Gorodetzky, seated by the bundles, was cool and cheerful.

"One can see that you're not used to this sort of thing," he whispered to Ashkenazi. "Take it easy. Everything will be all right!"

When the train was completed a mob of men, women, and children made a rush for it. Although it was winter, many people continued to live at the seashore, whither they returned late every night; and since this was the last train, it was jammed with travellers. Passengers of all kinds, in furs, in rags, in military clothes, struggled for places. Max Ashkenazi stood like one lost; he had never travelled on such a train. He had never had to fight for a seat. But Miron Markovitch was quite at home. He wormed and elbowed his way through with extraordinary rapidity. He found two places and covered them with the parcels. In an instant he was back on the platform, propelling Max Ashkenazi in front of him. And in a few minutes Miron Markovitch had already made friends with the other people in the car and, between joking and impudent begging, had made himself and Ashkenazi comfortable.

"Just a little room, comrades. Thanks, that's it, thanks very much," he kept coaxing in his broad Odessa Russian, rolling the *r* of the frequent *tovaritch*. The train pulled along slowly, whistling dismally into the night, stopping often. Max Ashkenazi tried to make himself as inconspicuous as possible. Time was eating like a worm at his intestines. He was tortured by the rich fur coat he was wearing, and by the little canvas bags.

Late in the night they arrived at a roadside station. Miron Markovitch picked up the bundles and signalled Ashkenazi to follow him. He led him out of the station and down to the seashore. A fierce wind was blowing. Max Ashkenazi struggled against it and followed Markovitch. The air was harsh and salty. The trees which grew almost to the water's edge whistled and shrilled in the wind. The waves slapped against the shore.

A figure emerged suddenly out of the darkness, making Ashkenazi start with terror. Markovitch grabbed him by the arm. "One of our men," he muttered, reassuringly.

The man drew close, took the parcels wordlessly from Markovitch, and led the way. Miron Markovitch began to say something, but Max Ashkenazi seized him fiercely and covered his mouth.

"For God's sake, stop talking!" he whispered.

The sound of the sea pleased him, even though it seemed to presage storm. It spoke of distance and freedom and salvation. Hope and fear struggled in his heart at the prospect of the hours to be passed on the water. He would have liked to ask the tall, silent man who was leading them whether he expected really dangerous weather, but he did not trust himself to speak.

They came to a small hut. The man in front dropped the packages and knocked. Someone opened. The interior of the hut was faintly illumined by a single weak lamp. Ashkenazi saw huge piles of sacks, stacks of barrels. Furs hung on the walls. The men in the hut did not exchange greetings with the newcomers. They sat, all of them, in silence, smoking.

Miron Markovitch lay down on a pile of sacks and fell asleep. He snored and puffed, making as much noise when he slept as when he was awake. Ashkenazi, too, sat down and tried to close his eyes, but they opened again of themselves;

his nerves were on edge.

Hours passed. Ashkenazi waited for the moment when they would tell him that the boat was ready and he could set out on his journey, but the men uttered no word. The wind outside kept up its wailing, the waves beat rhythmically against the shore. Max Ashkenazi looked again and again at his gold watch—the watch he had received as a present when he became a bridegroom—and noted the slow passage of the hours. The night seemed to be endless. At last his nerves relaxed, in sheer exhaustion, and his eyes closed. The dark hut with its sacks and mysterious figures dissolved, and in its place there grew up the lighted dining-room of his palace in Lodz. All the lamps were lit; the table was loaded with food; at the head of the table he himself, Max Ashkenazi, was happily installed; near him was his wife—not the second, but the first, Dinah. She was young and beautiful, as she had been in the days of his first love for her; but though she was so young, their children were already grown up. They, too, were seated at the table with shining faces, Ignatz on one side, Gertrude on the other. They were all there, ranged along the table: his parents-in-law, Reb Chaim and Priveh; his brother, Jacob Bunim. They ate and drank and laughed; he told them of his travels and adventures; they lifted their glasses to him; he opened a big leather valise and distributed many presents; then they left, and he was alone with his Dinah. She undressed; she put on a sweet and costly night-dress; she caressed him with her soft hands, she called him gently to her.

"Yes, Dinah," he whispered. "I'll be with you soon. . . ."

He lifted his hand to put out the light, but it refused to be put out. It kept glaring at him. He tried to thrust it away from him, but then he woke and was aware that he was staring at a lantern which someone was holding to his face. Two men in leather were shaking him by the shoulders.

"That's enough sleep. Time to get up."

Ashkenazi sprang to his feet. Something in the voice filled him with terror. The two men had revolvers stuck into their belts. He looked around for Gorodetzky.

"Miron Markovitch!" he called. "Miron Markovitch!"

The two men burst into laughter.

[561]

"Miron Markovitch got a sudden invitation to a wedding," one of them roared. "He left you his kindest regards, Gospodin Ashkenazi. Come on now, faster; we've got a truck waiting for you outside."

But he could not move. The ghastly truth dawned on him, the swindle of it, the unspeakable treachery of the little man with the red cheeks and the round, black eyes! Fooled! Delivered, in the most loathsome way, into the hands of the enemy! He wanted to scream into the black night, a wild protest against the indecency of human beings; he wanted to yell, out across the sea, the bitterness in his heart, his hatred of everyone, and of himself too, for his indescribable stupidity and simplicity and gullibility. Here, at the gate of liberty, turned back, ruined, undone! His blood seemed to be repeating all these words, but he could not open his mouth. His tongue was like a piece of hard shoe-leather nailed to his palate. He was paralysed with terror. His knees trembled, as though the sockets had been unscrewed.

"Make a move there!" the two men growled, and released their hold on him.

He could not make a move. The moment they let go of him he sank to the floor. The two men spat, bent down to him, and put their powerful hands under his armpits. Carelessly and negligently they lifted him and hauled him to the door. Outside stood a truck, with a driver in the seat. The two men pitched Ashkenazi into the truck like the packages which they threw in after him. Then they jumped in beside the driver.

"Full speed ahead, Vanya!" cried one of them. "It's late, and we've got a pile of work to do."

Max Ashkenazi had fainted with fear.

The automobile turned and sped along the road parallel with the shore. The sea thundered in the darkness, rolled up against the land, withdrew, returned again, in the rhythm of a million years; so it had washed this stretch of shore while generations, ages, nations, had come and gone. The wind sweeping in from the water wrestled with the hissing branches of the trees, tore at them as if to break them off, or else to tear the trees out by the roots.

The day of vindication and triumph came for Tevyeh the weaver; Colonel von Heidel-Heidellau, commandant of the city of Lodz, fled from that city under every circumstance of humiliation and disgrace.

The Baron had known something concerning the German defeats on the western front, the collapse of the Hindenburg line, and the defection of the allies. But nothing had been able to shake his obstinate belief in the ultimate triumph of his country. When he received a military dispatch informing him that the Kaiser had fled to Holland, and that the population of Berlin had risen, he turned very red, then very white, and then yellow, as yellow as a corpse.

"It's ridiculous!" he yelled at his adjutant. "It's perfectly ridiculous. Read it out, lieutenant, I can't see it any more."

The lieutenant read out the information in a loud steady voice. The Baron, hearing it now from someone else, broke down and began to sob like an old woman, striking himself in the head with both hands.

"*Verdammt! Verflucht!* Blast it, blast it, blast it!" he wailed.

He began to look like a wet and wounded old rooster who has just emerged from mortal combat with a young rival. His weakness and age broke through his stiff uniform. The lieutenant tried to bring him back to himself.

"Colonel!" he said, gently. "Baron! In God's name!"

"No! No! The disgrace of it!"

He had let himself go so completely that the water was

running from his nose and mouth as well as from his eyes. The dazzling colonel's uniform was dirtied like a little boy's smock.

The adjutant wiped off the stains with a handkerchief.

"Colonel! You must master yourself! You must be strong now."

"Everything lost! Gone! Dishonoured!" the old man continued to mumble. His harsh military voice had disappeared; he wailed in a high, feminine treble. He would not let himself be consoled by the lieutenant. Look! They, the Germans, had been so close to the great triumph! Half of Europe had been in their grasp. Their armies had been firmly established in France and in Belgium, in Roumania, in Turkey, in Poland, in the Ukraine, in the Baltic Provinces, and in the Crimea. Yes, they had even dreamed of Petrograd. Everywhere the triumphant German eagle. And now—collapse! Germany in an uproar! The Kaiser fled! Gone to take refuge with the Dutch, the wide-trousered fisher-folk! It was too much.

It was his own personal disgrace that tormented the Baron. What would they think of him in this city, which he had governed with an iron hand? There would be one shout of laughter from the horde of verminous Polacks. He would not dare to show himself. His own soldiers, too, would lose all respect for him. They would do what the Russians had done. They would rebel; they would tear the epaulets from the shoulders of the officers; they would arrest him; they would shoot him, perhaps. For he knew that they hated him, every one of them.

"There's only one way out," he groaned. "A bullet right into the brain. That's all, lieutenant."

But he did not shoot himself, Colonel von Heidel-Heidellau. He bethought himself, and relieved his feelings by a good half-hour of violent and obscene cursing. He cursed the German General Staff, he cursed the strategists, he cursed everyone who had been responsible for the defeat. He screamed at the top of his voice. He dragged out of the recesses of his memory every oath and obscenity he had ever heard in his student days at the beer-swilling parties, later in the barracks and among his fellow-officers. It all came tumbling out, like a stream of garbage. Finally he was exhausted and calmed. He wiped his face, straightened out his uniform, rearranged the medals on his breast, turned his moustaches up again, and considered what was to be done.

There were no orders from headquarters. The General Staff had lost its head and left every officer to his own devices. Baron von Heidel-Heidellau had a very foolish idea. He had received the news through military channels, and therefore, presumably, was the first in possession of it. He would therefore repress it. He sat down at his table and began to issue instructions to his adjutant in his old manner, just as if he not been slobbering and weeping like an old woman a few minutes before. Not a word was to get out! Not even his brother officers were to be told. Those damned newspapers were to be kept under the closest watch. Life in the garrison and in the city was to continue as if everything were still normal.

"*Ja wohl*, Colonel!" the adjutant answered.

"Strict discipline, lieutenant! If any new reports come, bring them to me at once."

The adjutant withdrew, determined to carry out the orders; but they were foolish and futile. The news was out. No one could tell what sources had brought it, but everyone had it. The Polish legionaries were suddenly transformed from despised and slightly comical imitation soldiers into proud, swaggering warriors. As if by concerted arrangement they stopped saluting the German officers on the streets of Lodz. The Polish boys of the city suddenly blossomed out in Legion hats; they formed into a procession, with Polish flags at the head, and marched through the streets. Crowds assembled everywhere, and the militiamen did not even try to disperse them. And then placards began to appear on the walls, with the Polish eagle at the top, and the news of the complete collapse of Germany below. The proclamations ended with a call to Poland to assert her rights as a free nation. The signatures at the bottom were those of the high officers of the Polish legions.

German soldiers stopped, and asked the Jews, whose language they partially understood, to tell them what was happening. The Jews explained, the Germans listened and did not seem to take it too dreadfully to heart. Most of them said, quite simply: "That means we go home at last."

The German soldiers of Posen had a smattering of Polish. They read the proclamations and translated them to their comrades. "I think we ought to join the Polish army," some of them said.

The situation was inverted. Just as, before, the German soldiers had swaggered through the streets, while the Poles had walked timidly in the gutter, now the Germans stepped off the sidewalk and the Poles were the masters. The morale broke; dispirited, undisciplined, and careless, the Germans neglected their appearance. They unbuttoned their uniforms; they carried their guns carelessly; they walked with unmilitary slovenliness, not in ranks but in crowds. They passed their officers with a faint suggestion of a salute, or none at all.

It was impossible to keep the news secret. No one obeyed the colonel's orders now. The German army began to melt away.

Before the day had ended, Polish soldiers were stopping Germans on the streets and relieving them of their arms. Officers resisted, refusing to give up their revolvers; but they were overcome. The *Landstürmer,* they who had overawed the country, and one of whom had been enough to keep a small town in order, yielded up their arms without a protest.

Together with the patriotic proclamations of the high Polish officers, others appeared on the walls of Lodz, proclamations beginning with the phrase: "Proletarians of the world, unite!" They were in Polish, in Yiddish, and even in German. They called on the workers of Lodz to seize this brilliant historic opportunity and to strike the final and decisive blow for freedom and fraternity.

Tevyeh was the storm-centre of this second demonstration. His hour had come! He saw the pillars of the old world cracking and toppling. First Russia, now Germany and Austria, soon the others. The disillusioned masses, armed by the very capitalists who were exploiting them, had turned. The whole world was flaming red. Far off, in India and China, in all the

[566]

colonies of the European masters, the masses were ready to rise.

His hour had come! After all the mockery and scepticism, the repression and contempt, he was emerging to triumph. For he had been right. He repeated this over and over again to his faithful workers at the kitchen. "This is the march of history! We foresaw it! We are ready for it!"

But in the midst of the triumph, while he prepared speeches and proclamations and resolutions, he also warned his men. The old world was breaking, but it was not yet broken. It was like a wounded beast, dying but still dangerous. In the victorious countries the workers were being dazzled by the empty triumph; they were being deafened by the trumpet-peals of the celebrations. A high wave of patriotism was carrying thousands of the workers in the wrong direction. Here too, in Poland, there was the same danger. The reactionaries were openly and brazenly at work; the church bells were ringing loudly; in the synagogues cantors and rabbis were extolling the God of victory and praising the new masters as they had praised the old.

All this needed watching, he shouted. Mass meetings must be held for the enlightenment of the workers. Clarity must be brought into their minds, with proclamations and pamphlets. Among the Jews, too, there were the Zionists to be combated; for they were misleading the Jewish masses as the Polish legionaries were misleading the Poles. During the German occupation no one had dared to speak of the Declaration issued by the English Lord Balfour, in the name of the British Government, promising Palestine to the Jews as a homeland. Baron von Heidel-Heidellau had suppressed the news and forbidden all mention of it. He would not have the Jews know of the benefits which the filthy English proposed to confer on them. Now, with the Germans gone, the Zionists were free to spread the news. The Jewish papers were full of it. In the synagogues prayers of praise were uttered in honour of the English Lord. Among all the other proclamations, as fiery as any, appeared those of the Zionists. There was even a great folk-demonstration; the scrolls of the Law were carried through the streets amid music and dancing. Tevyeh knew the force of propaganda. He knew how easily the masses could be intoxicated with the poison of nationalism. He therefore turned his guns on the Zionists, too, denounced them for trying to distract the attention of the workers from their real task, which was, in international unity, to struggle for the freedom of all; he mocked the pietists and the synagogue officials and the well-to-do who were their support, and painted in lurid colours the treachery of their alliance with English imperialist lords.

Tevyeh was everywhere, on all committees, in all groups, Polish, German, and Jewish. His voice was hoarse, his hands trembled, his body was feverish. He neither slept nor ate. There was much work, and the moment was crucial. He could not pause to think of himself.

He held it of primary importance to win over the German soldiers, whom disillusionment had turned into such promising revolutionary material. A special mass meeting was therefore called of the Soldiers' Councils which had sprung up among the Germans. As a gesture of triumph and defiance, it was to be held right in front of the palace in which Baron von Heidel-Heidellau was still lodged. The soldiers assembled by the thousand; the committees were swamped by the rank and file. One soldier after another addressed the excited mass, called on the soldiers to tear the insignia off their uniforms and to pin on their breasts the red colours of the revolution. The mass roared its approval.

The Baron pulled down the blinds of his window, not to see the horrible spectacle.

Tevyeh's turn came to speak. In a faulty Lodz Yiddish-German, which he had picked up from travelling merchants, he let loose his oratory over the crowd. They did not understand every word, but they caught his meaning; and they were hypnotized by the fury and passion which streamed from this haggard old man in the tattered proletarian clothes. Under the shaggy eyebrows the eyes flamed with faith and youth and courage, and with hatred against all those who stood in the way of the great liberation.

The roaring of the crowd became louder. The Baron could not help himself; he had to go to the window to see who was

[568]

inflaming the masses. He screwed the monocle into his eye and stared at the comical little figure gesticulating above the crowd. This was probably, he thought, that Jewish proletarian leader of whom he had heard much and on whom he had never been able to lay his hands. It was quite incredible. This scarecrow, this starved rat, was *his* opponent, Baron von Heidel-Heidellau's. His triumphant opponent. The shame of being defeated by such a miserable, pitiful enemy! The Baron's fingers itched. He wanted to take out his revolver and with a single shot bring down the filthy little agitator.

But it was more than he dared. The soldiers were applauding hysterically. At a signal from the orator they would have stormed the palace. The Baron pulled down the blind again and writhed with the bitterness of his thoughts. He remembered the Kaiser, and the grand old army; he remembered his estates in Prussia. All, he thought, would be at the mercy of this civilian vermin. Workers, the scum of the cities, would occupy all the high places henceforth. In Germany some dirty little saddle-maker was already at the head of the Government. And perhaps his own ancient lands would pass into the hands of Polacks. His eyes became wet again; his nose prickled with the onset of tears, and his old lips trembled.

Outside, on the edge of the vast crowd, Keile, the wife of Tevyeh, stood with her daughters and stared incredulously at the astounding spectacle.

"Look, look, look!" Keile kept repeating, plucking at her daughters. "If I didn't see it with my own eyes, I wouldn't believe it. The world's gone mad. . . ."

For Felix Feldblum, too, for the revolutionary who had suffered for the liberation of Poland in the belief that a Poland freed from foreign rule would set an example of justice and equality to the rest of the world—for him, too, the hour of triumph came. The crown of thorns which had rested on the brow of Poland for more than a hundred years was plucked off. The cathedral in Cracow, repository of the bones of Poland's kings and poets, was no longer a barracks and stable for the Austrian cavalry. The Polish flag fluttered from its highest turrent, as it fluttered everywhere in the land.

The youth of the city of Cracow had enrolled itself in a special legion which was now marching eastward on the city of Lemberg, to liberate it from the Ukrainians. Attached to this legion was the regiment in which Felix Feldblum had served, first as a private in the ranks and then as officer. His sword dangling by his side, his epaulets sitting crooked on his narrow shoulders, the elderly man strode at the head of his troops. Behind him his men marched, singing the Song of the Crocuses, the name which the Cracow legionaries had given themselves.

> General Roya on his horse!
> Behind him comes the Crocus band!
> Song on tongue and sword in hand,
> We'll drive the foeman from our land!
> We'll clean them out, the dirty crews,
> The Russians first and then the Jews.

The Jews of Lemberg heard of the approach of the "Cro-cuses" and trembled; evil days had come for them, and not for them alone.

Poland was filled with wandering bands of demobilized soldiers belonging to all nations. From the Ukraine, from the Crimea, from Volhynia and Podolia and White Russia, disorganized mobs of Germans were fleeing homeward. They crowded the trains, perched on the roofs of the cars, and clung to the steps; but even so, there were not trains enough to carry them. They were ragged and demoralized; they did not know what awaited them on the morrow. Many of them had become revolutionaries and had pinned red ribbons on their uniforms. Alsatian troops, feeling that Germany was done for, proclaimed their allegiance to France and marched along the roads singing French songs. Poles from the Posen district, who had begun the war as German soldiers, threw off their allegiance to Germany, and in faulty Polish picked up the patriotic songs of Poland. These "returning sons" were held in high esteem among the population, particularly among the young women. They were given first places in the churches and in popular demonstrations. Austrian troops, of every race in the crazy-quilt of the Empire, also filled the roads of Poland. Their morale was lowest. They had turned on their officers and plundered the commissariat; they sold their uniforms and their guns for a few copper coins. Every national group reverted to its own language and loyalty and attached the emblem of its freedom to its clothes. The Polish soldiers deserted in masses to the Polish regiments; the Czechs cut off from their caps the metal emblems of the Empire and pinned on the emblems of the new Czechoslovakia. The Hungarians, too, proclaimed their independence. Bosnians, Roumanians, Slavs, Ruthenians, Serbs, Croats—all sang their own songs in their own language, all marched toward their home-lands.

The Jews alone remained in their places, in the vicinity of their homes, their synagogues, and their ancient ceme-teries. But everywhere in Jewish towns and villages the walls were covered with placards and posters which told of the coming storm. The schoolboys of the newly liberated Polish state were busy chalking the walls with insults, slanders, and threats. "Poland for the Poles," said the posters, "and the Jews can get out and go to Palestine. And if they don't they know what to expect." Above the military music which accompanied the marching mobs in the cities began to be heard the shattering of glass as stones were thrown into Jewish homes.

Most wretched of all were the Jews of East Galicia, in the vicinity of Lemberg. The towns and villages had been laid waste by the Cossacks during the Russian invasion. Many Jews had been driven out of the district, some deported to Siberia. A great famine had followed the invasion, and pestilence had followed the famine. The tens of thousands of Jewish soldiers who had been drawn from the Galician population into the armies of an Austrian Empire were returning to misery and desolation.

Many of these soldiers, following the prevailing custom, had pinned Jewish Shields of David on their uniforms. But their fellow-soldiers mocked them. "Why don't you go to your own country? We don't want you here." The older Jews would have nothing to do with these emblems. They were sick of the war and of military emblems. They were sick of service, and discipline, and the un-Jewish ways they had been forced to follow in the army. When the general decay set in they let their ear-locks grow once more and took on their ancient habits. They reverted to type; they forgot the erect military walk; they flocked to the synagogues to pray and to study as of old. The immemorial burden of Jewishness, the double burden of this world and of the world to come, descended once more on their shoulders. The thread of their life had to be picked up where it had been dropped; they thought of their workman's tools, lying around somewhere in the garrets of their homes; the time had come to return to the normal—to making a living, bringing children into the world, bringing them up in Jewish ways, marrying off the daughters—the long, heavy, painful routine to which they were accustomed. In their houses of study, in their Chasidic synagogues, they gathered and sought comfort, lifting their eyes to heaven, to the Ruler of all rulers.

[572]

Their prayers were vain. The world would not return to its old, normal ways; war and violence would not cease. New, minor wars—the results of ancient enmities—broke out, between the Poles and the Ruthenians, between the Polish Pans and the peasantry. Every little group made a play for power. Now was the time, they said, or never. And the Jews were in the midst of it; whichever way the bullets flew, they cut across Jewish streets and homes; each side demanded the help of the Jews and denounced them as traitors if they refused to involve themselves in the quarrel.

The fiercest of these minor wars was being waged in Lemberg. The city was held by two rival armies, the Polish and the Ukrainian; each army occupied its own quarter and fired across the intervening space—occupied by the Jews—at the other.

Young Jews, soldiers and officers of the crumbled Austrian army, organized a Jewish self-defence, to keep out the thugs and robbers who had begun to make forays even in daytime. The Jews proclaimed themselves neutral between the Poles and the Ukrainians, hoping thereby to placate the ultimate victor. But the Poles were outraged by the neutrality of the Jews; and though the Polish command agreed to the Jewish policy of neutrality and signed an official agreement with the Jewish self-defence, it spread among its troops a spirit of hatred against the Jews and denounced them as enemies of Poland.

The rank and file of the Polish soldiers threatened the Jews openly. "Wait!" they shouted at the Jews. "We'll get the Ukrainians out, and then we'll show you how to be neutral!"

Nor did they forget. When the Ukrainians had withdrawn from Lemberg, the Polish troops organized an attack on the Jewish quarter, exactly as if it were an armed enemy fortress instead of a defenceless section of a conquered town. With the Polish troops came a rabble eager for plunder, city officials and nurses, thieves and prostitutes, church dignitaries and monks and housewives—a horde streamed toward the Jewish streets.

"Down with the Jews!" they yelled. "Hang them by their

[573]

ear-locks! Drive them out like rats!"

Officers marched openly at the head of the troops, one officer for every ten soldiers. They surrounded the headquarters of the Jewish self-defence and disarmed it; they shot its leaders and arrested the men.

Then the carnage and looting began.

The attack began with the precision of a battle. At exactly seven o'clock on a cold November morning the Polish legionaries surrounded Cracow Square with their machine-guns and armoured cars. Synagogue, Shulkev, Onion, and other streets were blockaded, so that no one could get out, and the order was given to open fire.

The bullets of machine-guns and rifles began to spatter the walls and break the windows; advancing slowly, the Polish legionaries flung hand-grenades at the walls and the barred doors. From within the houses a dreadful screaming arose; a few figures fled out of the houses and were shot down. The soldiers howled with glee and continued to throw their grenades.

When the population had been thoroughly terrorized and given a taste of what to expect in case of resistance, the officers gave the order to cease firing and sent out patrols to break into the houses. Orders came regularly from the city theatre, where the high command was in session. House by house the patrols advanced, burst open the doors, and began to throw the household goods into the street. In wealthier houses the men and women were told to stand up against the wall and put up their hands while the officers searched them for money, jewels, and other valuables. Here and there the soldiers wanted more than booty; the sight of some pretty woman fired their lust; husbands, brothers, and sons were bound down, and in their presence the women were raped by the mob. And if this was not enough, an insane blood-lust seized soldiers and officers; babies were stabbed in their cradles, in the presence of their mothers; men were smashed down with the butts of rifles; women were stabbed and ripped open with bayonets.

Outside in the streets a frenzied mob screamed for more blood, more booty. At the gates of the Jewish quarter were stationed military trucks into which perspiring, laughing soldiers packed the household goods thrown into the street, to be carted off to the points of assembly. There the civilian population struggled and fought in the division of the spoils. Working-women in shawls, elegant ladies in furs, street-girls, nurses, nuns, teachers, all pushed and yelled for their share.

"Give that to me, captain!" "No, to me! I want that!" they panted.

The well-to-do came in their carriages to carry off a larger share.

The shops in the Jewish quarter were emptied of clothes, food, and other merchandise. Truck-load after truck-load went out; two streams ran through the streets, to and from the gates of the Jewish quarter; full trucks in one direction, empty trucks in the other.

On the second day, when the looting was finished, the high command in the theatre gave orders to set fire to the Jewish quarter. The trucks now brought barrels of benzine, taken out of Jewish stores on the previous day. The walls of the Jewish houses were thoroughly soaked; cushions, bed-covers, and sacks of straw were also soaked in benzine and piled against the doors, so that no one could escape. Then the torch was applied.

A dreadful screaming rose from the Jewish houses.

"Fry in your own fat!" the soldiers and officers roared.

From the houses the Polish legionaries turned to the synagogues and houses of study. Four officers, each at the head of a squad of ten men, marched into the Forshtetter synagogue. They tore down the velvet curtain before the holy Ark, burst open the door, and looted the valuables inside; they took the silver crowns, the handles of the scrolls, the beakers and the candelabra. These, together with the silk and velvet covers for the holy days, they thrust into sacks. The naked scrolls were flung on the floor, trampled on, and befouled. When the interior of the synagogue was a ruin, the soldiers flung several hand-grenades into the naked wooden Ark, and the ancient building burst into flames.

Two thirteen-year-old boys who lived in Synagogue Street—David Reubenfeld and Israel Feigenbaum were their names—

rushed into the blazing building and picked up the befouled scrolls of the Law which lay on the floor. With these they ran out, thinking to save the sacred objects, but at the door of the synagogue they were shot down by Polish legionaries.

A like fate befell all the synagogues and houses of study in that quarter. Officers carried away all the silver from the temple on Shulkev Street. Some, not content with robbery, gave vent in a drunken frenzy to their hatred and contempt for the Jewish religion. They took the covers off the Ark, twisted them round their heads like turbans, danced around, and stood swaying back and forth in parody of Jews at prayer, for the laughter of the mob of soldiers. When they had had their fill of fun, the officers commanded the men to tear up the floor, pour benzine into the foundations, and set fire to the place.

In another house of prayer on Synagogue Street, Jews wrapped themselves in shrouds, put on their prayer shawls, and said the death-bed confessional, beating their breasts with their fists and reciting their sins. The doors were locked on them, and the synagogue set fire to. The Jews went on praying until the flames crept up to their prayer shawls and set them on fire. One officer, seeing the spectacle through the window, was horrified. He opened one of the side doors and bade the Jews get out. But in the noise, the wailing and confusion, he was not heard, and the Jews perished in the flames.

Three days and three nights the Jewish quarter was given over to pillage and destruction. The soldiers murdered and plundered; the houses and synagogues burned. The firemen of the city did not even approach the district.

On the fourth day the terrified Jews, cowed by disaster and humiliated by the disgrace of the attack, crept out of the ruins and began to seek the dead. The charred corpses were wrapped in praying-shawls, the unidentified bones were put into jars, so that they might be given decent burial. From among the still glowing ruins fragments of sacred vessels and scraps of parchment that had once been scrolls of the Law were rescued and put into other earthen jars, likewise for burial. Seventy-two dead lay in a row under the prayer shawls.

[576]

Sobbing men and screaming women sought among them for their own.

All the Jews of the city turned out for the mass funeral of the martyrs and the destroyed and desecrated scrolls. Among the thousands of men and women in black stalked one figure in a light-blue uniform—Felix Feldblum, officer of the Polish Legion, fighter for the freedom of Poland, one-time believer in her Messianic future.

Yakob Ashkenazi forgot the quarrels and enmities of the years and set out for Petrograd to find his brother Max and bring him home.

From every part of Russia refugees streamed back into Poland; they came singly, in twos and threes, in groups. Only Max Ashkenazi did not return. Nor was there any communication from him. His wife, old, sick, and broken, went daily to the railroad station and tottered around among the refugees, asking at random for word of him. But no one had seen him or heard what had happened to him. It was as though the earth had opened and swallowed him. The former widow Margulies tottered back to her desolate home, to return again the next day.

She still lived in the apartment which had once been the residence of the fat, dissolute Albrecht, once director of the Huntze factories. She had never returned to her palace, even after Baron von Heidel-Heidellau had left the city. Nor had she made any friends. She was still alone in Lodz, and her one hope was the husband who had disappeared in Russia. Except for her visits to the railroad station, she passed her time either in the office of the factory or in her apartment, in the company of the one maid she had retained. As in the time of the German occupation, she still carried on a fierce struggle for the remnants of the Ashkenazi possessions. The palace had been taken over by the Polish military, and where German officers had rioted and danced before, Polish officers now carried on. And if it had not been for the vigilance of this old, sick woman, the remains of the factory equipment would have been carried away by the Poles.

It was a bitter, miserable struggle. The officials of the new régime were as hostile and contemptuous as the Germans had been. A furious wave of anti-Semitism was passing through Poland, and the Lemberg pogrom had been the signal for a series of murderous assaults on Jews. The hungry and unemployed workers everywhere, and especially in Lodz, gathered in mobs and marched on the homes and factories of the Jewish industrialists. They demanded work when there was none; and when there was work, the unemployed demanded it on their own terms. They besieged the Jews in their homes and factories. The police did not interfere; the higher officials shrugged their shoulders. When rioters broke into the Ashkenazi factory, and the weary, half-paralysed old woman applied for protection to the police commissioner, she was thrust from the door.

She would not abandon her post. Umbrella in hand, her wrinkled, weary old face set determinedly, she fought and argued. She felt that she had nothing more to expect in life; but there was one ambition to which she clung with mortal obstinacy. She would see her husband again some day, she would turn over to him the keys of the factory and the palace; she would show him she had been a faithful guardian of his property; and then she would die.

But her husband did not come, nor was there any news of him. Madame Ashkenazi filled the newspapers with advertisements; she sent letters and telegrams to people in Russia, through the Red Cross. Not an echo came back. And then, one day, she made a bitter and desperate resolve. She went out into the street, her umbrella clutched in her hand, hailed a droshky, and asked to be driven to her brother-in-law, Yakob Ashkenazi, whom she had never seen.

She did not know what to expect. In that house, as she knew, there was the woman whom Max Ashkenazi had thrown over in order to marry her, the widow Margulies. There, too, lived the daughter who had married her uncle. From neither of these women, nor from Yakob Ashkenazi, who had been a lifelong enemy of his brother, was she likely to receive help and comfort. But in her helplessness she swallowed her pride; if there was the remotest chance of doing something for her husband, she would not let her own feelings stand in the way.

With trembling heart and hand she knocked at the door. To the servant girl who opened, she said, with forced and unnatural loudness: "Tell your master that Madame Mazova Ashkenazi wishes to see him. Repeat that name carefully— Madame Mazova Ashkenazi." From inside she heard laughter and the sound of a piano. Waiting in the dark corridor, the old woman felt her heart sinking lower and lower. She was not at all sure that they would receive her, and if they did, she did not know how they would talk to her. She waited a long time, and then suddenly the door at the farther end swung open and Yakob Ashkenazi, erect and broad-shouldered, his face lit with a smile of welcome, strode toward her.

"Welcome, sister-in-law," he said, heartily. "I'm very happy indeed to see you here." He took her uncertain hand in his and pressed it warmly.

A wave of relief and gratitude swept through the old woman. She returned the pressure of Yakob's hand. She was embarrassed. She suddenly did not know what to do with the umbrella which she held in her free hand. Yakob Ashkenazi took it from her, and then helped her to take off her coat, which she was reluctant to remove.

"I won't detain you long, Herr Ashkenazi," she murmured. "I've only come to ask your advice."

"But what are you talking about, sister-in-law?" he replied, in an astonished tone of voice. He still held her hand and drew her, not toward his office, but toward the dining-room. "You'll sit down and rest, and take a glass of tea with us."

The old woman could not move forward a step when she saw the two women, one elderly and one young. She had never met either of them, but she knew well who they were. Yakob Ashkenazi led her slowly forward.

"This is our sister-in-law, Madame Ashkenazi," he announced in a loud, friendly voice.

Embarrassed, the two women came closer and held out their hands to her.

"You are welcome. Please sit down." And Dinah, her voice, too, louder than usual, ordered the maid to bring in tea.

For a time the women looked at one another wordlessly. Madame Ashkenazi had long wanted to see both the mother whom she had replaced and the daughter about whom there had been so much talk. Old though she was, broken and without hope, there was womanly curiosity in the gaze which she fixed on her rival; and she could not help feeling how old, ugly, and hard she was by comparison.

Dinah and Gertrude looked with astonishment on her who had taken their place in the Ashkenazi palace. No, they could not approve Max Ashkenazi's choice; there was nothing attractive in this old woman. Dinah blushed like a school-girl, moved closer to Gertrude, and drew her shawl closer around her, as if she had felt a cold wind blowing through the room. Yakob tried to save the situation by talking loudly and cheerfully, but his remarks remained hanging in the air, and a painful silence descended on the group. Then suddenly little Priveh, the grand-daughter, burst into the room, carrying a doll. Blond-headed, gay, and unembarrassed, she ran up to the stranger.

"Look," she sang, "this is Mimi, my new doll, my little Mimi. She's got a blue dress and a red ribbon. I've got a new bear too; he's very big, and he bites. His name is Bumbu."

"You little darling!" murmured Madame Ashkenazi, and drew the child to her.

In an instant the embarrassment had disappeared. The three women began to play with the child. Dinah and Gertrude repeated clever sayings of hers. Yakob stood on one side, his face lit with happiness.

The old woman was no longer in a hurry to leave. How warm and friendly the house had become, how loving and generous these people were! They no longer stared at her. They pressed tea and cakes on her. Gertrude even addressed her as "Auntie." Then, quite easily and naturally the conversation passed to the subject which had brought the old

[581]

woman to the house—Max Ashkenazi. The tears began to stream from Madame Ashkenazi's eyes.

"God knows what has happened to him." Looking on her the other women began to weep too.

When they had recovered, they took council, and the two houses decided to unite their forces in the search for the missing man. Yakob Ashkenazi placed himself without reserve or thought of self at the disposal of the women.

The first thing for him to do, they decided, was to proceed to Berlin, the only city in which the new Russia was represented. Yakob Ashkenazi agreed at once, though even this preliminary step was beset with difficulties. Much ingenuity had to be exercised, much money spent, before he could get accommodation, for the trains were packed with demobilized soldiers. Nor was it easy to obtain a visa. But Yakob Ashkenazi had always had a way with him; there was something about his bearing, his regal figure, his friendly, commanding voice, that opened all doors to him. The lackeys who were accustomed to turning away thousands of applicants made way for him; and officials who listened with cruel indifference to the pleas of those who had been admitted found this self-assured, easy-spoken man hard to refuse. Money, persistence, and ease of manner won out for him. He obtained both the visa and a place on the train, and found his way to the embassy in Berlin, with the red flag flying over it.

The embassy officials were very courteous. They wrote down his brother's name and promised to make inquiries, the results of which they would transmit to him as soon as they arrived. Every day Yakob Ashkenazi visited the embassy, but no answer had arrived from Russia. After waiting several weeks, he realized that he was wasting his time. There was nothing for it but to proceed to Russia himself and to make his own investigations on the spot.

When he returned to Lodz and declared his intentions, he met with discouragement on every hand. He was warned of the folly and danger of venturing into a land torn by civil war. Yakob Ashkenazi would not listen. Of one thing he was certain. If his brother was alive, he was not remaining in Russia of his own free will. There was no business in that land to keep him there. Refugees were returning by the thousand, some under escort, others by their own devices. Only Max did not come, and Yakob, now that he had begun the search, could not rest in Lodz. He forgot the old rivalries and quarrels. He had never been a good hater. All that possessed him now was the desire to find his brother. He packed his valises, sewed large sums of money into his clothes, provided himself with all sorts of permits and official documents, and made ready to set out on the dangerous journey.

On the eve of his departure the three women sat with him. Every few minutes old Madame Ashkenazi would stretch out her trembling, half-paralysed hands, take hold of Yakob's, and cover them with kisses and tears. She had brought with her a package of jewels, which she insisted on turning over to him, so that he might use them on his mission, if necessary.

"Take them, brother-in-law," she wept. "They'll come in useful on such a journey. Jewels are currency everywhere and at all times."

Yakob Ashkenazi tried to refuse. But the old woman forced the package on him. When she had thrust them into his pocket, she took off a talisman which she wore round her neck and hung it round Yakob's.

"It's a family heirloom," she said. "It comes from the great Rabbi of Karlin. It will guard you on your travels. Wear it, for my sake."

Yakob had not the heart to say no, though he had not the slightest faith in the memory of the Rabbi of Karlin. He took the talisman and promised to wear it.

The generosity and courage which inspired Yakob evoked in Dinah and in Gertrude, too, a mood of tenderness and softness. He had long been an enemy of his brother, and they had had little cause to love Max Ashkenazi. But now everything was forgotten. Gertrude threw her arms round her husband's neck and praised him, called him her knight and hero. The admiration and affection of her first love for him seemed to have returned. Together the three women supervised all the preparations for the journey and provided him with linen not only for himself, but for his brother, as though they were certain that he would be found and brought back.

The train that carried Yakob Ashkenazi into Russia was filled with returning refugees and demobilized, or, rather, disorganized, soldiers. Many thousands had been released from the German concentration camps. Their beards matted and neglected, their faces haggard with the long years of privation, their clothes in tatters, their feet covered with rags or in wooden clogs, they struggled eastward toward their homes. They were returning to the Ukraine and Siberia, to the Caucasian country and the Crimea, to every corner of Russia. Abandoned by the officers who had led them into battle, helpless in the strange countries which had taken them prisoner and had now released them, hungry, sick, and half-naked, they dragged themselves along from city to city, sometimes on foot, sometimes in trains, begging their way, grateful for a crust of bread. There were among them big, hairy, blue-eyed Great Russians, black-eyed, flat-nosed Caucasians, slant-eyed, yellow-skinned Chuvashes, Kalmuks, White Russians, Jews, Ukrainians, Tatars, Cossacks, and Armenians of all ages and in all conditions. They came from remote villages, from forlorn mountains and valleys; and all of them hungered for one thing: home. No one asked them for permits and passports; they wandered in free bands across the frontiers.

They were disillusioned and embittered; all the high-flown phrases which had been dinned into their ears, Tsar, Fatherland, God, Empire, had become a mockery to them. In the name of these they had been torn from their piece of soil, from the plough, from wife and children, and delivered to disease, hunger, pain, humiliation, and death. Now they had been left to look after themselves, without help or counsel. The great wandering covered the roads and railways. In their midst sprang up thieves and traitors, and men who, with wild words, added to their already crushing burden of bitterness.

In the midst of this motley crowd of refugees sat Yakob Ashkenazi, well fed, well clad, waking envy and astonishment.

They sat around him, picking the vermin out of their tattered shirts, unbinding and rebinding their wounds. They talked loudly of the days to come and the happiness which waited for them at home.

"They've taken the land away from the nobles," one soldier said. "I'll get a big farm for myself. Everything's going to be fine."

"But they say the Reds have started a new war," answered another. "We'll have to fight again, and this time against our own."

"In the Ukraine the nobles and landlords have come back," a third volunteered. "The peasants are under the heel again, like in the old days. They're still drinking our blood."

"It's not true," put in another. "Only the Ukrainians want to keep their country for themselves. They don't want to give it away to the Russian pigs. That's why they're fighting. Every Ukrainian ought to come to the rescue."

"I don't give a damn who's fighting and what for," shouted a fifth, a young soldier. "I won't go to the front again, not for anybody. I've had enough. I want to live quietly, in peace, with my wife. I haven't seen her in years."

"She's probably got someone else by now," an elderly man mocked him.

"Shut your jaw, you dog," shouted the young soldier, "or I'll smash every bone in you. You don't know anything about it."

"Take it easy, young man," said a broad-shouldered, pockmarked soldier. "You haven't been keeping an eye on her bed, either. She'd be a God-damned fool to wait all these years for you. A woman is a bitch; if it isn't this dog, it's another—everyone knows that."

"That's so," said another, nodding. "My parents wrote me about my wife. That's what she did. She got herself another, and she's had two brats by him. Bastards, that's what they are."

"Well," they asked him, "what are you going to do about it when you get home?"

"I don't know yet," the bearded soldier answered. "I'll forgive her, maybe. And maybe I'll cut her throat."

The conversation drifted away from these homely subjects and took a wider range.

"They're setting fire to the churches," said one, in a corner.

"And they don't let you say any prayers, those Red devils."

"Jews are the big men among them, the leaders. They say that even the new Tsar is a Jew."

An old, haggard-faced peasant piped up suddenly: "He's got horns just like a devil. It was in all the newspapers. That's what somebody told me."

"Well, don't they say the Jews are to blame for everything? And, by God, so they are. They began the war, didn't they, to make money?"

"They ought to be wiped out."

"That's what we're doing in our country, in the Ukraine," a lame soldier said, proudly and ferociously.

The railroad car was filled with dirt, hatred, disillusionment, and animal stupidity. Yakob Ashkenazi felt the atmosphere around him heavy with enmity and disease. So it was in every train that he boarded. But he did not turn back. He went deeper and deeper into the country, travelling day and night, on trains that crawled with the slowness of dying worms through devastated and starving lands. The path by which he travelled was circuitous. He traversed many frontiers, though no one knew exactly where the frontier lay and who was the authority on either side of it. Every other day there were new laws and regulations to be taken into account. Only one thing was certain: murder and robbery reigned everywhere.

Slowly and with infinite obstinacy he advanced toward his goal. The money in his pockets opened one gate after another for him, and led him through the very dangers which it created. Even in Petrograd, now no longer the capital of the new Russia, among the leather-coated soldiers and officials of the Red régime, gold worked like magic and led him into the offices of Shchinsky's much trusted lieutenants, led him finally to the office of the prison in which his brother was held, and led him, at last, to his brother, to Max Ashkenazi, himself.

For several minutes the two brothers stood looking at each other dumbly in the office of the prison, seeking to recognize each other.

[586]

Yakob was paralysed and terrified by the sight of this tiny, shrivelled, tattered, and befouled old man who had been led into the room. His skin was yellow; his beard was matted and nondescript in colour; his clothes hung down in tatters. Nothing remained of the brother he had known. Likewise paralysed, his eyes fixed on his brother with a stony glare, Max Ashkenazi stood before the massive, dignified figure of Yakob.

He had been like this, rigid, stony, and wordless, since the moment when the two men at the seashore had snatched him back from the gates of freedom, flung him into the truck, and led him to prison. He had, at that instant, given up all hope, knowing that in the city of Petrograd, and indeed throughout the whole of Russia, there was not one human being who would make an effort to save him or who even cared what happened to him. He was lost to the world, done for, his fate sealed. There was nothing to look forward to but the sure end, approaching he knew not how fast, but quite inexorably. He was so sure of this that he had no inclination to try to save himself. He was in a stupor. He nodded dumbly to all the accusations which were brought against him; he made no protest when he was flung into the common cell.

His neighbours tried to draw him into conversation. They asked him what he had been arrested for and what he hoped to do about it. He did not answer. What was the good of talk? He was through, was he not? What matter who spoke? He did not even answer the Red guards when, bored by their long vigils, they questioned him about his previous life, about his activities and the country he came from.

"Just a block!" said one of them disgustedly.

"He's not human," said his neighbours.

During the first few days he muttered the Psalms to himself, remembering them out of his boyhood years. Every night the guards came into the cell to lead out a few men to be "cleaned"; every night those who had been led out were replaced by others. As often as the door opened in the night, and the leather-coated men with the lanterns entered, Max Ashkenazi was certain that his turn had come. He tried to prepare for the end. He prayed dumbly to God, begging forgiveness for the sins he had committed on earth. But he was not led out. Always it was someone else. But he remained so ready for the call that as often as the door opened he sprang up from the filthy straw sack on which he lay. One might have said that he was in a hurry to be done with it—that he was afraid of being missed or of arriving late.

The soldiers laughed at him.

"Lie down, old boy," they said. "It's not your turn yet."

His neighbours envied him.

"You'll be just the one to escape being shot," they surmised. "Anyway, you're only a speculator. They're easier on speculators than on political prisoners."

But he did not believe them. He was certain that it was only a matter of days. He did not know why he ate. He looked long and indifferently at the piece of bread and the wooden plate of greasy soup which he received once a day, before he ate them. The long waiting, the emptiness of the hours, the certainty of what was coming, cast him into a dark, silent, unresponsive mood. He was like a man abandoned to certain death in some lonely place where a human face was not to be seen. His neighbours talked excitedly among themselves, ate the meagre prison meals eagerly, devised impromptu games, cut chessmen out of paper and played on the floor. One man, in a military uniform, was for ever doing his exercises, in order to keep fit, though no one could have said what for. Max Ashkenazi only sat, a dumb, immovable figure, on his sack. He did not ask, as the others did, what kind of weather it was outside; he did not beg for little favours; he did not curse. He was deaf to everything. Only within, his thoughts were alive. He was drawing up the balance-sheet of his life, a senseless, bitter accounting; and this, too, was useless, but he was under some sort of compulsion to do it. Nothing else mattered to him. Nothing existed; not the curses and complaints of his fellow-prisoners; not the sunlight or rain or snow outside the prison. There was only death, which was approaching him steadily.

The men in the leather coats did not tell him when he might expect the end. They did not believe in advising their prisoners in such matters. Only from time to time they led him out of the cell and questioned him anew; the same questions, the same answers. Then they led him back. The final call for the prisoners, the call from which they never returned, always came unexpectedly, and in the night. Max Ashkenazi died more than once. He died every time the door was flung open in the night, and the men with the lanterns dragged out the condemned prisoners. So, having died, he had nothing to do with the processes that belonged to the living. He did not wash; he did not smooth out his hair and his beard in the mornings; he did not straighten out his clothes. His underwear clung to his body. He did not, like the others, carry on a fight against the rats and the vermin which infested the cell. He let everything happen to him. The soldiers looked at him contemptuously.

"That's what happens to their kind when they haven't got servants to look after them," they said. "They become living carcasses."

Now and again a prisoner took pity on him and tried to persuade him to take himself in hand. He paid no attention. He had lost all his outward senses but one; he was indifferent to pain, dirt, and insult. The one sense which was active, and which, from day to day, from week to week, from month to month, became sharper and sharper, was the sense of hearing. He could hear footsteps approaching a long way down the corridor. He would start up in the night long before the footsteps came to the door of his cell. He was ready, always ready.

So, when one of the men in a leather coat, with a Mauser strapped to his side, appeared at the door and shouted out his name, Max Ashkenazi rose automatically to his feet. He asked no questions. There was nothing to find out. In his dumb concentration on the one dread fact which had so long dominated his consciousness, he did not even notice that the daylight was staring in dully through the window-panes and did not remember that executions took place only at night. He followed, without feeling his limbs under him. When he was conducted, at last, into the big prison office, he heard the man in the leather jacket say something loudly, but he could not grasp the meaning of the words.

[589]

With bulging eyes, bloodshot from the sleepless nights, he stared at the big, imposing man in civilian clothes who faced him. He did not recognize his brother. In the many years since they had last seen each other, Yakob had changed greatly. But even if he had been the same as in his early manhood, Max Ashkenazi would not have recognized him. He did not see him clearly. He was accustomed to the half-darkness of the cell. He was blinded by the light, dulled by his long familiarity with the thought of death. There was an immovable darkness before his eyes, and a deeper, even more immovable darkness in the heart under the filthy rags, and in the brain behind the withered face, the tangled beard, to which clung the dirt and straw of his mattress.

Awhile the two men stared at each other, unable to move or utter a word. Then suddenly the big man ran over to the filthy, ragged little creature.

"Simcha Meyer!" he cried, and pressed the bundle of rags closely to him.

Those two half-forgotten names cut like knives through the dulled brain of Max Ashkenazi. The thick mist lifted from before his eyes, the rigidity in his limbs and in his heart relaxed, and he felt a faint warmth running through them again. He began to tremble violently. He could see at last. Out of the dry beds which his eyes had become during the months of imprisonment, tears, hot tears, began to flow again. His lips began to babble.

"Jacob Bunim," he blubbered, "Jacob Bunim."

Then suddenly he slipped from his brother's grasp, bent, seized his hands, and covered them with kisses, like a beggar kissing the hands of some passer-by who has thrown him a gold coin.

Jacob Bunim tore his hands away from his brother's lips.

"Simcha Meyer!" he cried, frightened. "What are you doing?"

But Max, hardly hearing, had thrown himself on the floor and was embracing and kissing his brother's feet. He clung to them convulsively and moaned with relief, like a dog which has been readmitted to the house on a stormy night.

"You won't leave me here, Jacob Bunim," he wept. "You'll

[590]

take me home, won't you? Tell me. . . ."

The stench that mounted from his brother's body choked Jacob Bunim. Filled with pity and disgust, he bent down and lifted the shivering body of Max. The tears ran unchecked down his cheeks and into his dyed beard.

They went out of the prison, these two brothers who had been divided by hatred for so many years, holding each other by the hand.

Yakob had succeeded. Money and personal charm, the two instruments which had opened so many other gates for him, had opened these gates too. Even the leather-coated men found something charming and irresistible about him. And then, the truth was that the Bolsheviks were not particularly embittered against Max Ashkenazi. They had kept him in prison as a matter of routine, but they were not at all interested in his commonplace crime. For a decent sum, not in worthless Russian paper, but in foreign currency, they were quite ready to release him and to give him all the documents he needed in order to cross the frontier and return to his home.

Simcha Meyer ran from the prison, pulling his brother by the hand, as if he was afraid that any moment the Bolsheviks would change their mind and drag him back.

"Come, Jacob Bunim," he muttered. "Walk faster. Let's get away from here."

Passers-by stopped to look at these two men, the tall, dignified, well-dressed foreigner and the little, haggard, filthy beggar who clung to his hand. Even in this city, which had seen so much, it was a curious sight. Women crossed themselves, and cripples hobbled after them with outstretched hands. Jacob Bunim hailed the first passing droshky, bundled his brother in, and mounted beside him. The stench that mounted from Simcha Meyer's body and rags still assailed his nostrils, and he wondered how the other was able to bear it. Indeed, he did not even seem to notice it, for he clung close to Yakob, as he babbled: "Let's go faster. Let's go away from here. I'm afraid to stay."

Yakob spoke long and soothingly to him, explaining that he was free, that he had nothing to fear and nothing to flee from; but Max could not get the truth into his head. In that long, dark vigil in the cellar he had become like a child—physically, as well as mentally. Yakob himself had to wash and scrub the befouled body of his brother, take the dirt out of his hair, and cut his nails for him. When he had made him half-presentable, he took him to a barber. Max looked smaller than ever when the wild growth of hair had been shorn from him and he was left only with a tiny point of a beard such as he had always worn. But the odour of the prison still clung to his body.

"Shall I pour some eau-de-Cologne on him?" asked the barber, of Yakob, as though the other were indeed a child.

"Pour it on," said Yakob.

"I was lucky enough to keep some from the old days," said the barber.

When Max, with Yakob's assistance, put on clean underwear, a clean shirt, and clean socks, a look of delighted amazement came into his face, as though he had begun to doubt that such things existed in the world. The linen did not fit him. He swam around in it. The white collar stood away from his scraggy neck. But the feel of it filled him with happiness.

"Linen! Clean, fresh, white linen," he murmured, fingering his shirt incredulously.

The hotel porter had made the old rags into a bundle, which he now held gingerly, with a look of disgust on his face. He asked what was to be done with them.

"Throw them out! Burn them!" exclaimed Yakob with a shudder.

He helped his brother lace his shoes, fasten his tie, and button his clothes. Max could not yet control the trembling

[593]

of his hands. When they sat down to a meal in the privacy of their room, Yakob unpacked the sausages, sardines, cakes, and chocolate which Dinah and Gertrude had packed for him. The sight of the good food made Max's hands tremble more than ever. After the filthy and meagre rations of the prison everything tasted to him like some divine manna. He could hardly carry the food to his mouth.

"They're presents for you, Simcha Meyer," said Yakob, "from Gertrude and Dinah. They packed them specially for you."

A faint tinge of colour crept into Max Ashkenazi's yellow face, and he dropped his eyes. For the first time in his life he felt the sensation of shame.

Yakob, too, dropped his eyes. This man was not at all like the brother he had known.

The arrangements for the homeward journey went through much more smoothly than even Yakob, the optimist, had dared to expect.

For the first stage, from Petrograd to Orsha, Yakob obtained, in exchange for a thick wad of foreign notes, two good places in a first-class car. With a bottle of cognac he bribed the conductor to admit both of them occasionally to his special compartment, where he made hot tea for the two of them. The train moved slowly, with many stops at wayside cabins and in the open fields. But day by day the frontier came closer. At Orsha, a town still occupied by German troops, they had to change trains. There was much questioning there, and much examination of baggage and papers. The leather-clad men with red stars on their coats rummaged minutely through all the possessions of the Ashkenazis, but they found everything in order. Then they advised them to find whatever accommodation they could in the city, since it would be weeks before they could be given places on a train. All the trains were packed with returning soldiers and prisoners of war.

Max fell into a panic once more. He would not believe he had been saved until he was once more on Polish territory and in his own home. The prospect of a long wait in the territory of the Bolsheviks filled him with terror, and he looked with helpless, frightened eyes at his brother. Yakob, however, was not to be put off so easily by a handful of sol-

[595]

diers. He demanded to be taken before the local commissar.

"Impossible!" was the stern answer. "He sees nobody."

"He'll see me," answered Yakob serenely; and there was something in his manner, a suggestion of authority, which impressed the leather-coated soldiers.

The very day of their arrival in Orsha, Yakob obtained an interview with the commissar. Doors seemed to open for him of themselves. Guards and orderlies fell back before this imposing person with the authoritative voice; and when he was admitted to the presence of the commissar, Yakob approached him easily and spoke to him as man to man. He carried his point. Instead of weeks, only a few days passed before they were given places on a military train. Max Ashkenazi, fingering his little beard nervously, as in the old days, gazed at his brother in amazement when he brought the good news to the little hotel.

"Nothing seems to stop you, Jacob Bunim," he said. "I don't know how you do it. . . ."

Indeed, he no longer recognized his brother, just as his brother had not recognized him. All his life he had foolishly considered Yakob a brainless, feckless, incompetent trifler. He saw before him a man of character, imagination, and daring. He was ashamed now, not only of the hatred he had always felt toward his brother, but of the contempt in which he had held him. "After all," he asked himself, "how many brothers have I, that I should have behaved toward him as I did?" One brother, a twin. It was his fault, Max's, that he had not known how to appreciate him, make a friend of him, and go through life hand in hand with him. Always there had been enmity, envy, and quarrels. The stupidity of it! Here, in this crucial moment, when disaster had overwhelmed him and he had given up hope, it was this brother who had come to his rescue, left his home and his business, risked everything, and pulled him back from the very gates of death. It would be different from now on! A new life of love, comradeship, mutual help, joys shared together, and, if it came to that, sorrows.

Yes, it would be a new life in all respects. He would be a true brother to Jacob Bunim—he always thought of him by

[596]

the old name—and a true father to his children. He would find his son again. If necessary he would, after a few weeks' rest, go to France and trace Ignatz. He would bring him home, set him up in business, make a man of him, prepare him to become, some day, his heir, the carrier of the Ashkenazi name. He would take Gertrude to his heart, too. She was a good girl, when all was said and done; for in spite of the way he had treated her, she had remembered him in the hour of his need and encouraged her husband, his brother, to set out on the perilous journey. He would undo all the evil he had done and prove himself a father, as she had proved herself a daughter. As for her marriage with Jacob Bunim, she had only shown thereby her understanding of the value of the man; for Jacob Bunim was worth a thousand Simcha Meyers, and it was right and proper that Gertrude should have fallen in love with him. Then there was their child, his grand-daughter, a sweet little girl, Priveh, whose photograph Jacob Bunim had brought with him and on whose face Max was never tired of looking.

The name of the little girl sent a pang of regret and shame through Max Ashkenazi every time his brother mentioned it. It was the name of his dead mother-in-law. How meanly he had behaved toward her and toward her husband, Reb Chaim! He had taught her to hate him. Once she had even flung a glass of tea in his face; and as he thought back, he could not blame her for it. He was ashamed of the incident and of the provocation which had been responsible for it. How stupid he had been! How blind, how insane, in his feverish desire for wealth, and more wealth, and still more wealth! If only he could recall those times! If only he could make restitution to the dead Priveh and her husband, Reb Chaim, for the brutality and treacherousness of his behaviour. But they were dead, and there would never be a reconciliation. Only Dinah was left, and she had forgiven him. Side by side with the shame that seemed to be poured through his veins, Max Ashkenazi felt a strange warmth and gratitude. He looked back bitterly at the folly and emptiness of his life. If in those far-off days he had only had the sense and the clarity of vision which he had now! He would not

[597]

have ruined his own life, together with the lives of others. He had sacrificed them all, his wife and children, his father-in-law and his mother-in-law, his own brother. "I've been bad, bad, bad," he muttered to himself; "there was evil in my blood."

Max Ashkenazi felt an unwonted gratitude toward his second wife, too. Yakob spoke enthusiastically of her, praised her character and intelligence, told how, alone in the city, she had guarded, as well as she could, her husband's property, and how, in the end, she had humbled herself and come to her brother-in-law for help, not for her own sake, but for his, Max Ashkenazi's. But it was only gratitude and respect that he felt toward her, the woman of character. His affections were stirred by the thought of Dinah, his first love, the mother of his children. If he could only return straight to her! How good it would be to pass the remainder of his life with her and with his brother and the children! It would be hard now, after these tangled years, to rebuild a relationship; and it would be hard to go on living that empty life in the huge, cold palace with that mannish woman who was now his wife.

But he would face it and make the best of it. This was his firm determination. Still, the difficulties of the future weighed heavily, and all the efforts of his brother to instil some cheerfulness into him were without effect. Nothing was left in Max Ashkenazi of the old hardness and self-assurance and contempt for the world's opinion. He was frightened. He was like a little boy who had misbehaved and who wanted to rehabilitate himself in the eyes of his parents, but was afraid to speak to them. He would have liked to tell all this to his brother, but he felt the uselessness of it. Throughout the long journey the rhythm of the wheels kept time with the rhythm of self-accusations in Max Ashkenazi's heart.

Beyond Orsha the train travelled faster. In Minsk, which was, like Orsha, still in the possession of the Germans, they had to change again. They passed a night in a hotel. In the morning they were informed that the next permit would carry them only as far as Lapy. There they would have to be re-examined.

[598]

"Lapy is Poland," the German soldiers told them. "You're home then."

But on the stretch between Minsk and Lapy the two brothers were made to feel that they would not be very much "at home" in Poland, as the German soldiers had promised. The nearer they drew to the Polish frontier, the more impudent became the behaviour of the Polish travellers toward the Jews. A spirit of hatred filled the railroad cars. Threats and insults were heard on every hand.

"Hey, Sheeny, take up less room there. Decent people want to be comfortable too," they began. "Why don't you travel the other way, toward Palestine?"

"Wait till we're past the Germans," one of the Poles promised. "Wait till we're in our own country."

"That's the idea," another agreed. "We'll have a little party like the one in Lemberg."

"Has anyone round here got a pair of scissors?" asked a young Pole. "Some of these Sheeny-beards need cutting."

"Not now," he was warned. "Wait till we get to Lapy, where there aren't any Germans."

The Jews shrank into corners, helpless before the mounting fury of the mob. Max fixed his frightened eyes on his brother. The other stared back boldly at the peasants, with eyes that glowed indignantly. The brothers were silent.

The train stopped in the fields.

"Everybody out!" the German conductors shouted. "We're a couple of kilometres from Lapy. This train doesn't go any farther."

The passengers climbed out. Close to the railroad track was a wooden hut, and outside the door a soldier, with the Polish eagle fastened to his cap, stood guard. Between two trees was stretched a linen streamer, with a welcome to the returning Poles. The crowds of Poles burst into the national anthem. Women flung themselves on the ground and kissed the soil. One of them rushed up to the soldier and embraced him.

"Jesu!" she gasped. "A Polish soldier, in a Polish uniform!"

Her voice was drowned out by the screams of an old Jew who was caught in a ring of young hooligans. They flung him round in a circle, smashing their fists into his face.

"Well, we're 'at home,'" muttered Yakob.

The crowd straggled along the sandy road parallel with the railroad for several kilometres. In front of the station of Lapy, over which fluttered a white and red flag, stood a squad of gendarmes, with long swords dangling at their sides.

"Jews and Bolsheviks to one side!" the corporal shouted.

The waiting-room was adorned with a naked Jesus on the cross, a Polish eagle, portraits of generals, and innumerable Polish flags. It was crowded from door to door with travellers and their baggage and armed soldiers. At a plain wooden table a man sat opposite a gendarme and with both fists beat at his breast.

"Here," he pleaded, "open my heart and take a look inside. I swear by God and by His Holy Mother that I am not a Bolshevik. I've come a long way, from the other end of the world, from Siberia, and I've lost my papers."

The gendarme grinned. "We know those stories, brother. You were a Bolshevik commissar. . . . We know your kind. The prison for you, and the whip. . . ."

Max Ashkenazi felt as though his heart had been emptied of blood. Something in the looks of that gendarme, the cruel grin, the pleasurable licking of the lips, boded evil. Yakob had become pale. The two brothers sat motionless, waiting their turn. After a few minutes a soldier came up and escorted them to the table, saying: "There's a good time waiting for you."

The man who had been beating his breast was led away through one of the doors. The gendarme looked up at the two Jews, and an expectant leer distorted his face.

"Well, where do you two Sheenies come from?" he asked.

Yakob took out his papers and laid them on the table. The gendarme did not even look at them.

"Get undressed!" he ordered, curtly.

The two brothers looked at each other in stony silence. The waiting-room was jammed. At the wooden table, next to the gendarme, sat a girl in uniform. The gendarme banged on the table and yelled to his men: "Strip them naked."

Amid the laughter of the crowd the soldiers threw themselves on Max and Yakob and began to tear the clothes from them. The gendarme at the table was suddenly replaced by an officer, a young, thin-faced Pole, with a sharp nose and little moustaches. He wore, slung across one shoulder, the coat of a Hungarian hussar. Yakob broke free from the soldiers who were tearing off his clothes and flung himself toward the officer.

"Lieutenant!" he cried. "My brother and I are manufacturers of Lodz. We own houses there. We place ourselves under your protection."

The officer threw off his hussar's coat, and removed his cap, revealing a mop of blond, stiff hair which stood out like pig's bristles. He looked out of his narrow grey eyes at the big, dignified figure of Yakob.

"So, manufacturers of Lodz, and owners of your own houses," he repeated. "Not Bolsheviks at all, then."

"God forbid, lieutenant," said Max, thrusting eagerly forward. His coat and vest had been ripped from him. "I've just come from Russia, where I was imprisoned by the Cheka. Here are my papers to prove it."

"Very well, we'll see," said the thin officer. "Shout at the top of your voice: 'To hell with Leon Trotsky!' "

"To hell with him by all means!" said Max Ashkenazi, fervently.

"I told you to shout it!" said the officer, angrily. "At the top of your voice."

"To hell with Leon Trotsky!" repeated Max Ashkenazi, more loudly.

"Louder!" yelled the officer.

Max Ashkenazi repeated the words again, but the officer was still not satisfied.

"Louder, you filthy Jew! Louder! Till your teeth rattle!"

Max Ashkenazi shouted with all his remaining strength, amid the laughter of the soldiers and of the girl in uniform.

"Now shout: 'To hell with all the Yids!' " the officer commanded. "At the top of your voice!"

The sweat was streaming down Max's face. He could not open his lips. His breath came in spasms. The officer smacked him across the face with his hat.

[601]

"Shout! Or I'll tear the guts out of you!"

Yakob tried to twist himself free from the soldiers who held him. They tightened their grasp on him.

"Shout!" yelled the officer again.

Max Ashkenazi looked round at the excited mob of peasants and soldiers. He saw the delight on their faces, the frenzied desire to crush and humiliate him. He gave way.

"To hell with all the Yids!" he whispered. Then louder, and louder again, he repeated the words.

The mob neighed with happiness.

"That's fine!" said the little officer. "Now you can give us a little dance, Mr. Manufacturer and house-owner of Lodz. A little dance and song, to entertain our soldier-boys here. Come on, now, lively!"

Again Yakob tried to tear himself free from the men who held him, and again they tightened their grasp, driving their fists into his ribs.

"Don't do it, Max, don't do it!" he shouted.

Max did not hear him. He cast round him, at the mob of tormentors, a look in which all the poisonous contempt in his soul found expression; and he did as he was told. He turned and twisted before the soldiers.

"Faster, livelier!" they shouted, clapping their hands.

Max went on twisting and turning until he collapsed and lay on the floor covered with perspiration and panting brokenly.

"Let him lie there!" the officer commanded. "Now for the other Jew."

The gendarmes brought Yakob forward and released him. He stood deathly white, but erect and dignified.

"Go on with the dance," the officer commanded.

Yakob did not budge.

"Dance, you dirty Jew!" the officer shouted, and brought his fist down on the table. "Dance or it will be worse for you."

Still Yakob did not budge.

The blood rushed into the little officer's face. The soldiers were all looking now, from him to the big, silent, dignified man and back again, waiting to see what would be the upshot of the struggle between these opposed wills. The officer rushed round the table and grabbed Yakob by the beard.

"Dance!" he shouted, and tried to pull Yakob down.

At that instant Yakob tore himself free, stepped back, lifted his arm, and slapped the officer with such force that the latter staggered back until he was brought up against the wall.

The audience was paralysed, and a mortal silence filled the room. Only the girl in uniform rose and ran over to the officer. Then Max Ashkenazi, on the floor, crawled toward his bother. "Yakob! Yakob!" he whispered, his voice filled with fright.

The officer straightened up, his face contorted. With a trembling hand he fumbled at his holster and drew out his pistol. It took him a long time to get the pistol free. Then he lifted it and screamed: "Stand back!"

The gendarmes made a rush away from Yakob Ashkenazi. Several times the officer shot point-blank at the big, white silent figure. Then he turned. "My hat and coat!" he gasped. They were handed to him. Without donning them he rushed from the room.

Max Ashkenazi had crawled over to the bloody figure of his brother and was holding him in his arms.

"Why did you do it, Jacob Bunim?" he wailed. "Why?" And he tried to lift the body. But there was no response. A thin trickle of blood ran out from the forehead over the beard. Yakob was dead.

The naked figure of Jesus looked down on the scene.

Max Ashkenazi lay wailing on his brother's body, oblivious of his surroundings. The crowd stood silent—wretched little creatures suddenly aware of their meanness and smallness. Smallest of all felt Max Ashkenazi, as he lay on the corpse of his twin brother, who had triumphed over him again, but now for the last time.

During every moment of the seven days of mourning which, following the ancient ritual, Max Ashkenazi observed for his brother, his thoughts were concentrated on himself and his fate.

After the funeral he was brought in a droshky to his daughter's house, which he had never entered before. In stocking-feet they sat on low stools, father and daughter. The mirrors and pictures were covered with black crape. All were silent.

During the first day of mourning he could take no food. His mouth would receive nothing but the smoke of cigarettes, which he lit steadily, one after another. Dinah brought milk to the two mourners, to strengthen them; but Max pushed the glass away. He only kept smoking. The ashes fell neglected on his stockinged feet. He spoke to no one, and he did not hear when he was spoken to. He had open before him the Book of Job, and his eyes rested immovably on the words:

"Let the day perish wherein I was born, and the night perish in which it was said: There is a man child conceived. . . . Let them curse it that curse the day, who are ready to raise up their mourning. . . ."

Gertrude, sitting by her father, bent down her eyes to the book and looked on the strange letters which she could not read; but she could feel rising out of them the echo of her despair. Her father did not try to comfort her. He had nothing to say to his daughter, for whose happiness he had never

[604]

taken thought, and whose house he had never entered before. With this first visit he had brought death and mourning to those who had forgiven him and had tried to save him—his first gift to her after her marriage. He did not lift his eyes from the book; he could not look on the people whom he had treated so ill all the days of his life, his daughter Gertrude and his first wife, Dinah. His second wife came to the house and sat down on a stool beside him. She caressed his shoulder dumbly, with her heavy, half-paralysed hand, but to her, too, he said not a word.

"Is there not an appointed time to man upon earth?" he read in the Book of Job. "Are not his days also like the days of an hireling? . . ."

On the second day visitors came to condole with him. Because of the disaster which had befallen him his neighbours forgot how he had lived apart from them; they forgot the evil things he had done them; they came to the one-time king who sat now on a low stool, in stocking-feet. They spoke to him about the city, about business, about factories. Max Ashkenazi heard them unwillingly. What mattered business and factories now? He had nothing left to work for. He was done for. He had thrown away his life. He had wanted to begin life anew, to live in affectionate closeness with his own; but God had decreed otherwise. On the threshold of this new, reformed life he had been flung back; he had been driven out of the house of the living like a leprous dog. No! He was destined only to bring misery to others. So it had been in the days when, blinded by ambition and the lust for power, he had been the author of evil; so it was now, when, having become wiser, he still remained, against his will, an instrument of evil. He who sows hatred reaps misery. There was no place for him now in the world of the living. His fate was sealed. There remained only a few years now, years of darkness and mourning and emptiness. It was useless and pointless to make a new beginning. For what, after all, were his needs? He had never, in all his life, desired much for himself and his own satisfaction; he desired nothing at all now. A piece of dry bread, a shirt to cover his nakedness, a corner in which to lean his head. That was all. How wise, how right, had been the sages of old! There was no difference between man and beast. The yoked beast carries its burden; man does likewise. The beast fails in the end, and is trodden underfoot; and this is the end of man too.

On the third day he thrust out of his mind these thoughts concerning the vanity of life and turned once more to thoughts of human duty. It was wrong to break down completely, for now the lives of others depended on him; his was the sole responsibility for them. He himself might feel that life was at an end, and he desired nothing more, but there were others who needed him. All of them, Dinah, Gertrude, the son in France, and this old woman, his second wife, too. She was sick and alone. His was the duty to care for all of them. It was impossible, it was wrong, to let everything drift. On the contrary; he had to take hold of everything, harness his last energies, rebuild the foundations of the house, so that the Ashkenazi family might endure. It was so in ancient days, among Jews; when a man died, his surviving brother took upon himself the perpetuation of the house of the dead man. This house of Ashkenazi must not be permitted to vanish from the face of the earth. He would make himself responsible, replace evil with good, and bring such restitution as he could to those he had harmed.

Therefore he listened more willingly now to the visitors who spoke about business and factories and doings in the city of Lodz. He listened, but he did not take part in the conversation. His thoughts were with the living again, but not with the city of Lodz and not with the land which had treated him with unspeakable cruelty, had trodden on him and poured out the blood of his house. Not for all the wealth in the world would he remain here any longer, to be covered with filth, to be humiliated and degraded daily. He would go away to Palestine, as the Zionists among his friends counselled him. He had never believed in them till now; he had looked upon them as foolish dreamers, who hoped to transform a nation of merchants into tillers of the soil and followers of the plough. Now he saw his mistake. What did wealth mean, factories and houses and merchandise, if the stranger could take it away overnight? Better to build for

[606]

oneself, in one's own land. He would leave Poland; he would sell whatever remained to him, at whatever price he could get for it, and go with his family to Palestine. There he would be among fellow-Jews, among his own, under his own vine and his own fig-tree; a quiet, modest life; food from his own field, milk from his own cows; no more fever and struggle. There were so many Jews leaving Poland for Palestine; they went by the train-load, all kinds, young and old, the religious and the irreligious. As soon as the week of mourning was over he would liquidate his possessions and flee from the presence of these hordes which thirsted for Jewish blood.

He spoke of this to his visitors, and they praised his decision.

"True words," they said. "Do this thing, Herr Ashkenazi, and half the Jews of Lodz will follow your example."

But on the fourth day Max Ashkenazi rejected the plan; he would not plough the soil and plant vineyards. That was a task for the young, whose bodies were fresh and who were not fit for anything else. He, Max Ashkenazi, could not become a farmer. It was too simple for him, too primitive. You put seeds in the earth, and ears of corn grew; and sometimes they did not grow. One earned very little at best. And then you had to look perpetually at the sky; sun and wind and rain were your partners, capricious and unpredictable. It needed so much strength, too. "In the sweat of thy face shalt thou eat bread. . . ." This was written of the peasant. He, Max Ashkenazi, was not built for that. Every man to that for which he was best fitted; it was ridiculous to put a heavy spade in the delicate hand of a diamond-polisher. Peasants were made for that. If he, Max Ashkenazi, were to go to Palestine as a peasant, he would serve neither his people nor himself. Far better to cling to the big things he had always dreamed of. Wealth did not lie in the soil; it lay in industry. He, Max Ashkenazi, would develop the industry of Palestine, as he had developed the industry of Lodz. He would build factories in the Holy Land, provide employment for thousands of workers, import merchandise from every country, attract capital, become the king of Palestine. That was worth while; for such an objective he would have

[607]

the strength to begin anew. Ah, he would show them what he could do with that country! Just because it lacked industries. How long was it since Lodz itself was a dreamy village? But men of courage and imagination and initiative, workers and planners, had appeared on the scene, and Lodz had become a world city. What he had helped do for Lodz, he would now do for Palestine, for his own land. In his imagination Max Ashkenazi addressed himself to the world as Jacob of old had addressed himself to Laban the Syrian: "When shall I provide for mine own house also?" He had worked enough for the Labans of Poland, who, like Laban the Syrian, had robbed and deceived the Jacobs who had laboured for them.

On the fifth day this plan, too, died in Max Ashkenazi's mind. He was calmer now, and he began to consider the folly of setting out, at his age, to conquer new worlds. He would start nothing hastily. To build up the industries of Palestine would, indeed, be a fine thing, and a Jewish thing; but suppose they turned out to be only castles in the air? It would be easy enough to build a factory there; but what was the good of a factory without markets? True, Lodz had once been what Palestine was now: waste sand. But Lodz was part of a great country which needed and could absorb merchandise. Even Poland now, cut off from Russia, had a population of millions. What was Palestine? A land of Arabs who dressed in rags, needed nothing and bought nothing. And then, to compete with the English was no light matter, either. They were good merchants. The handful of Jews in the Holy Land was no basis for an industry. Besides, every Jew who had gone to Palestine considered himself a mixture of saint and hero. Jews were good to have at one's table, not to do business with. There was also the question of water in Palestine; it was doubtful whether the local water was good for the washing of textiles. All sorts of other difficulties occurred to him. It was, after all, a land which lived on charity, on gifts from abroad. It was altogether too risky, then; he would not expose himself to defeat, and to the derision which would follow defeat. For if he failed, the Jews themselves would laugh at him.

[608]

On the sixth day Max Ashkenazi found himself listening with the liveliest interest to the business conversations which were started by the merchants and manufacturers who came to visit him. All of them were anxious to know whether, in spite of his professed interest in Palestine, he was going to reopen his factory in Lodz. The world was slowly coming to after the war. Agents and buyers were beginning to appear in Lodz, like the first swallows in spring. Markets were opening tentatively in the neighbouring agrarian countries. It was a question of studying their demands and creating the kind of goods they wanted. All eyes were turned, therefore, on Max Ashkenazi, one-time king of the Lodz industrialists, who had returned to his native city; it was as if he alone could give the word and set the example and the pace.

"Herr Ashkenazi," they said to him, in the words which some had used about Palestine, "you begin and the rest will follow."

On the seventh day of mourning Max Ashkenazi rose from the low stool and began to walk in his stocking-feet on the soft carpet of his daughter's living-room.

No! he exclaimed inwardly. He would not give in; and he would not surrender his position here. Just because the gentiles wanted it. He would see them damned before he would let them triumph over him so easily. Working day and night, he had, with his own two hands, erected a mighty industry, while they, the masters of the land, had lived carelessly and dissolutely, spending *their* days and nights with wine, women, and cards, whether at home or in Paris or in other gay cities abroad. Now they wanted to take everything over, ready-made for them, driving from the country those who had done the building. By God, he would remain on the spot, and give nothing away! If only Jacob Bunim had been differently made! The two of them would be working hand in hand now, to become masters of the city. But Jacob Bunim had trodden in the path of the gentiles, had pursued folly, had worshipped the emptiness of pride; and that had been his undoing. Jews should not imitate the vanities of the gentiles—give up life for an empty word called honour. If a pack of dogs attacks a man, shall the man consider himself degraded thereby? True, dogs have teeth and are stronger than men; but they are dogs none the less, and a man remains a man none the less. Our grandfathers and great-grandfathers were wiser, reflected Max Ashkenazi, when they despised the gentile inwardly and refused to take to heart his so-called insults, as one does not take to heart the howling of a dog in the street. One did not give up one's life for such things. The power of Israel did not lie in physical strength, but in thought. Always, from the earliest times on, the gentiles had heaped insults on the Jew and had tortured him physically; and the Jew had remained silent, knowing he was the sheep among wolves. He was in exile. It was folly to fight with the stronger. Had the Jew followed the example of the gentiles, he would long ago have disappeared from the face of the earth. But he had understood that his ways were not as their ways, and their conception of honour was not his. Therefore he had endured; and often he had grown to such strength that the gentiles who despised him had been compelled to seek favours from him. This was the strength of the Jew, and this was his revenge. For hundreds of years the Jews had danced and sung at the bidding of gentiles, because there was no way out, because the murderers demanded it. In these hours of bitterness it was wrong to throw one's life away; one tried to soothe the rage of the murderer; one did not provoke him.

If only Jacob Bunim had understood this! If he had only understood that the insult which the strong offer the weak returns on the head of the strong. They insult themselves; and their punishment is certain. Was it not written in the Ethics of the Fathers: "Because thou didst drown a man, thou hast been drowned; and they that drowned thee shall be drowned"? He, Max Ashkenazi, had implored his brother to offer no resistance. But he had not listened. All his life Jacob Bunim had trodden the path of folly, had obeyed the impulses of the blood instead of the dictates of his reason. Jews are forbidden to taste blood or to obey its impulses.

The tears filled Max Ashkenazi's eyes as he thought of his brother. They would not work hand in hand, Jacob Bunim and he. But he alone would take up the gage; single-handed he would fight the hordes who wanted to drive him out of

[610]

the country. He would become king of Lodz once more, and his enemies would once more stand before him, hat in hand, begging favours.

This once they had caught him in a tight place, tortured him and spat on him. He would pay them back, both for himself and for his brother. Let him only get the factory working again. Money was the only weapon which the Jew could wield, and this weapon he, Max Ashkenazi, would use like a two-edged sword. He would not play the fool; he would not, in a moment of blind rage, abandon the field to the triumphant foe. This was not Max Ashkenazi's way.

On the eighth day he donned his shoes, shaved the seven-day growth of bristles off his face, put on a new coat, the lapel of which was not torn in sign of mourning, and went out into the city which he had once abandoned, in order to conquer it anew.

Somewhere within, the seemingly inexhaustible sources of energy were open again. With a fury and stubbornness which matched the years of his prime, Max Ashkenazi advanced again toward the position he had lost.

As always, it meant long labour, planning, endurance, and will-power. Life had never given him anything for nothing; it did not relent now.

The first struggle centred on his palace. This, on the retreat of the German army of occupation, had passed into the hands of the Polish military, who had ultimately turned it over to the Voivode or Governor of the city. Panch Panchevski was his name, of the bluest blood in Poland, a prince by descent, though in these democratic days he was not permitted to add his titles to his signature. He had to be Panch Panchevski in the Republic, like any ordinary citizen. He submitted to the law very ungraciously, but he never forgot his princely privileges, and he would not agree to take up his official residence in the barrack-like house of the former Russian police commissioner. A man of his descent had to have a palace; and Ashkenazi's palace was the place for him.

When Ashkenazi—immediately after the period of mourning—sent a curt but polite request to the Voivode to vacate the palace, the latter ignored it. He did not believe the Jew would dare to do anything about it. He threw the letter into the waste-paper basket and merely smiled. There was nothing wrong about a Jew asking for his house; but the Jew would not dare to insist. Prince, or, rather, Citizen Panch Panchevski was quite wrong. The Jew did insist; and he insisted through the most skilful and most expensive lawyers; he insisted all the way through the lower to the higher courts. He brooked no delay, either. The Voivode used influence to get the case delayed; the Jew used money to get it speeded up. Formally the Jew was in the right, and the sour-faced, long-whiskered Voivode knew it.

In the end Panch Panchevski tried to compromise. He would pay a good rent for the palace if Ashkenazi would not disgrace him by throwing him out. But that was just what Ashkenazi wanted to do. For he was not so much in love with the palace as a residence. He only wanted to show that he was still Max Ashkenazi, who could not be put upon by anyone. And he needed the palace for his own prestige. It was part of his great come-back.

Panch Panchevski left the palace, his tail between his legs. True, before he vacated he had his servants turn the place upside down, smash the mirrors, and ruin the furniture. But he did go out. And Lodz rang again with Max Ashkenazi's name.

"You can't keep that man down," they said, shaking their heads. "He's got twenty thousand devils inside of him."

Ashkenazi moved back into his palace, and on the very day of his triumph set about the rehabilitation of his factory. This was in even more woeful condition than the palace. All the beltings and boilers were gone; so were most of the machines. What Ashkenazi had not moved into Russia the Germans had either moved into Germany or left in ruins. To set the factory in motion again, Ashkenazi would need ten times the capital he now possessed.

He turned first to the State Bank. Dressed in his finest suit of clothes, a thick cigar in his mouth, his mind filled with subtle and persuasive arguments, he paid a visit to the local State Bank director. The latter, formerly a Russian bank official, knew Ashkenazi well and received him courteously. He offered his condolences on the tragic loss which Max Ashkenazi had recently suffered. He listened respectfully to Max Ashkenazi's plans, nodding the bullet head

[613]

above the triple chin. Yes, he agreed, it would certainly be an excellent thing to build up the local industry again. It would be a patriotic act of the first magnitude. It would help to decrease unemployment, and thus restore a spirit of law and order among the workers, who, with their meetings, protests, and demonstrations, were a great source of worry to the authorities. From every point of view, a most desirable plan.

But when it came to the question of the big credits which Max Ashkenazi needed, the director lost his enthusiasm.

"There's our difficulty, Herr Ashkenazi," he said, nervously, drumming on the desk. "The Polish Bank just isn't in a position to extend big credits. If conditions were better . . . as soon as we've taken the country in hand . . . you won't have to ask twice. . . ."

But the truth was that the new masters of Poland were not particularly desirous of extending help to the Jewish city of Lodz. At the meetings of the local industrialists, the Voivode, Panch Panchevski, spoke movingly of his plans to rebuild the city which the Germans had ruined; but everyone knew that he had no affection for Lodz, the Jerusalem of Poland. He hated the Jews who had arrived from the villages empty-handed and were now silk-hatted industrialists who drove about the streets in their own cars. He was Voivode of the city, but he did not care what happened to it.

He had another reason besides his hatred of Jews. To be Voivode of the second city in Poland was quite a distinction; but Panch Panchevski felt he was entitled to more. He had dreamed of an ambassadorship to Paris or Rome, where he would find himself in the company of an ancient European aristocracy, not in that of a crowd of greasy manufacturers, garlic-eating Jews and shopkeepers. But in the new Poland the high positions of state did not fall to the nobility. They were snatched up by lawyers, publicists, party workers; and often enough by riff-raff, by men who had worn convict-clothes. Here and there a few aristocrats had been given high positions—not the highest, though—and then, of course, on the condition that they obeyed the law and did not sign themselves by their aristocratic titles. The very highest positions

[614]

were filled by plebeian nobodies. In Warsaw, in the Government offices, sat men to whom Prince Panch Panchevski would not have offered his hand in the old days. Now they were his superiors. His direct superior was a former jail-bird; the Russians had imprisoned him for revolutionary activity. Now he issued orders to Prince Panch Panchevski.

He could have forgiven everything, but not this last insult, this appointment to the city of Lodz, where he had to deal every day with Jews, treat them as equals, even invite some of them to the annual ball. And then there were foreign journalists, scribblers—mostly Jews, too—correspondents of foreign papers, who wanted to know this and that and the other about attacks on Jews in the streets of Lodz. He had to receive them all, be very friendly, assure them over and over again that in Poland the Jews were certain of equality before the law. Very recently there had been a miserable business with a foreign diplomat, an important personage, who had been sent into Poland to investigate the pogroms, with particular reference to the behaviour of the army. And this foreign diplomat, who had come down from Warsaw in the company of important Polish officials, had been a Jew, too. On the Sabbath he had even gone to the Jewish synagogue. And he, Prince Panch Panchevski, had had to dance attendance on him, give him information, and toast his health at public banquets. The worst of it was that, according to the newspapers, this diplomat was descended from Polish Jews; his grandfather had been an inn- or shop-keeper in a Polish village.

So it was; Prince Panch Panchevski, father of the city, hated it not less than von Heidel-Heidellau had hated it in his time, and as often as he came in contact with the Jewish industrialists, merchants, and intellectuals, he felt a revulsion in his blue and princely blood. It was not that he was an enemy of the Jews; they had their place in the country, he believed; but that place was not at the head of a city's industries. He remembered out of his boyhood the frightened, ragged Jews of the village, shrinking, bearded figures in long gaberdines, who would stoop before the local squire and kiss the hem of his garment. Those Jews were all right. As long as

[615]

the prince remained a prince, the peasant a peasant, the Jew a Jew, Prince Panch Panchevski felt benevolently inclined. In fact, he could not imagine Poland without its Jews, and it made him feel good when, driving along a country road, he encountered one of those stooping, cringing, bearded pedlars who got out of the way and humbly removed his cap as the Polish aristocrat drove by. But what kind of world was this, he asked himself, where Jews, clean-shaven, in modern dress, speaking Polish, masqueraded as bankers and industrialists and intellectuals and had a say in the management of affairs?

In the days when Russia had ruled Poland, Prince Panch Panchevski had been forced to look on while the Russian Governor had paid court to these very Jews, preferring their homes and palaces and entertainments to those of the impoverished and subject Poles. Now that the Poles were masters again in their own land, said the Prince to himself, a new order would be introduced, or, rather, the old, original order would be restored, and the golden days would return; the Polish nobleman would once more take up the sceptre, the peasant his spade, and the Jew his bundle of wares.

However, the Prince discovered that the peasants and the city rabble refused to be put in their places. This was their hour, even more than his. But when it came to the Jews, there was some hope that they could be taught a lesson. Many of the cabinet ministers in Warsaw were enemies of the Jews. There was a strong movement to push the latter out of trade and industry and substitute Poles. Lodz was as good a place as any to begin with; the Jews could be smoked out, and instead of these hook-nosed kings of the textile industry there would arise dynasties of pure-blooded, snub-nosed, flaxen-haired sons of Poland.

The Voivode did all in his power to further this movement. He instructed the director of the State Bank to withhold credit from Jewish manufacturers, but to extend it liberally to every Pole who proposed to buy a factory from a Jew or build a new one. He also gave his warm support to the new Polish industrial company, "Unity," founded by the Christian Party. He had one of the cabinet ministers come down

[616]

to Lodz to officiate at the opening of the first factory built by Unity. Priests and cardinals were there, too, and they sprinkled the doors and floors with holy water. Prince Panch Panchevski also called in the heads of the Christian labour union, and persuaded them to reach a permanent agreement with the directors of the Unity factories. But, above all, the Prince used his utmost influence to obtain credits for the new Polish enterprises; and in order to encourage both himself and the governmental leaders, he saw to it that bundles of stocks were distributed where they would do most good.

The Jews sent one deputation after another to Warsaw. They argued with the Prime Minister that if they could not get credits from the Government they could not open their factories, and unemployment would increase from year to year. But when it came to Jewish industrialists the Prime Minister, like the Voivode, always insisted that the future of Poland depended on the development of her soil and her natural resources. They did not dare to state openly that if there was going to be any kind of industry in Poland, it would have to be in the hands of Poles rather than of Jews. It would not have been diplomatic to make such a statement; the Jews had a nasty habit of raising the cry of discrimination, and that produced a bad impression abroad. So it was done diplomatically. The Prime Minister, the Voivode, the bank director, all praised the Jews for their initiative and their high patriotic intentions; but money, they complained, was scarce. Credits had already been extended for agriculture; a little had also gone to Polish industrialists; what could the poor Government do?

And then, if any credits had been extended to Jews, Max Ashkenazi would have been last on the list. The Voivode never forgave him for driving him out of the palace; and his favourite dream was of the day when Ashkenazi, unable to open his factory, would be compelled to sell both factory and palace to the highest bidder. Then Unity would acquire the first, and he himself, Prince Panch Panchevski, the second.

Max Ashkenazi spent several weeks trying to break through the barriers. Friends advised him to follow the example of other Jewish manufacturers and get himself a Christian partner, for whose sake the State Bank would extend credit. Many a name ending in "berg" and "son" and "stein" had hurdled all obstacles by yoking itself with a name ending in "ski." Nor were there lacking pure-blooded Poles eager to go into partnership with a Jew. Editors of Catholic newspapers which denounced these unholy alliances were themselves among the sinners. One Pole, with exceptionally high connections, sent word indirectly to Max Ashkenazi that he was ready to offer the mantle of his name with which to cover the fatal defect. He had no money of his own; but he could obtain plenty of credit if he became the nominal head of the factory and was actually an important partner.

The friend who brought the offer worked hard on Ashkenazi.

"Take him while the taking's good!" he advised. "If you won't, someone else will. Take him; the bank will have to give him credit. And then you and he can both snap your fingers at the Voivode."

Max Ashkenazi refused. Ever since he had become an independent manufacturer he had refused to consider partnerships. Besides, he would see the Polish aristocrat damned before he would offer him a fortune for the mere use of his snobbish name. He was not of a mind, either, to obliterate the name Ashkenazi. He had worked a lifetime to give it a reputation. It had one of the best; and if they refused to honour it in Poland, well, there were countries where it sounded better, in the ears of business-men, than all the "skis" in the world. He would do without Polish credits. He would go to London and Manchester, where his name would always mean something. He would explain to English bankers and merchants what had happened to him in Russia. He would get machinery and raw materials on his reputation. He had been their biggest customer before the war. He would be their biggest customer again. All he needed was temporary assistance; and if they had any sense, those English magnates, they would realize that they could not make a better investment.

He laid his plans secretly, as he had done in the old days when he had gone to Frankfurt in search of a chemist. He prepared a long and careful report on industrial conditions,

[618]

costs, markets, and prospects. He took with him, too, the records of his past achievements. Without knowing a word of English, he arrived in London and found his way to the men he needed. From London he proceeded to Manchester. He interviewed bankers, machine-manufacturers, wool and cotton importers. He found, as he had expected, that his name was still good. They received him, these cold English men of affairs, like a king. True, like a fallen king, but a king for all that. The Jewish sound of his name did not worry them, as it had worried the Polish politicians. They listened carefully to his plans, which an interpreter translated out of Lodz German into English. And they found the plans good.

Max Ashkenazi returned to Lodz, but not alone. There went with him an expert, a representative of the consortium which had decided to extend the necessary credits, a red-headed Englishman who understood little German, but as against that understood everything about a factory. They decided that, since the factory was going to be renovated throughout, they might as well install the latest machinery, such as no other factory in Poland possessed, so that when they were ready for production they would be able to leave their competitors behind. The English financiers did not pursue a penny-wise pound-foolish policy. When the Ashkenazi factory reopened, it was the wonder of Poland.

There was the devil to pay in the anti-Semitic press, which launched a patriotic crusade against the Jewish "king" who had gone abroad for his credits, enslaving his country's industries to foreign capitalists. The cartoonists were busy for weeks portraying Max Ashkenazi with a long, crooked nose, and on his head a tilted crown from beneath which peeped out the ear-locks of a Jewish pietist. He looked, in all these pictures, like a gross, fleshy sensualist. But he did not care what they wrote about him or how they drew him. If anything, he found pleasure in the feeling that they had to reckon with him. And if they hated him and attacked, that only proved that he was a living force. Again all Lodz and most of Poland spoke of Max Ashkenazi. Again he sat through the days in his private office, a uniformed watchman at the door. Again they came respectfully into his presence, directors, engineers, draftsmen, architects, Polish business-men, penniless aristocrats; they came and stood humbly before him; they spoke softly, they sought to placate him; their big mouths, covered with blond moustaches, were half-open, ready to chant in chorus, to everything he said: "*Tak yest, Panie Presisie*—it's just as you say, Mr. President."

Poverty-stricken counts and barons, and demobilized officers of every rank, besieged his office, bringing letters of introduction and asking for jobs, however unimportant. How shamelessly obsequious they were! He looked through the window and saw the long line of workmen who, hat in hand, waited for an interview. Many of them still wore their military coats. Who could tell if among them there were not some who had made merry over his agony in that horrible little railroad station? There they were now, waiting at his gates from the earliest morning hours on, imploring work from him.

The Unity factories, into which untold millions had been sunk, were idle half the time; Max Ashkenazi's factory worked full speed. The sour-faced princely Voivode in the high, old-fashioned collar, and with the little golden cross on his tie, had presided at the opening of the factory. He had publicly congratulated Max Ashkenazi; in the name of the city he had thanked him for bringing back the tide of industry to Lodz. Ashkenazi had shaken his hand, and the two men had smiled at each other. They both felt as if they had grasped a fistful of thorns.

The huge, blackened chimneys again sent their thick clouds into the sky. Again the sirens of the Ashkenazi factory screamed through the early morning air, driving the workers from their beds. Merchants, agents, buyers and sellers again filled the offices. The heavy carts rolled in and out of the factory yards. Travelling salesmen went through the towns and villages; Ashkenazi's goods covered the land and began once more to spill out into neighbouring countries.

Max Ashkenazi passed often through Piotrkov Street, but now no longer in a horse-drawn carriage. He sat, instead, in a lustrous open automobile, a uniformed chauffeur at the wheel. The claxon sounded a special call, impudent and cheerful, to all the passers-by, to all the horses and carriages, to make room for the master of Lodz.

The crowds on Piotrkov Street turned their heads and looked at the withered little figure reclining in the back seat; and as in the old days they said:

"That's Max Ashkenazi; you can't keep him down."

The fever of the inflation time burned hot in the veins of Lodz.

On the surface it looked as though the good old days had returned. On Piotrkov and adjacent streets crowds gathered and milled. Men with pencils stuck behind their ears argued and bargained fiercely, scribbling on pieces of paper or on the walls. The cafés were crowded and noisy. Buyers and sellers, agents, remnant-dealers, commission merchants, sat at the dirty little tables, shoved their hats back on their heads, calculated, told stories, and laughed loudly. Invisible goods changed hands a dozen times. Everyone seemed to be making money.

But this money, the new issue of the Polish Republic, fell in value from day to day. Between morning and night it declined to such a degree that everyone tried to spend it as early as possible. At dawn the housewives went out to the markets and bazaars to get the maximum for their money, and they bought whatever they found, food, cloth goods, household utensils, even if they did not need them, so as not to be caught with paper money at the end of the day. Prices rose by the hour. Before he had finished weighing his goods, the merchant might change his mind and ask for more. The peasants and peasant women stood guard over their stocks of potatoes and drove the excited crowds of housewives away with their whips.

The factories of Lodz all worked full time now, three shifts a day. The manufactured goods did not rest a moment in the warehouses, but went straight from the factory to the buyers, who did not pause to reflect whether they needed the consignments or not. The manufacturer was ready to give; the merchant was ready to take. A frenzy had seized on the country. Industrialists obtained credits from the banks, indifferent to the charges; merchants obtained goods from industrialists; little shopkeepers obtained the same goods from the wholesalers. Everyone wanted commodities of some kind; no one wanted the paper money of the Republic. The workers were kept busy day and night satisfying the demand; they in turn increased the demand by spending every paper mark as soon as they received it. No one understood, and no one cared to understand, how this wild miracle was working; as long as it worked, as long as the crazy paper bridge held, everyone joined in the wild dance.

The newspapers printed one edition after another, only to keep the public informed as to the rates of exchange. The Government presses worked overtime, like the factories, to flood the country with money. The paper was of the cheapest, but from week to week the number of zeros on the currency increased; hundreds became thousands, tens of thousands, millions. Beggars offered a ten-thousand-mark note by a passer-by would throw it back in his face.

Professors and economists wrote pessimistic articles, foretelling disaster. The anti-Semitic papers accused the Jews of being responsible for the decline of the mark. Placards and posters appeared on the walls, picturing fat Jews seated on bags of gold and spurning with their feet the paper money of the Republic. Workers and peasants, gathering before these posters, spat angrily and cursed the Jews. Sometimes they would vent their rage on some passing old-clo' dealer, tear the sack from his back, and scatter the rags in the street, to avenge themselves on the Jews who were hoarding the gold of the country and ruining its currency. In every town, in every side street, little speculators bought and sold; the police hunted the speculators, put some of them in prison, drove others off the street—but the furious commerce went on.

In the universal madness, when everyone was shouting that it was time to call a halt, no one actually dared to stop; the

[623]

pull of the stream was too strong. Planlessly, fantastically, they went on. Houses were built, children were married off, a new generation was brought into the world; and everyone knew that it could not last. Soon, very soon, the collapse would come.

The only ones not to participate in the lunatic prosperity of that period were the workers. Their wages increased from week to week, but the increases were more than swallowed up by the decline of the currency. The housewives went out in the morning with packs of money and brought back half-empty baskets. They were bewildered by the astronomical sums which were now associated with a loaf of bread and a salt herring. In Balut the hand-looms rattled day and night. Like flies struggling in a spider's web, men, women, and children sat on their stools, working convulsively. But the harder they worked, the less they earned, and the millions of marks they collected on Friday did not suffice to carry them over the Sabbath. Black bread served for the Sabbath benediction, and a piece of herring was considered a dainty.

Still, as in the old years, Tevyeh the weaver continued his agitation among the workers, and Konitzky the official sent out his spies and stool-pigeons and agents provocateurs. The former penned proclamations explaining to the unhappy masses how the rich were accumulating real wealth in the form of houses, factories, and farms, while the poor got only the paper marks which slipped through their fingers; the latter placed at the service of the new state the psychological skill which he had once employed on behalf of his Russian masters. Still a colonel, Konitzky had abandoned the Russian Orthodox Church and turned good Roman Catholic, as became a Pole. In his office hung, not the portrait of the Tsar, but that of the head of the free and independent Polish Republic; he took his orders now, not from a Russian official, but from a patriotic Pole whom, in the old days, he had had imprisoned for revolutionary activities. But the methods which Konitzky used were still the same; the strong he repressed brutally, the weak he corrupted and turned into agents provocateurs. Nothing had changed in the city of smoke, stench, gold, and hatred.

[624]

Ashkenazi's factories were the busiest in those feverishly busy days. The new machines spat out fabrics faster than anyone else. It was Ashkenazi first, no one second. But the re-crowned king of Lodz felt no happiness, and the satisfaction which he had anticipated with the restoration of his position still eluded him.

He saw only too clearly what awaited the country in the near future. The tumult of the machines and the roaring in the streets did not deceive him or confuse his vision. He knew that the day of reckoning was close, that the paper bridge would collapse, and with it this frantic dance of prosperity. All would be engulfed, the innocent with the guilty. Not that he cared about innocence or guilt; he was a business-man, and all he was concerned with was the making of money. But the truth was that the innocent would be in worse case than the guilty, and, speaking in purely economic terms, he, Max Ashkenazi, was among the innocent. For in spite of the ceaseless torrent of abuse which issued from newspapers, politicians, and moralizing publicists against the industrial-ists, who were called the exploiters of the country, it was they, the so-called patriots, who were reaping the harvest, and they who would be responsible for the famine to follow. They were the ones who issued those fantastic credits, bought themselves houses and fields and farms, gave themselves shares in co-operatives and factories, and then paid the Government back in worthless paper. They were the robbers and exploiters.

The real manufacturers—not the Unity factories—received, if anything, only the most meagre assistance. They had to get their raw material abroad. There the credit was not unlim-ited. The day would come when worthless Polish paper would not cover the foreign currency needed; the exporters would want gold. And then the collapse would come.

Ashkenazi realized, too late, that in the matter of the Eng-lish credits he had obtained, he had overreached himself. His calculations had been logical enough, but of what avail was logic in a world that had gone insane? Among lunatics the sane man is a fool. He had planned sensibly, far-sightedly. But these were times which mocked all plans. Neither shrewd-ness nor foresight nor reliability nor reputation nor all the

[625]

other virtues of the solid industrialist and business-man counted now. Only chance ruled; or if it was something more than chance, it was a combination of all the qualities which made for failure in healthy and normal times: falsehood, unreliability, instability, and recklessness.

Those that saw him seated in his office, issuing his curt and exact orders, could not guess that behind the façade of confidence there was the beginning of a panic. Ashkenazi would have liked to withdraw from the ring which, spinning faster and faster, would fly asunder before long. But he did not know how to get out. He was carried along—his own considerable weight adding to the momentum which, at the critical moment, would send the fragments scattering far and wide.

He felt like the captain of a ship caught in a blind storm; the most sensible thing would be to furl sails, drop anchor, and with bare masts wait for the storm to blow over. But just this was what he could not do, or dared not do—close the factory. He knew that his workmen would not permit it. They would rise against him and smash the place up. The public would be with them, not only the trade unions, the Jewish and Christian Socialists, the liberals, the anti-Semites, and the press at large, but the very men who were profiting by the storm and who wanted its prolongation. If he, by closing his factory, precipitated the crisis, he would be accused as its author. Then there was the Voivode, who was lying in wait for him, ready to avail himself of the first opportunity to repay him for the affair of the palace. It was quite possible that if he tried to shut down, the Government would take over the factory and carry on; and that all the more readily because he was a Jew. There it was! A man's property was no longer his own, to do what he liked with. Things were really no better in Poland than in Russia, except that in Russia they robbed all the "robbers," while in Poland they concentrated on the Jews. If he only gave them the slightest pretext they would be at him like a pack of wolves. Oh, the law was on his side right enough; but by the time he had set the law in motion, he would be without factory and without palace.

[626]

It was out of the question, then, to make a stand against the furious storm. Nor did he find any sympathy with his fears when he ventured this opinion to business acquaintances.

"Let it ride, Mr. President," they said to him. "You can't tell how it will end—perhaps not as badly as you think. And meanwhile we live. Tomorrow is God's worry."

Empty words they were to him. The fecklessness of these people reminded him of his dead father-in-law, Reb Chaim Alter, who had always relied on miracles to get him out of nasty situations. The miracles did not happen. Miracles never happened. And it was galling to him to think that if anyone escaped catastrophe now, it would be the men who had been devoid of sense and foresight and responsibility. Others would profit, too: the authors of the evil, the printers of the worthless money, the recipients of the credits.

He knew that his efforts were futile, his motions mere gestures, but he still worked from early morning till late at night. He rose from his bed, like the commonest of his labourers, with the first shrilling of the factory siren. His wife, old and sick and half paralysed, tried to keep him at home.

"Stay in bed this morning, and rest, Max," she pleaded with him. "You may as well, for all the business you'll do, God help us. At least you can look after your health."

"I can't sit here," he muttered. "I can't sit still."

The butler brought him a hearty breakfast, but Max Ashkenazi scarcely touched it. The king of Lodz ate, at most, a beggar's breakfast, a crust and half a glass of milk. Since the Petrograd days he had had no appetite. What kept him going were the worries which were killing him.

On his family affairs not less than in his business, Max Ashkenazi's high intentions and far-sighted plans had completely miscarried.

He had done everything to start a new life, just as he had resolved in those wretched prison days in Petrograd, confirming the resolution later during the period of mourning for his brother. All that he had now belonged to those whom wittingly and unwittingly he had wronged all his life: to his daughter, who for his sake was now a widow; to his son Ignatz, whom he brought back from Paris in order to play the father to him; and to his former wife, Dinah. But this household, which he had so ruthlessly shattered, refused to be put together again. He could not, he discovered, restore overnight what he had spent a lifetime in destroying.

Immediately after ejecting the Voivode from his palace, he had proposed to Gertrude that she and her child come to live with him. The truth was that he had not struggled so obstinately for the recovery of his palace because of his own needs. He had never been happy in it. The vast rooms had always oppressed him; they oppressed him more than ever in these latter years of sickness. The dining-room, with its immense, elaborate table, at which he sat opposite his second wife, had always been hateful to him. The ceremonial meals were eaten—if any eating was done—in silence. There was nothing that he and the unhappy old woman who was his second wife cared to talk about.

But how changed it would all be, he thought, if he could only bring his daughter and his little grand-daughter into the place! New voices, a new warmth, a feeling of life in blossom, not life in decay, would enter the enormous, frosty palace. The old woman who shared the palace with him was as eager as he to win the young people over, and she herself made several efforts to persuade Gertrude to join them. From Gertrude's first refusal they gathered that she could not think of leaving her mother alone in Yakob Ashkenazi's house. Max consulted his wife and found her willing to ask Dinah in, too. They would set up a separate apartment for mother and daughter and grand-daughter. Between Max Ashkenazi's wife and Dinah there was no enmity; the two women had passed beyond the age of jealousy for a man's sake; they were concerned more with holding on to the remnants of their family life than with perpetuating their quarrels. Even so, however, Dinah could not bring herself to live in the same house with her former husband and his second wife. She shrank from the painful implications of the situation. So she remained in Yakob Ashkenazi's house, and her daughter and grand-daughter remained with her.

Between Gertrude and her father there was nothing that might have tempted her to leave her mother, or even to press her hard to take up her home in Max Ashkenazi's palace. Gertrude was sorry for her father. She was touched by his loneliness, and by his efforts to make restitution to her and her mother; but there was no love in her heart for him. Throughout the years he had laboured to uproot in her every vestige of filial affection; now it was too late to plant it again. There were times when she felt something like a superstitious revulsion from her father. It seemed to her that he had been chosen by fate as an instrument for the undoing of her life, so that even when he himself meant well, the momentum of years of evil intention produced the same results as of old. She never reproached him. She knew how wretched he was inwardly; she saw that, in destroying the lives of others, he had utterly destroyed his own. But from this feeling of pity to one of active love was a long way.

Her father provided lavishly for her and her mother, yet

often she could not bring herself to visit him, and weeks would pass without contact between them. Dinah drove her daughter to visit the old man, reminding her that, after all, he was her father.

The only time when Max Ashkenazi forgot his business worries, and with them the wretchedness of his life, was when his daughter came to visit him with little Priveh. Whether they came announced or unannounced, there were always presents ready for them. He took the child on his old, bony knees and dandled her; he played with her on the rug, as he had never played with his own children; and his wife, who had never had children of her own, took Priveh in her old, half-paralysed arms and pressed the child to her. But all the affection they poured out on the little one could not win her over. Innocently and frankly she tugged at her mother's skirt.

"Mamma! I want to go home. I want to go to my other grandma."

Her going left the palace more desolate than ever.

Max Ashkenazi brought his son to Lodz. It had not been easy to persuade Ignatz to visit his father, much less to promise that he would go into his father's business. Many letters passed between the two, and large sums of money had to be forwarded to Paris, before Ignatz gave his consent. When he arrived, Max Ashkenazi did not recognize his son. Nothing of the boy he had known was visible in this large, heavy man with the deep voice and the outlandish manners. The years which Ignatz had spent in the army had coarsened him. Max Ashkenazi had to stand on tiptoe to kiss his son, who in return barely touched with his lips the withered cheeks of his father. He seemed to have no relationship to the old man, neither affection nor gratitude nor even curiosity. They communicated with difficulty, for Ignatz had forgotten most of his Lodz German, the language in which he had once conversed with his parents. His language was now French, of which his father did not understand a word. What gave Ignatz, in his father's eyes, the last touch of remoteness and strangeness was the heavy scar of a knife-wound across his face. It had a wild, pagan, un-Jewish look about it.

[630]

"I got that at the front," said Ignatz, with a proud laugh. "I came by it honestly."

Max Ashkenazi's heart sank when he encountered his son; it sank still further when the latter presented the Frenchwoman he had brought with him, a bony brunette, with large black eyes in which there was not a spark of Jewishness. The long, coloured ear-rings, the jingling bracelets on her hands, the slender legs showing under the short skirt, the fantastic clothes she wore, made Ashkenazi think of the Hungarian dancers he had seen in the cabarets which he had frequented reluctantly for business reasons. The woman spoke only French. Max Ashkenazi was certain that this woman was not Jewish. She was probably French; perhaps even a gypsy, or a half-breed from one of the French colonies. He blushed when the woman flung her arms round him and kissed him loudly, exclaiming: "*Mon père, mon père!*"

When she had done kissing him, she snatched up her little hairy dog and kissed it with the same fervour.

Max Ashkenazi did not dare to ask his son who this woman was. Definitely, she was not Jewish. He saw it in her looks, he felt it in her behaviour. She was without manners and without shame. In the presence of Max Ashkenazi and of his wife, she would throw herself on her husband, and cover his face with passionate kisses. She did not behave like one who had ever lived in a decent home. At such moments Max Ashkenazi blushed and looked away.

A few days after his son's arrival Max Ashkenazi began to talk with him about the future. Whatever business conditions might be now, he felt instinctively that the firm of Ashkenazi would survive, and he wanted his son to enter it and learn how to manage it, so that he might in time take it over and perpetuate the name. But the reluctance which Ignatz had indicated in his letters hardened into definite distaste when the problem became actual. He refused to set foot in the factory. He could not bear the noise of it even from the outside, as he could not bear the sight of the thousands of workmen pouring out of its gates. A sullen hostility settled on his face when his father began to talk business to him. He spent his days swimming, fencing, hunting, playing with the little

[631]

dog, and quarrelling with his wife. The bony brunette had a violent temper. Max Ashkenazi did not understand a word of what either of them said when they quarrelled in his presence, but her voice was shrill and hateful. On one occasion she flew at her husband with her finger-nails, and then Ignatz slapped her face once, twice, and three times, so loudly that the sound echoed throughout the house. Max Ashkenazi was paralysed. For days afterwards he could not look his wife or any of the servants in the face. Such things did not happen in Jewish homes, but among drunken gentile workers. What was almost worse than the incident itself was its sequel. For the dusky Frenchwoman seemed to find nothing outrageous in it all. A few minutes after she had been slapped, she was kissing the hands of her husband passionately. It was utterly revolting.

Her table-manners sickened the old man. She ate with lusty animal appetite and drank heavily. She loved spicy foods. She gave her own instructions to the cook for strange dishes. She behaved as though the house were a hotel, and everyone in it there to serve her whims.

Often Ignatz would disappear for the whole day, taking with him his father's automobile. He was a mad driver. He flew through the city, out into the country, along lanes, frightening pedestrians and animals. He managed somehow to avoid bad accidents, but police reports came in thickly, and Max Ashkenazi became tired of settling up for his son.

Worse than this, however, were Ignatz's insatiable demands for money, and the reputation as a spender which he quickly developed in Lodz. He became known as a frequenter of shady cabarets, *cafés chantants* and gambling-dens. His companions were the scum of these dens, professional gamblers, pimps, and cashiered officers. More than once he was brought home, late at night, too drunk to walk or to utter a word.

Whenever Max Ashkenazi tried to argue with him, pointing out that it was impossible to go on in this way, Ignatz would grow black with resentment and threaten to go back to Paris.

"But what will you do there?" his father asked.

"I'll join the Foreign Legion and go to Africa," his son an-

[632]

swered, furiously, his eyes flaming up with hatred against his father. "I'm sick of this place, anyway."

Max Ashkenazi could not let his son go. He clung obstinately to the idea that in the end his kindness would triumph. He paid Ignatz's debts again and again, hoping against hope that he would wear down the insane spirit that had seized his son. Sometimes the couple—Ignatz and his Frenchwoman, of whom Max Ashkenazi was not even certain that she was legally married to his son—would disappear for days at a time. They went to Warsaw, which reminded them of Paris. They went into the country. They could not stand Lodz. They would return as unexpectedly as they had disappeared, but in spite of the brief change they were as wild and as unmanageable as ever.

But from one of these trips the young couple did not return, and a week after their disappearance Max Ashkenazi received a telegram under a Paris date-line, giving the name of a hotel and asking for money. Then Max Ashkenazi admitted to himself what he had, in truth, long ago realized; his son was a hopeless case. There was nothing Jewish about him. If he resembled anyone at all, it was the Huntze sons.

He telephoned to Dinah, whom the antics of Ignatz had reduced to a state of nervous prostration.

"As long as we know where he is, and how he is," he said to her, comfortingly, "let him stay in Paris. It's better for all of us."

But he could not comfort himself. Whichever way he turned, failure stared him in the face; and worst of all was his failure with his son. It seemed to him that this, at least, was unmerited. Whatever sins he had been guilty of, they had not been gross and stupid sins of the flesh, and there seemed to be a special cruelty in his son's defection. It was as though Providence had conspired against his desire to reform: the children for whose sake he had once again taken up the burden of the struggle stood off from him and reduced his self-sacrifice to an absurdity. It was all useless.

He could not find the strength to go on, and yet he did go on. He continued to make the gestures. He sat in his office, calculated, planned, and gave orders, but he saw no sense in it. The nights were intolerable, filled as they were with his loneliness and the sick moaning of his wife. The spurt of energy which had issued from his spiritual conversion died down when he realized that his conversion would be fruitless. Hidden and suspended sicknesses of the body came into the open, but he had neither the patience to listen to doctors nor the desire to struggle against his own disintegration.

His wife pestered him with advice. She brought distinguished physicians to the house, but Max Ashkenazi paid no attention to their prescriptions. He knew in advance what they would tell him to do: give up work, go abroad to the springs, forget his worries. It was ridiculous! How could he rest, how could he remain calm, with his life tumbling in ruins about him, and with the final catastrophe looming over him? What medicines could make whole a life wasted and mis-spent? At which resort could he find refuge from the consciousness of complete failure?

During the long, sleepless nights he wandered in dressing-gown and slippers through the vast rooms of the palace, pausing always to return the sly grin of the bronze Mephistopheles in the dining-room.

LXX

Lodz was done for.

The paper chain which had held the city together in its mad, whirling dance burst at last and flew asunder into a million fragments. The badly printed marks with the innumerable zeros finally lost all value and were replaced by a new silver currency. Overnight Lodz was paralysed.

Warehouses and shops remained full of merchandise; there were no buyers. Piotrkov and adjacent streets suddenly emptied, as though a pestilence had swept through the city. No more crowds milling at the corners; no more shouting of figures and prices. The cafés were empty too, and the waiters stood around idly or chased the flies from the counter. If clients came in, they sat long at the tables before they ordered anything.

"Tea for the gentlemen?" the waiter would ask.

"Later," they replied.

They still wrote figures on the marble tops of the tables, but these were calculations respecting the past. Who had made money in the catastrophe, and how much? Who had lost everything? What had happened to the old, solid firms? Who were the new masters?

It was an insane world. The reliable manufacturers, the men with solid reputations, were the ones who had been ruined. The ones to emerge triumphantly from the tremendous débâcle were the swindlers, the fly-by-night speculators, those who a few years before had been errand-boys, waiters, hangers-on, tipsters, nobodies.

Bankruptcies became so common that they no longer attracted attention. From abroad came the representatives of the wool and cotton firms which had extended credits to the factories; they found, instead of money, repudiated paper marks with countless zeros on them. Judges and lawyers worked overtime. Notaries were kept busy transferring personal property from husbands to wives. The activity of decay replaced the activity of life.

No smoke went up from the chimneys into the sky above the city. Workers wandered by thousands through the streets or stood in long lines before the employment agencies. There were jobs to be had—but not in Poland. France needed miners and was importing them from abroad. Men were ready to leave home and family for the sake of bread. There sprang up in Lodz, in these days, a new industry—the exploitation of the unemployed. Shipping agents circulated in the crowds, persuading workers to migrate to countries where there was "work for everyone." Well-dressed strangers represented themselves as foreign consuls and issued valueless visas. Meanwhile anti-Semitic orators sprang up at the street corners and denounced the Jewish manufacturers who were responsible for the ruin of Lodz: it was all a deep plot, the purpose of which was to force the Poles to leave their own country, which would then fall into the hands of the Jews. As against these, revolutionaries distributed proclamations denouncing the rich, Jew or gentile; and police agents, spies, students, and patriotic women hunted the revolutionaries down and assaulted them openly.

"Down with the Trotskys!" they yelled. "Send them off to Palestine!"

In Balut the hand-looms stood motionless again, covered with white sheets; the sick and hungry children sat at the windows staring out into the grey streets. Old, bearded rag-and-bone dealers wandered through the back alleys, but there were neither buyers nor sellers. Beggars in filthy rags bent over the garbage-boxes, rummaging them from top to bottom. Cripples, real and pretended, wandered with outstretched hands from door to door.

[636]

There was no hope for these, the workers of Balut. During the mad days of the inflation their miserable hand-looms had put up the last fight against the steam factories. But it would never happen again. Nor would they—if life ever returned to Lodz—be drawn into the factories. Those were filled with Poles and Germans. They could not even ask for the pitiful unemployment dole, these weavers of Balut. Panch Panchevski had so framed the relief laws that only employees in factories were entitled to the dole. The hand-loom weavers and their apprentices were left out.

The strongest among the young weavers applied for heavy unskilled work, such as road-building, ditch-digging, and the like. But the Government offices refused to employ Jews. Everywhere the cry was: "You're not wanted, Ikey Mo. Go to Palestine."

The only live place in Lodz was actually the railroad station. The population of the city was scattering. Women and children were setting out for America, to the head of the family; fathers and mothers were going out to join their children. Former villagers, their city jobs gone, remembered suddenly that they had once dug gardens and planted potatoes, and they determined to try their luck in the colonies of the Argentine.

Zionist pioneers, young men and women with bronzed faces from their farm training, and soldierlike kit-bags on their backs, were setting out for Palestine. They went in bands, the blue-white flag carried at the head of the procession. They sang their new Hebrew songs and danced their Palestinian dances on the railroad platforms. The crowds that came to see them off danced and sang with them and shouted after the disappearing train the immemorial Jewish phrase:

"Next year in Jerusalem."

Others were setting out for Palestine, too, but unlike the *chalutzim,* or pioneers, they went furtively, without music and dancing. They travelled first and second class. They had, not kit-bags, but valises and portmanteaus and trunks. The men wore fur coats, the women were bediamonded. They were going to Palestine, not to till the soil, but to buy city lots, open shops, and build factories. For what was the good of staying on in Lodz? It would be years before the city would recover—if it ever would—from the disease of over-production. Lodz was sick; it was putrefying alive. Over its prostrate body crawled, like blood-sucking vermin, the tax-collectors, who concentrated their activity on the Jews.

They did not want to know whether or not the taxpayer had the wherewithal to meet his obligations. If there was no money—which was often enough the case—they took the looms out of the cellars, the goods from the shelves, even the furniture, and the utensils from the kitchens. The Government carts made the rounds and carried off the distrained goods to the warehouses. It became a common thing to see a housewife running down the street after one of these laden governmental carts, wringing her hands and pleading with the officials to give her back the pots and pans which they had removed from her kitchen.

The Government did not want to know whether business was good or bad. It needed money; it levied its taxes. Shops were closed, shelves emptied; the women had to give up their diamonds, the men their gold watches. It was senseless, then, to remain in Lodz if one could go elsewhere betimes. So the middle class, too, turned to Palestine, but turned to it reluctantly, with fear, with a feeling of strangeness. Their intention was to build a new Poland there, a new Lodz, a new Piotrkov Street. They had no connection with those brown-faced, open-throated pioneers who danced joyously on the railroad platform and sang the songs of Palestine in a nasally oriental Hebrew. They kept themselves apart. They did not speak Hebrew, but Lodz German. They inquired about the climate in that queer country, Palestine; they inquired about local customs. They inquired about the language. The only Hebrew they knew consisted of a few prayers; besides, the way the pioneers and the Palestinians spoke the language, it sounded more like Arabic. How alien it all was to them! They feared the tropical sun; they heard with uneasy surprise about the palm-trees and the camels— things they had been told of in their childhood, when they had studied the Bible. The women wanted to know whether the latest dances were known in Palestine, and whether there

[638]

were such things as masquerades and dances.

"*Boszhe kochani!*" they sighed. "Who knows what kind of life we're going to!"

They set out for Palestine as if they were setting out into exile.

Lodz was crumbling. At the end of one hundred years the process was being reversed. Once the roads had been thick with immigrants swarming into the growing city; now they were thick with emigrants swarming out of the dying city. The only difference was that now there were trains to help in the transportation of families and their possessions. But the same natives gazed with the same astonishment on these passers-by. In the fields through which the crowded trains passed slowly, the peasants, both men and women, paused, leaning on plough or rake, to gaze on these strangers. Half-naked children ran out of the huts and crawled through the wattled fences to get a better glimpse of the crowded train windows.

There was no hope for Lodz, the city which had sprung up so rapidly on the sandy lots by the Lodka. Separated from the great Russian market, it was like a branch severed from a tree. For a little while it might retain the semblance of life, and even put forth blossoms. But it was doomed.

That semblance of life, that brief blossoming, was now over. Death came to Lodz, and to the man who had acquired the title of King of Lodz. It was as though he had been unable to give up the ghost as long as the pulse of the city still beat, however faintly. But with the extinction of the last glimmer of vitality in Lodz, he, too, closed his eyes. He could not breathe the air from which the smoke of the factories had been wholly removed. He stifled in the tranquillity of the atmosphere. He could not eat or drink. He turned his face away from his wife, from the doctors, from the food which was prepared for him. He knew that the end had come.

On the last night, unable to sleep, unable to bear his utter loneliness, he crawled out of his bed. He went to the window and looked down into the empty factory yard. Not a light burned there. Not a sound came from it. He turned away, appalled, went over to the bookcase, and switched on the light. He looked at the rows of heavily bound, gilt volumes, with their Gothic lettering and their thick pages. They did not interest him; they had no meaning for him. Very painfully he bent down to the bottom shelf, where, out of sight, there stood a few Hebrew books. He drew out an old, tattered Bible and went to bed again.

By the red electric light, under the picture of a satyr pursuing a naked girl, he turned the pages slowly, and his eyes moved over the heavy words of Proverbs and Ecclesiastes, concerning the vanity of life and the insignificance of man. These were the words that he had always hated, from childhood onward, like the mumbling of old dotards. Now he found them strangely intimate and true. He closed his eyes and continued to turn the pages automatically. Suddenly he came to a page which had been turned down. He opened his eyes and saw that he had reached the Book of Job; the turned-down page was one which he had been reading during the mourning period for his brother, Jacob Bunim. Eagerly, as if something were about to be revealed to him, he scanned the lines, murmuring the words aloud:

"So Satan went forth from the presence of the Lord, and smote Job with sore boils from the sole of his foot unto his crown; and he took himself a potsherd to scrape himself withal; and he sat down among the ashes. . . . Now, when Job's three friends heard of all this evil that was come upon him, they came every one from his own place; Eliphaz the Temanite, and Bildad the Shuhite, and Zophar the Naamathite: for they had made an appointment together to come to mourn with him and to comfort him. And when they lifted up their eyes afar off, and knew him not, they lifted up their voice, and wept; and they rent every one his mantle, and sprinkled dust upon their heads toward heaven. So they sat down with him upon the ground seven days and seven nights, and none spake a word unto him; for they saw that his grief was very great. After this opened Job his mouth and cursed his day. . . ."

From adjoining rooms clocks sounded out the hour with slow ceremonial rhythm.

[640]

Max Ashkenazi laid the volume down on the pillow and put his hand behind his ear, in order to count the strokes. In that instant he felt a sudden and fearful tightness at his heart, as though it had been gripped by a pair of iron pincers. He uttered a frightened croak and reached for the electric cord dangling over his bed. But by the time the manservant arrived, Ashkenazi was dead.

His head had fallen across the rumpled pages of the Bible. His hand clutched convulsively the electric cord.

$\mathfrak{All}$ Lodz came to the funeral of Max Ashkenazi. Piotrkov Street was black with pedestrians and carriages. There were bearded pietists in black gaberdines, manufacturers in silk hats, ladies in dark dresses, shopkeepers in stained clothes, servants, workers, apprentices, *yeshivah* students, beggars and cripples. All of Jewish Lodz, from Piotrkov Street to Balut, had assembled to conduct to his eternal rest the eternally restless man of Lodz.

They saw in the death of Max Ashkenazi the death of the city, and his funeral was that of Lodz. Row by row they advanced, mourning for themselves and their world. At the head, immediately behind the coffin, which no flowers adorned, went three women wrapped in black. Their faces were covered, but everyone knew who they were: the two wives of Max Ashkenazi and his daughter. With bowed heads, and supporting each other, the three women followed with faltering steps the slow carriage.

The grave-diggers had prepared a small grave, as if for a child. A stranger recited over the coffin the Kaddish which Max Ashkenazi's son should have recited. Strangers threw the first handfuls of earth into the open grave. "Dust thou art, to dust returnest, and all that is in thee is earth," they murmured.

A thick mist had descended from the skies over Lodz. A wind rose and blew the dust of the cemetery in the eyes of the mourners. Heavily and slowly, like the rolling mists

[642]

above them, they turned back to the desolate and alien city.

"Sand," they muttered, covering their eyes with their hands. "Everything we have built was built on sand."

The evening came on with swift strides. In the black sky above the mourners a flock of birds flying in a half-moon formation passed with shrill cries.

☰ A NOTE ON THE TYPE IN WHICH ☰
THIS BOOK IS SET

The text of this book was set on the linotype in Baskerville. The punches for this face were cut under the supervision of George W. Jones, an eminent English printer. Linotype Baskerville is a facsimile cutting from type cast from the original matrices of a face designed by John Baskerville. The original face was the forerunner of the "modern" group of type faces. ¶ John Baskerville (1706-75), of Birmingham, England, a writing-master, with a special renown for cutting inscriptions in stone, began experimenting about 1750 with punch-cutting and making typographical material. It was not until 1757 that he published his first work, a Virgil in royal quarto, with great-primer letters. This was followed by his famous editions of Milton, the Bible, the Book of Common Prayer, and several Latin classic authors. His types, at first criticized as unnecessarily slender, delicate, and feminine, in time were recognized as both distinct and elegant, and both his types and his printing were greatly admired. Printers, however, preferred the stronger types of Caslon, and Baskerville before his death repented of having attempted the business of printing. For four years after his death his widow continued to conduct his business. She then sold all his punches and matrices to the Société Littéraire-typographique, which used some of the types for the sumptuous Kehl edition of Vol-
—taire's works in seventy volumes.—

COMPOSED, PRINTED, AND BOUND
BY H. WOLFF, NEW YORK. PAPER
MADE BY CURTIS & BROTHER,
NEWARK, DEL. DESIGNED
BY ERNST REICHL